Introduction to the Quantum Theory

Introduction to the

Quantum Theory

David Park

Williams College

McGraw-Hill Book Company

New York   San Francisco   Toronto   London

Introduction to the Quantum Theory

Copyright © 1964 by McGraw-Hill, Inc. All Rights Reserved.
Printed in the United States of America. This book, or parts thereof,
may not be reproduced in any form without permission of the publishers.
Library of Congress Catalog Card Number 63-20191
48479

Cover photograph: From *Principles of Modern Physics* by Robert B. Leighton.
Copyright 1959. McGraw-Hill Book Company. Used by permission.

2 3 4 5 6 7 8 9 – M P – 9 8 7 6

Preface

The purpose of this book is to give a substantial introduction to quantum mechanics at a fairly low mathematical level—the second year of calculus should suffice. It reflects the belief that as much as possible of any student's training in physics should be in quantum-mechanical terms, and that the earlier these terms are introduced the better. Except for a few necessary ideas about operators and Fourier integrals, I have tried to avoid the teaching of mathematics. Physicists who have used mathematics for many years tend to forget how hard the learning was, and I think it is quite difficult enough to absorb a lot of new ideas in physics without having to deal with them in terms barely understood.

The lectures out of which this book has developed have been given to students about half of whom have gone on to doctoral studies. I have therefore tried to design something which can serve as a starting point for more advanced study but which at the same time is complete in itself. Even though most people believe that every physicist must understand quantum mechanics, it does not follow that all must be prepared to do detailed calculations. I have therefore included many applications to fields of general interest but nothing about transformation theory, for example, and I have regretfully omitted the Dirac electron because I can see no way of making sense of it in modern terms without a detailed disentanglement of states of positive and negative energy. In selecting material I must confess that I have thought rather more about the needs of the nontheorists who need their knowledge in order to read the literature and to understand better what they are doing than of specialists for whose final training I am not in any case responsible.

These considerations have also influenced me in the direction of the deductive approach followed here. Many excellent teachers present quantum mechanics primarily as a technique for computation. Apart from the fact that the student thus misses being introduced by an expert to an extensive and self-consistent intellectual structure of great beauty, I have seen evidence that this procedure does not always work very well. Nothing, of course, will prevent a natural-born physicist from learning to understand quantum mechanics, or better, from learning to work at physics in such a way as to realize that there is nothing to understand. I have in mind, however, the considerable majority of all physicists, particularly the nontheorists among them, to whom the right ideas do not always come naturally. To them it makes a difference how the subject is presented. The assumption behind the practical approach is that if a student learns to solve problems, the proper understanding will come naturally as he does so. I have met a number of intelligent physicists for whom this simply is not so—having in the course of time lost hold of the computational devices, they have lost all, and no instinct remains to guide them.

I have organized this book in a somewhat unusual way. Part I is a formal introduction to the theory, proceeding as far as a discussion of many-body wave functions and aiming at mathematical simplicity. Part II is a series of chapters designed to illustrate the application of quantum mechanics to specific problems in atomic, nuclear, and solid-state physics. These are supposed to show what kind of thing one actually does with the theory, the kind of results one obtains, and what they have to do with experiment.

It is not intended that the reader should master all of the theory in Part I before starting the applications in Part II. The following chart shows where each chapter of Part II can be introduced into the study of Part I without presupposing anything that comes after.

	Theory	Application
Chap. 4	Systems in One Dimension	Chap. 12
Chap. 5	Hermitian Operators and Angular Momentum	Chap. 13
Chap. 7	Systems in Two and Three Dimensions	Chap. 14 (Secs. 1 and 2)
Chap. 8	Approximate Methods of Calculation	Chaps. 14 (Secs. 3 and 4), 15, 16, and 18
Chap. 9	The Theory of Scattering	Chap. 17
Chap. 10	Electromagnetic Radiation	Chap. 17
Chap. 11	Systems Containing Identical Particles	Chaps. 15, 16, and 19

The book is divided into parts only in order not to encumber the logical development and to enable the teacher to select the applications according to the length of the course, the interests of the class, and the amount of other reading that he may wish to include.

The text contains a number of problems in which steps of the proofs and related ideas are explored. The problems vary widely in difficulty, some even being trivial, but they are more than most people need be asked to do, and the teacher will probably want to do some of them in class.

A word about the units used in this book. Officially, they are rationalized mks system, which seems to be establishing itself in undergraduate teaching in this country. But talk of atomic diameters in meters or masses in kilograms still rings harshly on the ear, and in addition I have had to listen to passionate denunciations of the electrical units from physicists who, though they would not set the gravitational constant equal to unity, would prefer to dispense with ε_0 and μ_0, not to mention 4π. While it is undoubtedly true that Coulomb's law, and the many formulas in atomic physics which derive from it, look best in the old form, it seems to me that nothing is as important as being able to perform useful computations without thinking about units. Fortunately, a compromise is possible. I write Coulomb's law as e'^2/r with $e'^2 = e^2/4\pi\varepsilon_0$. e' does well enough in most situations, and if one wishes to calculate a transition probability or a susceptibility, one can easily reinstate the e.

Acknowledgements. To my colleague Professor Franzo Crawford and to an unknown reviewer for their comments on the manuscript and to Mr. S. Gerald Kirsch for his assistance in getting it ready. To Miss Pamela Tombs and to Katharine and Rachel Park for their help with proofreading and the index. Finally, it is a pleasure to thank my students, who have listened to the development of these ideas over more than a decade and whose shrewd questions and blank stares have often shown me the way to go. For what it is worth, I dedicate my book to them.

David Park

To the Reader

It will be well to try to make clear at the outset what is entailed in learning this subject. It is not merely learning some new physics. It is much more learning to look at old physics in a new and better way—it sounds new because the ordinary vocabulary of science and everyday life is not well adapted to the uses of quantum theory, and it is better because the new theory is in agreement with experiment over a far wider range of phenomena than the old. It obtains its results in most cases by reasoning which cannot be explained in classical terms, but this does not mean that it renders the classical theory wrong or obsolete. It concerns itself largely with questions to which the older viewpoint cannot be applied, but the latter has, it seems, a permanent place in physics because it deals in a natural way with phenomena which ordinarily present themselves to the human senses. There exists, therefore, a very special relationship between quantum mechanics and Newtonian physics, and it will be noticed that all the final results of calculations in the new theory are expressed in the language of the old. It is thus in the calculation of physical results that one makes the closest contact with what is familiar, and that is why this book offers a variety of worked-out examples of the theory's application in its Part II. Most people will probably learn more from this part than from the first.

A word of advice. Do not ignore the problems in reading the text; they are in many cases designed to call attention to matters that you may not have noticed. Most of the book is designed to be read with a pencil and paper at hand, and the reader is not supposed to be able to master it otherwise. Steps are omitted from some of the proofs and some of the calculations are curtailed, not because the author is lazy but in order to encourage the reader to participate. Such gaps are very narrow in the beginning and get wider toward the end. None is very wide; if it appears so, you are probably off the track.

A final word. This is a physical theory, constructed out of concrete physical ideas. It is expressed mathematically because that is the way to express this kind of thinking. Everything possible has been done to make this book easy mathematically; things which the author has been unable to simplify he has omitted. If, therefore, you have trouble at any point, try to see whether the difficulty is in physics or in mathematics. Divide and conquer.

Contents

part **ii**   APPLICATIONS

part I
Theory

Prudence, indeed, will dictate that governments long established should not be changed for light and transient causes; and accordingly all experience hath shown that mankind are more disposed to suffer, while evils are sufferable, than to right themselves by abolishing the forms to which they are accustomed.

Thomas Jefferson

1

The Inadequacy of Classical Physics

Anyone preparing a revolution must expect to be asked whether the step is really necessary, and he will, if he is wise, begin his manifesto by showing that it is so. To see that the Newtonian view of physical reality must be superseded, we shall therefore start by examining in the light of ordinary, intuitive notions of reality some straightforward experiments which various people have done. These notions of reality form the framework of physical ideas in which we were all brought up and out of which Newtonian physics and its offshoots have developed. Details of the experiments will be omitted on the assumption that the reader will have encountered most of these things before.

1.1 The Wave Nature of Light

Our definite knowledge about the wave nature of light begins with Dr. Thomas Young, who in 1802 published a paper on optical interference (a term which he introduced) in which the phenomena are explained in terms which would be perfectly acceptable today. Earlier workers had imagined light as a beam of corpuscles (Newton), a sequence of puffs in a luminiferous medium (Huyghens), and occasionally as a wave in which a definite frequency corresponds to a pure color (Euler), but Young was the first to see that by assuming that light is a wave, he could explain quantitatively a wide variety of diffraction phenomena which were then known. To do this he formulated what we shall call the *principle of superposition:* that if two light waves arrive at the same point, their effect is exactly equivalent to that of a third wave whose displacement at that point is equal to the (algebraic) sum of the displacements of the component waves. The superposition of two beams of light of the same wavelength can be carried out in two ways: *coherently*, so that there is a definite and constant phase relation between the two beams, or *incoherently*, so that there is not. The characteristic interference phenomena of light are found only when the superposition is coherent, and this must be achieved by deriving both beams from a common source. Otherwise, the addition of two beams merely produces an intensity which is the sum of the separate intensities. (Though there is a definite phase relation between the two beams at every moment, it is not constant, and an average washes out the interference patterns.)

The typical arrangement for demonstrating the coherent superposition of two light beams is illustrated in Fig. 1.1, which shows the beams coming from a common source, being divided by a diaphragm, and recombining at a screen, which may be a photographic plate. The intensity pattern at the screen is accounted for by supposing that the wave amplitudes add. The possibility of performing such an addition is quite evident if the waves are mechanical in nature (Young thought they probably were) so that the displacement is a mechanical displacement. It is not quite so evident if one doesn't know what kind of waves they are, but that the superposition of two light beams forms a third is conclusively shown by Young's experiments.

Fig. 1.1 **Diffraction of light by double slits.**

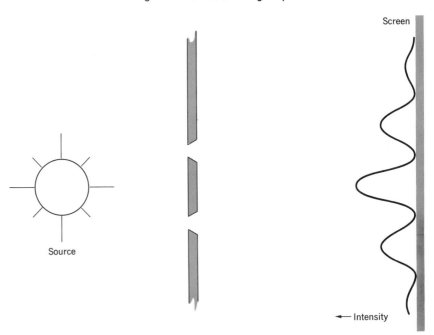

Screen

Source

←— Intensity

Later, in 1817, Young proposed to account for polarization phenomena by supposing the waves to be transverse—he used the now common analogy with waves on a rope. But this by no means answers all the questions that one can ask about light. First there is the nature of the medium in which the undulations occur, the so-called ether. Popular writings on relativity often assert that the ether has finally been done away with. This is by no means the case,[1] but at least we know that there is nothing remotely resembling a fluid or solid medium with mechanical waves running through it. More important for our purposes is the fact that a knowledge of the properties of light waves traveling in free space by no means completely characterizes light. It does not enable one to understand its emission or absorption, for example, or to predict what will happen when the waves move from air into glass or vice versa. (In this case the refraction can be explained à la Huyghens, but not the partial reflection that occurs.) We need an equation, or a set of equations, which will describe all these things and of which the monochromatic plane waves of a simple diffraction experiment represent particular solutions.

What is known about these aspects of light can be summed up in the idea of an electromagnetic wave. In 1861, James Clerk Maxwell succeeded in characterizing the electric and magnetic fields, their relation to charges and currents, and the relations between them in terms of a set of eight partial differential equations.[2] As long as the fields are static or nearly so, the general physical content of these equations can be understood from a knowledge of Coulomb's law and the right-hand rule for magnetic fields. But when time variation becomes important, entirely new phenomena begin to emerge, and, in particular, Maxwell found that it is possible to have wavelike configurations of electric and magnetic fields which are entirely disconnected from their sources and propagate through space at the well-known speed c. In subsequent years it was proved that the visible spectrum of light and its prolongations at each end are electromagnetic waves of this kind.

With Maxwell's equations one can explain a great variety of phenomena relating to the propagation, dispersion, reflection, refraction, and interference of electromagnetic waves, essentially all of which are found to correspond with known properties of light. Thus they provide the rigorous mathematical foundation of Young's hypothesis.

1.2 The Particle Nature of Light

The idea of light as a stream of particles originated with the ancients but in modern times stems from Newton. His espousal of it at first

---

[1] See Einstein's essay "Ether and Relativity" in *Sidelights on Relativity*, Methuen & Co., Ltd., London, 1922.

[2] See Appendix 5.

seems paradoxical, especially in view of his own experiments on interference, diffraction, and polarization, but he argued that only the corpuscular theory of light can explain sharp shadows. The wave theory would lead one to expect to receive light, as easily as one receives sound, from around the corner of a building. (How can Newton's argument be countered today?) Deeper than this, however, Newton was a thoroughgoing atomist, and it went against his instinct of the uniformity of nature to suppose that matter is one thing and light something entirely different. In this, as we shall see, he was perfectly right.

The first contemporary suggestion of the discrete nature of light is found in the work of Max Planck in 1900. It is unnecessary to discuss this work in detail, and the reader will probably have encountered it elsewhere,[3] but we shall summarize it by saying that in order to calculate the spectral distribution function of black-body radiation, Planck assumed a hollow cavity lined with little oscillators, and he then found that the correct distribution could not be obtained as long as it was assumed that the oscillators can gain and lose radiant energy continuously. He was obliged to assume that each oscillator of frequency ν is able to exist only in discrete states whose energies are separated by the interval $h\nu$, where h is Planck's constant,

$$h = 6.6256 \times 10^{-27} \text{ erg-sec} \tag{1.1}$$

Planck's conclusions related to the material oscillators lining the cavity; but it is clear that the energy at frequency ν given out by such oscillators will occur in quanta of energy $h\nu$, so that a discontinuity is thereby introduced into the radiation field as well. It was not at first clear whether this was an essential property of radiation or whether it was merely related to the particular system considered. Further, there was, of course, no reason to think that the radiant energy would stay together once it was emitted; rather, one would expect it to spread out like the circular ripple caused by a stone falling into water. But in 1905, Einstein, considering the radiation in a cavity as a gas of particles, showed that if each particle has an energy $h\nu$, then it is possible to understand Planck's formula for the entropy of black-body radiation as though it were a formula from the kinetic theory of gases.[4]

Einstein was at once able to explain several puzzling facts about radiation, notably that a change in the intensity of the light ab-

[3] For example, F. K. Richtmyer, E. H. Kennard, and T. Lauritsen, *Introduction to Modern Physics*, 5th ed., McGraw-Hill Book Company, Inc., New York, 1955, chap. 4. This book is an excellent reference for many of the subjects discussed in this chapter.

[4] A. Einstein, Ann. Physik, **17,** 132 (1905). The agreement is good only at large values of ν because, as will be seen in Chap. 18, the kinetic theory of a gas of light quanta has a somewhat different statistical basis than that envisaged in the classical theory.

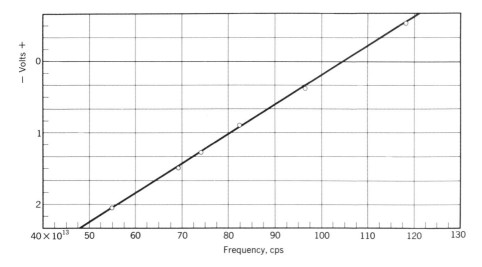

Fig. 1.2 Millikan's data for the potential necessary to stop the fastest photoelectrons produced by monochromatic light plotted against the frequency of the light. [From Phys. Rev., **7,** 355 (1916), by permission.]

sorbed in the photoelectric process does not affect the energy of the photoelectrons, but produces a proportionate change in their number. Introducing the work function φ, where $e\varphi$ represents the least energy required to remove an electron from the metal surface, Einstein predicted that the kinetic energy of the fastest electrons emitted would vary with ν according to

$$(\tfrac{1}{2}mv^2)_{\max} = h\nu - e\varphi \tag{1.2}$$

This relation proved exceptionally difficult to verify, but at length, in 1915, Millikan was able to show that it was accurately fulfilled.[5] Figure 1.2, taken from Millikan's second paper, shows the agreement between theory and experiment. By this time Einstein's theory had received another independent test in its application to Bohr's theory of atoms, and Einstein received a Nobel prize for it in 1921.

If light is considered to be made up of particles all traveling with the fundamental velocity c, then these particles should possess momentum as well as energy. The relation between energy E and momentum p in relativistic mechanics is

$$E^2 = (cp)^2 + (mc^2)^2 \tag{1.3}$$

[5] R. A. Millikan, Phys. Rev., **7,** 18, 355 (1916). The final value obtained for h is $(6.57 \pm 0.03) \times 10^{-27}$ erg-sec. As has often happened in the measurement of fundamental constants, the author was optimistic in his estimate of uncertainty.

for a free particle whose rest mass is m. [Derived as Eq. (14.25), we can here set $V = 0$.] If a photon is a particle whose rest mass is zero, this gives

$$E = cp \qquad (1.4)$$

Unfortunately, this relation cannot be used very simply to test the light quantum hypothesis, since the densities of energy and momentum in a radiation beam are predicted by Maxwell's electromagnetic theory to be in the same ratio. But experiments measuring the recoil of a single microscopic particle under the action of a single quantum are decisive. It was shown by Compton[6] in 1922 that the ordinary conservation laws of energy and momentum require that if a photon is scattered through an angle ϑ by collision with a free electron of mass m, its wavelength should increase by an amount $\Delta\lambda = (2h/mc) \sin^2 \frac{1}{2}\vartheta$, a relation which has been verified in extensive X-ray experiments by Compton and others. The explicit appearance of h in this formula, unlike (1.4), shows that the phenomenon cannot be explained on the basis of Maxwell's theory.

Problem 1.1 Use the relativistic formulas for momentum and energy to derive the above formula governing Compton scattering. Why are the experiments performed using X rays?

Problem 1.2 Show that it is impossible for a photon striking a free electron to be absorbed and not scattered.

Even more direct, though far more difficult, is the verification that when an atom emits a quantum of energy $h\nu$ in one direction, it recoils with a momentum $h\nu/c$ in the opposite direction. Though the recoil velocity of the atom is very much less than its thermal velocity, a delicate experiment by Frisch[7] showed that sodium atoms in a narrow beam are deviated from their paths by about the expected amount when they are caused to radiate.

Problem 1.3 What is the expected recoil velocity of a sodium atom which when at rest emits a quantum of its D radiation ($\lambda = 5890$ Å)? Design a beam experiment in which one might hope to detect this recoil.

In view of the known successes of Maxwell's theory, it looks at this point as though the reader were being invited to conclude that light is at the same time a wave and a particle. Such a conclusion is, of course, absurd; the two models are irreconcilable. A closer look, however, reveals that whereas the wave picture is established by its correspondence with Maxwell's theory and the phenomena of interference and diffraction which it explains, the particle picture has a rather different basis. In fact, all we have shown is that the

[6] A. H. Compton, Phys. Rev., **21**, 483 (1923).
[7] R. Frisch, Z. Physik, **86**, 42 (1933).

electromagnetic field carries momentum and energy and that, when it exchanges them with matter, it does so discontinuously; this fact does not justify one in assuming that light consists of particles. But the notion of a light quantum as a particle carrying energy and momentum (and frequency!) is still a convenient aid to visualizing certain processes, and for this reason we shall not try to banish it. This question is further discussed in Sec. 2.1, but it is clear at the outset that the development of a consistent and unambiguous terminology, in which one can discuss experiments of all different kinds, is going to require an imaginative insight which takes us rather far from the classical notions of reality.

In order to make as clear as possible the nature of the difficulties to be overcome, let us consider again the interference experiment illustrated in Fig. 1.1. The particle picture is of no help here, for it makes sense to talk of the intensity of a beam of particles but not its amplitude, and the construction of the interference pattern explicitly requires the superposition of the amplitudes of the component waves. A further indication of the shortcomings of this picture is given by experiments on interference between light beams which are so faint that, in the particle picture, there would almost never be two particles inside the apparatus at the same time.[8] A particle, if such there were, would go through only one slit. Thus the existence of the other slit would make no difference and an incoherent superposition would result. In fact, however, when a long exposure is made, ordinary wave interference fringes are produced, the conflict between wave and particle pictures being made especially striking by the fact that, as always, the darkening of the photographic plate is due to the blackening of certain grains while others are left unaffected. This represents a typical quantum phenomenon.

It is worth noting what would happen if one were to move the photographic plate to a position just behind the double slit and expose it for an interval brief enough that not more than one quantum would be likely to pass through the apparatus. In that case (omitting observations in which no quantum is found), a grain of the emulsion just behind one slit or the other would be blackened. The wave goes through both slits (as witness the diffraction pattern) but the "particle" goes through only one. Put more exactly, we see that a given wave, though it exists at many points, is absorbed at only one, and an examination of the grains of a photographic image gives one the strong impression that these points are located at random. The result of this last conceptual experiment is somewhat paradoxical, since if the photographic plate just behind the slits shows that the "quantum"—that is, the energy—flowed through one of the slits, it is still not at all plain how the other slit

⁸ G. I. Taylor, Proc. Cambridge Phil. Soc., **15**, 114 (1909); A. J. Dempster and H. F. Batho, Phys. Rev., **30**, 644 (1927).

can influence the diffraction pattern. The paradox can be resolved (Sec.3.5), but before we can do so some new ideas must be developed.

1.3 The Behavior of Electrons

The existence of electrons as particles and even the magnitude of the electronic charge were inferred during the late nineteenth century from experiments on gaseous ions, and it was presently shown (by J. J. Thomson and others) that the electrons in a beam of electrons obey Newton's laws of motion as regards the acceleration and deflection of the beam.

Problem 1.4 Electrons are accelerated by falling through a potential V and are then deflected by passing between a pair of parallel plates of given size across which there is a transverse electric field of E V/m. Through what angle is the beam deflected? (Neglect edge effects in comparison with the dimensions of the plates.)

Problem 1.5 Outline, giving the necessary elementary analysis, a way of finding the mass of the electron experimentally. How does one know the mass of a neutron?

For electrons confined to a small region of space, as in an atom, the situation is more obscure, since Newton's laws can give no explanation of the stability of an atomic system. That this is so is seen in Rutherford's planetary model of hydrogen, since an electron may revolve around a proton in an elliptical orbit that is of any size whatever, and depends only upon the initial conditions. This fact can be seen in a formal way if we note that the only constant parameters which enter the theory are the masses and charges of the component parts and that no constant of the dimension of a length can be formed from these numbers. (The reader should prove this for himself.) Thus Newtonian mechanics unaided is unable to account for the well-known stable structure, fairly rigid and a few times 10^{-8} cm in size, which all atoms exhibit in their collisions. The remark that with the introduction of h one can form the quantity $4\pi\varepsilon_0 h^2/me^2 \approx 20 \times 10^{-8}$ cm using the m and e of the electron led Niels Bohr, in the year following Rutherford's discovery, to the hypothesis that h enters the theory as a mechanical quantity.[9]

Bohr's famous assumptions which led him to explain the spectrum of atomic hydrogen, are, first, that the atom obeys the laws of Newtonian mechanics except that

the electron's orbital angular momentum is restricted to be an integral multiple of $h/2\pi$

[9] N. Bohr, Phil. Mag., **26**, 1, 476, 875 (1913) and subsequent papers in the same journal. It is assumed that the reader is already familiar with the general content of Bohr's theory. The remarks which follow are intended not to explain the theory, but only to call attention to certain of its features.

But the electromagnetic radiation from the atom does not follow Maxwell's theory; rather, it takes place one photon at a time, so that

> a quantum of radiation is emitted when the electron changes from one orbit to another of lower energy, the quantum's energy $h\nu$ being equal to the energy released

and

> an electron in its orbit of lowest energy does not radiate

(The fact that most of the ideas expressed and implied here had been put forth by others at various earlier dates does not in the least detract from Bohr's merit in being the first to combine them into a definite theory.) We shall speak here only of circular orbits; elliptical orbits require a further hypothesis.

Let a be the radius of the orbit and Ω the electron's angular velocity. Then Bohr's first hypothesis is that all possible orbits must satisfy

$$m a \Omega^2 = \frac{e^2}{4\pi\varepsilon_0 a^2} \tag{1.5}$$

and

$$m a^2 \Omega = n\hbar \qquad (n = 1, 2, 3, \ldots) \tag{1.6}$$

where we have introduced the notation

$$\hbar = \frac{h}{2\pi} = 1.0545 \times 10^{-34} \text{ J-sec} \tag{1.7}$$
$$= 1.0545 \times 10^{-27} \text{ erg-sec}$$
$$= 6.5820 \times 10^{-16} \text{ eV-sec}$$

and we shall rarely refer again to plain h. From these relations one finds that the radii of the possible orbits are [10]

$$a_n = n^2 a_0 \tag{1.8}$$

where the quantity

$$a_0 = \frac{4\pi\varepsilon_0 \hbar^2}{me^2} = 0.5292 \text{ Å} \tag{1.9}$$

is known as the radius of the first Bohr orbit. This accounts for the mechanical stability of hydrogen atoms. The electron's total energy in its nth orbit is

$$W_n = -\frac{1}{n^2} \text{ Ry} \tag{1.10}$$

---

[10] Obviously, the notation would be more consistent if we were to write a_1 instead of a_0, but convention rules otherwise.

where

$$\mathrm{Ry} = \frac{me^4}{2(4\pi\varepsilon_0\hbar)^2} = 13.60 \text{ eV} \qquad (1.11)$$

In terms of this quantity, the angular velocity of the electron in its orbit is

$$\Omega_n = \frac{2 \, \mathrm{Ry}}{n^3\hbar} \qquad (1.12)$$

Problem 1.6 Derive Eqs. (1.8), (1.10), and (1.12).

The possible spectral frequencies will be given by

$$\omega = \frac{1}{\hbar} \mathrm{Ry} \left(\frac{1}{n_f{}^2} - \frac{1}{n_i{}^2} \right) \qquad (n_f < n_i) \qquad (1.13)$$

where ω is 2π times the usual frequency. This coincides with Balmer's famous empirical formula.[11] As already mentioned, there will, of course, be elliptical orbits as well; but these are found to introduce no new energies, and so they will introduce no further spectral lines.[12]

It would appear from Bohr's model that the principles governing the radiation of light from an atom are completely different from those of classical physics. There is the explicit occurrence of $\hbar$ in the energy formula arising from both the angular-momentum hypothesis and the light-quantum hypothesis, and there is also the basic fact that the emitted frequencies are associated with *differences* in the states of the atom rather than with the states themselves. In fact, classical physics predicts that the fundamental frequency of the radiation emitted by an electron in a certain orbit will be that of the electron in that orbit and that there will be higher harmonics as well,[13]

$$\omega_{cl} = k\Omega_n \qquad (k = 1, 2, 3, \ldots) \qquad (1.14)$$

A look at (1.8) now shows that a remarkable situation exists. If n is chosen large enough, the radius of the "atom" will reach a size (say, 1 m) where one would expect the classical theory to be valid. We therefore have in this range two different theories applying to the same phenomenon, and we must see whether their results agree. The lowest frequencies emitted will correspond to transitions between states for which n_f is not much less than n_i. If $n_i - n_f$, which we shall call Δn, is much less than n_i, then we can expand

---

[11] J. Balmer, Ann. Physik, **25**, 80 (1885); see also Richtmyer et al., *op. cit.*, sec. 74.

[12] Ruark and Urey, *Atoms, Molecules and Quanta*, McGraw-Hill Publishing Company, Inc., New York, 1930, chap. 5.

[13] The harmonics are due essentially to Doppler shifts in the fundamental frequency as the particle moves toward and away from the observer.

the parentheses in (1.13) as

$$\frac{1}{n_f^2} - \frac{1}{n_i^2} = \frac{1}{(n_i - \Delta n)^2} - \frac{1}{n_i^2} = \frac{1}{n_i^2}\left[\frac{1}{(1 - \Delta n/n_i)^2} - 1\right]$$

Expanding the fraction in powers of $\Delta n/n$ gives

$$\frac{1}{n_f^2} - \frac{1}{n_i^2} = \frac{1}{n_i^2}\left[1 + 2\frac{\Delta n}{n_i} + \cdots - 1\right] = \frac{2\,\Delta n}{n_i^3}$$

where we have neglected higher-order terms which are unimportant when $n_i \rightarrow \infty$. This gives

$$\omega = \frac{2\,\Delta n}{n_i^3\hbar}\,\mathrm{Ry} = (\Delta n)\Omega_{n_i} \qquad (\Delta n = 1, 2, 3, \ldots) \tag{1.15}$$

by (1.12). Comparing this with (1.14), we see that there is an exact correspondence between the predictions of the classical and the quantum theories in the limiting case in which the two theories overlap. The fact that in this limit, which is characterized by large quantum numbers, quantum and classical theory must agree was termed the *correspondence principle* by Bohr in 1923, and it is one of the stringent formal requirements that any law of quantum theory must satisfy.

The correspondence principle governs the intensities as well as the frequencies of spectral lines in the limit of large quantum numbers. If the classical theory does not yield a certain frequency at all, in quantum theory the corresponding transition should not take place. The *selection rules* to which this argument gives rise are found to hold for small quantum numbers also, as is seen in an example which will be worked out in Sec. 10.3.

Problem 1.7   Discuss the correspondence limit of Eq. (1.4).

Problem 1.8   Show, using Taylor's series, that the frequency of light emitted in a transition out of a state whose energy is W_n is given by

$$\hbar\omega = \Delta n\,\frac{\partial W_n}{\partial n} - \frac{1}{2}(\Delta n)^2\,\frac{\partial^2 W_n}{\partial n^2} + \cdots \tag{1.16}$$

where Δn is the change in the quantum number n. Compare this with (1.15) and state the conditions under which the second term can be neglected in discussing Bohr's theory.

There is another important aspect of Bohr's theory which it will be interesting to compare later with the quantum-mechanical result. Suppose that an atom is put into a weak, uniform magnetic field. It is shown in classical electrodynamics that the atom will continue to function undisturbed, except that it will precess as a whole around the direction of the field (see Fig. 1.3). Let the atom's original angular momentum be P, which according to Bohr's

B

P

Fig. 1.3 Larmor precession of Bohr's hydrogen
atom in a magnetic field.

postulates will be equal to $l\hbar$, with l a positive integer.[14] The extension of Bohr's original theory to other types of periodic motion such as this precession led to the conclusion that not only the magnitude of the angular-momentum vector but also the value of its component in the direction of the field (call it z) take on discrete values:

$$P_z = m\hbar \qquad (1.17)$$

where m is an integer. Figure 1.4 shows the evenly spaced z components corresponding to $l = 3$; clearly, m can go in integer steps from $-l$ to $+l$, a total of $2l + 1$ different values. This phenomenon is known as *spatial quantization*.

It is quite generally true in classical physics that a group of electrons executing orbits whose total vector angular momentum is **P** will exhibit a magnetic moment proportional to it,

$$\mathbf{M} = \gamma\mathbf{P} \qquad (1.18)$$

with γ, the *gyromagnetic ratio*, given by

$$\gamma = \frac{e}{2m_e} \qquad (1.19)$$

where m_e is the electron's mass. (The same is true of the spin motion also, except that the gyromagnetic ratio is twice as great. This leads to complications which we wish to avoid here.) Since the energy of a magnetic dipole in a magnetic field of induction **B** is $-\mathbf{B} \cdot \mathbf{M}$, or in this case

$$-\mathbf{B} \cdot \mathbf{M} = -BM_z = -B\gamma P_z = -m\gamma\hbar B \qquad (-l \leqslant m \leqslant +l) \qquad (1.20)$$

we see that an atom in this situation has a potential energy which changes in steps as its orientation in space changes. This produces

---

[14] We neglect the effects of electron spin in this discussion. The reader who has studied Bohr's theory in any detail will recognize that the letters l and n are interchangeable in the following discussion because, in the special case of an inverse-square interaction, the energy corresponding to a given orbit depends only on the electron's angular momentum and not on the shape of the orbit.

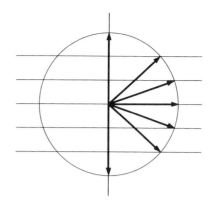

Fig. 1.4 Spatial quantization of the direction of an
angular-momentum vector $l = 3$ in Bohr's theory.

the splitting of spectral lines known as the Zeeman effect.[15] It is
not necessary here to go into the proofs of formulas such as (1.17)
and (1.18), since we shall rederive them from quantum mechanics
as we go along.

A more direct example of spatial quantization is given by the
Stern-Gerlach experiment,[16] in which the magnetic field, made
inhomogeneous, actually produces a physical separation of a beam
of atoms into components corresponding to the different values of
P_z. One would expect to find $2l + 1$ such components.

In both the experiments just described, there is poor agreement
between Bohr's theory and the empirical facts. Generally, there are
more lines than the theory predicts; this is due to the effect of electron spin, and it can be taken into account satisfactorily if one also
assumes that the orbital quantum number l can go down to zero.
With atomic hydrogen, for example, the Stern-Gerlach experiment
reveals only two traces,[17] and this is explainable if one assumes that
the electron has a spin angular momentum whose z component is
equal to $\frac{1}{2}\hbar$ and which can therefore take on two different orientations, while it has no orbital moment at all. Setting n equal to zero in
(1.6) is difficult to explain intuitively (what is the nature of an
orbit with no angular momentum?), and it also produces bad results in (1.10); we have here a paradox which quantum mechanics
will resolve.

The most peculiar thing about space quantization is this:
It is established at once, and it is independent of the strength of the
field. In fact, it exists in arbitrarily weak fields and so presumably
in the limit of no field. But in the limit, where is the z axis? The
paradox here is conceptual rather than experimental, since one
cannot detect the space quantization without applying a field, but
it is perhaps the most extreme illustration of how far one can be led

[15] Richtmyer et al., *op. cit.*, sec. 129.
[16] *Ibid.*, sec. 298.
[17] T. E. Phipps and J. B. Taylor, Phys. Rev., **29**, 309 (1927).

by Bohr's postulate of the quantization of periodic motions, a postulate which is purely *ad hoc*, with nothing in ordinary experience or intuition to justify it.

As to the ultimate results of Bohr's theory, its failures are as striking as its successes. It ended up by explaining very well the spectrum of hydrogen (and of alkali elements like sodium and potassium which have hydrogen-like spectra), but it provided no understanding of the structure or spectrum of even the next most complicated element, helium. It established the nomenclature and basic concepts for explaining atomic spectra as well as the entire periodic system of the elements; yet, except for a few arguments based solidly on the correspondence principle, it was unable to derive more than the simplest quantitative results in those fields. Further, an essential part of Bohr's theory is a set of selection rules designed to state which of the dynamically possible transitions will and which will not take place. In atomic spectra, for example, they take the form

$$\Delta l = \pm 1 \qquad \Delta m = \pm 1, 0 \tag{1.21}$$

The purely empirical character of these rules was evidence of a serious gap in the theory.

Problem 1.9 Verify (1.18) and (1.19) for an electron moving in a circular orbit.

Problem 1.10 To illustrate Larmor's theorem, imagine an electron in a circular orbit under the influence of a force attracting it toward the center. Let its angular momentum be $n\hbar$. Now let a magnetic field B be slowly turned on, perpendicular to the plane of the orbit. Assuming that n does not change, and neglecting all effects proportional to B^2, show that the electron's angular velocity in its orbit changes by $\pm eB/m$, regardless of the nature of the attracting force or the size of the orbit.

1.4 The Wave Theory of Matter

Finally, in the latter part of 1923, a new idea led to an explanation of the mysteries and inaccuracies of Bohr's theory. As things stood in 1923, one could draw up the following table:

	Light	Matter
Classical aspect	Wave phenomena (Maxwell's equations)	Particle phenomena (Newton-Einstein equations)
Quantum aspect	Particle phenomena $(E = \hbar\omega \qquad p = E/c)$	Bohr's rules $(P = n\hbar,$ etc.$)$

On the first line we have well-established phenomena governed by detailed mathematical equations: Maxwell's equations on the one hand and Newton's laws, supplemented by Einstein's relativistic modifications, on the other. On the second line the phenomena are again well established, but instead of a system of equations we have only a few empirical and not wholly successful rules for calculation. The principal problem facing physics at that moment was the completion of this table.

The necessary new idea was furnished by Louis de Broglie,[18] then a graduate student in Paris, who noted that one could attain a sort of symmetry in the foregoing table by saying that matter resembles light in having both wave and corpuscular aspects. His arguments[19] were based on relativistic properties, and so we shall not reproduce them here; a somewhat less persuasive account can be given as follows. The equations $E = \hbar\omega$, $p = E/c$ were successful in describing the particle properties of light. Let us turn them around and use them to describe wave properties of matter. Yet there is a difficulty posed by the presence of c in the equations. A nonrelativistic theory should not contain c, and the obvious correctness of Bohr's results, in which c is not involved, suggests that (at low energies) it should not enter the wave theory. The difficulty is removed by rewriting the second equation in terms of the light's wavelength λ, or rather this quantity divided by 2π, which we shall call $\lambdabar$:

$$E = \hbar\omega \qquad \text{Einstein} \tag{1.22}$$

$$p = \frac{\hbar}{\lambdabar} \qquad \text{de Broglie} \tag{1.23}$$

De Broglie suggests that a beam of particles of energy E and momentum p is to be characterized by a wavelength $2\pi\lambdabar$ and a frequency $\omega/2\pi$, and in his first paper he predicts that suitable experiments on a beam of electrons would reveal interference phenomena analogous to those of light.

Problem 1.11 What would be the approximate wavelength and frequency associated with an electron traveling at 1 cm/sec? A 1-eV electron? A pitched baseball?

It is now easy to give a physical picture of the origin of Bohr's angular-momentum rule. We have noted that quantization occurs only in systems which are restricted in space. This suggests resonances of some kind, characterized by standing waves. Consider, for

[18] The correct pronunciation of this name is difficult to render into English, but it rhymes exactly with the French word *feuille*. The reader may take comfort in the fact that most French people mispronounce it too.

[19] Compt. Rend., **177**, 107, 148 (1923). See also P. G. Bergmann, *Introduction to the Theory of Relativity*, Prentice-Hall, Inc., Englewood Cliffs, N.J., 1942, p. 143.

  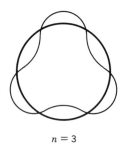

$n = 1$ $n = 2$ $n = 3$

Fig. 1.5 Orbital standing waves according
to de Broglie's hypothesis.

example, a hydrogen orbit of radius a. If the electron forms a standing wave in this orbit, then, as shown in Fig. 1.5, the circumference
will be an integral number of wavelengths, or

$$2\pi a = n\lambda \qquad (n = 1, 2, \ldots)$$

From this and (1.23) we have for the angular momentum

$$P = mva = n\frac{mv\lambda}{2\pi} = n\hbar$$

which is exactly Bohr's rule for angular momenta. The important
idea here is that the discrete atomic energy states are analogous to
the discrete overtones of a vibrating system such as a violin string
or a column of air. This suggestion is the basis of our present understanding of stationary atomic states.

The first paper closes with the words, "We are now in a position
to explain the phenomena of diffraction and interference in terms
which take account of the existence of light quanta." In fact, it was
reserved for others to do this, since de Broglie had not fully realized
how the principle of superposition applies to matter waves. But he
had discovered a new aspect of the uniformity of nature, the universality of the relation between waves and particles, calling for a
new form of dynamics which should be to Newtonian dynamics as
wave optics is to geometrical optics.

The wave nature of electrons was exhibited four years later
in the beautiful experiments of Davisson and Germer, of the Bell
Laboratories,[20] who directed a beam of electrons onto a suitably
oriented nickel crystal. The reflected beams showed a lobed pattern

[20] Phys. Rev., **30**, 705 (1927). It is interesting that Davisson's original
experiment started out as a study of secondary electron emission from a tungsten target, and that if the target had not accidentally been overheated in the
course of outgassing, it would have remained so. The heat caused the worked
tungsten surface to recrystallize into a single crystal suitable for detecting diffraction effects.

which could be analyzed exactly analogously to the Laue patterns of X-ray diffraction[21] and were in excellent agreement with de Broglie's formula. But one may still ask whether the wave property is a general one—does it apply to composite objects as well as electrons and photons? The answer was provided in a remarkable experiment by Stern and his collaborators,[22] who produced a beam of slow helium atoms by means of a mechanical velocity selector and diffracted it from a lithium fluoride crystal. The measured wavelength corresponded exactly with (1.23) if p was taken to be the momentum of the system as a whole.

Problem 1.12 The wavelength λ as measured in this experiment was about 0.60 Å. What was the velocity of the incident He atoms? To what temperature would this velocity correspond?

It is natural to ask how fast a matter wave travels through space. Suppose first that we have a uniform, "monochromatic" beam containing only a single frequency and wavelength:

$$\sin 2\pi \left(\frac{x}{\lambda} - \nu t \right)$$

or, introducing the abbreviation $k = 2\pi/\lambda = 1/\lambda$,

$$\sin (kx - \omega t)$$

The velocity of a point in this wave which has a certain fixed phase, say, a particular crest or trough, is clearly ω/k, corresponding to the usual expression $\lambda\nu$. If we consider a free particle with velocity v, for which

$$E = \hbar\omega = \tfrac{1}{2}mv^2$$
$$p = \hbar k = mv$$

(1.24)

this *phase velocity* v_φ is

$$v_\varphi = \frac{\hbar\omega}{\hbar k} = \tfrac{1}{2}v$$

(1.25)

At first sight this seems to be in error, but one must be careful. The reason why there is no conflict with experiment here is that v_φ is not an observable quantity. A uniform beam is essentially a stationary object, for it has no distinguishing mark by which its velocity could be measured. The beam needs to be modulated in some way; and we shall show that the speed of the modulated pattern is in fact v, the corresponding particle velocity. Of this we shall give two proofs, a general one in Sec. 3.4, which is so general that one can't really see how it works, and a more specific one now.

[21] Ruark and Urey, *op. cit.*, chap. 21.
[22] Estermann, Frisch, and Stern, Z. Physik, **73**, 348 (1931).

The simplest way to represent a modulated beam is by the *coherent* superposition of two beams having somewhat different frequencies and wavelengths, for example

$$\sin\left[(k + \Delta k)x - (\omega + \Delta\omega)t\right] + \sin\left(kx - \omega t\right)$$

This sum is equal to

$$2\cos\left(\frac{\Delta k}{2}x - \frac{\Delta\omega}{2}t\right)\sin\left(k'x - \omega't\right) \tag{1.26}$$

where k' and ω' are the averages of the two constituent wave numbers and frequencies. The first cosine represents the modulation; and *its* phase velocity, which is termed the *group velocity* of the combination, v_g, is $\Delta\omega/\Delta k$. For a practical experiment, $\Delta\omega$ and Δk would have to be rather small compared with ω and k (how small?); it is convenient to take the limit and write

$$v_g = \frac{d\omega}{dk} \tag{1.27}$$

with ω expressed as a function of k. With (1.24) this is dE/dp, and with $E = p^2/2m$ for a free particle we have

$$v_g = v \tag{1.28}$$

so that the apparent contradiction is reconciled. This method of resolving the difficulty should be taken as warning that quantum mechanics, like electromagnetism, contains unphysical quantities, and one must therefore always think about it in experimental terms. This is a hard lesson to learn, and it is here, and not in the mathematics, that most of the difficulty of the subject lies.

1.5 The Principle of Superposition

The foregoing explanation of the velocity paradox involves no new assumptions; for the basic trick, the representation of a modulated wave as the superposition of two (or more) unmodulated ones, has already been seen to be essential to the explanation of interference phenomena. One has to be able to add amplitudes. But it is precisely this coherent superposition of amplitudes that is unknown in the classical theory of particles, which explains why the theory can never in any way explain interference phenomena. We have referred to the idea that the amplitude corresponding to a physical object may be written as the sum of other amplitudes as the *principle of superposition*. It is as fundamental to quantum mechanics as it is to optics and acoustics. And one is quite accustomed to treating electrical problems in the same way. To analyze the action of an LC filter in smoothing a rectified voltage, one performs a Fourier analysis of the latter, considers it as the sum of the sinusoidal voltages, and calculates the response of the filter to each. Whether the applied signal actually "is" an irregular waveform or the sum of sinusoidal ones is a meaningless question. It is both, or it may be represented in other ways—for example, as the sum of a series of brief pulses. The superposition may correspond to an actual physical superposition (coherent!) of two systems, or it may be merely a mathematical device to simplify calculation. In many cases it can be regarded both ways.

In order to express this principle mathematically, we must have something to superpose, something which will be analogous to the potentials superposed in network analysis or the vectors **E** and **H** which one superposes in Maxwell's theory. We shall call this quantity by the neutral name *wave function* and denote it by $\psi(x,y,z,t)$. It is a scalar quantity and, as in the other two cases just mentioned, we shall suppose that it specifies all that can be known about the system it represents. A major problem before us is to find the exact physical interpretation of ψ. The object of any theory is to enable one to understand specific experimental results from a general standpoint, so that we must have a set of rules which will enable us, knowing ψ, to predict what results a certain measurement will give.

A second major problem can be spotted in the table on page 16. The reason why the classical theories are so richly documented by experiment is that they are based on *equations of motion*. As set forth in the table, the quantum aspect is not so fortunate, since it is expressed only in a set of rules due to Einstein, Bohr, and now de Broglie. The quantum theory cannot hope to have anything like the power and generality of the classical theory until it too is expressed in terms of an equation of motion.

The analogy of Maxwell's theory suggests that ψ will satisfy a partial differential equation. Such an equation cannot be derived *a priori* any more than Newton's second law can be; but we can at least suggest something of how such an equation can be arrived at, and learn something about ψ in the process. Let us consider the uniform wave corresponding to a beam of free particles moving along the x axis. Its ψ will be a periodic function of $(kx - \omega t)$, where k and ω satisfy (1.24) and are therefore related by

$$\hbar\omega = \frac{\hbar^2 k^2}{2m} \tag{1.29}$$

The differential equation must be a reflection of this relation. By differentiating ψ with respect to x or t, we obtain a multiplicative factor of k or ω. It must therefore be differentiated once to get ω and twice to get k^2. The only function which remains of the same form whether differentiated once or twice is the exponential, so that writing

$$\psi = A e^{i(kx-\omega t)} \tag{1.30}$$

where A is a constant amplitude, we readily find that

$$i\hbar\,\frac{\partial\psi}{\partial t} + \frac{\hbar^2}{2m}\frac{\partial^2\psi}{\partial x^2} = \left(\hbar\omega - \frac{\hbar^2 k^2}{2m}\right)\psi = 0$$

This equation

$$i\hbar\,\frac{\partial\psi}{\partial t} + \frac{\hbar^2}{2m}\frac{\partial^2\psi}{\partial x^2} = 0 \tag{1.31}$$

is satisfied by the proposed wave function (1.30), though it is not the only such equation, nor is (1.30) the only wave function which fulfills the requirements from which it was derived. But it is the simplest possibility, and it happens to be experimentally the right one. It is derived above only for the simple exponential wave function (1.30), but it is valid for any k and the corresponding ω. If we assume (see Sec. 2.4) that all possible wave functions can be represented by Fourier superposition of such exponentials, we conclude that they all satisfy (1.31), since the sum of any set of solutions of (1.31) is itself a solution. (Why?)

Equation (1.31) was first given by Erwin Schrödinger at Zurich in 1926; his derivation depends on aspects of Newtonian mechanics somewhat more advanced than those we are using here, but, together with the interpretation of ψ, which was arrived at later, it completed the first stage in the development of quantum mechanics.[23] In the form (1.31) it refers only to free particles moving in one dimension. We shall see how to introduce forces in Chap. 3.

Schrödinger's equation is a single partial differential equation and therefore simpler than Maxwell's eight equations (which can be reduced to three), but it introduces a great novelty, $\sqrt{-1}$. One is used to encountering this quantity in alternating-current theory, but only because it is put there as a computational device. The basic equations, like the currents and voltages, are real. But here i enters into both the equation (1.31) and its simplest form of solution, (1.30). It is to be presumed that the actual results of quantum mechanics, expressed as observable quantities, will be real numbers, and much will be made of this fact later; but an equation is not an observable thing, and there is no reason why it should not involve i. Further, we shall see that ψ is not itself an observable, though its wavelength, for example, is. This is less surprising if one remembers that E and H are not observables either, though they have a simple connection with observable quantities in terms of forces which they exert. The ψ function has no simple connection of this kind.

Problem 1.13 Replace Schrödinger's complex equation with a pair of real equations by (a) writing $\psi(x,t) = \psi_1(x,t) + i\psi_2(x,t)$ with ψ_1 and ψ_2 real and separating real and imaginary parts, (b)

---

[23] Schrödinger's work is brilliantly described in his *Collected Papers on Wave Mechanics*, Blackie and Son, Ltd., Glasgow, 1928.

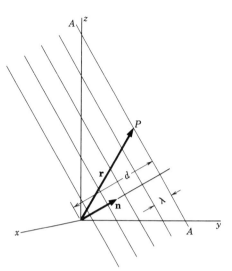

Fig. 1.6 Side view of plane waves in three dimensions. The wavelength is λ, and $\mathbf{n}$ is a unit vector normal to the plane of the waves.

writing $\psi(x,t) = A(x,t)e^{i\varphi(x,t)}$ with A and φ real and finding the real equations satisfied by A and φ. Is any simplicity gained by this?

The foregoing considerations are all for one spatial dimension. To generalize to three dimensions, we need an expression analogous to (1.30) which will describe a plane wave. Figure 1.6 shows the wave fronts of such a wave as a series of parallel planes separated by a distance λ. Let $\mathbf{n}$ be a unit vector normal to the wave fronts. Then if $\mathbf{r}$ gives the position of any point P on a certain wave front A, it satisfies the relation $\mathbf{n} \cdot \mathbf{r} = d$, where d is the normal distance from the origin to the wave front A. The spatial part of the phase of this wave front with respect to a plane passing through the origin is $2\pi d/\lambda = d/\lambda = (\mathbf{n} \cdot \mathbf{r})/\lambda$. Analogously to the number k introduced above, let us define

$$\frac{\mathbf{n}}{\lambda} = \mathbf{k} \tag{1.32}$$

the *propagation vector* of the wave. Then, including the time factor, the wave function for a plane wave is

$$\psi = Ae^{i(\mathbf{k}\cdot\mathbf{r}-\omega t)} \tag{1.33}$$

In three dimensions, the momentum vector of a particle has the magnitude of $\hbar/\lambda$ and the direction of $\mathbf{n}$; it is given by

$$\mathbf{p} = \hbar\mathbf{k} \tag{1.34}$$

analogously to (1.24). Finally, the natural generalization of (1.31) is

$$i\hbar \frac{\partial\psi}{\partial t} + \frac{\hbar^2}{2m} \nabla^2\psi = 0 \tag{1.35}$$

and it is easy to verify that if (1.33) is put in, one again finds (1.29). Thus, (1.35) is Schrödinger's equation for a free particle in three dimensions.

The occurrence of stationary energy levels in nature can be qualitatively understood from (1.31); for its spatial part, see (1.36) below, has exactly the same form as the equation which arises in the study of a vibrating string (see any text on mechanics or general theoretical physics). A treatment in parallel columns, starting with (1.31), will exhibit the similarities and differences.

Vibrating string	**Schrödinger's equation**
$$\frac{\partial^2 u}{\partial x^2} = \frac{1}{v^2}\frac{\partial^2 u}{\partial t^2}$$	$$\frac{\partial^2 \psi}{\partial x^2} = -i\,\frac{2m}{\hbar}\frac{\partial \psi}{\partial t}$$

where v is the velocity of waves in the string. We now consider the "normal modes," that is, the modes of motion which are simply periodic in time.

Let $u \propto \cos \omega t$

$$\frac{\partial^2 u}{\partial x^2} = -\left(\frac{\omega}{v}\right)^2 u$$

Let the string, of length L, be fastened at both ends, so that $u(0) = u(L) = 0$. The solution of the last equation is

$$u = A \sin \frac{n\pi x}{L}$$

$$(n = 1, 2, 3, \ldots)$$

with

$$\left(\frac{\omega}{v}\right)^2 = \left(\frac{n\pi}{L}\right)^2$$

or

$$\omega = n\pi \frac{v}{L}$$

Let $\psi \propto e^{-iEt/\hbar}$

$$\frac{\partial^2 \psi}{\partial x^2} = -\frac{2mE}{\hbar^2}\psi \qquad (1.36)$$

Let the particle be confined to a region of length L by impenetrable walls at which the wave function vanishes, $\psi(0) = \psi(L) = 0$. Then

$$\psi = B \sin \frac{n\pi x}{L}$$

$$(n = 1, 2, 3, \ldots)$$

with

$$\frac{2mE}{\hbar^2} = \left(\frac{n\pi}{L}\right)^2$$

or

$$E = n^2 \frac{\hbar^2}{2m}\frac{\pi^2}{L^2}$$

The string's energy depends on the amplitude of its vibration as well as its density ρ, and it is calculated as[24]

$$E = n^2 A^2 \rho v^2 \frac{\pi^2}{4L}$$

We see how stationary energy levels are going to be explained as standing-wave phenomena, but we note the characteristic difference that the energy of the matter wave does not depend on its

[24] C. A. Coulson, *Waves*, Interscience Publishers, Inc., New York, 1944.

amplitude. This is, of course, already reminiscent of the photo-electric effect, in which the energy of the ejected electrons is independent of the amplitude of the incident light waves; but in order to understand it, we shall have to have a clear idea of what the wave function ψ actually represents. Subsidiary questions are "What is the special importance of normal modes?" and "Why does one impose the boundary condition that $\psi(0) = \psi(L) = 0$?" Such questions can be answered only if we have a precise physical interpretation for ψ; the next chapter is devoted to this. Chapter 3 shows how to write down the wave equation for a particle acted upon by external forces and discusses some general quantum-mechanical properties of physical systems. Then Chap. 4 will return to a more detailed study of phenomena of free and bound electrons, considered in one dimension for simplicity, and including discrete energy levels as we have roughly sketched the theory above.

2

The Wave Function

In the last chapter we talked about matter waves and gave them a definite frequency and wavelength; by doing so we were able to throw light on some of the characteristic phenomena of microphysics. In this chapter we shall find a physical interpretation for these waves and try to answer the obvious question, "What is it that is waving?" It is clear that to go from a picture of elementary processes in terms of particles to one in terms of waves is such a large conceptual jump that the question of interpretation is not one which can be answered in a few lines. We shall therefore first write down a physical interpretation for the wave function ψ and then see at some length how it is possible to infer information regarding particles from a knowledge of it.

2.1 The Meaning of ψ

Throughout most of the nineteenth century it was generally assumed that physical phenomena have their ultimate explanation in terms of conventional mechanics and that Newton's laws, or something like them, are thus the cornerstone of physics. The main obstacle to this view was electromagnetism, where the facts are reasonably simple but to explain them in terms of mechanical processes in an ether involves one in enormous complexities. Finally, it became clear from Einstein's work that to explain electromagnetic waves in terms of undulations of a mechanical medium is impossible; the world learned to its profit that the E and H of Maxwell's theory are fields and that the waves are waves in these fields. Similarly, we shall assume that ψ is a field, a function of

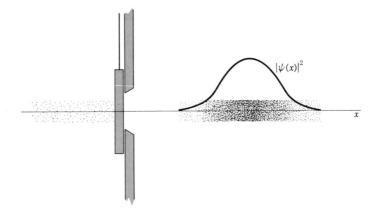

Fig. 2.1 A briefly open shutter allows a group of electrons to pass through. $|\psi|^2$ measures their intensity.

x, y, z, and t, and that it is defined throughout the region of space and interval of time under consideration. We shall think of it as a function of those four variables which is continuous and differentiable except possibly at a few points.

The intensity of a wave is proportional to the square of its amplitude. This is true of mechanical waves in material media, and also of electromagnetic waves. We have noted in the preceding chapter that a peculiar feature of ψ is that its values are complex numbers.[1] We shall therefore—insisting that intensity must be represented by a real number—guess that the intensity of a matter wave is proportional to the square of the absolute magnitude of ψ, that is, the quantity $\psi^*\psi$ or, as it is usually written, $|\psi|^2$.

Suppose, for example, that a shutter (Fig. 2.1) opens and closes on a beam of electrons so that only a short group passes through. The intensity is essentially zero outside the group and is at a maximum at the center. Its graph has been sketched in the figure.

But suppose that the intensity of the beam incident from the left is much reduced, so that only one electron passes through while the shutter is open (Fig. 2.2). Now what does $|\psi|^2$ signify? To say that $|\psi|^2$ is an intensity is quite sufficient when one is talking of an almost continuous beam of electrons, where the particle properties are not in evidence. But when one wishes to discuss the clicks of a Geiger counter or the blackening of individual grains in a photographic plate—that is, as soon as the energy $\hbar\omega$ is appreciable and there are not too many quanta—the language has to be made more precise. Suppose that a light wave of a certain intensity blackens, on the average, 20 grains/mm² of a plate exposed to it for 1 sec. The first thing we note is that knowing the intensity of the beam does not enable us to predict which grains will be blackened or even exactly how many will be blackened in a particular square milli-

---

[1] Appendix 1 contains a brief discussion of complex numbers.

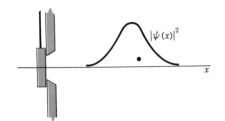

Fig. 2.2 Situation as in Fig. 2.1 except that the incident beam is so weak that only a single electron passes through.

meter. All it enables us to say is what will happen if we perform the experiment many times and average the results. But it is also the business of physics to specify what will happen in individual cases. If the experiment is to be performed only once, then clearly the language of averages is inappropriate. We must specify a probability. Probabilities are the natural extension to a small number of cases of the ideas which we have previously expressed in terms of averages.

Suppose, for example, that it is known (as in Fig. 2.2) that only a single electron is present. The quantity $|\psi(x,t)|^2$ will have to do with the probability of finding a single electron if one looks for it at the point x at the instant t. More exactly, one searches not at a point, but in a small region around that point. Therefore, we shall postulate that $|\psi(x,t)|^2\, dx$ is equal to the probability of finding the electron[2] in the element dx, centered at the point x at the time t. Finally, the integral of $|\psi|^2$ over the entire space available to the electron is the total probability of finding it there. To the extent that an electron is a permanent thing it must certainly be found somewhere, and we shall designate this certainty by a probability of 1:

$$\int |\psi(x,t)|^2\, dx = 1 \tag{2.1}$$

where the integration is over the entire range of values of x, normally from $-\infty$ to $+\infty$.

More realistically, of course, things in nature are distributed in space and not along lines. Thus we shall take $|\psi(x,y,z,t)|^2\, dx\, dy\, dz$ to be the probability that at the time t the electron is located in the volume element $dx\, dy\, dz$ centered at the point (x,y,z). Analogously to (2.1), we must have

$$\int |\psi(x,y,z,t)|^2\, dx\, dy\, dz = 1 \tag{2.2}$$

---

[2] If there is more than one electron (and, of course, there usually is) the wave function involves coordinates referring to each of them and is more complicated in form, though the interpretation is still essentially the same. We shall discuss this further in Chaps. 7 and 11. Meanwhile, it should be noted that if one is trying to think quantum-mechanically about the behavior of a swarm of electrons whose mutual interactions can be neglected, it is all right to visualize $|\psi(x,y,z,t)|^2$ as being proportional to the density of the swarm, provided that one realizes that this rough picture is of limited validity.

integrated over all space. Wave functions satisfying this condition are said to be *normalized*; if a wave function is not normalized, it can be made so by multiplying it by some *normalizing factor N* so that

$$\int |N\psi|^2 \, dx \, dy \, dz = |N|^2 \int |\psi|^2 \, dx \, dy \, dz = 1$$

or

$$|N|^2 = (\int |\psi|^2 \, dx \, dy \, dz)^{-1}$$

N is now any number of the form

$$N = e^{i\lambda}(|N|^2)^{\frac{1}{2}}$$

where λ is a real number, but unless there is some reason not to do so, we shall always take N to be real and positive. We shall see later that most formulas which yield physically significant results in quantum mechanics are independent of λ, either because they do not involve the phase of ψ at all or because they involve the product $\psi^*\psi$, from which the phase factors cancel.

People who do not like quantum mechanics have objected against the introduction of probabilities into a physical theory on the grounds that the value of a probability depends on the state of one's knowledge, so that a purely subjective element is being introduced into the description of nature. They argue, very properly, that a cardinal assumption of all science is that nature exists independently of ourselves, and that our theories must therefore deal only with objective properties of the world. It must therefore be explained at the outset that a probability, as we have defined it, is an objective number, and its value depends not on the extent of the observer's knowledge but on the nature of the observations he is equipped to make. Thus a quantum-mechanical argument must always take account of the kinds of measurement which can be performed. As we shall see in Sec. 2.4, this is required physically because measuring instruments perturb a system in ways which are sometimes uncontrollable. The occurrence of probabilities is thus in perfect logical consistency with the limitations forced upon us by experience. From a methodological point of view, what has happened is that quantum mechanics is not meaningful or consistent unless the (often imaginary) physical systems which it discusses are considered to include the measuring apparatus by which one obtains information about them.[3]

To describe any physical system, we list its properties. They can be divided into two sets: those which depend on the way the system is made (that is, charges and masses, etc., which are never directly observable), and those which depend also on its past

[3] The suggestion that de Broglie's waves might be waves of probability was first made by Einstein in 1925. To Max Born is due the systematic introduction of probability into quantum mechanics a year later.

history. This second set of properties defines the *state* of the system. Thus all hydrogen atoms are made alike, but two may differ in their properties because they are in different states. We shall say that the wave function ψ describes completely the state of the system to which it belongs, in the sense that if we know the function ψ at the time t, this enables us to give a complete description of the system at that time. But a complete description in quantum mechanics is less complete than classical mechanics imagines it to be. The wave function, for example, tells us only the probability that an electron will be found at a particular point; a more exact specification cannot be given. The Newtonian clarity, which communicated itself so strongly to educated thought in the eighteenth and nineteenth centuries, is no longer a part of physics.

2.2 Expectation Values

Quantum mechanics yields its numerical results sometimes as definite predictions, as with the energy levels of stationary states, and sometimes as a choice of numbers with greater or less probability attached to them, as with the position of the particle in Fig. 2.2. In order to specify this position, even though roughly, we consider a measurement of the particle positional coordinate x and imagine that the whole experiment has been repeated many times, always with the same function ψ, and that the various values of x have been written down and averaged. We call this average the *expectation value* of x, and we denote it by $\langle x \rangle$. To see how it is calculated, let us consider a particularly simple case in which there are only three possible values of x: $x = 3$, 4, and 5, and that the probabilities of finding these values are $\frac{1}{5}$, $\frac{3}{5}$, and $\frac{1}{5}$, respectively. Suppose now that a large number N of readings are taken. The readings will come out approximately

$$x = 3 \qquad \tfrac{1}{5}N \text{ times}$$

$$x = 4 \qquad \tfrac{3}{5}N \text{ times}$$

$$x = 5 \qquad \tfrac{1}{5}N \text{ times}$$

and averaging them, we have

$$\langle x \rangle = \frac{1}{N} \left(\tfrac{1}{5}N \times 3 + \tfrac{3}{5}N \times 4 + \tfrac{1}{5}N \times 5 \right)$$

$$= \tfrac{1}{5} \times 3 + \tfrac{3}{5} \times 4 + \tfrac{1}{5} \times 5 = 4$$

The significant thing is that N drops out and that we have a simple formula for the expectation value in terms of the possible values of x, which we shall call x_n, with $n = 1,2,3$, and their respective probabilities p_n,

$$\langle x \rangle = \sum_n x_n p_n \tag{2.3}$$

summed in our case from $n = 1$ to $n = 3$, or more generally over all possible values of n.

Returning to our original problem, where x can take on a continuum of values, we divide the x axis into elements of length dx so that the probability of the particle's being in the nth element is $|\psi(x,t)|^2 \, dx$, where x is the value of the coordinate belonging to that element. Replacing the sum by an integral, we have

$$\langle x \rangle = \int x |\psi(x,t)|^2 \, dx \tag{2.4}$$

integrated over the entire region in which the wave function is defined. Clearly, since we have not integrated over t, $\langle x \rangle$ will be a function of t. The whole discussion of probabilities leading to this formula may be replaced by the simple prescription: $\langle x \rangle$ is at the center of gravity of the distribution $|\psi|^2$. And the reader will have no trouble in seeing that if ψ is defined in three dimensions,

$$\langle x \rangle = \int x |\psi(x,y,z,t)|^2 \, dx \, dy \, dz \tag{2.5}$$

with analogous formulas for $\langle y \rangle$ and $\langle z \rangle$. And in general, for any quantity f which is defined as a function of x, y, and z,

$$\langle f \rangle = \int f(x,y,z) |\psi(x,y,z,t)|^2 \, dx \, dy \, dz \tag{2.6}$$

This formula shows how to find the expectation value of any dynamical variable which depends only on a particle's position. But there are many dynamical variables which depend on the particle's state of motion as well, and in the next section we shall see how the expectation values of some of these may be found.

2.3 Probabilities and the Principle of Superposition

It was observed in the course of Sec. 1.5 that a simple wave of the form

$$\psi_k(x,t) = A(k)e^{i(kx - \omega_k t)} \tag{2.7}$$

satisfies Schrödinger's equation for any value of k. We have written ω_k to emphasize that ω depends on k through (1.29), and $A(k)$ for the amplitude appropriate to any particular value of k. The calculations to follow will be done in one dimension for convenience; generalization to three dimensions introduces little that is new. Since the sum of any set of solutions of Schrödinger's equation is again a solution, we may multiply the above solution by dk and sum for any values $A(k)$ to get a solution

$$\psi(x,t) = \int A(k)e^{i(kx - \omega_k t)} \, dk \tag{2.8}$$

Problem 2.1 Verify, by differentiating under the integral sign, that (2.8) indeed satisfies (1.31).

Given $A(k)$, then—if we are clever enough to do the integral—we can find the value of ψ at any point x and any time t. But the opposite also can be done; for Fourier's integral theorem allows us to find $A(k)$ if ψ is known. It is easiest to consider the instant $t = 0$ (which can, of course, be any instant). Then (2.8) becomes

$$\psi(x,0) = \int A(k)e^{ikx}\,dk \tag{2.9a}$$

and Fourier's theorem[4] states that

$$A(k) = (2\pi)^{-1}\int\psi(x,0)e^{-ikx}\,dx \tag{2.9b}$$

Thus, since a knowledge of either function enables us to find the other, it is clear that, like ψ, the function $A(k)$ completely specifies the state of a free-particle system. And since $\psi(x,0)$ can be any normalizable function whatever, it is clear that every possible wave function describing a non-interacting particle in one dimension can be written in the form (2.8) by suitable choice of the function $A(k)$. We have already a physical interpretation for ψ. Now we shall find one for $A(k)$.

The general approach to be followed can be understood from a simple example. Suppose that the unnormalized wave function for a single particle in some region of interest is represented as a sum of plane waves belonging to two different momentum states, $\hbar k_1$ and $\hbar k_2$,

$$\psi = e^{ik_1x} + 3e^{ik_2x} \qquad (t = 0) \tag{2.10}$$

(Far from the region, the wave function must decrease so that it can be normalized.) We shall *assume* that a precise measurement of the particle's momentum can only result in one of the two values mentioned and that the squares of the amplitudes of the two terms correspond to the probabilities of finding them. Thus in this example the probability of finding $p = \hbar k_1$ is $\frac{1}{10}$ and that of finding $p = \hbar k_2$ is $\frac{9}{10}$. (These assumptions will be justified in Secs. 5.2 and 3.6 respectively.)

An expression like (2.9a) is merely an extension of (2.10) to a continuous range of variation of k, and our interpretation of $A(k)$ will be exactly analogous to our interpretation of $\psi(x)$:

$|A(k)|^2\,dk$ represents the probability that the particle's momentum lies between $\hbar k$ and $\hbar(k + dk)$.

We say "represents" because there may still be some factor of proportionality involved. To investigate this, we note that the total probability should be unity. We therefore need to evaluate the integral

$$J = \int|A(k)|^2\,dk$$

---

[4] Fourier integrals are discussed in Appendix 2.

To do so, we write one factor of the integrand in the form (2.9b),

$$J = (2\pi)^{-1} \iint A^*(k)\psi(x,0)e^{-ikx} \, dx \, dk$$

Now we use the complex conjugate of (2.9a) to evaluate the k integral, giving

$$J = (2\pi)^{-1} \int |\psi(x,0)|^2 \, dx$$

Let us assume that at time $t = 0$ the wave function ψ is normalized. The last integral is thus equal to 1, so that $J = (2\pi)^{-1}$. To normalize $A(k)$ properly, we therefore define a new quantity which we shall call the *momentum wave function*,

$$\varphi(k) = (2\pi)^{\frac{1}{2}} A(k) \tag{2.11}$$

so that

$$\psi(x,0) = (2\pi)^{-\frac{1}{2}} \int \varphi(k) e^{ikx} \, dk \tag{2.12}$$

$$\varphi(k) = (2\pi)^{-\frac{1}{2}} \int \psi(x,0) e^{-ikx} \, dx \tag{2.13}$$

and

$$\int |\varphi(k)|^2 \, dk = 1 \tag{2.14}$$

where

$|\varphi(k)|^2 \, dk$ equals the probability that the particle's momentum lies between $\hbar k$ and $\hbar(k + dk)$ (2.15)

To construct the momentum wave function from the coordinate wave function at times different from zero is not difficult. We rewrite (2.8) as

$$\psi(x,t) = (2\pi)^{-\frac{1}{2}} \int \varphi(k) e^{-i\omega_k t} e^{ikx} \, dk \tag{2.16}$$

and note that, for an arbitrary t, $\varphi(k)e^{-i\omega_k t}$ now takes the place of the previous $\varphi(k)$. Thus (2.13) becomes

$$\varphi(k) = (2\pi)^{-\frac{1}{2}} e^{i\omega_k t} \int \psi(x,t) e^{-ikx} \, dx \tag{2.17}$$

It should be noted that although t appears on the right side, $\varphi(k)$ is independent of t, meaning that, quite naturally, the various momenta present in a free-particle wave function do not change with time.

Problem 2.2   Prove that

$$\int |\psi(x,t)|^2 \, dx = \int |\varphi(k)|^2 \, dk = 1$$

so that if the coordinate wave function of a free particle is normalized initially at $t = 0$, it remains normalized as time goes on.

2.4 The Momentum Representation

From the fact that a knowledge of ψ enables us to find φ, and vice versa, it follows that these two functions contain exactly the same information and merely give us two different representations of the same state. We shall refer to a description in terms of ψ as the coordinate representation and to a description in terms of φ as the momentum representation.

We can use the momentum representation to find expectation values involving the momentum just as we use the coordinate representation to find expectation values involving the coordinates. For example, analogously to (2.4) we have clearly

$$\langle p \rangle = \hbar \int k |\varphi(k)|^2 \, dk \tag{2.18}$$

We now ask a very important question whose answer will lead us to one of the central mathematical devices of quantum mechanics: How can we find $\langle p \rangle$ working in the coordinate representation? Evidently this is possible, for we have seen that φ and ψ contain exactly the same information. To see how it is done, we substitute (2.17) for the factor of $\varphi(k)$ in (2.18):

$$\langle p \rangle = (2\pi)^{-\frac{1}{2}} \hbar \int\int k \varphi^*(k) e^{-ikx} e^{i\omega_k t} \psi(x,t) \, dx \, dk$$

We wish to be able to evaluate the k integral by means of the complex conjugate of (2.16), but the factor of k stands in the way. We therefore get rid of it by writing

$$k e^{-ikx} = i \frac{\partial}{\partial x} e^{-ikx}$$

so that

$$\langle p \rangle = (2\pi)^{-\frac{1}{2}} i\hbar \int\int \varphi^*(k) e^{i\omega_k t} \psi(x,t) \frac{\partial}{\partial x} e^{-ikx} \, dx \, dk$$

which on integrating by parts becomes

$$\langle p \rangle = -(2\pi)^{-\frac{1}{2}} i\hbar \int\int \varphi^*(k) e^{i\omega_k t} e^{-ikx} \frac{\partial}{\partial x} \psi(x,t) \, dx \, dk \tag{2.19}$$

and this can be integrated over k to give

$$\langle p \rangle = -i\hbar \int \psi^*(x,t) \frac{\partial}{\partial x} \psi(x,t) \, dx \tag{2.20}$$

This remarkably simple formula is exactly equivalent to (2.18), and it is scarcely more complicated. Writing the two as

$$\langle p \rangle = \int \varphi^*(k) \hbar k \varphi(k) \, dk$$

$$= \int \psi^*(x,t) \frac{\hbar}{i} \frac{\partial}{\partial x} \psi(x,t) \, dx$$

we see that just as $\psi(x,t)$ is equivalent to $\varphi(k)$, so the operator $(\hbar/i)(\partial/\partial x)$ may be said to represent in the coordinate representation the same thing that $\hbar k$ does in the momentum representation. We shall summarize these facts in a new notation by introducing a symbol $\hat{p}$ to denote the momentum operator and writing

$$\langle p \rangle = \int \varphi^*(k)\hat{p}\varphi(k)\,dk \tag{2.21}$$

where

$$\hat{p} = \hbar k \qquad \text{momentum representation} \tag{2.22}$$

and again

$$\langle p \rangle = \int \psi^*(x,t)\hat{p}\psi(x,t)\,dx \tag{2.23}$$

where

$$\hat{p} = \frac{\hbar}{i}\frac{\partial}{\partial x} \qquad \text{coordinate representation} \tag{2.24}$$

The choice of which form of $\hat{p}$ to use is clearly determined by the representation one is using. Some further features of these operators appear in the following problems.

Problem 2.3 Show that if the operator giving $\langle p \rangle$ in the momentum picture is $\hbar k$, then that giving $\langle p^2 \rangle$ is $(\hbar k)^2$, and that if that giving $\langle p \rangle$ in the coordinate picture is $(\hbar/i)(\partial/\partial x)$, then that giving $\langle p^2 \rangle$ is $[(\hbar/i)(\partial/\partial x)]^2 = -\hbar^2\partial^2/\partial x^2$.

Problem 2.4 If the operator giving $\langle x \rangle$ in the x picture is just x, what is it in the momentum picture? What operator gives $\langle x^2 \rangle$?

Problem 2.5 Justify the integration by parts leading to (2.19). (Remember that $\psi(x,t)$ is a normalized function of x.)

Operators

The use of operators where one might expect to use numbers is a basic part of quantum mechanics. Essentially, an operator is merely an instruction to do something to the quantity which follows it. Thus $\partial/\partial x$ means "take the partial derivative of what follows with respect to x," and sin means "write down the sine of the number which follows." One does not, of course, always do as one is told, for operators themselves often have properties leading to what may be called an algebra of operators, as for example

$$\frac{\partial}{\partial x}\frac{\partial}{\partial y} - \frac{\partial}{\partial y}\frac{\partial}{\partial x} = 0 \tag{2.25}$$

which is short for saying that

$$\frac{\partial}{\partial x}\frac{\partial}{\partial y}f(x,y) - \frac{\partial}{\partial y}\frac{\partial}{\partial x}f(x,y) = 0$$

for any (continuous and differentiable) $f(x,y)$. This is analogous to the rule $xy - yx = 0$ in ordinary algebra. An ordinary number can play the part of an operator, and in quantum mechanics it often does; for example, x by itself may mean just the number x, but in the combination $xf(y)$ it means "take the product of the number $f(y)$ by the number x."

Most of the operators we shall encounter in quantum mechanics are either differentiations or else numbers used in this way; an exception will be found in the chapter on spin.

Problem 2.6 It sometimes makes a difference that operations are carried out in a particular order. Show that

$$\frac{\partial}{\partial x} x - x \frac{\partial}{\partial x} = 1 \tag{2.26}$$

and explain exactly what this relation means mathematically. Evaluate

$$\frac{\partial}{\partial x} y - y \frac{\partial}{\partial x} \tag{2.27}$$

Three dimensions

The foregoing discussion has all been carried out, for convenience, in one dimension. Extension to three dimensions introduces nothing new. Fourier's integral representation can be applied three times to give the formula

$$\psi(x,y,z,0) = \iiint A(k_x,k_y,k_z)e^{i(k_x x + k_y y + k_z z)}\, dk_x\, dk_y\, dk_z$$

where the k's are variables of integration running from $-\infty$ to $+\infty$. It is natural to regard them as the three components of a vector and abbreviate the above to

$$\psi(\mathbf{r},0) = \int A(\mathbf{k})e^{i\mathbf{k}\cdot\mathbf{r}}\, d\mathbf{k} \tag{2.28}$$

We now recognize $e^{i\mathbf{k}\cdot\mathbf{r}}$ as a plane wave traveling in the direction given by $\mathbf{k}$, corresponding to a particle with a momentum of magnitude $\hbar k$; and the most general ψ has thus been expressed as a superposition of such waves, traveling in all directions with all momenta and all different amplitudes. The momentum wave function in three dimensions is defined by

$$\psi(\mathbf{r},0) = (2\pi)^{-3/2}\int \varphi(\mathbf{k})e^{i\mathbf{k}\cdot\mathbf{r}}\, d\mathbf{k} \tag{2.29}$$

and may be calculated from

$$\varphi(\mathbf{k}) = (2\pi)^{-3/2}\int \psi(\mathbf{r},0)e^{-i\mathbf{k}\cdot\mathbf{r}}\, d\mathbf{r} \tag{2.30}$$

We shall interpret $|\varphi(\mathbf{k})|^2\, dk_x\, dk_y\, dk_z$ as the probability that the x component of the particle's momentum is between $\hbar k_x$ and $\hbar(k_x + dk_x)$ and similarly with the y and z components, and the reader will easily verify that

$$\int |\varphi(\mathbf{k})|^2 \, d\mathbf{k} = 1 \tag{2.31}$$

Clearly, the y and z components of momentum are represented in the coordinate representation by differential operators like (2.24), so that we can write

$$\hat{\mathbf{p}} = \frac{\hbar}{i} \, \mathbf{\nabla} \tag{2.32}$$

where $\mathbf{\nabla}$ is the usual vector operator of differentiation.

Problem 2.7 In classical mechanics, the angular momentum of a particle about the origin of coordinates is given by the cross product $\mathbf{P} = \mathbf{r} \times \mathbf{p}$. Write the operator corresponding to $\mathbf{P}$ in both the coordinate and momentum pictures.

Newton's first law

Finally, we wish to call attention to the fact that the machinery introduced above supplies us with the quantum-mechanical form of Newton's first law of motion. This law is designed to give the answer to the problem "If at time $t = 0$ I know the position and momentum of a particle, where is the particle to be found at any subsequent time t if no forces act upon it?" In quantum mechanics, the analogous question asks "If I know the wave function of a free particle at $t = 0$, what form does the function take at any subsequent time?" Again let us use one dimension for convenience. At $t = 0$, we can find the momentum wave function $\varphi(k)$ from (2.13), and at all subsequent times the development of ψ follows from φ according to

$$\psi(x,t) = (2\pi)^{-\frac{1}{2}} \int \varphi(k) e^{i(kx - \omega_k t)} \, dk \tag{2.33}$$

Thus, $\psi(x,t)$ is found from $\psi(x,0)$ at the price of carrying out two integrations.

It is possible to find $\psi(x,t)$ from a knowledge of $\psi(x,0)$ because Schrödinger's equation is of first order in t. This is in contrast with Newtonian physics, where the equation of motion is of the second order and we must give both $x(0)$ and $\dot{x}(0)$ in order to solve it. But it agrees with the general requirement that ψ should contain all possible information about the particle, since in order to make a prediction we cannot ask for more than that.

Problem 2.8 Suppose that $\psi(x,0)$ is of the form

$$\psi(x,0) = C e^{-x^2/4\Delta^2 + ik_0 x}$$

Sketch $\psi(x,0)$ and $|\psi(x,0)|^2$. Find the value of C which normalizes ψ. Find $\psi(x,t)$ and $|\psi(x,t)|^2$ and sketch them for several successive later values of t. Give a detailed account of the physical significance of the various features of the functions $\psi(x,0)$, $\varphi(k)$, and $\psi(x,t)$. The integral formula

$$\int_{-\infty}^{\infty} e^{-a^2x^2+bx}\, dx = \frac{\pi^{1/2}}{a}\, e^{b^2/4a^2} \qquad (\text{Re }a^2 > 0) \tag{2.34}$$

will be of use.

2.5 Indeterminacy

We have seen that the description of the state of a particle by mean of its coordinate wave function does not enable us to know exactly where the particle is to be found, and similarly a description by the momentum wave function does not in general tell us the exact momentum. The descriptions are essentially incomplete, from a classical point of view, in that the values of measurable quantities are not exactly determined even by an exact knowledge of the particle's state. In this section we shall discuss the extent of these indeterminacies in position and momentum and then find a physical interpretation for them.

Suppose that the shutter in Fig. 2.2 is opened abruptly and then closed again, allowing a single particle to pass through (Fig. 2.3). A wave function whose spatial dependence is of the form Ae^{ik_0x} arrives from the left. On the right, we have

$$\psi(x) = \begin{cases} 0 & (x < -\tfrac{1}{2}l) \\ Ae^{ik_0x} & (-\tfrac{1}{2}l < x < \tfrac{1}{2}l) \\ 0 & (\tfrac{1}{2}l < x) \end{cases} \tag{2.35}$$

where for ease of calculation we have taken the center of the pulse as the origin of x. (The time dependence is unimportant here, and we may take t to be zero.) Clearly, the particle's position is specified

Fig. 2.3 A square pulse of waves formed by opening and closing an absorbent shutter.

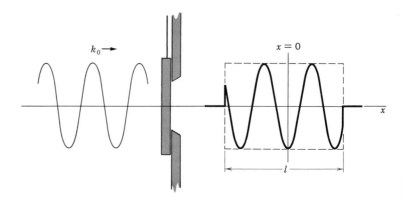

only to the extent that it is located between $-\frac{1}{2}l$ and $\frac{1}{2}l$; we shall say that the indeterminacy, or uncertainty, in its position is about l,

$$\Delta x \approx l$$

Now let us find the corresponding uncertainty in momentum Δp. To do this, it will be convenient to evaluate the momentum wave function,

$$\begin{aligned}
\varphi(k) &= (2\pi)^{-\frac{1}{2}} \int \psi(x)e^{-ikx} \, dx \\
&= (2\pi)^{-\frac{1}{2}} A \int_{-\frac{1}{2}l}^{\frac{1}{2}l} e^{ik_0 x - ikx} \, dx \\
&= \left(\frac{2}{\pi}\right)^{-\frac{1}{2}} A \, \frac{\sin \frac{1}{2}(k_0 - k)l}{k_0 - k}
\end{aligned} \tag{2.36}$$

This function is plotted in Fig. 2.4. It has a maximum of $k = k_0$ and falls off fairly rapidly on each side. (The presence of negative k's, corresponding to Fourier components moving toward the left, merely means that this idealized waveform cannot be produced.) To get an idea of the uncertainty in momentum, let us look at the width of the central maximum, down to the first zero on each side. It is

$$\Delta k \approx \frac{4\pi}{l}$$

from which, with $\Delta x \approx l$ and $\Delta p = \hbar \, \Delta k$,

$$\Delta p \, \Delta x \approx \hbar \tag{2.37}$$

where we have omitted the 4π because it does not affect the magnitude significantly and because it depends on the rather unsophisticated way in which Δp and Δx have been defined. The formula will be rederived in Sec. 3.5. The uncertainty Δk is introduced into the wave number of an initially monochromatic beam by the action of the shutter. Thus the value given by (2.37) is a minimum; for one could as well have a mixture of frequencies to the left of the shutter,

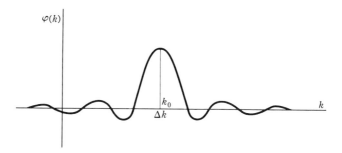

Fig. 2.4 Fourier transform of a square pulse.

in which case Δk would be larger and Δx no smaller. We express this fact by rewriting (2.37) as

$$\Delta p \, \Delta x \gtrsim \hbar \tag{2.38}$$

We see from this idealized example that the relation between the indeterminacies Δp and Δx is a reciprocal one: the one may approach zero only if the other approaches infinity. An extreme example of this is an infinite plane wave e^{ikx}, where the momentum, we have seen, is certainly $\hbar k$ but where there is an equal likelihood of finding the particle anywhere along the beam, from $-\infty$ to $+\infty$.

Another example of indeterminacy may be found in the relation between the spread of kinetic energies ΔE present in a *wave packet*, as a bounded wave like that of Fig. 2.3 is called, and the time Δt it takes to go past a certain point. Clearly, if Δp is not too large,

$$\Delta E = \Delta \frac{p^2}{2m} = p \frac{\Delta p}{m}$$

and

$$\Delta t = \frac{\Delta x}{v} = \frac{m \, \Delta x}{p}$$

therefore

$$\Delta E \, \Delta t = \Delta p \, \Delta x \gtrsim \hbar \tag{2.39}$$

Problem 2.9 Find $\langle p \rangle$ in the coordinate representation for a bounded wave packet of the form (2.35).

Solution. We shall solve this problem for a general normalized wave function which can be written in the form

$$\psi(x) = e^{ik_0 x} S(x)$$

where $S(x)$ is a real function of x which is (or tends to) zero outside certain limits. In the problem of the square pulse as stated, normalization requires that $S(x) = l^{-\frac{1}{2}} \; (-\frac{1}{2}l < x < \frac{1}{2}l)$ and zero elsewhere. Now

$$\langle p \rangle = \frac{\hbar}{i} \int e^{-ik_0 x} S(x) \frac{\partial}{\partial x} e^{ik_0 x} S(x) \, dx$$

$$= -i\hbar \int S(x)[ik_0 S(x) + S'(x)] \, dx$$

$$= \hbar k_0 \int S^2(x) \, dx - i\hbar \int S(x) S'(x) \, dx$$

$$= \hbar k_0 - \frac{1}{2}i\hbar S^2(x) \Big|_{-\infty}^{\infty} = \hbar k_0$$

where we have used the normalization of the wave function and the vanishing of S at $\pm \infty$.

Problem 2.10 A pulse of electrons 1 nanosecond long from a beam with an energy of 1 eV moves into free space. Find Δx and

Δp. What is the minimum uncertainty in the velocity of an electron in the pulse? What will be the values of Δx and Δp after 1 sec? Comment on the use of the inequality sign in (2.38).

Problem 2.11   Prove (2.39) again by a calculation analogous to that leading to (2.38) except that time is now taken as the independent variable instead of x. Imagine that one is at a fixed point x and consider ψ as a function of t.

The wave theory cannot specify simultaneously the exact positions and momenta of the particles in a beam. The situation here is a little analogous to that which exists in the kinetic theory of gases—one can make quite detailed predictions as to the behavior of the gas as a whole without knowing anything more than probabilities concerning the positions and movements of the individual molecules. Yet there is this difference. The kinetic theory as developed by Boltzmann and Gibbs and others rested on an underlying theory, Newtonian mechanics, which took account of the exact behavior of individual molecules. Where is the exact theory underlying wave mechanics?

Indeterminacy as a fact of nature

The answer to this question was not given till 1927, after wave mechanics, in the hands of Schrödinger and his followers, had already shown its ability to explain a great variety of hitherto obscure phenomena. It was provided by Werner Heisenberg, who had in the preceding two years been busy with the development of a parallel branch of quantum theory which originated not from de Broglie's hypothesis, but from a more abstract study of the nature of the physical laws responsible for the observed properties of atomic spectra.[5]

Heisenberg's insistence on the essential role played by observable quantities provided an answer to the question whether wave mechanics is incomplete as a mode of description of physical phenomena. In general terms, his answer was this: A quantity such as p or x should be termed an observable only insofar as it is capable of being observed, and the only rational criticism of a theory containing a result such as (2.38) would be to show that it disagrees with observation. That is, in this case, one would have to be able to set up

---

[5] The resulting theory took the form of a calculus, known as *matrix mechanics*, relating observable quantities to one another according to certain rules; and as worked out by Heisenberg and his collaborators in 1925 and 1926 it had proved itself capable of explaining atomic phenomena as well as wave mechanics did. Computationally, however, matrix mechanics is generally difficult to apply, and so it will not be discussed further in this book. It turned out after a while that the theories of Heisenberg and Schrödinger were essentially the same and could be derived from one another by mathematical transformations, and today's theory makes use of ideas of each in the regions in which they are most convenient.

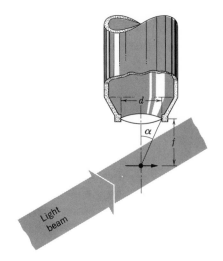

Fig. 2.5 Bohr's gamma-ray microscope.

an experiment by which one could know, more accurately than (2.38) allows, the simultaneous values of p and x for a particle. The crux of Heisenberg's argument is that this is physically impossible. The quantum nature of interactions on the atomic scale introduces uncontrollable disturbances of the system under measurements, resulting in a real uncertainty, or indeterminacy, of the type expressed by Eq. (2.38).

It is often said that indeterminacy is a "consequence" of quantum mechanics which can be derived by arguments such as that leading to (2.38). But surely this misses the point. The indeterminacy of quantum mechanics, expressed by (2.28), could only be considered as a blemish on the theory until it was shown, independently of the theory, that indeterminacy is a basic fact of nature. This basic fact could perfectly well have been discovered many years before 1927 if it had occurred to anyone to think about it.

Bohr's microscope

Bohr[6] has given a famous example of the operation of this principle. Consider, he said, the use of a microscope to determine the x component of the position of a particle in a beam moving with a given momentum in the x direction (Fig. 2.5). It is well known that the diffraction angle of light entering the objective lens is λ/d, where λ is the light's wavelength, so that the microscope will be unable to resolve the electron's position to within a distance

$$\Delta x = f\frac{\lambda}{d} = \frac{2\pi f \lambda}{d}$$

[6] N. Bohr, Nature, **121**, 580 (1928).

On the other hand, a light quantum will exchange momentum with the particle according to the laws of the Compton effect, and the x component of the momentum exchanged will be uncertain owing to the impossibility of knowing through what part of the objective lens the photon enters the microscope. The amount of this uncertainty is

$$\Delta p_x = p_\lambda \frac{d}{f}$$

where p_λ is the momentum of the quantum of wavelength λ and we have assumed that $f \gg d$. (If $f \approx d$, all the relations become more complicated but the result is the same.) If now de Broglie's relation holds for quanta, the product of the last two operations is $\Delta p_x \Delta x = 2\pi\hbar$, which is consistent with (2.38).

It should be noted, we are not saying that an indeterminacy is introduced into the result of the experiment just because the light interacts with the particle. This is to be expected, and because one understands the Compton effect it can be fully allowed for. In particular, we have not worried about the y component of the particle's recoil. And if it were known in what direction a photon would have to bounce off the particle in order to enter the microscope, the x component could likewise be taken into account. The point is that we do not know the direction exactly, since although we know that the photon entered the lens, we can never know exactly where it went in. Thus the x component of the deflected photon's momentum contains an uncertainty which is passed on to the particle, and it is this that prevents us from using the microscope observation to make a clear prediction of what the particle will do next.

Diffraction of a beam

We shall now give another simple example of indeterminacy, the use of a slit to collimate a beam. Figure 2.6 shows a beam of particles having initially $p_y = 0$ which is passed through a slit in an attempt to localize the beam in the y direction. But here the wave aspect of matter becomes important. The slit will produce diffraction, whose angular size will be $\alpha \approx \lambda/d$. The momentum associated with a diffracted part of the beam has a y component which may (assuming that α is small) be as large as αp, and this is Δp_y, the unavoidable disturbance in p_y produced by the measuring act. Since one is not attempting to localize the particle in the beam more exactly than is given by the slit width d, we have

$$\Delta y \, \Delta p_y \approx d \frac{\lambda}{d} p = \hbar \tag{2.40}$$

But this is only the situation immediately behind the slit. The beam broadens as it leaves the slit, and the y coordinate of a particle

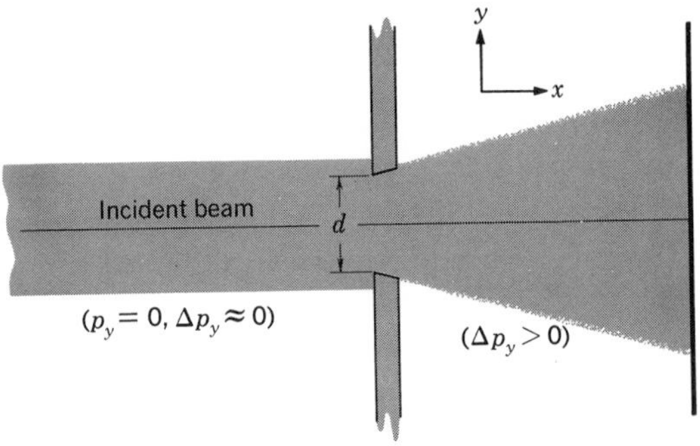

Fig. 2.6 Diffraction of a
beam of particles.

in it becomes correspondingly more and more uncertain. The
momentum uncertainty remains constant, so that (2.40), again, is
a lower limit.

It should be noted that there are two kinds of indeterminacy
statements in quantum mechanics which have often been confused:
that which is an essential ingredient of physical knowledge (Heisenberg's) and the kind just mentioned, which may have its origin in
Heisenberg's but which thereafter increases without limit in the
course of the system's natural evolution.

Problem 2.12 In a study of the action of gravity on elementary particles, an initially parallel beam of very slow electrons
passes vertically upward through a slit 2 cm long and 1 mm wide.
The electrons rise 10 m and then fall back again. What is the size
and shape of the region over which they are spread out when they
reach the ground? Roughly what fraction of them fall back
through the slit?

The two examples just given illustrate Heisenberg's *principle
of indeterminacy*, which states that there are certain pairs of dynamical variables, notably a component of position and the component of momentum in the same direction, whose values as determined in any given experiment must remain undetermined to an
extent given by (2.38). The fact that experiment cannot transcend
this accuracy means that no more precise mathematical description
than that given by quantum mechanics is needed in order to describe any experiment. If it is agreed that the final criterion for the
truth of any physical theory is its agreement with experiment, then
the general framework of quantum mechanics (whether or not its
details are correct) may be adequate and may not need to be supplemented by anything more definite. There is not, however,
universal agreement on this point, and Einstein, Schrödinger, and
de Broglie, among others, always looked for an interpretation of
quantum mechanics which was more like that of classical physics.
They hoped thereby to be led to a more complete theory which
would perhaps reduce to quantum mechanics when certain approxi-

mations were made, but so far neither they nor their followers have produced an alternative theory whose scope and elegance are comparable to those of quantum mechanics.

Waves and particles

In the foregoing arguments we have referred to both the wave aspects and the mechanical aspects of matter, and the novice in quantum theory often blames himself for failing to understand such arguments because he does not see how anything can be a wave and a particle at the same time. It is important to realize that this is exactly what cannot happen, for quantum mechanics refers to experiments, and no experiment can give such a paradoxical result. This is true because of indeterminacy. An example will help to clarify matters.

Let us look again at G. I. Taylor's experiment mentioned in Sec. 1.2. From the wave point of view it offers no difficulties, since even a very weak wave should show ordinary interference phenomena. The difficulty comes if we try to explain it from the particle point of view. We do not understand how a particle can interfere with itself. Further, the interference pattern is formed only if both slits are open, and yet a particle must go through only one slit, and one cannot see how the other slit can make any difference.

This puzzle centers around the apparently obvious point that a particle must go through one slit or the other. Let us see whether this statement could be verified experimentally, in the interference of two beams of light. Figure 2.7a shows the two-slit experiment of Fig. 1.1 with a device D, mounted behind slit 1, which recoils slightly with the passage of a photon. Figure 2.7b shows a possible form for D. Let us now analyze the measurement, remembering that D itself must be subject to indeterminacy.

If we want to use the apparatus to determine whether a photon goes through slit 1, then D must be confined to a region which in the arrangement shown has a length of about $\frac{1}{2}l$ if it is to intercept only the beam from slit 1. The momentum of D is therefore undetermined to the extent $2\hbar/l$, and the recoil momentum must be greater than this to be detectable,

$$\Delta p > \frac{2\hbar}{l}$$

When a photon loses this momentum, its wave number changes, and since $p = \hbar k$, we have

$$\Delta k = \frac{\Delta p}{\hbar} > \frac{2}{l}$$

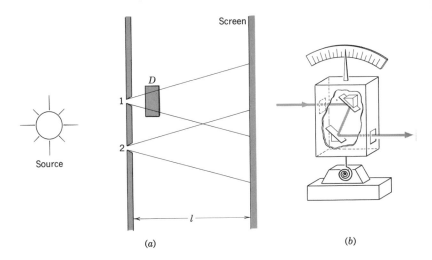

Fig. 2.7 (a) Arrangement for determining whether a given photon has passed through slit 1 or slit 2. (b) Device D to register the passage of a photon. Each mirror receives an impulse, but that on the upper mirror exerts the greater torque, so that D deflects toward the right.

The wave then travels a distance of at least $\tfrac{1}{2}l$ after interacting with D, and in this distance its phase changes by at least

$$\Delta\varphi = \tfrac{1}{2}l\,\Delta k > 1 \text{ radian}$$

This is enough to obliterate the interference pattern on the screen, since the pattern can be formed only when there is a definite phase relation between beams 1 and 2. Thus if one finds out which slit the photon went through, there is no interference pattern, and hence no paradox. If it is impossible to be sure whether something went through just one slit, then there is no paradox either.

Complementarity

It is impossible to perform a single experiment which will allow the position and momentum of a particle to be known simultaneously with an accuracy which violates (2.38), and yet one can perform certain experiments which make Δx very small and others which do the same for Δp. It is impossible to establish in a single experiment that something is both a wave and a particle, and yet each aspect has been fully explored. We build up our picture of reality from experiments which do not duplicate each other but rather complement each other. The resulting composite picture shows the world as classical physics sees it, but indeterminacy prevents us from using this picture to make definite predictions of physical phenomena. (In this sense, it is often said that causality is no longer strictly preserved in physics.) On the other hand, the laws of quantum theory are perfectly definite, but because a quantum-mechanical calculation analyzes the world only as revealed in some particular experiment, the calculation does not fully express our sense of reality as derived from many complementary experiments. Thus the classical view and the quantum view also stand in a complementary relation to each other. This relation was first pointed out by Bohr in 1928 and called by him the *principle of complementarity*.[7] Bohr has discussed a number of instances of complementarity outside of physics, for example, that which exists between the exact definition of a term and its use in creative thought, but in general its further implications remain relatively unexplored.[8]

Ideal measurements

We must now stop for a moment to think what it means to say that a certain dynamical variable Q has a certain value. It is clear from the foregoing that it may mean nothing unless we specify and take into account the means by which the value can be measured. But is it then possible? Suppose that every way of measuring Q produced an uncontrollable disturbance of the value of Q in the system after it was measured. Then it would be of no possible use to be able to say that Q has a certain value. Clearly, things are not that bad, for we know that useful predictions can in fact be made—for example, the wavelength of the hydrogen alpha line in a spectrum plate to be exposed tomorrow morning. If we measure the momentum of a particle, with great accuracy, by deflecting the particle in a magnetic field, then Δx will be large and we shall not be able to locate the particle accurately, but we can at least predict what momentum will be found if it is measured again. Similarly, if we measure the position of the particle precisely by means of a very hard gamma ray, then we may no longer know the momentum, but we can be sure that a second photon arriving immediately after the first will show it in very nearly the same position.

We are therefore led to postulate the existence of a certain class of ideal measurements which allow predictions to be made. They will be specified exactly in Sec. 3.6; for the moment we sum up the postulate in two general statements.

The results of an ideal numerical measurement on a physical system are a number and a measured system. Since systems change

---

[7] N. Bohr, *loc. cit.;* W. Heisenberg, *The Physical Principles of the Quantum Theory,* University of Chicago Press, Chicago, 1930. See also Bohr, *Atomic Theory and the Description of Nature,* Cambridge University Press, London, 1932, as well as the discussions between Bohr and Einstein recorded in P. A. Schilpp (ed.), *Albert Einstein, Philosopher-Scientist,* Library of Living Philosophers, Inc., Evanston, Ill., 1949.

[8] N. Bohr, *Atomic Physics and Human Knowledge,* John Wiley & Sons, Inc., New York, 1958; *Essays 1958–1962,* John Wiley & Sons, Inc., New York, 1964.

with time, we define the latter to be as it was left immediately after the measurement was performed. Now,

1. If the measurement is repeated *at once* on the measured system, it will give the same result as the first measurement.　(2.41)

2. The state of the system after an appreciable interval can be found by using the equation of motion of the system.　(2.42)

If measurements such as these did not exist, at least in principle, then it would not be possible to give any precise meaning to the statement that a particular physical quantity has a particular value. We shall see in Chap. 5 that their existence is very important for constructing the mathematical apparatus of the theory.

3

General Principles

Using the language of everyday life, a physicist will speak of properties of a physical system such as mass, energy, and momentum as though they were qualities inherent in the system itself. Pressed to explain himself, he states that they are the results which would be obtained from measurements. But we have seen that the result of a measurement depends in general on the way in which it was carried out and that, in addition, there exists a reciprocal indeterminacy affecting certain pairs of measurements. Thus the physicist's own standard of truth sometimes prevents him from ascribing objective physical properties to a system. Classical physics assumes that it is possible to ignore this inconsistency and deal with the values of dynamical variables in an objective way. The fact that quantum mechanics does not seem to be able to make this idealization leads one to formulate its problems in terms of the total situation including the measuring apparatus, in essentially the following terms: If I measure a physical quantity Q in a system S by means of an apparatus A according to a procedure P, what answer will I get? (Of course, people who are expert in quantum theory know how much of this prescription they can leave out, but it is rather dangerous for the beginner to leave out any of it.) The purpose of this chapter is to build up some of the technical apparatus which is necessary in order to put into practice the elementary principles developed in Chap. 2, and our first task is to see how to introduce the idea of a force into what has up to now been a theory of free particles.

3.1 Interactions

We shall start with the time-independent wave equation (1.36) in the coordinate representation

$$-\frac{\hbar^2}{2m}\nabla^2\psi = E\psi \tag{3.1}$$

and seek to generalize it to include external interactions. The clue to how to proceed is given by the momentum operator $\hat{p}$ introduced in (2.24), in terms of which we can rewrite (3.1) as

$$\frac{\hat{p}^2}{2m}\psi = E\psi \tag{3.2}$$

Here the operator on the left clearly represents the kinetic energy $p^2/2m$, and the whole equation may be taken as saying that the energy of a free particle is entirely kinetic. Similarly, the time-dependent equation (1.35) may be written as

$$\frac{\hat{p}^2}{2m}\psi = i\hbar\frac{\partial\psi}{\partial t} \tag{3.3}$$

Equation (3.2) applies to states with a definite energy E, whereas (3.3) applies to those as well as to states formed by a superposition of states of different energies.

When interactions are present, we shall express them in terms of the potential energy $V(x,y,z)$, which we write as $V(\mathbf{r})$ for short, by replacing the energy operator in (3.2) and (3.3) by an operator corresponding to the relation

$$\frac{\hat{p}^2}{2m} + V(\mathbf{r}) = E \tag{3.4}$$

In the coordinate representation it is perfectly possible to specify V simultaneously with ψ, since both are functions of x, y, and z. Thus one might expect that no further operators need be introduced. It should be possible to write down the equation of motion in the general case in terms of the operator

$$\hat{H} = \frac{\hat{p}^2}{2m} + V(\mathbf{r}) \tag{3.5}$$

so that the time-independent equation becomes

$$\hat{H}\psi = E\psi \quad\text{or}\quad -\frac{\hbar^2}{2m}\nabla^2\psi + V(\mathbf{r})\psi = E\psi \tag{3.6}$$

and the time-dependent one becomes

$$\hat{H}\psi = i\hbar\frac{\partial\psi}{\partial t} \quad\text{or}\quad -\frac{\hbar^2}{2m}\nabla^2\psi + V(\mathbf{r})\psi = i\hbar\frac{\partial\psi}{\partial t} \tag{3.7}$$

The operator $\hat{H}$ recalls the hamiltonian function of classical dynamics, which expresses the total energy of a system in terms of the values of its coordinates and momenta. We shall refer to $\hat{H}$ as the *hamiltonian operator*, or the hamiltonian, for short.

Equation (3.7) appeared in Schrödinger's first papers in 1926.[1] The argument just given is supposed to make the equation plausible. It is less convincing than Schrödinger's original argument, but the latter makes use of ideas of classical mechanics which are beyond the scope of this book. At all accounts, one does not *derive* this equation at all, for it is more general than all that preceded it, and we can only show that it implies Newton's mechanics and not the reverse. This will be done in the following pages.

Equation (3.7) was derived from a formula of nonrelativistic mechanics and is not itself relativistic in form, so that it will not give correct results when applied to high-energy processes. The relativistic form of Schrödinger's equation was given in 1927 by P. A. M. Dirac, an English research student working at Cambridge,[2] but it is not a simple generalization and leads to complexities which we need not go into.

We have now set forth the two fundamental hypotheses of quantum mechanics: the equation governing the evolution of ψ and the formula for expectation values which enables us to derive observable numbers from a knowledge of ψ. Other basic questions will arise, relating, for example, to the boundary conditions to be satisfied by Schrödinger's equation, but they are less crucial and will be dealt with as they arise.

It is perfectly legitimate to apply to a system with interactions the procedure for calculating expectation values derived in the preceding chapter for force-free particles. The situation is just the same as in classical mechanics. If I speak of the momentum of a certain particle at the moment t, it does not bother me that the momentum is continually changing under the action of the forces. I can imagine a measurement so nearly instantaneous that the forces have no time to change it appreciably while it is being carried out, or I can imagine that the interactions are all suddenly turned off, so that the momenta remain at their values at time t and can be measured at leisure. In either case, it is as though the particle were observed in the absence of interaction, and in the same spirit we use the free-particle formula for finding $\langle p \rangle$ (or whatever it may be) from the value of ψ at the instant t.

3.2 The Current Vector

We have mentioned the conservation of electrons from an integral point of view, showing that it is equivalent to the requirement that (2.2) holds independently of time, and have verified in Probs.

[1] E. Schrödinger, Ann. Physik, **79**, 361, 489 (1926).
[2] Proc. Roy. Soc. (London), Ser. A., **117**, 610 (1928). See any more advanced text on quantum mechanics.

2.2 and 2.8 that it does so. In this section we shall discuss the same thing from a differential point of view.

Our first problem is to derive a mathematical expression of the fact that electrons are neither created nor destroyed. Considering an element of volume $\Delta\tau$, let $\rho(\mathbf{r},t)\,\Delta\tau$ be the quantity of charge it contains. We now postulate that the only way in which this quantity can change is by a flow of charge through the boundary. If $\mathbf{dS}$ is an outward-oriented element of the surface of $\Delta\tau$, then the outward flow per second through $\mathbf{dS}$ is $\rho\mathbf{v}\cdot\mathbf{dS}$, where $\mathbf{v}$ is the charge's velocity of motion, and the total outward flow is $\int_{\Delta\tau}\rho\mathbf{v}\cdot\mathbf{dS}$. This must be equal to the rate of decrease of the charge in $\Delta\tau$:

$$-\frac{\partial}{\partial t}(\rho\,\Delta\tau) = -\frac{\partial\rho}{\partial t}\,\Delta\tau = \int_{\Delta\tau}\rho\mathbf{v}\cdot\mathbf{dS}$$

or, in the limit,

$$\frac{\partial\rho}{\partial t} = -\lim_{\Delta t\to 0}\frac{\int_{\Delta\tau}\rho\mathbf{v}\cdot\mathbf{dS}}{\Delta\tau}$$

But this limit is exactly what defines the *divergence* of a vector quantity,[3] so that, in the two most usual notations, we can write

$$\frac{\partial\rho}{\partial t} = -\operatorname{div}\rho\mathbf{v} = -\boldsymbol{\nabla}\cdot\rho\mathbf{v} \tag{3.8}$$

This is called the *equation of continuity*, and it is basic to the theory of any flow process in which something is conserved.

In order to see the form taken by this law in quantum mechanics, let us consider first a stream of electrons, with charge density given by $e|\psi|^2$. The time derivative of the density is

$$\frac{\partial}{\partial t}(e\psi^*\psi) = e\left(\psi^*\frac{\partial\psi}{\partial t} + \frac{\partial\psi^*}{\partial t}\psi\right)$$

from which the time derivatives can be eliminated by the use of Schrödinger's equation (3.7) and its complex conjugate. We find that the terms containing the potential energy cancel and

$$\frac{\partial}{\partial t}(e\psi^*\psi) = -\frac{e\hbar}{2im}(\psi^*\nabla^2\psi - \psi\nabla^2\psi^*) \tag{3.9}$$

The quantity in parentheses on the right is the divergence of the vector $\psi^*\boldsymbol{\nabla}\psi - \psi\boldsymbol{\nabla}\psi^*$. Thus in quantum mechanics also there is an equation of continuity, which we write as

$$\frac{\partial}{\partial t}(e\psi^*\psi) = -\boldsymbol{\nabla}\cdot\mathbf{s} \tag{3.10}$$

[3] G. Joos, *Theoretical Physics*, Hafner Publishing Company, Inc., New York, 1950, 1958.

where

$$\mathbf{s} = \frac{e\hbar}{2im} (\psi^* \boldsymbol{\nabla} \psi - \psi \boldsymbol{\nabla} \psi^*) = \frac{e}{m} \, \text{Re} \psi^* \hat{\mathbf{p}} \psi \tag{3.11}$$

This quantity takes the place of the former $\rho \mathbf{v}$ and, like it, denotes a directed flow of current per unit area. More precisely, $|\psi|^2 \, \Delta\tau$ represents the probability of finding a single electron within $\Delta\tau$, so that (3.10) is equivalent to the statement that if the probability of finding an electron in $\Delta\tau$ decreases, there must be a corresponding increase in the probability of finding it elsewhere, given by the *probability current* $\mathbf{s}$ flowing through the boundary of $\Delta\tau$. The reader may wish to follow the argument backward from (3.9), using Gauss's divergence theorem, to show that (3.9) implies the constancy of the total probability.

Problem 3.1 Show that (3.10) and (3.11) are equivalent to (3.9), and verify that a wave function normalized according to (2.2) at one instant remains so thereafter.

Problem 3.2 Find the current density carried by a plane wave Ae^{ikx} in one dimension, showing that it is in fact what one would expect from the formula $\rho \mathbf{v}$, and verify that it satisfies the equation of continuity in one dimension.

3.3 Time Dependence of Expectation Values

Quantum mechanics yields most of its results in terms of expectation values. These are determined by a knowledge of the wave function according to formulas like (2.6) and (2.23) and their analogues in the momentum representation. Generalizing from them (see also Prob. 2.3) we shall postulate that the expectation value of a dynamical variable Q in a certain state is always given by

$$\langle Q \rangle = \int \psi^* \hat{Q} \psi \, d\mathbf{r} \tag{3.12}$$

where $\hat{Q}$ is some operator which corresponds, in the sense of the examples cited above, to the dynamical variable Q. This postulate amounts to saying that we intend to restrict our idea of a legitimate dynamical variable to quantities whose expectation values can be represented in this way. It will be seen later that even in spite of this apparently arbitrary restriction, there are still more dynamical variables in quantum than in classical theory.

Since ψ is a function of time, the expectation value $\langle Q \rangle$ is also in general a function of time. In this section we shall see what can be said about the time dependence of $\langle Q \rangle$ if one does not go to the trouble of solving the wave equation. Let us take the time derivative of $\langle Q \rangle$. It is

$$\frac{\partial}{\partial t} \langle Q \rangle \rightarrow \frac{d}{dt} \langle Q \rangle = \int_\infty \left[\frac{\partial \psi^*}{\partial t} \hat{Q} \psi + \psi^* \frac{\partial \hat{Q}}{\partial t} \psi + \psi^* \hat{Q} \frac{\partial \psi}{\partial t} \right] d\mathbf{r}$$

The middle term exists only if $\hat{Q}$ involves t in an explicit way, and it is zero in most applications. Using (3.7) and its complex conjugate,

$$\hat{H}\psi^* = -i\hbar \frac{\partial \psi^*}{\partial t}$$

we have

$$\frac{\partial}{\partial t}\langle Q \rangle \to \frac{d}{dt}\langle Q \rangle = \frac{1}{i\hbar}\int_\infty [-\hat{H}\psi^* \cdot \hat{Q}\psi + \psi^*\hat{Q}\hat{H}\psi]\,d\mathbf{r} + \left\langle \frac{\partial \hat{Q}}{\partial t}\right\rangle \tag{3.13}$$

where the dot in the first term is a reminder that the operator $\hat{H}$ differentiates only the ψ^* immediately following it. The first term will now be rewritten. It is

$$-\frac{\hbar^2}{2m}\int_\infty \nabla^2\psi^* \cdot \hat{Q}\psi\,d\mathbf{r} + \int_\infty V(r)\psi^*\hat{Q}\psi\,d\mathbf{r} \tag{3.14}$$

The first term of this expression can be transformed according to Green's theorem in vector analysis, which states that if u and v are two scalars,

$$\int(u\nabla^2 v - v\nabla^2 u)\,d\mathbf{r} = \int(u\nabla v - v\nabla u)\cdot d\mathbf{S} \tag{3.15}$$

where the first integration is over the volume of an arbitrary region and the second is over its surface; $d\mathbf{S}$ represents a surface element with its normal directed outward. It is clear that if the integral $\int\psi^*\hat{Q}\psi\,d\mathbf{r}$ is not to diverge, $\psi^*\hat{Q}\psi$ must decrease rapidly enough with increasing distance; and it is not hard to show that, as the volume of integration in (3.15) is made larger with v equal to ψ^* and u equal to $\hat{Q}\psi$, the surface integral then approaches zero.

Problem 3.3 Assuming (1) that u and v are spherically symmetrical and (2) that $\int uv\,d\mathbf{r}$ is finite, show that the surface integral in (3.15) vanishes when the volume integration is over all space, so that

$$\int u\nabla^2 v\,d\mathbf{r} = \int v\nabla^2 u\,d\mathbf{r} \tag{3.16}$$

Equation (3.16) now enables (3.14) to be rewritten as

$$\int_\infty \hat{H}\psi^* \cdot \hat{Q}\psi\,d\mathbf{r} = \int_\infty \psi^*\hat{H}\hat{Q}\psi\,d\mathbf{r}$$

where we have used the fact that V is a function of x,y,z to take it past ψ^* (but not past $\hat{Q}$, which may involve differentiation!). Thus, (3.13) becomes (with a sign change)

$$\frac{\partial}{\partial t}\langle Q \rangle \to \frac{d}{dt}\langle Q \rangle = \frac{i}{\hbar}\int_\infty \psi^*(\hat{H}\hat{Q} - \hat{Q}\hat{H})\psi\,d\mathbf{r} + \left\langle \frac{\partial \hat{Q}}{\partial t}\right\rangle \tag{3.17}$$

where in the notation of (3.12), the integral is again an expectation value. The combination of operators in parentheses is of such common occurrence in quantum mechanics that it receives a special name and notation:

$$\hat{A}\hat{B} - \hat{B}\hat{A} = [\hat{A},\hat{B}] \tag{3.18}$$

is called the *commutator of* $\hat{A}$ *and* $\hat{B}$. Thus, finally,[4]

$$\frac{d}{dt}\langle Q \rangle = \left\langle \frac{i}{\hbar}[\hat{H},\hat{Q}] + \frac{\partial \hat{Q}}{\partial t} \right\rangle \tag{3.19}$$

We can use this theorem at once to prove two basic results, the persistence of normalization and the conservation of energy.

a   The persistence of normalization

We have already remarked in connection with (2.2) that it has to be shown that the normalization integral is independent of time. This we do by setting $\hat{Q}$ equal to unity in (3.19). Since $1\hat{H} = \hat{H}1 = \hat{H}$, the commutator vanishes as does the time derivative, and we have

$$\frac{d}{dt}\int \psi^*\psi \, d\mathbf{r} = 0 \tag{3.20}$$

b   The conservation of energy

Since the hamiltonian involves the kinetic energy $p^2/2m$ and the potential energy $V(\mathbf{r})$, whose values cannot simultaneously be known, one cannot at first thought say anything exact about the conservation of their sum (though we shall see later that energies can sometimes be known exactly). But setting Q equal to H in (3.19) again gives identically zero, so we have

$$\frac{d}{dt}\langle H \rangle = 0 \tag{3.21}$$

and the conservation of energy, as a *statistical* result, is thereby rigorously established.

Problem 3.4   What happens to (3.21) if the potential energy depends explicitly on time? What is the analogous result in classical physics? Work out an example.

To go further, it will be convenient to work out a few basic rules about commutators.

We start by evaluating a commutator which is fundamental, that connecting a component of momentum with a function $f(x,y,z)$. We introduce an arbitrary $\psi(x,y,z)$ on the right for the operators to act on:

$$[\hat{p}_x,f(\mathbf{r})]\psi(\mathbf{r}) = \frac{\hbar}{i}\left[\frac{\partial}{\partial x}f(\mathbf{r})\psi(\mathbf{r}) - f(\mathbf{r})\frac{\partial}{\partial x}\psi(\mathbf{r})\right]$$

$$= \frac{\hbar}{i}\frac{\partial}{\partial x}f(\mathbf{r}) \cdot \psi(\mathbf{r})$$

[4] The reader will notice an inconsistency of notation here. We write $\langle Q \rangle$ to mean "the expectation value of the variable Q" and $\langle \hat{Q} \rangle$ to mean "the expectation value of the operator which represents Q." The two are equal, but the emphasis is somewhat different.

where the dot, as before, indicates where the operation $\partial/\partial x$ stops. Since this is true for any ψ, we can consider the relation to be independent of ψ and write it as

$$[\hat{p}_x, f(\mathbf{r})] = \frac{\hbar}{i} \frac{\partial f(\mathbf{r})}{\partial x} \tag{3.22}$$

and similarly for $\hat{p}_y$ and $\hat{p}_z$. As a special case of (3.22) we have

$$[\hat{p}_i, r_k] = \begin{cases} \dfrac{\hbar}{i} & (i = k) \\ 0 & (i \neq k) \end{cases} \tag{3.23a}$$

and together with this we mention for completeness that

$$[r_i, r_k] = 0 \tag{3.23b}$$

and

$$[\hat{p}_i, \hat{p}_k] = 0 \tag{3.23c}$$

Problem 3.5   Derive Eqs. (3.23) (See Prob. 2.6).

Problem 3.6   Show that the quantities p_i and $\hat{r}_k$ in the momentum representation (see Prob. 2.4) also satisfy Eqs. (3.23).

Equations (3.23) were first written down by Heisenberg's collaborators Max Born and Pascual Jordan in 1925, before the advent of Schrödinger's wave mechanics. Equation (3.23a) is worth a little thought. The crucial thing about it is the smallness of the number on the right. For a marble rolling across a table, for example, classical mechanics might say that p_x is 50 g-cm/sec and x, measured from the table's edge, is 20 cm. The product $p_x x$ is therefore 10^3 g-cm²/sec; what one should notice now is that, according to (3.23a), $x\hat{p}_x$ differs from $\hat{p}_x x$ only a number of absolute value in the neighborhood of 10^{-27} g-cm²/sec. Classical mechanics assigns numerical values to p_x and x simultaneously, and, of course, they commute. Equation (3.23a) is an indication of the impossibility of assigning the values simultaneously, and in fact in Sec. (3.5) we shall use it to derive the uncertainty principle in its general form.

Most operators which do not commute with functions of x,y,z are functions of the momentum $\hat{p}$. In taking commutators of such functions it is useful to have a few general rules, which will usually reduce any commutator to expressions of the form (3.22). They are

$$[\hat{A}, \hat{B}] = -[\hat{B}, \hat{A}] \tag{3.24}$$
$$[\hat{A} + \hat{B}, \hat{C}] = [\hat{A}, \hat{C}] + [\hat{B}, \hat{C}] \tag{3.25}$$
$$[a, \hat{A}] = 0 \tag{3.26}$$

where a is any constant number

$$[a\hat{A},\hat{B}] = a[\hat{A},\hat{B}] \tag{3.27}$$

$$[\hat{A}\hat{B},\hat{C}] = \hat{A}[\hat{B},\hat{C}] + [\hat{A},\hat{C}]\hat{B} \tag{3.28}$$

The order of factors in (3.28) should be particularly noted.

Problem 3.7 Prove the identities (3.24) to (3.28).

We can now proceed to the establishment of two more consequences of (3.19).

c The motion of a wave packet

We have previously shown that a particle's momentum is equal to its mass times the group velocity [Eq. (1.27)] for a wave pattern of a very particular sort. But this type of treatment is not adequate to the general case, in which the shape of a wave packet changes as the packet moves along. We may then ask how the centroid of the packet moves, that is, what is $\frac{d}{dt}\langle x \rangle$? By (3.19), we have to find $[\hat{H},x]$, which we shall write as

$$\frac{1}{2m}[\hat{p}_x^2 + \hat{p}_y^2 + \hat{p}_z^2 + V(\mathbf{r}),x]$$

This can be examined in the light of the foregoing identities and (3.23). The only nonvanishing term is

$$\frac{1}{2m}[\hat{p}_x^2,x] = \frac{1}{2m}(\hat{p}_x[\hat{p}_x,x] + [\hat{p}_x,x]\hat{p}_x)$$

$$= \frac{1}{2m} 2\frac{\hbar}{i}\hat{p}_x$$

where we have used (3.28) and (3.23). Thus, by (3.19),

$$m\frac{d}{dt}\langle x \rangle = \langle \hat{p}_x \rangle \tag{3.29}$$

which once more asserts the validity of the classical connection between momentum and velocity *on the average*, even though they cannot both at once be known exactly.

Problem 3.8 Discuss the content of (3.29) as applied to a moving baseball.

d Newton's second law

Having established the observational meaning of the variable we have called momentum, we are in a position to determine the relation between Newtonian mechanics and the theory we have developed here. We have already studied the quantum-mechanical analogue to Newton's first law; we now take a look at the second.

The problem is to evaluate $\dfrac{d}{dt}\langle p_x \rangle$, and this requires the commutator $[\hat{H},\hat{p}_x]$. It is easily shown to be equal to

$$[\hat{H},\hat{p}_x] = -\frac{\hbar}{i}\frac{\partial V}{\partial x}$$

so that

$$\frac{d}{dt}\langle \hat{p}_x \rangle = -\left\langle \frac{\partial V}{\partial x} \right\rangle \tag{3.30}$$

Thus there exists a relation among expectation values which exactly parallels Newton's second law expressed in terms of the potential energy. It is the most direct line of connection between quantum mechanics and the classical theory, and it encourages us to look at Newtonian physics as a series of relationships among the expected results of measurements.

To complete the connection with classical physics, let us abbreviate $-\partial V/\partial x$ as $f(x)$ and suppose that ψ is in the form of a wave packet centered at $\langle x \rangle$ and that $f(x)$ varies fairly slowly across the packet, as in Fig. 3.1. Then expanding $f(x)$ in a Taylor series about $\langle x \rangle$ up to the third term gives

$$\langle f(x) \rangle = \langle\, f(\langle x \rangle) + (x - \langle x \rangle)f'(\langle x \rangle)$$
$$+ \tfrac{1}{2}(x - \langle x \rangle)^2 f''(\langle x \rangle)) \,\rangle + \cdots$$
$$= f(\langle x \rangle) + \tfrac{1}{2}\langle (x - \langle x \rangle)^2 \rangle f''(\langle x \rangle) + \cdots$$

If the second term, reflecting the finite width of the wave packet, is negligible, then (3.29) and (3.30) give

$$m\frac{d^2}{dt^2}\langle x \rangle = f(\langle x \rangle)$$

which is (in one dimension) exactly Newton's equation for $\langle x \rangle$ as a function of t. It is clearly adequate for the situations normally dealt with in classical mechanics. For a macroscopic system, the statistical distributions in x and p_x may be taken to be infinitely narrow, so that any measurement gives essentially a definite value and the whole terminology of expectation values becomes unnecessary. Equation (3.30) then has exactly the same content as Newton's second law.

Equations (3.29) and (3.30) are known as Ehrenfest's theorems.

Fig. 3.1   Wave packet in a slowly
varying field of force.

Problem 3.9 Derive Eq. (3.30).

Problem 3.10 What is $d\langle V \rangle / dt$ for the type of system we have been considering? What is the relation of the answer with that given by Newtonian mechanics?

Problem 3.11 In classical mechanics, a particle bound to a fixed center by a force depending only on the distance from that center has a constant angular momentum. The classical formula for angular momentum is $\mathbf{P} = \mathbf{r} \times \mathbf{p}$. What is the quantum-mechanical analogue of this formula? Prove both the classical conservation law and the corresponding one in quantum mechanics.

3.4 Hermitian Operators

We have mentioned earlier that the result of a measurement should be a real number. Since all such results are supposed to be expectation values of the form (3.12), this requirement imposes certain limitations on the dynamical variables Q appearing in the theory. Writing

$$\langle Q \rangle = \langle Q \rangle^* \tag{3.31}$$

we have

$$\int \psi^* \hat{Q} \psi \, d\mathbf{r} = \int \psi \hat{Q}^* \psi^* \, d\mathbf{r}$$

or

$$\int \psi^* \hat{Q} \psi \, d\mathbf{r} = \int (\hat{Q}\psi)^* \psi \, d\mathbf{r}$$

in keeping with the general style which places ψ^* to the left of ψ.

In its most general form, this relation involves an integration over all the coordinates of all the particles. If there are n particles, these are $3n$ coordinates (see Chap. 11); and if spin is to be included, one must carry out a summation over spin variables as well (see Chap. 6). It will save writing if instead of saying all this we merely omit the $d\mathbf{r}$ and write

$$\langle Q \rangle = \int \psi^* \hat{Q} \psi$$

and

$$\int \psi^* \hat{Q} \psi = \int (\hat{Q}\psi)^* \psi \tag{3.32}$$

meaning "integrated and summed over all the coordinates describing the system." Operators satisfying (3.32) were first studied in the nineteenth century by the French mathematician Charles Hermite, and in his honor they are usually referred to as *hermitian operators*, although perhaps the phrase *real operators* would be preferable.

Problem 3.12 If a number a is regarded as an operator, with ordinary multiplication its operation, what is $\langle a \rangle$? Prove that a is hermitian if and only if it is real.

Problem 3.13 Prove that if $\hat{Q}$ is hermitian and a is a number, $a\hat{Q}$ is hermitian if and only if a is real.

In writing integral expressions such as the normalization condition (2.2) or the expectation value (3.12) we assume, of course, that the integrals exist. But here we encounter a real difficulty in quantum mechanics, the fact that states which extend over all space often cannot be normalized. Let us consider, for example (in one dimension) the wave function $e^{i(kx-\omega t)}$ already encountered in (1.30), which corresponds to a definite value of the momentum, $\hbar k$. But this function is unnormalizable, for $\int |e^{i(kx-\omega t)}|^2 \, dx = \int dx$ is infinite. The way we shall get around this is to assume that the entire system is of finite size. It cannot, however, be boxed in by barriers of any kind, since these would give rise to extraneous reflected waves with momentum $-\hbar k$. The way to avoid reflected waves is to make the region finite by closing it on itself in a large loop of length L. The wave function is, of course, continuous, and so the only boundary condition to be satisfied is that ψ be periodic, with $\psi(x + L) = \psi(x)$.

Problem 3.14 Show that in this situation not all values of momentum are possible. What happens to this restriction in the limit as $L \to \infty$?

From a geometrical point of view, we have produced a normalizable wave function in one dimension by curving the one-dimensional coordinate space of the system (it is sometimes called the *configuration space*) into a two-dimensional loop. A two-dimensional configuration space can likewise be given periodic boundary conditions by wrapping it on a (three-dimensional) toroid. The wave function in three dimensions can be made similarly periodic by the simple expedient of writing

$$\psi(x + L_x, y + L_y, z + L_z) = \psi(x,y,z)$$

The fact that in order to realize the arrangement physically one would have to venture into four dimensions is of no importance. This conceptual device is of great use in quantum mechanics because it gets us out of a mathematical difficulty without having to introduce any new mathematical procedures.[5] It is an artifice which enables us to discuss a physical system in terms of simple plane waves even though no normalizable state can be quite so simple.

Problem 3.15 What is the limiting form of $|\varphi(k)|^2$ corresponding to the very long wave packet envisaged in footnote 5? (Use the

[5] Another way out, which we shall not use in this book, is to consider the exponential wave functions as the limiting case of a very long pulse like that of Prob. 2.8. Here Δx approaches infinity and Δp approaches zero, but the function is perfectly normalizable. The theory of scattering (see Chap. 9) can be given a simple and rigorous basis in this way.

results of Prob. 2.8). Sketch $|\varphi(k)|^2$ for progressively larger values of Δx, remembering (2.14), and interpret the result physically.

A problem similar to that of normalization arises in connection with hermitian operators. This term is somewhat misleading because it implies that hermiticity (the property of being hermitian) is a property of the operator alone. To see that such is not the case, let us take Q to be a component of momentum. By partial integration,

$$\langle p_x \rangle = \iiint \frac{\hbar}{i} \psi^* \frac{\partial \psi}{\partial x} \, dx \, dy \, dz$$

$$= \iint \left[\frac{\hbar}{i} \psi^* \psi \right]_x dy \, dz - \iiint \frac{\hbar}{i} \frac{\partial \psi^*}{\partial x} \psi \, dx \, dy \, dz$$

where the integrated part on the right is evaluated at the limits of the x integration. Thus,

$$\iiint \psi^* \hat{p}_x \psi \, d\mathbf{r} = \iiint (\hat{p}_x \psi)^* \psi \, d\mathbf{r} + \frac{\hbar}{i} \iint [\psi^* \psi]_x \, dy \, dz$$

One sees here that $\hat{p}_x$ is hermitian, by virtue of its factor of i, which effects the required sign change, only if $[\psi^* \psi]_x$ vanishes. This will be the case if the integration is over an infinite region and ψ is normalized, for $\psi^* \psi$ will then vanish as x approaches $\pm \infty$. Alternatively, if the system is closed upon itself, when x traces out its full circumference, ψ returns to its initial value and $[\psi^* \psi]_x$ vanishes by subtraction. And finally, if the system is enclosed in a finite box with impenetrable walls, ψ will vanish at these walls and $\hat{p}_x$ is once more hermitian. In any case, we see that hermiticity is a property of

   a. the operator
   b. the wave function
   c. the region of integration

We shall express this by saying that a certain operator is hermitian for a given wave function in a given region of hermiticity. It should be noted that the difficulties we have been discussing do not arise for a real physical system, however large, except when one is trying to idealize it by pretending that it is infinite. In actuality, every wave function which describes a possible physical system may be taken to vanish strongly at infinity. It is therefore normalizable, and the hermiticity of $\hat{p}$ follows at once. The only situation in which more need be said arises when ψ becomes infinite at some point. Then, as we shall see in Sec. 7.3, the requirement that all possible systems have wave functions with respect to which the hamiltonian operator is hermitian will turn out to be necessary in order to specify solutions of Schrödinger's equation uniquely.

We shall now prove a theorem on hermitian operators which will later be very useful. It is that if ψ_1 and ψ_2 are any two functions for which $\hat{Q}$ is hermitian, then

$$\int(\hat{Q}\psi_1)^*\psi_2 = \int\psi_1^*\hat{Q}\psi_2 \tag{3.33}$$

Proof. Clearly, if $\hat{Q}$ is hermitian for ψ_1 and ψ_2, then it is also hermitian for $\psi_1 + \lambda\psi_2$, where λ is any complex number. Thus

$$\int(\psi_1^* + \lambda^*\psi_2^*)\hat{Q}(\psi_1 + \lambda\psi_2) \quad \text{is real}$$

Expanding this gives

$$\int\psi_1^*\hat{Q}\psi_1 + |\lambda|^2\int\psi_2^*\hat{Q}\psi_2 + \lambda\int\psi_1^*\hat{Q}\psi_2 + \lambda^*\int\psi_2^*\hat{Q}\psi_1 \quad \text{is real}$$

The first two terms of this are real because $\hat{Q}$ is hermitian. The sum of the last two terms is real for arbitrary λ only if the integrals are complex conjugates of each other, that is, if

$$\int\psi_1^*\hat{Q}\psi_2 = (\int\psi_2^*\hat{Q}\psi_1)^*$$

from which follows (3.33).

Problem 3.16 Verify that the hamiltonian operator $\hat{H}$ satisfies (3.33).

Problem 3.17 Use the relation (3.33) to derive again Eq. (3.19), making the proof this time as short and neat as possible.

It is natural to ask whether the sum or product of two hermitian operators $\hat{P}$ and $\hat{Q}$ is again hermitian. It is easy to see that the sum is hermitian. The product is not necessarily so, as we can see by finding the complex conjugate of its expectation value:

$$\langle PQ \rangle = \int\psi^*\hat{P}\hat{Q}\psi$$
$$\langle PQ \rangle^* = \int(\hat{P}\hat{Q}\psi)^*\psi$$

Now use (3.33), with $(\hat{Q}\psi)^*$ as ψ_1^* and ψ as ψ_2:

$$\langle PQ \rangle^* = \int(\hat{Q}\psi)^*\hat{P}\psi$$

and again, with ψ as ψ_1 and $\hat{P}\psi$ as ψ_2:

$$\langle PQ \rangle^* = \int\psi^*\hat{Q}\hat{P}\psi$$

or

$$\langle PQ \rangle^* = \langle QP \rangle \tag{3.34}$$

The product $\hat{P}\hat{Q}$ is not hermitian, but one can easily form from it two expressions which are hermitian: $\hat{P}\hat{Q} + \hat{Q}\hat{P}$ and $i[\hat{P},\hat{Q}]$. The expression $\hat{P}\hat{Q} + \hat{Q}\hat{P}$ is called the *anticommutator* of $\hat{P}$ and $\hat{Q}$, and the reader who has solved Prob. 3.10 will already have encountered an example of it. In general, quantum mechanics replaces products of dynamical variables by symmetrized operator products of this type. Clearly, $\hat{P}\hat{Q}$ is hermitian if and only if $\hat{P}$ commutes with $\hat{Q}$. The fact that i times the commutator of two hermitian operators is again hermitian is reflected in the commutation relations (3.22), if one notes that a real number satisfies the definition of a hermitian operator (Prob. 3.12).

As a special case of a product, we note that $\hat{Q}^2$ is hermitian if $\hat{Q}$ is hermitian, and we can see at once that $\langle \hat{Q}^2 \rangle$, like its classical analogue Q^2, is not a negative number, for

$$\langle \hat{Q}^2 \rangle = \int \psi^* \hat{Q}^2 \psi = \int (\hat{Q}\psi)^* \hat{Q}\psi$$
$$= \int |\hat{Q}\psi|^2$$

which is the sum of contributions none of which are negative, that is,

$$\langle \hat{Q}^2 \rangle \geqslant 0 \qquad (3.35)$$

Physical quantities represented by hermitian operators are the backbone of quantum mechanics, and the next two sections will discuss two of their characteristic features. First we shall treat the Heisenberg indeterminacy relations in an exact and general way, and then we shall see how to characterize a state in which the indeterminacy in some physical quantity is zero.

3.5 The Indeterminacy Relations

We showed in the preceding chapter that the description of the kinematical and dynamical properties of particles by a wave function contains certain essential indeterminacies, that is, that it cannot always be made precise. This lack of precision manifests itself not in the expectation value of an operator, which can, of course, be found with an accuracy limited only by one's ability to compute, but in the fact that the actual results of readings will have a more or less fuzzy statistical distribution around the expectation value. But we can calculate the widths of such distributions, and we shall express the indeterminacy principle in terms of them.

The departure of a reading of a quantity Q from the expectation value of Q may be represented by the operator $\hat{Q} - \langle \hat{Q} \rangle$. Clearly, this is zero on the average,

$$\langle \hat{Q} - \langle \hat{Q} \rangle \rangle = \langle \hat{Q} \rangle - \langle \hat{Q} \rangle = 0$$

for this is what defines the expectation value. But the square of this quantity does not in general average to zero, for it is never negative. Let us define ΔQ as the positive square root of

$$(\Delta Q)^2 = \langle (\hat{Q} - \langle \hat{Q} \rangle)^2 \rangle \qquad (3.36)$$

which we can conveniently rewrite as follows,

$$(\Delta Q)^2 = \langle \hat{Q}^2 - 2\langle \hat{Q} \rangle \hat{Q} + \langle \hat{Q} \rangle^2 \rangle$$
$$= \langle \hat{Q}^2 \rangle - 2\langle \hat{Q} \rangle^2 + \langle \hat{Q} \rangle^2$$
$$= \langle \hat{Q}^2 \rangle - \langle \hat{Q} \rangle^2 \qquad (3.37)$$

If every reading of Q is certain to give the value $\langle \hat{Q} \rangle$, then ΔQ is certainly zero; but if the Q's are statistically distributed, then ΔQ is positive and is a measure of the breadth of the distribution. In statistical theory it is known as the *standard deviation* of the values of Q.

Problem 3.18 What are $\langle x \rangle$ and Δx for the wave function shown in Fig. 2.3?

Problem 3.19 What are $\langle x \rangle$ and Δx for the initial wave function of the particle in Prob. 2.8?

Problem 3.20 Let n be the number of spots shown by a die thrown at random. What is $\langle n \rangle$? What is Δn?

Problem 3.21 N coins are thrown onto a table and n heads appear. Find $\langle n \rangle$ and Δn.

To derive the indeterminacy relations between two quantities P and Q in terms of the standard deviations of their statistical distributions, let $\hat{P}$ and $\hat{Q}$ be the corresponding operators in some representation and let their commutator be written as

$$[\hat{P}, \hat{Q}] = i\hat{C} \tag{3.38}$$

where the i has been introduced in order that $\hat{C}$ shall be a hermitian operator. Now let us examine the real number

$$G = \int |(\hat{P} + i\lambda\hat{Q})\psi|^2$$

considered as a function of the real number λ. As in the derivation of (3.35), G must be positive or zero. Writing it out in detail, we have, by (3.33),

$$G = \int [(\hat{P} + i\lambda\hat{Q})\psi]^* \cdot (\hat{P} + i\lambda\hat{Q})\psi$$
$$= \int (\hat{P}^* - i\lambda\hat{Q}^*)\psi^* \cdot (\hat{P} + i\lambda\hat{Q})\psi$$

(the dot, as before, shows where $\hat{P}$ and $\hat{Q}$ stop operating)

$$G = \int \psi^* (\hat{P} - i\lambda\hat{Q})(\hat{P} + i\lambda\hat{Q})\psi \geqslant 0$$

Expanding the product (but keeping track of the order of factors) and using (3.38), we find

$$G = \langle \hat{P}^2 \rangle - \lambda\langle \hat{C} \rangle + \lambda^2\langle \hat{Q}^2 \rangle \geqslant 0 \tag{3.39}$$

which must be true for any real value of λ. In view of (3.35), G is certainly not negative when λ tends toward 0 or ∞, but even the smaller intermediate values are also not negative. The graph of G as a function of λ must therefore look something like Fig. 3.2.

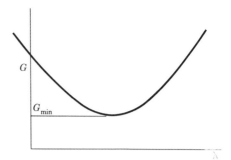

Fig. 3.2 *G* as a function of λ.

G is smallest when $dG/d\lambda = 0$, or $\lambda = \langle \hat{C} \rangle / 2\langle \hat{Q}^2 \rangle$, so that

$$G_{\min} = \langle \hat{P}^2 \rangle - \frac{1}{4} \frac{\langle \hat{C} \rangle^2}{\langle \hat{Q}^2 \rangle} \geqslant 0$$

that is

$$\langle \hat{P}^2 \rangle \langle \hat{Q}^2 \rangle \geqslant \tfrac{1}{4} \langle \hat{C} \rangle^2 \qquad (3.40)$$

To derive the uncertainty principle, we replace $\hat{P}$ and $\hat{Q}$ in (3.40) by $\hat{P} - \langle \hat{P} \rangle$ and $\hat{Q} - \langle \hat{Q} \rangle$, respectively. The new $\hat{P}$ and $\hat{Q}$ have the same commutation relation (3.38) as the old, but now comparison with (3.36) enables us to write

$$\Delta P \, \Delta Q \geqslant \tfrac{1}{2} |\langle \hat{C} \rangle| \qquad (3.41)$$

where ΔP and ΔQ are the standard deviations of the results of measurements of P and Q. This is an exact and general form of the uncertainty relation. It has two sorts of consequences. If $\hat{C}$ is a number, then $\langle \hat{C} \rangle = C$, independently of ψ. As an example, we have from (3.23a)

$$\Delta p_i \, \Delta r_j \geqslant \begin{cases} \tfrac{1}{2}\hbar & (i = j) \\ 0 & (i \neq j) \end{cases} \qquad (3.42)$$

This verifies that, as we found in two examples in Sec. 2.4, the reciprocal indeterminacy affects only corresponding components of position and momentum. In the language of classical dynamics, such coordinates and momenta are said to be *conjugate* to each other.

If, on the other hand, $\hat{C}$ is an operator, then $\langle C \rangle$ will depend on the state of the system, and one has a more general type of indeterminacy. Relations of this kind have been discussed very little in the literature of quantum mechanics.

Problem 3.22 Show that

$$\Delta H \, \Delta x \geqslant \frac{\hbar}{2m} \langle \hat{p}_x \rangle$$

and show how this relation is fulfilled in the wave packet of Prob. 2.8.

Problem 3.23   There is no reason other than the convenience of the result why λ must be chosen to be real. Carry out the proof again with $G = \int |[\hat{P} + (\kappa + i\lambda)\hat{Q}]\psi|^2$ and show that the uncertainty product $\Delta P\,\Delta Q$ calculated in this way is always at least as large as (3.41).

We can go a little further than the inequality (3.41) and ask what happens when the equality holds, that is, for what kind of state does one have the absolute minimum of uncertainty,

$$\Delta P\,\Delta Q = \tfrac{1}{2}|\langle C\rangle|$$

Tracing back the proof, one sees that the condition for this is $G = 0$, or

$$[\hat{P} - \langle P\rangle + i\lambda\,(\hat{Q} - \langle Q\rangle)]\psi = 0 \tag{3.43}$$

Usually only one sign is possible for λ, the other being unsuitable for some reason.

Problem 3.24   What kind of wave function in one dimension minimizes $\Delta p_x\,\Delta x$? What role does λ play in this wave function?

3.6   Simple States

Most of the discussion thus far has been in terms which make it appear that any measurement carried out on a number of identical physical systems will give a variety of answers statistically distributed about some average value. This is often, but not necessarily, the case. In fact, we have already considered wave functions of the form (1.30) in which only one value of momentum is present and, correspondingly, the position is perfectly undetermined. Likewise, the sharpness of spectral lines (though none are perfectly monochromatic) implies that stationary atomic states are quite definite in their energy values. Such a sharp state we call simple; and though it is usually unattainable in practice, it is convenient to have as an idealization.

Expressed mathematically, a simple state is characterized by the fact that one or more dynamical variables can be measured in it with vanishing standard deviation. By (3.36) this means that for one or more Q's,

$$(\Delta Q)^2 = \int\psi^*(\hat{Q} - \langle Q\rangle)^2\psi = 0$$

Using the hermiticity of Q gives

$$\int|(\hat{Q} - \langle Q\rangle)\psi|^2 = 0$$

and this is possible only if

$$(\hat{Q} - \langle Q\rangle)\psi = 0$$

Actually, $\langle Q \rangle$ is a poor notation to use when the value is a perfectly definite quantity. Instead of it we shall introduce the letter q, and in general the lower-case letter corresponding to any dynamical variable, to denote its definite value in a system where it has a definite value. [An exception will be made for $\hat{H}\psi = E\psi$ as in (3.6).] The wave function of such a system now satisfies not only Schrödinger's equation but also a relation of the form

$$\hat{Q}\psi = q\psi \tag{3.44}$$

where q is a (real) number, for each dynamical variable Q which takes on a definite value. This is in fact exactly the content of an equation such as (1.34), characterizing a pure momentum state. Equation (3.6) deserves a little more comment. If a certain state corresponds to a definite energy, then it satisfies

$$\hat{H}\psi = E\psi \tag{3.45}$$

Comparison with (3.7) shows that the state can also be characterized as being simply periodic, for

$$i\hbar \frac{\partial \psi}{\partial t} = \hat{H}\psi = E\psi$$

so that ψ is proportional to $e^{-i\omega t}$, where $E = \hbar\omega$. This fact was taken to be intuitively clear, at least in a rough way, in the discussions preceding the writing down of Schrödinger's equation in Sec. 3.1. If ψ depends on the time only through a factor $e^{-i\omega t}$, it is clear that $|\psi|^2$ is independent of time. This leads to the designation of states of definite energy as *stationary states;* they correspond to the stationary states of the Bohr theory. Problem 3.26 shows that not only $|\psi|^2$ but the expectation value of any dynamical variable is constant in such a state.

Relations of the form (3.44) are of great importance in physics, since they define the problem of calculating the possible values of anything that can be measured exactly. The calculation of atomic energy levels is of this character, and there are many other instances involving spins, angular momenta, etc., which occur frequently in practice. In good English, the various solutions ψ of (3.44) are called the *proper functions* of $\hat{Q}$, and the value of q corresponding to a given ψ is the *proper value* belonging to it. In German these terms are *Eigenfunktion* and *Eigenwert*. It is almost universal among English-speaking physicists to occupy the middle ground and call them *eigenfunctions* and *eigenvalues*. Further, it is convenient to denote the state of a system whose wave function is an eigenfunction of $\hat{Q}$ as an *eigenstate* of $\hat{Q}$. Like "liverwurst," these half-translations are now a part of the language.

The concept of eigenfunction enables us to state more exactly the specification of an ideal measurement made in Sec. 2.4. If a measurement is made and then at once repeated, (2.41) states that the second measurement will give exactly the same result as the first one. Thus the result of the second measurement is an eigenvalue of the operator associated with the measured quantity, and the state of the system just before the second measurement is the corresponding eigenstate. And, of course, the result of the first measurement was the same eigenvalue. We therefore conclude that

1. The possible results of any ideal measurement of a quantity Q are the eigenvalues of the associated operator $\hat{Q}$, and the state of the system immediately after the measurement is the corresponding eigenstate of $\hat{Q}$.

Statement (2.42) can similarly be supplemented by the following remark. If ΔQ remains zero as time goes on, the state of the system will remain an eigenstate of $\hat{Q}$. It is easy to see that this is the case if $\hat{H}$ commutes with $\hat{Q}$. Therefore,

2. If $\hat{H}$ and $\hat{Q}$ commute, then the system's wave function remains an eigenfunction of $\hat{Q}$, and any subsequent measurement of Q will give exactly the same value as before.[6]

Problem 3.25 Prove that if $[\hat{H},\hat{Q}] = 0$, then $d\Delta Q/dt = 0$.

Problem 3.26 If $\hat{Q}$ is an operator which does not involve the time explicitly and if ψ is any eigenfunction of $\hat{H}$, show that the expectation value of $\hat{Q}$ in the state ψ is independent of time.

Problem 3.27 Evaluate $d \langle \mathbf{r} \cdot \hat{\mathbf{p}} \rangle / dt$. If the expectation value is taken in a stationary state, show that this leads to the *virial theorem*

$$\langle T \rangle = \tfrac{1}{2} \langle \mathbf{r} \cdot \boldsymbol{\nabla} V \rangle \qquad (3.46)$$

where T is the kinetic energy.

Problem 3.28 Find the relation between $\langle T \rangle$ and $\langle V \rangle$ for a simple harmonic oscillator (one dimension) and for a hydrogen atom (three dimensions). Compare these results with those of classical physics. (For the hydrogen atom a circular orbit will suffice.)

Suppose now that we wish to give some meaning to the statement that P has the value p and Q has the value q for a given system. To do so, we imagine an experiment in which P is meas-

---

[6] There has been considerable discussion about the conclusion that a measurement of Q abruptly throws a system into one or another of the eigenstates of $\hat{Q}$, and the whole idea has often been denounced as unphysical. More careful investigation, however, shows that at least in some cases this transition is far from instantaneous and unphysical, for the system actually makes the transition into the eigenstate during the finite time occupied by the measurement and in a manner which is governed exactly by the equations of motion of the entire system. The calculations are rather difficult, but the interested reader will profit from a look at a paper by H. S. Green, Nuovo Cimento, **9**, 880 (1958).

ured, yielding the value p and leaving the system in the eigenstate of P belonging to that eigenvalue. Next we measure Q. This yields q and changes the system to the corresponding eigenstate of Q. This is in general no longer an eigenstate of P, and so we have lost the original value of p. Let us assume that p and q belong to continuous ranges of possible values. It can then be shown that if we are content with a precision ΔQ in the value of q, so that we do not know exactly the state into which the system is thrown by the measurement, then it is possible to change the previous eigenvalue of P only by an amount within ΔP of p, where ΔP and ΔQ are related by (3.41). If P and Q commute, then it is possible to find states which are eigenstates of P and Q at the same time, so that the two measurements are compatible and $\Delta P = \Delta Q = 0$. This will be proved in Sec. 5.3.

Examples

We shall now give three very simple examples of the occurrence of the eigenfunction-eigenvalue relation, from which the reader can judge something of its scope and importance.

1. *Angular momentum.* A particle moves in the xy plane with constant angular momentum about the z axis. We shall find the possible results of a measurement of the angular momentum, together with the corresponding eigenfunctions.

As in Prob. 2.7, the angular-momentum operator will be

$$\hat{P}_z = x\hat{p}_y - y\hat{p}_x = \frac{\hbar}{i}\left(x\frac{\partial}{\partial y} - y\frac{\partial}{\partial x}\right) \tag{3.47}$$

It will be convenient to adopt polar coordinates, given by

$$x = r\cos\varphi \qquad y = r\sin\varphi$$

in terms of which we find the simpler form

$$\hat{P}_z = \frac{\hbar}{i}\frac{\partial}{\partial\varphi} \tag{3.48}$$

Problem 3.29 Show that (3.47) is the same as (3.48).

The possible results of a measurement of P_z are now the eigenvalues P_z in the equation

$$\hat{P}_z\psi = \frac{\hbar}{i}\frac{\partial\psi}{\partial\varphi} = P_z\psi$$

the solution of which is

$$\psi = \psi_0 e^{(i/\hbar)P_z\varphi} \tag{3.49}$$

where ψ_0 contains whatever other variables (time, etc.) are necessary to describe the system. Equation (3.49) is a relation between ψ and P_z, but it does not tell us anything about the possible values of P_z. To find them, we must invoke the boundary condition satisfied by ψ, which in this case is as follows. The angle $\varphi = 0$ is the same as the angle $\varphi = 2\pi$, and if the wave function is to be *single-valued*, that is, have only one value for any given value of φ, we must have $\psi(0) = \psi(2\pi)$. Therefore,

$$1 = e^{2\pi i P_z/\hbar}$$

This is true only if

$$P_z = m\hbar \qquad (m = \ldots, -2, -1, 0, 1, 2, \ldots) \tag{3.50}$$

and corresponding to any value of m (the so-called magnetic quantum number) the wave function is

$$\psi = \psi_0 e^{im\varphi} \tag{3.51}$$

We have thus explained from first principles the origin of Bohr's postulated quantum rule (1.17). The subject of angular momentum is considerably more complicated than this, however, and we shall defer further consideration of it until Chap. 5. There we shall discuss angular momentum in terms of three dimensions.[7]

Problem 3.30   What is the uncertainty relation satisfied by ΔP_z and $\Delta\varphi$? How is this relation reflected in the wave function (3.49)?

2. *Linear momentum.*   Here the eigenvalue equation (in one dimension) is

$$\hat{p}\psi = p\psi \qquad \text{or} \qquad \frac{\hbar}{i}\frac{\partial\psi}{\partial x} = p\psi$$

whence

$$\psi = \psi_0 e^{(i/\hbar)px} \tag{3.52}$$

where again ψ_0 contains t and any other variables and p is the momentum eigenvalue. To go further, we need boundary conditions. We have mentioned in Sec. 3.4 the device of imposing periodic boundary conditions in order to obtain a normalizable wave function, and Prob. 3.14 showed how the possible values of p are restricted in this case. In infinite space, however, there are no boundary conditions at all; p is therefore quite arbitrary, and a free particle can have any momentum one chooses to give it.

3. *Energy.*   Suppose for simplicity that the particle is restricted to a finite region of length L along the x axis, moving freely within this region but prevented from leaving it by a force barrier so strong that ψ vanishes at and beyond each boundary.

---

[7] The property of single-valuedness postulated above apparently cannot be justified in a discussion restricted to two dimensions. For its justification in three dimensions, see E. Merzbacher, Am. J. Phys., **30**, 237 (1962).

The equation $\hat{H}\psi = E\psi$, or

$$-\frac{\hbar^2}{2m}\frac{\partial^2\psi}{\partial x^2} = E\psi \qquad [\psi(0) = \psi(L) = 0]$$

has already been solved in Sec. 1.5, where it was found that the possible values of E are

$$E = \frac{\hbar^2}{2m}\left(\frac{n\pi}{L}\right)^2 \qquad (n = 1, 2, 3, \ldots) \tag{3.53}$$

We see from the foregoing three examples how the eigen-function-eigenvalue relation, taken together with appropriate boundary conditions, leads to the quantizing of the possible measured values of a dynamical variable which is a characteristic feature of modern physics.

3.7 Superpositions

We have mentioned before that the effects in quantum mechanics which are the most inexplicable from the standpoint of a classical theory of particles arise from the principle of superposition, the fact the sum of the ψ's representing two different states of a system again represents a possible state of the system. In Chap. 1 we discussed the formation of a two-slit diffraction pattern from this point of view, stressing that the superposition involved must be coherent. Let us look at this requirement a little more closely. Suppose that the two slits are illuminated by two identical sources of light, and suppose them faint enough that there are only one or two photons in the apparatus at a time. The wave packet corresponding to any particular photon is of the order of 1 m long.[8] If two photons of the same wavelength enter through the two slits at about the same time, the field amplitude at the photographic plate will be the sum of the two component fields and an interference pattern will result, in the sense that the probability of receiving a photon will have alternate maxima and minima across the plate. In this sense, all superpositions are coherent. But since the phases of the two photons differ at random, the center of the pattern will be located at random on the plate. Another pair of photons produces its own instantaneous probability pattern, but superposed at random on the first, and the result of a long exposure will be a uniformly darkened plate. Let the field amplitudes at the plate from the two slits of Fig. 3.3 be proportional to $\cos(kl_1 - \omega t + \alpha_1)$ and $\cos(kl_2 - \omega t + \alpha_2)$, respectively, where the phase factors are written ex-

---

[8] This comes about because it takes a photon of the order of 10^{-9} sec to be emitted (this is the lifetime of the excited state). A careful discussion of the finite path differences over which interference is possible with incoherent sources is given by B. Rossi, *Optics*, Addison-Wesley Publishing Company, Inc., Reading, Mass., 1957, pp. 146–153.

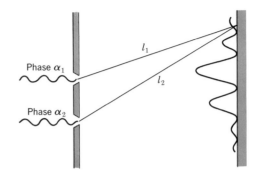

Fig. 3.3 Formation of an interference pattern by coherent illumination from two slits.

plicitly to emphasize their independence. The resultant field intensity is proportional to

$$[\cos (kl_1 - \omega t + \alpha_1) + \cos (kl_2 - \omega t + \alpha_2)]^2$$
$$= \cos^2(kl_1 - \omega t + \alpha_1) + 2 \cos (kl_1 - \omega t + \alpha_1)$$
$$\cos (kl_2 - \omega t + \alpha_2) + \cos^2 (kl_2 - \omega t + \alpha_2)$$
$$= \cos^2 (kl_1 - \omega t + \alpha_1) + \cos [k(l_1 + l_2) - 2\omega t + \alpha_1 + \alpha_2]$$
$$+ \cos [k(l_1 - l_2) + \alpha_1 - \alpha_2] + \cos^2 (kl_2 - \omega t + \alpha_2)$$

If now we average this expression over a good many cycles of ωt, it becomes

$$\tfrac{1}{2} + 0 + \cos [k(l_1 - l_2) + \alpha_1 - \alpha_2] + \tfrac{1}{2}$$

and a further average over either α gives the value 1, independent of the path difference. This corresponds to a uniform blackening of the plate. It is incoherent superposition. If on the other hand both beams originate in the same source, the phases will bear a definite relation to each other, with $\alpha_1 - \alpha_2 = \delta$, a fixed number even though both α's vary at random from one wave train to another. Averaging the intensity over α_1 with this proviso on α_2 leaves it unchanged, $1 + \cos [k(l_1 - l_2) + \delta]$, which shows the regular maxima and minima as a function of the path difference which characterize the diffraction pattern.

The above remarks apply with minor changes to Schrödinger wave functions. Suppose, for example, that two electron states ψ_1 and ψ_2 are superposed in a way which randomizes their relative phases, giving a resultant wave function

$$\psi = e^{i\alpha_1}\psi_1 + e^{i\alpha_2}\psi_2$$

Rather than calculate the intensity, let us find the expectation value of a dynamical variable Q in this mixed state,

$$\langle Q \rangle = \int (e^{-i\alpha_1}\psi_1^* + e^{-i\alpha_2}\psi_2^*)\hat{Q}(e^{i\alpha_1}\psi_1 + e^{i\alpha_2}\psi_2) \, d\mathbf{r}$$
$$= \int \psi_1^*\hat{Q}\psi_1 \, d\mathbf{r} + e^{-i(\alpha_1 - \alpha_2)}\int \psi_1^*\hat{Q}\psi_2 \, d\mathbf{r} + e^{i(\alpha_1 - \alpha_2)}\int \psi_2^*\hat{Q}\psi_1 \, d\mathbf{r}$$
$$+ \int \psi_2^*\hat{Q}\psi_2 \, d\mathbf{r} \qquad (3.54)$$

Averaging over α_1 and α_2 chosen at random gives

$$\langle Q \rangle = \int \psi_1^* \hat{Q} \psi_1 \, d\mathbf{r} + \int \psi_2^* \hat{Q} \psi_2 \, d\mathbf{r}$$
$$= \langle Q \rangle_1 + \langle Q \rangle_2 \tag{3.55}$$

which is simply the sum of the $\langle Q \rangle$'s belonging to the two states individually. This is just what one expects on the basis of classical mechanics, and it might be termed classical superposition. If, however, the phases have a fixed relationship as before, then the two central terms of (3.54) are (except perhaps for special ψ's) no longer zero. It is the cross terms arising in this way from the superposition of amplitudes that have no analogue in classical physics and are responsible for interference phenomena and others which we shall encounter later. One of the pleasant surprises of quantum statistical mechanics is that for a wide range of phenomena it yields essentially the same results as the classical theory, and this fact can be traced, as in the above example, to the randomness of the phases involved.

3.8 Summary

The essential results of this chapter, detached from the arguments relating them to experience, are these:

1. All possible information about a physical system is contained in its wave function ψ.

2. The expectation value of the measurement of the dynamical variable represented by the operator $\hat{Q}$ is

$$\langle Q \rangle = \int \psi^* \hat{Q} \psi$$

3. The evolution of a physical system in time is described by the wave equation

$$i\hbar \frac{\partial \psi}{\partial t} = \hat{H} \psi$$

where $\hat{H}$, the hamiltonian operator, has a form which depends on the assumptions made, but which in the nonrelativistic, one-particle theory discussed up to now is

$$\hat{H} = \frac{\hat{p}^2}{2m} + V(\mathbf{r})$$

where

$$\hat{\mathbf{p}} = \frac{\hbar}{i} \nabla$$

and $V(\mathbf{r})$ is the particle's potential-energy function. (The case of a particle in a magnetic field will be treated in Chap. 7.)

4. As a consequence of the preceding,

$$\frac{d}{dt}\langle\hat{Q}\rangle = \frac{i}{\hbar}\langle[\hat{H},\hat{Q}]\rangle + \left\langle\frac{\partial\hat{Q}}{\partial t}\right\rangle$$

where $[\hat{H},\hat{Q}]$ means $\hat{H}\hat{Q} - \hat{Q}\hat{H}$.

5. The statistical distribution of the results of measurements about their mean value is characterized by the standard deviation

$$\Delta Q = [\langle(Q - \langle Q\rangle)^2\rangle]^{\frac{1}{2}} = [\langle Q^2\rangle - \langle Q\rangle^2]^{\frac{1}{2}}$$

(and by higher statistical moments similarly defined).

6. Dynamical variables whose expectation values are real are described by hermitian operators, whose most useful characteristic is that

$$\int(\hat{Q}\psi_1)^* \cdot \psi_2 = \int\psi_1^*\hat{Q}\psi_2$$

7. A pair of noncommuting hermitian operators satisfy an indeterminacy relation of the form

$$\Delta P\,\Delta Q \geqslant \frac{1}{2}|\langle[\hat{P},\hat{Q}]\rangle|$$

8. Noncommutativity implies that after successive measurements of P and Q, a system is left in a state which depends on the order in which P and Q were measured, so that there is an indeterminacy in the degree to which values of P and of Q may simultaneously be ascribed to the system.

9. A state in which measurements of Q yield a definite value is called a simple state, and the condition $\Delta Q = 0$ implies that there exists a wave function ψ and a number q such that

$$\hat{Q}\psi = q\psi$$

10. The possible results of a measurement of Q are the eigenvalues of $\hat{Q}$, and the system is left after the measurement in the corresponding eigenstate.

11. Superposition of two wave functions to form a third can occur in two ways: with random phases (incoherent) and with the phases in a fixed relation (coherent). The latter gives rise to interference phenomena which have no analogue in classical mechanics.

4

Systems in One Dimension

In order to illustrate some of the characteristic results of quantum mechanics without encountering too many of its characteristic difficulties, we shall first treat some one-dimensional problems which are idealized but which nevertheless have the essential features of situations encountered in practice.

The systems are, of course, somewhat artificial, but no more so than those involving an insect crawling on a massless rod or a bead sliding down a frictionless wire that one encounters in books on classical mechanics. The point here is that we are trying to avoid solving partial differential equations until (in Chap. 5) we have developed some simplifying tricks. Every example to be treated here throws some light on an analogous situation that exists in the real world.

4.1 Simple Barriers

Let us suppose that it is possible to produce a truly monoenergetic beam of electrons of energy E. The time dependence of ψ will now be be simply periodic and we shall neglect it. The space dependence is given by (3.6), or, in one dimension

$$-\frac{\hbar^2}{2m}\frac{\partial^2\psi}{\partial x^2} = [E - V(x)]\psi \tag{4.1}$$

We note that if V were independent of x, this equation would be easy to solve. The examples to follow will exploit this fact.

Assume that it is possible to create a discontinuous potential as shown in Fig. 4.1. Let a beam of electrons be incident from the

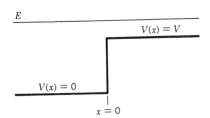

Fig. 4.1 A semi-infinite rectangular potential barrier.

left, of the form

$$\psi_{\text{inc}} = A e^{i p_1 x / \hbar} \tag{4.2}$$

We are going to find the effect of the discontinuity in potential upon this beam. It is easy to write down wave equations valid within each of the two regions of the figure:

region 1 $$-\frac{\hbar^2}{2m} \frac{\partial^2 \psi_1}{\partial x^2} = E \psi_1 \tag{4.3}$$

region 2 $$-\frac{\hbar^2}{2m} \frac{\partial^2 \psi_2}{\partial x^2} = (E - V) \psi_2 \tag{4.4}$$

We must now distinguish between two cases, according as $E - V$ is positive or negative. In the former case, classical physics asserts that the particle will penetrate region 2 and travel freely there, albeit with reduced velocity; whereas if $E < V$, the particle cannot get in.

Case 1: $E > V$

The terms E and $E - V$ (Fig. 4.1) represent the kinetic energies of electrons in the two regions, and it will be convenient to express them in terms of their associated momenta $\hbar k_1$ and $\hbar k_2$, respectively:

region 1 $$E = \frac{\hbar^2 k_1{}^2}{2m} \qquad \frac{\partial^2 \psi_1}{\partial x^2} = -k_1{}^2 \psi_1 \tag{4.5}$$

region 2 $$E - V = \frac{\hbar^2 k_2{}^2}{2m} \qquad \frac{\partial^2 \psi_2}{\partial x^2} = -k_2{}^2 \psi_2 \tag{4.6}$$

the solutions of which are

region 1 $$\psi_1 = A e^{i k_1 x} + B e^{-i k_1 x} \tag{4.7}$$

region 2 $$\psi_2 = C e^{i k_2 x} + D e^{-i k_2 x} \tag{4.8}$$

where the constants of integration, from the mathematical point of view, are arbitrary. From the physical point of view they are not arbitrary, however, since two of them can be assigned values in terms of the imagined conditions of the experiment. We have already assumed (4.2). The D term in (4.8) represents electrons incident on the apparatus from the right. We assume that there are none, and so set D equal to zero. Thus, A is given and B and C are unknown, the three of them representing respectively the ampli-

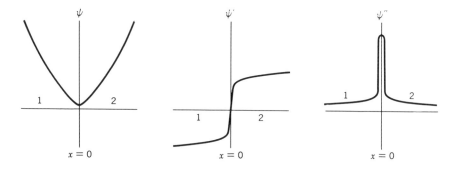

Fig. 4.2   (a) Wave function with an abrupt change of slope at
$x = 0$. (b) Its first derivative. (c) Its second derivative.

tudes of an incident and a reflected wave in region 1 and a transmitted wave in region 2.

The solutions in the two regions must now be joined together.
We obtained them by requiring that the wave equation be obeyed
within the two regions; now we require that it be obeyed at the
boundary. Clearly, this requires that ψ be continuous there:

$$\psi_1(x) = \psi_2(x) \qquad \text{at } x = 0 \tag{4.9}$$

But let us assume that ψ_1 and ψ_2 come together in a cusp. Figure 4.2a
shows a section of a slightly rounded "cusp"; (b) shows the derivative ψ' in the same region; and (c) shows the second derivative. If
now the cusp is sharp, corresponding to a real discontinuity in the
slope, the peak in ψ'' becomes infinitely high and narrow.[1] But in
(4.1), nothing becomes infinite, so that a ψ with a cusp would fail
to satisfy the equation at the point $x = 0$. We thus require that the
slope of ψ be continuous at the boundary,

$$\frac{\partial \psi_1(x)}{\partial x} = \frac{\partial \psi_2(x)}{\partial x} \qquad \text{at } x = 0 \tag{4.10}$$

The foregoing considerations can be expressed rigorously
as follows: Write (4.1) in the general form

$$\frac{\partial^2 \psi(x)}{\partial x^2} = f(x)\psi(x)$$

and integrate it from x_1 to x_2, where $x_1 < 0$ and $x_2 > 0$:

$$\psi'(x_2) - \psi'(x_1) = \int_{x_1}^{x_2} f(x)\psi(x)\, dx$$

[1] Functions which become discontinuous in this way, called *delta functions*,
are of quite general use in various branches of applied mathematics and physics.
See, for example, D. Bohm, *Quantum Mechanics*, Prentice-Hall, Inc., Englewood Cliffs, N.J., 1951, pp. 212–214. Delta functions will recur in Sec. 8.7.

Now let x_1 and x_2 approach zero from opposite sides. Since the integrand is finite, the integral approaches zero, and the two values of ψ' becomes equal.

The two conditions applied to ψ as given by (4.7) and (4.8) yield

$$A + B = C \tag{4.11}$$

and

$$k_1(A - B) = k_2C \tag{4.12}$$

whose solutions, in terms of the given A, are

$$C = \frac{2k_1}{k_1 + k_2} A \tag{4.13}$$

and

$$B = \frac{k_1 - k_2}{k_1 + k_2} A \tag{4.14}$$

These give the relative amplitudes of the transmitted and reflected waves. It is customary to define the coefficients of transmission and reflection at a barrier, T and R, as the ratios of the transmitted and reflected current densities to those which are incident. Using (3.11) and canceling common factors, we have

$$T = \frac{k_2}{k_1} \left| \frac{C}{A} \right|^2 \tag{4.15}$$

and

$$R = \left| \frac{B}{A} \right|^2 \tag{4.16}$$

We thus have

$$T = \frac{4k_1k_2}{(k_1 + k_2)^2} \tag{4.17}$$

and

$$R = \left(\frac{k_1 - k_2}{k_1 + k_2} \right)^2 \tag{4.18}$$

from which one can verify that as is necessary,

$$T + R = 1 \tag{4.19}$$

It will be noted that the reflection depends on the difference of the two momenta, but not on which is larger, so that a step down in potential produces the same reflection as a corresponding step up.

The whole situation here is thoroughly analogous to the reflection of an electromagnetic wave by a discontinuity in the index of refraction n of the medium through which it passes. At normal

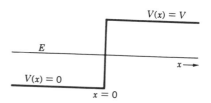

Fig. 4.3 Semi-infinite rectangular potential barrier higher than the total particle energy.

incidence, the reflection coefficient is $(n_1 - n_2)^2/(n_1 + n_2)^2$, exactly analogously to (4.18); this amounts to about 4 percent at each surface of a piece of glass.[2]

Case 2: $E < V$

In this case (Fig. 4.3) the kinetic energy to the right of the barrier would be negative, so that in classical physics the particle could not enter at all. In order to bring out the similarities with case 1, we introduce $\hbar k_1$ and a "pseudomomentum" $\hbar \kappa_2$ analogous to the previous $\hbar k_2$, so that, analogously to (4.5) and (4.6), we have

region 1
$$E = \frac{\hbar^2 k_1{}^2}{2m} \qquad \frac{\partial^2 \psi_1}{\partial x_1{}^2} = -k_1{}^2 \psi_1 \tag{4.20}$$

region 2
$$V - E = \frac{\hbar^2 \kappa_2{}^2}{2m} \qquad \frac{\partial^2 \psi_2}{\partial x_1{}^2} = \kappa_2{}^2 \psi_2 \tag{4.21}$$

whence

region 1
$$\psi_1 = A e^{ik_1 x} + B e^{-ik_1 x} \tag{4.22}$$

region 2
$$\psi_2 = C e^{-\kappa_2 x} + D e^{\kappa_2 x} \tag{4.23}$$

At this point of the preceding discussion, we set D equal to zero *by hypothesis* (no particles are incident from the right). Now also we set D equal to zero, but on different grounds. We do so because the wave function increasing toward the right is not a possible one, since it represents a divergently increasing possibility of finding a particle as one goes farther and farther into the forbidden region.[3]

The joining conditions (4.9) and (4.10) now lead as before to

$$A + B = C \tag{4.24}$$

and

$$k_1(A + B) = i\kappa_2 C \tag{4.25}$$

[2] An elementary discussion of this effect is given by Sarbacher and Edson, *Hyper and Ultrahigh Frequency Engineering,* John Wiley & Sons, Inc., New York, 1943, sec. 4.4. For a general treatment, see R. W. Ditchburn, *Light,* Interscience Publishers, Inc., New York, 1953, chap. 14.

[3] In the final analysis the two arguments are not so different, since one could imagine a different situation in which the barrier comes to an end farther to the right with an intense beam incident there. This, decaying exponentially *toward the left,* would be of the form $De^{\kappa_2 x}$. Our condition $D = 0$ amounts to asserting that such is not the case.

The latter is the same as (4.12) if we replace k_2 by $i\kappa_2$. This, in fact, is just what one would expect in comparing (4.21) with (4.6), since $k_2{}^2$ has been replaced by $-\kappa_2{}^2$. We can thus pass in a remarkably simple way to the solution of the new problem and can write down the solution at once from (4.13) and (4.14):

$$C = \frac{2k_1}{k_1 + i\kappa_2} A \tag{4.26}$$

$$B = \frac{k_1 - i\kappa_2}{k_1 + i\kappa_2} A \tag{4.27}$$

whence the reflection coefficient, by (4.16), is

$$R = 1 \tag{4.28}$$

This is natural, since the wave entering the forbidden region is exponentially damped, so that everything incident is ultimately reflected.

To obtain a picture of the wave function in this situation, we substitute (4.27) back into (4.22) and write the result as

$$\psi_1 = \frac{A}{k_1 + i\kappa_2} [(k_1 + i\kappa_2)e^{ik_1 x} + (k_1 - i\kappa_2)e^{-ik_1 x}]$$

We now write $k_1 + i\kappa_2$ in polar form as $\rho e^{i\varphi}$, with

$$\rho^2 = k_1{}^2 + \kappa_2{}^2 = 2mV/\hbar$$

$\tan \varphi = \kappa_2/k_1$, so that

$$\psi_1 = 2Ae^{-i\varphi} \cos (k_1 x + \varphi)$$

whereas from (4.23) and (4.26),

$$\psi_2 = 2 \frac{k_1}{\rho} Ae^{-i\varphi}e^{-\kappa_2 x}$$

Since A is arbitrary, we can now denote $2Ae^{-i\varphi}$ as a new amplitude A':

$$\psi_1 = A' \cos (k_1 x + \varphi) \tag{4.29a}$$

$$\psi_2 = \left(\frac{E}{V}\right)^{1/2} A'e^{-\kappa_2 x} \tag{4.29b}$$

These expressions are represented graphically in Fig. 4.4, in which one can see several things: the meaning of φ, the continuity of ψ and its first derivative, and the fact that the nearer E is to V in (4.29b), the smaller is φ. This last fact can be seen analytically from

$$\tan \varphi = \frac{\kappa_2}{k_1} = \left(\frac{V - E}{E}\right)^{1/2} \tag{4.30}$$

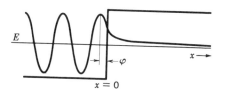

Fig. 4.4 Standing wave in the vicinity of the
barrier shown in Fig. 4.3, drawn
with the line E as an axis.

It will be instructive at this point to look at the problem which
has just been solved from the standpoint of the equation of continuity. To the left of the barrier one has waves of the form

$$\psi_1 = Ae^{ikx} + Be^{-ikx}$$

(the subscripts will be dropped). The one-dimensional   current
density corresponding to this ψ is, by (2.28),

$$s_1 = \frac{e\hbar}{2im}\left(\psi^*\frac{\partial\psi}{\partial x} - \psi\frac{\partial\psi^*}{\partial x}\right)$$

$$= \frac{e\hbar}{m}\,\mathrm{Im}\left(\psi^*\frac{\partial\psi}{\partial x}\right)$$

where Im denotes that one is to take the imaginary part of what
follows. This is equal to

$$s_1 = e\frac{\hbar k}{m}\,(|A|^2 - |B|^2)$$

which is clearly the difference between the current moving to the
right and that moving to the left.

To the right of the barrier, the general solution (4.23) is

$$\psi_2 = Ce^{-\kappa x} + De^{\kappa x}$$

and the corresponding current vector is

$$s_2 = 2e\frac{\hbar\kappa}{m}\,\mathrm{Im}\,(C^*D)$$

Since ψ throughout this chapter is assumed proportional to $e^{-iEt/\hbar}$,
the density $|\psi|^2$ is a constant, and the equation of continuity (3.10)
reduces here to $\partial s/\partial x = 0$, which is evidently satisfied on both sides
of the boundary. In order that it be satisfied *at* the boundary, we
must have

$$k(|A|^2 - |B|^2) = 2\kappa\,\mathrm{Im}\,(C^*D) \tag{4.31}$$

from which several pertinent conclusions will be drawn in the course
of this chapter. For the moment, we note merely that if D is set equal
to zero, as we have done, there can be no current to the right of the
barrier and $|A|^2$ must equal $|B|^2$, that is, there is total reflection.
But if the boundary conditions are such that D need not be set equal

to zero, then there is a possibility of current flow even in the region which is forbidden from the classical point of view.

Problem 4.1   Derive the above expressions for s_1 and s_2.

4.2   Potential Wells

We shall now use the same methods to study a situation in which stationary energy states occur and which explains qualitatively the reason for atomic and nuclear energy levels. Let the potential be in the form of a rectangular well, as in Fig. 4.5. At the same time, by making V positive, we can study the penetration of a potential barrier of finite width, as opposed to the infinite barrier of Fig. 4.1. We shall, therefore, investigate three cases: the first is when there is a beam of particles of energy E ($E > 0$) incident from the left and V is either positive or negative but $V < E$. The second is when V is high enough ($V > E$) that the central region, now become a barrier, is forbidden from the classical point of view; and the third is when V is again negative and E is also negative, so that the regions to right and left are forbidden and the particle is confined in the neighborhood of the well.

Case 1: $V < E,\ E > 0$

The wave functions in the three regions are, as before,

Region 1 $\psi_1 = Ae^{ik_1x} + Be^{-ik_1x}$ $[\hbar k_1 = (2mE)^{\frac{1}{2}}]$ (4.32)

Region 2 $\psi_2 = Ce^{ik_2x} + De^{-ik_2x}$ $[\hbar k_2 = (2m(E - V))^{\frac{1}{2}}]$ (4.33)

Region 3 $\psi_3 = Fe^{ik_1x}$ (4.34)

and the boundary conditions at $x = -a$ and $x = +a$ in turn give the four equations

$$Ae^{-ik_1a} + Be^{ik_1a} = Ce^{-ik_2a} + De^{ik_2a}$$

$$k_1(Ae^{-ik_1a} - Be^{ik_1a}) = k_2(Ce^{-ik_2a} - De^{ik_2a})$$

$$Ce^{ik_2a} + De^{-ik_2a} = Fe^{ik_1a}$$

$$k_2(Ce^{ik_2a} - De^{-ik_2a}) = k_1Fe^{ik_1a}$$

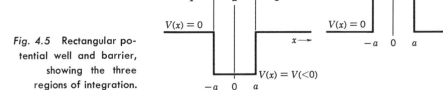

Fig. 4.5 Rectangular potential well and barrier, showing the three regions of integration.

These equations are solved by the method of determinants (or by solving the last two for C and D in terms of F, putting these into the first two, and finding A and B in terms of F). The results are most simply expressed as

$$A = Fe^{-2ik_1a}\left[\cos(2k_2a) - \tfrac{1}{2}i\left(\frac{k_1}{k_2} + \frac{k_2}{k_1}\right)\sin(2k_2a)\right] \tag{4.35}$$

$$B = \tfrac{1}{2}iF\left(\frac{k_2}{k_1} - \frac{k_1}{k_2}\right)\sin(2k_2a) \tag{4.36}$$

From the first of these we form the transmission coefficient of the entire barrier, which is most conveniently expressed in terms of its reciprocal:

$$\frac{1}{T} = \left|\frac{A}{F}\right|^2 = \cos^2(2k_2a) + \frac{1}{4}\left(\frac{k_1}{k_2} + \frac{k_2}{k_1}\right)^2\sin^2(2k_2a)$$

$$= 1 + \frac{1}{4}\left(\frac{k_1}{k_2} - \frac{k_2}{k_1}\right)^2\sin^2(2k_2a) \tag{4.37}$$

or, finally, using the definitions of k_1 and k_2,

$$\frac{1}{T} = 1 + \frac{1}{4}\frac{V^2}{E(E-V)}\sin^2(2k_2a) \tag{4.38}$$

The reflection coefficient is

$$R = 1 - T \tag{4.39}$$

Problem 4.2   Carry out the algebra leading to Eq. (4.35).

Problem 4.3   Find R directly and verify that it satisfies (4.39).

The qualitative behavior of T and R as functions of the energy E is sketched in Fig. 4.6.

The most immediate application of this theory is to the collision of slow electrons with atoms. Although the situation is here three-dimensional, at low energies it is reasonable to compare it to the encounter of an electron with a potential well in one dimension. The attractive potential exists because as the impinging electron enters the atom, the nuclear charge is no longer screened from it by the atomic electrons. Since R is a measure of the obstruction offered by

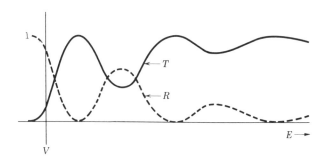

Fig. 4.6 Transmission and reflection coefficients of a rectangular potential barrier.

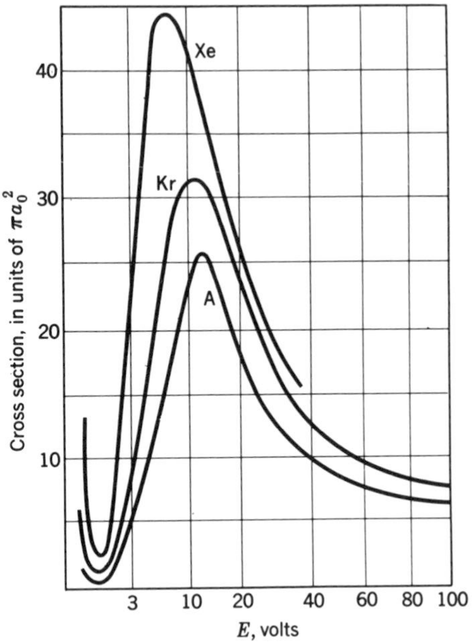

Fig. 4.7 Ramsauer effect in rare gases, showing their transparency to low-energy electrons. Adapted from Massey and Burhop, *Electronic and Ionic Impact Phenomena*, Clarendon Press, Oxford, 1952. By permission of the Oxford University Press.

the obstacle, one would expect that the scattering cross section for slow electrons would go through a minimum at some point. The results of measurements on rare-gas atoms in the low-energy range are shown in Fig. 4.7. The striking decrease in cross section, as a result of which the gases are almost transparent to electrons of about one volt, was discovered by Ramsauer in 1920 and independently later by Townsend and Bailey. It seems to be characteristic of many elements, subject only to the difficulty of obtaining monatomic vapors. The absence of further maxima and minima is due to complications involving states of differing angular momenta which set in at higher energies.[4]

Case 2: $V > E > 0$

The treatment in case 1 must be changed when the barrier becomes high enough to be impenetrable from the classical point of view. This is mirrored in the fact that k_2 in (4.33) now becomes imaginary. As in the last section, we write it as $i\kappa_2$ and note that none of the algebraic details of the theory are thereby changed. We can therefore rewrite (4.35) and (4.36) at once [using $\sin(ix) = i \sinh x$, $\cos(ix) = \cosh x$] as

$$A = Fe^{-2ik_1a}\left[\cosh(2\kappa_2 a) - \tfrac{1}{2}i\left(\frac{k_1}{\kappa_2} - \frac{\kappa_2}{k_1}\right)\sinh(2\kappa_2 a)\right] \tag{4.40}$$

$$B = -\tfrac{1}{2}iF\left(\frac{\kappa_2}{k_1} + \frac{k_1}{\kappa_2}\right)\sinh(2\kappa_2 a) \tag{4.41}$$

[4] See H. S. W. Massey and E. H. S. Burhop, *Electronic and Ionic Impact Phenomena*, Clarendon Press, Oxford, 1952, for literature references and further details.

from which

$$\frac{1}{T} = \left| \frac{A}{F} \right|^2 = \cosh^2 (2\kappa_2 a) + \frac{1}{4}\left(\frac{k_1}{\kappa_2} - \frac{\kappa_2}{k_1}\right)^2 \sinh^2 (2\kappa_2 a)$$

$$= 1 + \frac{1}{4}\left(\frac{k_1}{\kappa_2} + \frac{\kappa_2}{k_1}\right)^2 \sinh^2 (2\kappa_2 a)$$

or

$$\frac{1}{T} = 1 + \frac{1}{4}\frac{V^2}{E(V - E)} \sinh^2 (2\kappa_2 a) \tag{4.42}$$

This is the formula for the transparency of a barrier which, classically speaking, should not be transparent at all. [The possibility of such transparency was mentioned in the remarks following (4.31).] It gives rise to a number of interesting and typically quantum-mechanical effects such as the slow emission of alpha-particles from a nucleus (Chap. 12) and the *field emission* of electrons from a metal surface under the influence of a strong applied electric field.

Problem 4.4   A 20-mA beam of 5-V electrons is directed toward a potential barrier of height 30 V and width a_0 [see (1.9)]. How many electrons per second get through?

Case 3: $V < E < 0$

Here the wave function must decay exponentially on either side of the potential well and the problem of matching solutions is somewhat different, since we are now specifying a boundary condition on each side instead of only one. The situation is illustrated in Fig. 4.8, where for all given values of a, V, and E we can attain a smooth matching at the left side of the well but have no further adjustable parameters available to make ψ continuous at the right. Only for certain values of E will a smooth match be possible at both edges of the well, and it is therefore only for these values that allowable solutions of (4.1) exist. Three possibilities, corresponding to successively higher values of E, are shown in Fig. 4.9. In the case illustrated, only these three values of E are possible. In actual cases, the number of energy states may be finite (for example, one for the deuteron, cf. Chap. 17) or infinite, as for hydrogen (Chap. 14). We shall mention here only a simple limiting case, already discussed at the end of Chap. 1, in which the well becomes infinitely deep

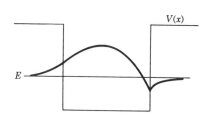

Fig. 4.8   Wave function in a potential well, showing the difficulty of matching ψ and its derivative at both sides of the well if E is chosen arbitrarily.

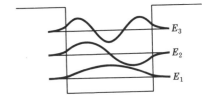

Fig. 4.9 Properly matched eigenfunctions, drawn about the corresponding energy levels, for the rectangular potential well.

$(V \to -\infty)$. In this case it is convenient to change the reference level for energy from the top of the well to the bottom and the origin of x to the left side of the well. The wave function must vanish exactly (why?) at each edge. The only combination of exponentials which vanishes at $x = 0$ is the sine, and so

$$\psi = A \sin kx \qquad \hbar k = (2mE)^{\frac{1}{2}}$$

In order for the sine to vanish at the other side of the well we must have

$$\sin ka = 0$$

or

$$ka = \pi n \qquad (n = 1, 2, 3, \ldots)$$

or

$$E = \frac{(n\pi\hbar)^2}{2ma^2} \qquad (n = 1, 2, 3, \ldots) \tag{4.43}$$

A few of the corresponding wave functions are shown in Fig. 4.10.

Problem 4.5 Why are the nonpositive values of n not included in (4.43)?

One has in case 3 the basic reason given by quantum mechanics for the occurrence of definite energy states in nature. They are a standing-wave phenomenon, as was first suggested by de Broglie.

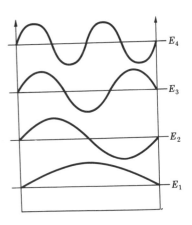

Fig. 4.10 Eigenfunctions and eigenvalues for a square well of infinite depth.

The relation of energy values to the existence of physically admissible solutions of the wave equation was worked out for the case of hydrogen by Schrödinger in his first papers[5] on wave mechanics.

Problem 4.6   Show that there are no possible states for which $E < V < 0$.

Problem 4.7   What minimum energy, in the case just considered, is required by the uncertainty principle? The argument here is that we know the electron's position to within a distance $\Delta x \approx a$. It is therefore impossible to assert that the momentum is zero, even in the lowest state, since Δp cannot be zero. What is the smallest value that can be assigned to the momentum? To what energy does this correspond? Compare the answer with (4.43).

Although the foregoing represents very much of an idealization, it still reproduces one of the most significant features of quantum-mechanical behavior, the essential continuity of phenomena at the absolute zero of temperature. We see that all motion does not cease when a system is in its lowest possible energy state and that, in fact, this state is not qualitatively different from the others except that no further energy can be removed from it.

4.3 Classical Considerations on ψ

We now go on to a discussion of the wave function in general cases (but still in one dimension) in which the potential may vary arbitrarily with position. A typical example, embodying a variety of features, is shown in Fig. 4.11. In order to estimate what ψ will be like for such a system, let us look at it first from a purely classical point of view. Here the forbidden region bc divides the system into two separate parts. In the left part a particle will oscillate between a and b, which are known as *turning points*. A quantum-mechanical treatment will show that, as in Sec. 4.2, this trapping results in the existence of discrete energy states (see Sec. 4.5), although these states will not be completely stable because the particle has a finite probability of penetrating the barrier and leaking away (see Chap. 12, where the theory of α decay is treated according to such a model). Finally, on the right, the particle will accelerate away from the turning point c. If there are many particles, then $|\psi|^2$ may be taken to describe their density in a purely classical sense. We now ask: How does this density depend on x?

The answer to this question is provided by the equation of continuity (3.10), which is a basic ingredient of any theory in which something is conserved.

[5] Ann. Physik, **79**, 361, 489 (1926), translated in *Collected Papers on Wave Mechanics*, Blackie & Son, Ltd., Glasgow, 1928.

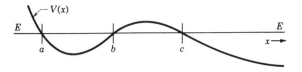

Fig. 4.11 Typical potential curve showing bound, forbidden, and free regions.

A stationary state, as we have defined it, is characterized by having ψ proportional to $e^{-iEt/\hbar}$, so that $|\psi|^2$ is constant. The analogous classical situation is therefore one for which ρ is independent of time, so that, in one dimension, $\partial(\rho v)/\partial x = 0$, or

$$\rho = \frac{\text{const}}{v} \tag{4.44}$$

where v is the velocity of motion. (This relation characterizes the jamming up of automobiles at a place where there is an obstruction in the highway and their thinning out where passage is easier.)

The region ab in Fig. 4.11 contains particles traveling in each direction, and (4.44) should apply to each stream. Expressing v in terms of energy so that we may consider it as a function of x, we have

$$|\psi|^2 = \frac{\text{const}}{\{2m^{-1}[E - V(x)]\}^{1/2}} \tag{4.45}$$

so that one can expect ψ to be of the general form

$$\psi = \frac{A\,e^{i[S(x)-Et/\hbar]}}{[E - V(x)]^{1/4}} \tag{4.46}$$

This quantity actually diverges at the turning points, where the potential-energy curve intersects E, which corresponds to the fact that the classical particle stops at this point and reverses its motion. In quantum mechanics the situation is more complicated than this, for there is a certain degree of penetration of the barrier, and one therefore expects that ψ may be continuous there as in the examples we discussed in the preceding section.

One can also guess what $S(x)$ will be on the basis of de Broglie's relation. If $p(x)$ is the particle's (classical) momentum at the point x, the phase change of the wave between x and $x + dx$ should be

$$\frac{dS(x)}{\lambda} = \frac{1}{\hbar}\,p(x)\,dx = k(x)\,dx$$

and the total phase change from some initial point, such as $x = a$, should be

$$S(x) = \int_a^x k(x)\,dx$$

Expressing this in terms of the energy, we finally have for the spatial part of the wave function estimated from classical considerations and de Broglie's principle,

$$\frac{A}{[E - V(x)]^{1/4}} \exp \left(\frac{i}{\hbar} \int_a^x \{2m[E - V(x)]\}^{1/2} \, dx \right) \tag{4.47}$$

In the next section we shall derive this result, under a suitable approximation, directly from Schrödinger's equation, and we shall also investigate what happens on the other side of the barrier, where classical considerations can tell us nothing.

4.4 The WKB Approximation

In this and the following section we are going to investigate an approximate procedure for solving Schrödinger's equation in one dimension. The general method has been known for some time, but it was first applied to quantum mechanics independently and almost simultaneously by Wentzel, Kramers, and Brillouin in 1926. It is sometimes useful in practice as a computational device, though it tends to result in an integral which is difficult to evaluate, but its main pedagogical interest is that in content it lies somewhere between classical mechanics and quantum mechanics and provides a number of bridges between the two. We shall, for example, again encounter (4.47), but in addition to WKB method will give a corresponding formula valid in the forbidden region.

Let us start from the time-independent Schrödinger equation in one dimension and try to find a solution of it in the form

$$\psi(x) = F(x)e^{iS(x)} \tag{4.48}$$

where F and S are real functions, at least in the classically allowed region where the discussion of the preceding section applies. It will be convenient to write Schrödinger's equation as

$$\psi''(x) = -k^2(x)\psi(x) \tag{4.49}$$

with

$$k(x) = \left\{ \frac{2m}{\hbar^2} [E - V(x)] \right\}^{1/2} \tag{4.50}$$

This last notation is just that in (4.6), for example, except that here we allow V to be a function of x. Substituting (4.48) into (4.49), performing the differentiations, canceling the exponential, and separating the terms with and without i, we have

$$(F'' - FS'^2 + k^2F) + i(2F'S' + FS'') = 0 \tag{4.51}$$

It is quite arbitrary what we do next. A single unknown function, ψ, has been replaced by two unknown functions; we could choose either F or S to be anything at all and then adjust the remaining one so that (4.48) is satisfied. We have noted, however, that both the amplitude and the phase in (4.48) should be real (except perhaps for an arbitrary constant multiplying the amplitude). Thus, to get a result which is formally like a wave with amplitude and phase, we *treat F* and *S* in (4.51) as real numbers and require that each term in (4.51) be equal to zero:

$$F'' - FS'^2 + k^2F = 0 \qquad (4.52)$$

$$2F'S' + FS'' = 0 \qquad (4.53)$$

The second equation can be integrated at once. Multiplying it by F, we see that the left side is a perfect derivative, $(F^2S')'$, so that we have found F as a function of S:

$$F(x) = \frac{C}{[S'(x)]^{1/2}} \qquad (4.54)$$

where C is arbitrary.

Up to this point everything is exact. But (4.52) is readily seen to be a very difficult equation—in fact more complicated than (4.49) itself. We must therefore approximate, and this we do by neglecting the first term in (4.52), that is, by assuming that the amplitude changes far more slowly than the phase. With this approximation, (4.52) gives

$$S'(x) = \pm k(x) \qquad (4.55)$$

or

$$S(x) = \pm \int k(x) \, dx \qquad (4.56)$$

where we write the indefinite integral because any constant of integration would merely give a multiplying factor which could be absorbed in C. With (4.55) we can evaluate $F(x)$ in (4.54), so that the completed approximate solution is

$$\psi(x) \approx \frac{C}{[k(x)]^{1/2}} \exp\left[\pm i \int k(x) \, dx\right] \qquad (4.57)$$

just as in (4.47) except for the sign $\pm$, which means only that the wave may be traveling in either direction. The general solution is, of course, a combination of the two forms with arbitrary coefficients.

We can now complete the wave function by extending it into the region beyond the turning points. Here $k(x)$ becomes imaginary. As before, in (4.21), we write it as

$$k(x) = i\kappa(x) \qquad (4.58)$$

where

$$\kappa(x) = \left\{\frac{2m}{\hbar^2}[V(x) - E]\right\}^{1/2} \qquad (4.59)$$

With new amplitude constants C' we have

$$\psi(x) \approx \frac{C'}{[\kappa(x)]^{1/2}} \exp\left[\pm \int \kappa(x) \, dx\right] \qquad (4.60)$$

in which the ascending and descending exponential behavior which we have previously noted in the case of the rectangular barrier is again present.

The nature of the approximation

We must now pause to see exactly what approximation has been made, since it makes no sense to require that F'' be small without specifying with respect to what it is to be small. We write (4.52) as

$$\frac{F''}{F} = S'^2 - k^2$$

and specify that (4.57) should be a good approximation to S' in the sense that the difference between the terms on the right is much smaller than either of them:

$$|S'^2 - k^2| = |F''/F| \ll S'^2$$

Now we replace F by means of (4.54) to get

$$\left| \frac{3}{4} \left(\frac{S''}{S'} \right)^2 - \frac{1}{2} \frac{S'''}{S'} \right| \ll S'^2$$

Let us satisfy this inequality by demanding that it be satisfied by each term alone:

$$\tfrac{3}{4} S''^2 \ll S'^4 \qquad \tfrac{1}{2}|S'''| \ll |S'|^3$$

Neglecting the unimportant numerical coefficients, we see by differentiation that the second relation is automatically satisfied if the first one is, so we need look only at the first. By (4.55) it gives $|k'| \ll k^2$ or, with $k = 1/\lambda$,

$$|\lambda k'| \ll k \qquad\qquad (4.61)$$

which states that the fractional change in k per wavelength must be small. This condition is well known in the theory of waves as the one which must be satisfied if the wave is to progress through a medium of varying index of refraction without giving rise to an appreciable reflected wave. We see it here in a new, though closely related, context. Alternatively, expressing k by means of (4.50), we can express the condition for either sign of $E - V$ as

$$\left| \frac{V'}{(E - V)^{3/2}} \right| \ll \left(\frac{m}{\hbar^2} \right)^{1/2} \qquad\qquad (4.62)$$

The approximation which we have obtained in this way can be regarded from a formal point of view as what one gets if one tries to express the solution of Schrödinger's equation as an exponential[6]

---

[6] D. Bohm, *Quantum Mechanics*, Prentice-Hall, Inc., Englewood Cliffs, N.J., 1951, p. 264.

with the exponent expanded in powers of $\hbar$. The formulas given here correspond to keeping the first two terms of the expansion. Higher terms can be obtained,[7] but they are not very useful in practice.

Since the expressions (4.57) and (4.60) are only approximations to ψ, it is important to know how good these approximations are. We know, for example, that they fail at the turning points by becoming infinite. To get an idea of their validity at points other than the turning points, we can see whether (4.62) is satisfied, but let us also calculate the current density by the use of (3.11). The calculation is straightforward, and for a wave function (in the allowed region) of the form

$$\psi(x) = Ak^{-\frac{1}{2}} \exp\left[i\int k(x)\,dx\right] + Bk^{-\frac{1}{2}} \exp\left[-i\int k(x)\,dx\right] \tag{4.63}$$

it gives

$$s = \frac{e\hbar}{m}\left(|A|^2 - |B|^2\right) \tag{4.64}$$

showing the two currents carried in opposite directions. The striking thing about this expression is that it is independent of x, meaning, as noted above, that the current is conserved, even up to the turning point. In the forbidden region, if we write

$$\psi = C\kappa^{-\frac{1}{2}} \exp\left(-\int \kappa\,dx\right) + D\kappa^{-\frac{1}{2}} \exp\left(\int \kappa\,dx\right) \tag{4.65}$$

the current density is

$$s = 2\frac{e\hbar}{m}\,\mathrm{Im}\,(C^*D) \tag{4.66}$$

and again it is conserved.

Problem 4.8 Derive (4.64) and (4.66).

4.5 The Connection Formulas

Because the WKB approximation to ψ diverges at the turning points, the problem of joining together solutions of the forms (4.63) and (4.65) is considerably more difficult than with the rectangular barriers of the preceding section. The derivation of the *connection formulas*, which give C and D in terms of A and B, is beyond the scope of this book,[8,9] but the exact validity of the conservation of

[7] *Ibid.*

[8] See E. C. Kemble, *The Fundamental Principles of Quantum Mechanics*, McGraw-Hill Book Company, Inc., New York, 1939, or E. Merzbacher, *Quantum Mechanics*, John Wiley & Sons, Inc., New York, 1961. An important modification is given by R. E. Langer, Phys. Rev., **51**, 669 (1937). I. Imai, Phys. Rev., **74**, 113 (1948), has shown how to make an accurate approximation in the neighborhood of the turning points which, however, leads to the same connection formulas as given here.

[9] Readers who are familiar with the ideas of the theory of functions of a complex variable will find a very interesting application in Furry's treatment

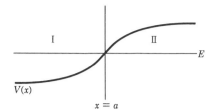

Fig. 4.12   Potential curve having a forbidden region
at the right of the turning point.

current in this approximation enables one to say a good deal about them on elementary grounds.

Let the potential barrier be as in Fig. 4.12, with the forbidden region on the right, and let the constants of integration be chosen in (4.63) and (4.65) so as to write

region I $\psi(x) = Ak^{-\frac{1}{2}} \exp\left[i\int_a^x k(x)\,dx\right]$

$$+ Bk^{-\frac{1}{2}} \exp\left[-i\int_a^x k(x)\,dx\right] \qquad (4.67)$$

region II $\psi(x) = C\kappa^{-\frac{1}{2}} \exp\left[-\int_a^x \kappa(x)\,dx\right]$

$$+ D\kappa^{-\frac{1}{2}} \exp\left[\int_a^x \kappa(x)\,dx\right] \qquad (4.68)$$

where it should be noted that the integrals in (4.67) are negative. (It seems easiest, though, to choose this standard way of writing in which the variable x is always in the same place in the formula.) Because of the linearity of the Schrödinger equation, the connection formulas will be of the form

$$
\begin{aligned}
C &= cA + c_1 B \\
D &= dA + d_1 B
\end{aligned}
\qquad (4.69)
$$

where c, d, c_1, and d_1 are complex numbers. But now we note that if the original equation (4.1) is satisfied by ψ as given in (4.67) and (4.68), it will also be satisfied by its complex conjugate, which is of the same form except that A, B, C, and D are replaced by their conjugates and the roles of the right- and left-traveling waves in (4.67) are interchanged. This means that the connection formula (4.69) should still remain valid under the substitutions

$$A \to B^* \qquad B \to A^* \qquad C \to C^* \qquad D \to D^*$$

and it is easy to see that this requires

$$c_1 = c^* \qquad d_1 = d^* \qquad (4.70)$$

of the same problem; Phys. Rev., **71**, 360 (1947). The entire subject is of considerable interest mathematically, and is well treated by J. Heading, *An Introduction to Phase-Integral Methods*, John Wiley & Sons, Inc., New York, 1962.

so that

$$C = cA + c^*B$$ (4.71)
$$D = dA + d^*B$$

We now put these expressions into (4.66) and require that the current be conserved by equating the result to (4.64). This gives

$$|A|^2 - |B|^2 = 2(|A|^2 - |B|^2) \text{ Im } (c^*d)$$

or

$$\text{Im } (c^*d) = \tfrac{1}{2}$$ (4.72)

Finally, we derive the formulas valid when the barrier is to the left of the turning point by interchanging right and left everywhere in the preceding argument. This amounts to interchanging A with B and C with D. From (4.71) we have

$$C = d^*A + dB \qquad \text{barrier to left}$$ (4.73)
$$D = c^*A + cB$$

The most straightforward way of proceeding now is to abandon the WKB approximation and construct a solution to Schrödinger's equation which is exact in the neighborhood of the turning points and can be joined smoothly to the WKB function a short distance to each side. This procedure is rather long,[8,9] and we give only the result here,

$$c = \tfrac{1}{2}e^{-i\pi/4} \qquad d = e^{i\pi/4}$$ (4.74)

Thus we have the following summary, with $e^{i\pi/4}$ denoted by ϑ.

Barrier to right:

$$C = \tfrac{1}{2}(\vartheta^*A + \vartheta B) \qquad A = \vartheta C + \tfrac{1}{2}\vartheta^*D$$ (4.75)
$$D = \vartheta A + \vartheta^*B \qquad B = \vartheta^*C + \tfrac{1}{2}\vartheta D$$

Barrier to left:

$$C = \vartheta^*A + \vartheta B \qquad A = \tfrac{1}{2}\vartheta C + \vartheta^*D$$ (4.76)
$$D = \tfrac{1}{2}(\vartheta A + \vartheta^*B) \qquad B = \tfrac{1}{2}\vartheta^*C + \vartheta D$$

Bound states

As an example of the use of these formulas, we shall derive their most useful consequence, which is the implicit equation for the energy levels of a bound system. Let the potential be as shown in Fig. 4.13.

In region I the C amplitude is zero, so that, using (4.76) for A and B, we find

$$\psi_{II}(x) = D\vartheta^*k^{-\frac{1}{2}} \exp\left[i\int_a^x k(x)\, dx\right]$$
$$+ D\vartheta k^{-\frac{1}{2}} \exp\left[-i\int_a^x k(x)\, dx\right]$$
$$= 2Dk^{-\frac{1}{2}} \cos\left[\int_a^x k(x)\, dx - \tfrac{1}{4}\pi\right]$$ (4.77)

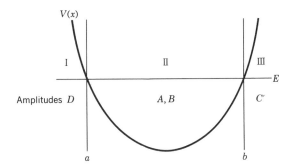

$V(x)$

I   II   III

E

Amplitudes D A, B C'

a b

Fig. 4.13 Potential curve, together with amplitudes in the three regions of integration, for a symmetrical potential well.

To match this with the wave function in region III, we write

$$\int_a^x k(x)\,dx = \int_a^b k(x)\,dx + \int_b^x k(x)\,dx$$

The definite integral is called the *phase integral*, and it will be denoted as

$$\int_a^b k(x)\,dx = \varphi$$

With this, the first form of (4.77) gives

$$\psi_{\text{II}}(x) = D\vartheta^* e^{i\varphi} k^{-\frac{1}{2}} \exp\left[i\int_b^x k(x)\,dx\right]$$
$$+ D\vartheta e^{-i\varphi} k^{-\frac{1}{2}} \exp\left[-i\int_b^x k(x)\,dx\right]$$

It is now straightforward to construct the solution in region III by the use of (4.75). We find

$$\psi_{\text{III}} = C'\kappa^{-\frac{1}{2}} \exp\left(-\int_b^x \kappa\,dx\right) + D'\kappa^{-\frac{1}{2}} \exp\left(\int_b^x \kappa\,dx\right)$$

where

$$C' = D\sin\varphi \qquad D' = 2D\cos\varphi$$

But the boundary conditions require that D' be zero, and this occurs if φ is an odd multiple of $\frac{1}{2}\pi$. It is convenient to consider two cases:

$$\varphi = (2n + \tfrac{1}{2})\pi \qquad C' = D \tag{4.78}$$

and

$$\varphi = (2n + \tfrac{3}{2})\pi \qquad C' = -D \tag{4.79}$$

in both of which, since φ is positive, n represents a nonnegative integer. Since φ has a numerical value which depends on that of E, these relations implicitly determine the allowed energy values of the system.

Problem 4.9 Equations (4.78) and (4.79) represent one extreme, in which the potential energy changes slowly relative to the wave function. At the other extreme, consider the case shown

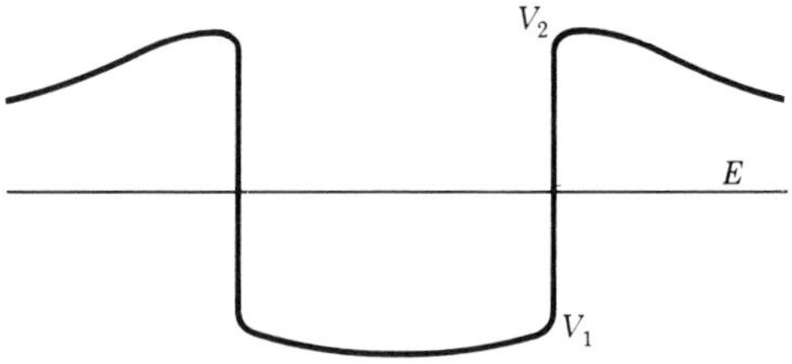

Fig. 4.14 Potential well infinitely steep in
the neighborhood of the turning points.

in Fig. 4.14, in which the well is infinitely steep at the turning
points. What are the conditions analogous to (4.78) and (4.79)?
Why are they difficult to apply in practice? Show that if $V_2 - E \gg E - V_1$, they reduce to

$$\varphi = (2n + 1)\pi \qquad C' = D$$
$$\varphi = (2n + 2)\pi \qquad C' = -D$$

where $n = 0, 1, 2, \ldots$.

The wave function in the allowed region is now given by (4.77)
subject to the conditions (4.78) and (4.79). The phase of the cosine
starts at $-\tfrac{1}{4}\pi$ when $x = a$, and at the opposite turning point it has
become $\varphi - \tfrac{1}{4}\pi$, that is, $(2n + \tfrac{1}{4})\pi$ or $(2n + \tfrac{5}{4})\pi$, according as
the wave functions in regions I and III are of the same sign ($C' = D$)
or the opposite ($C' = -D$). We shall refer to these, somewhat
roughly, as wave functions of symmetrical and antisymmetrical
type.

Normalization

We have now to find D from the normalization condition (2.1).
But since the wave function itself is not exact, this need not be done
exactly, and in fact there is usually no important loss of accuracy
if we neglect the exponentially decreasing parts in the forbidden
regions. We may thus impose the condition

$$4|D|^2 \int_a^b \frac{dx}{k(x)} \cos^2 \left(\int_a^x k(x')\, dx' - \tfrac{1}{4}\pi \right) \approx 1$$

Let us suppose that n is a fairly large integer, since it is in this case
that the WKB approximation gives the best results anyhow. The
cosine term goes through about n complete cycles as x ranges from
a to b, and we can replace it by its average value of $\tfrac{1}{2}$, so that

$$2|D|^2 \int_a^b \frac{dx}{k(x)} \approx 1$$

The integral is a rather interesting one, and it can be expressed in
two ways. First, by differentiating the expression for φ with respect

to E, we find that

$$\frac{\partial \varphi}{\partial E} = \frac{\partial}{\partial E} \int_a^b \left\{ \frac{2m}{\hbar^2} [E - V(x)] \right\}^{\frac{1}{2}} dx = \frac{m}{\hbar^2} \int_a^b \frac{dx}{k(x)} \qquad (4.80)$$

Second, if we write the last integral as

$$\frac{\hbar}{m} \int_a^b \frac{dx}{\{(2/m)[E - V(x)]\}^{\frac{1}{2}}}$$

we see that the radical represents the velocity of a particle oscillating between a and b as one would compute it classically, so that in these terms the integral is

$$\frac{\hbar}{m} \int_a^b \frac{dx}{dx/dt} = \frac{\hbar}{m} \int_a^b dt = \frac{\hbar}{m} \left(\frac{T}{2} \right) = \frac{\hbar}{2m\nu}$$

where T is the period and ν is the ordinary frequency of the particle's motion. Thus,

$$|D|^2 \approx \frac{m/2\hbar^2}{\partial \varphi / \partial E} = \frac{m\nu}{\hbar} \qquad (4.81)$$

Furry[10] has shown that this is a good approximation even when one does not assume that n is large.

Problem 4.10 Derive Eq. (4.80) in detail.

Problem 4.11 Does the radiation from the bound system described by a WKB wave function obey the correspondence principle?

Solution. According to (1.16), the frequency ω of light emitted by a radiating system is approximately

$$\omega = \hbar^{-1} \, \Delta n \, \frac{\partial E_n}{\partial n}$$

Since the WKB energy levels E_n are determined as solutions of the implicit equation $\cos \varphi = 0$ or $\varphi(E_n) = (n + \frac{1}{2})\pi$, we have

$$\frac{\partial \varphi}{\partial n} = \frac{\partial \varphi}{\partial E_n} \frac{\partial E_n}{\partial n} = \pi$$

so that

$$\frac{\partial E_n}{\partial n} = \frac{\pi}{\partial \varphi / \partial E_n} = 2\pi\hbar\nu$$

and

$$\omega = \Delta n \, (2\pi\nu)$$

as in (1.15). As we have seen in Sec. 1.3, a correspondence of this sort is necessary in order that quantum theory shall give the same

[10] *Ibid.*

results as classical theory in their common region of validity, that is, if one attempts to use quantum mechanics, with enormous quantum numbers, to calculate some process which properly belongs in the domain of classical theory.

The remarkable results which come out of the WKB approximation must not blind us to the fact that it is only an approximation and that its results are too much like those of classical physics. Its worst inaccuracy is that it predicts no reflection at a change in potential. If there is a turning point where the potential changes, the matching procedure, which can be derived only by going outside the approximation, yields a reflected wave; otherwise, there is none at all. This is true notably in situations like those of Figs. 4.1 and 4.5 and their smoothed-out analogues, and it is the reason why the WKB theory of scattering (see Prob. 9.27) is of limited use.

4.6 The Anharmonic Oscillator

In order to see in a worked-out example how the foregoing relations determine energies, wave functions, and normalizations, we shall apply them to a problem which arises in connection with the theory of molecular spectra: motion in a potential of the form

$$V(x) = -\lambda x^4$$

leading to a cubic law of force. In classical terms, the oscillator bound in this way differs from that bound by a force obeying Hooke's law in that its frequency and amplitude of motion are not independent. For this reason it is called an *anharmonic oscillator*. The phase integral is

$$\varphi = \left(\frac{2m}{\hbar^2}\right)^{\frac{1}{2}} \int_{-a}^{a} (E - \lambda x^4)^{\frac{1}{2}} \, dx \qquad a = \left(\frac{E}{\lambda}\right)^{\frac{1}{4}}$$

and the substitution $x^4 = (E/\lambda)y$ gives

$$\varphi = \frac{1}{2}\left(\frac{2m}{\hbar^2}\right)^{\frac{1}{2}} \frac{E^{\frac{3}{4}}}{\lambda^{\frac{1}{4}}} \int_0^1 (1 - y)^{\frac{1}{2}} y^{-\frac{3}{4}} \, dy \tag{4.82}$$

The integral is expressed in terms of Euler's beta function as[11] $B(\frac{1}{2},\frac{3}{2})$, and its numerical value is 3.4960. Solving (4.78) and (4.79) for E, we find that

$$E_{n,z} = 2.183\left(2n + \frac{z}{2}\right)^{\frac{4}{3}} \lambda^{\frac{1}{3}} \left(\frac{\hbar^2}{2m}\right)^{\frac{2}{3}}$$

[11] H. B. Dwight, *Tables of Integrals and Other Mathematical Data*, 3d ed., The Macmillan Company, New York, 1957, 855.4 and Table 1005. For the relevant theory see W. E. Osgood, *Advanced Calculus*, The Macmillan Company, New York, 1937, pp. 484, 480.

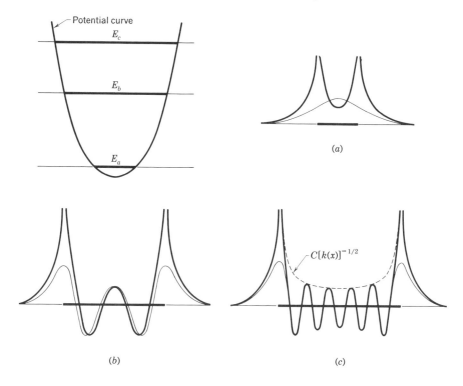

Fig. 4.15 Comparison between exact wave functions (thin lines)
and WKB wave functions (heavy lines) for a typical oscillator.
Darkened stretches of the horizontal axis
show the allowed regions.

where $z = 1$ or 3 for even or odd ψ, respectively. For the first four
states, with n equal to 0 and 1, we write

$$E_{n,z} = K_{n,z}\lambda^{1/3}\left(\frac{\hbar^2}{2m}\right)^{2/3}$$

where $K_{n,z}$ is as given in the accompanying table together with more
exact values[12] and percentage errors. It is clear (and it is typical

State		$K_{n,z}$(WKB)	$K_{n,z}$ (exact)	Error, percent
n	z			
0	1	0.866	1.060	18
0	3	3.748	3.800	1.4
1	1	7.408	7.456	0.63
1	3	11.612	11.645	0.28

[12] R. McWeeny and C. Coulson, Proc. Cambridge Phil. Soc., **44**, 413 (1948).

of the WKB approximation generally) that subject to the difficulty of evaluating the relevant integrals, this method needs to be supplemented by something more accurate only for the lowest states.

For each value of E, the normalization constant is given by (4.81) and (4.82) as

$$D = 0.218 \left(\frac{2m}{\hbar^2}\right)^{1/4} (E\lambda)^{1/8}$$

Figure 4.15 shows sketches of the WKB approximations to exact wave functions of this kind for small, medium, and large values of n. It is obvious why the approximation improves for large values of n.

Problem 4.12   Imagine three atoms in a line, at equilibrium under a force which depends only on the distance between them. The atom in the middle is given a small, rapid displacement Δy perpendicular to the line. Show that the potential energy associated with the displacement is proportional to $(\Delta y)^4$.

4.7   The Double Potential Well

As a second application of the WKB method we shall look at the somewhat more complicated situation shown in Fig. 4.16. It is supposed to represent in a very schematic way the forces acting on an electron in a homopolar molecule, such as H_2 or N_2, where the electrons are attracted equally toward each of two centers of force. Our aim is to show that the presence of an electron can result in an attractive force between the two halves of the molecule; that is, we are going to give a schematic explanation of a simple type of chemical bond. It is important to realize that classical mechanics cannot do this. In classical mechanics the electron would attach itself to one half of the molecule, and the two atoms would then drift apart. We shall find that in quantum mechanics the lowest energy state is one in which the electron is shared equally between the two halves and that it tends to draw them together.[13]

As before, we solve the wave equation approximately in each of the several regions of the figure, starting at the left.

Region I $\psi_{\mathrm{I}} = D_1 \kappa^{-1/2} \exp\left(\int_a^x \kappa \, dx\right)$

Region II $\psi_{\mathrm{II}} = A_2 k^{-1/2} \exp\left(i \int_a^x k \, dx\right)$

$$+ B_2 k^{-1/2} \exp\left(-i \int_a^x k \, dx\right) \qquad (4.83)$$

where, by (4.76), $A_2 = \vartheta^* D_1$ and $B_2 = \vartheta D_1$. In order to match solutions at b, we write $\int_a^x k \, dx$ as $\int_a^b k \, dx + \int_b^x k \, dx$. The first of

----

[13] This subject will be taken up again and a more realistic calculation performed in Chap. 15.

Fig. 4.16 Potential curve
with two minima,
showing five regions
of integration.

these is the phase integral φ which we have already introduced in talking about a single well. With this, (4.83) becomes

$$\psi_{II} = \vartheta^* D_1 e^{i\varphi} k^{-\frac{1}{2}} \exp\left(i \int_b^x k\, dx\right)$$
$$+ \vartheta D_1 e^{-i\varphi} k^{-\frac{1}{2}} \exp\left(-i \int_b^x k\, dx\right)$$

Region III $\psi_{III} = C_3 \kappa^{-\frac{1}{2}} \exp\left(\int_b^x \kappa\, dx\right) + D_3 \kappa^{-\frac{1}{2}} \exp\left(\int_b^x \kappa\, dx\right)$

and the use of (4.75) gives

$$C_3 = D_1 \sin \varphi \qquad D_3 = 2D_1 \cos \varphi \tag{4.84}$$

In order to match solutions at c, we introduce the quantity

$$\sigma = \int_b^c \kappa(x)\, dx \tag{4.85}$$

somewhat analogous to φ, and write ψ_{III} as

$$\psi_{III} = D_1 e^{-\sigma} \sin \varphi \kappa^{-\frac{1}{2}} \exp\left(-\int_c^x \kappa\, dx\right)$$
$$+ 2D_1 e^{\sigma} \cos \varphi \kappa^{-\frac{1}{2}} \exp\left(\int_c^x \kappa\, dx\right) \tag{4.86}$$

Region IV $\psi_{IV} = A_4 k^{-\frac{1}{2}} \exp\left(i \int_c^x k\, dx\right)$
$$+ B_4 k^{-\frac{1}{2}} \exp\left(-i \int_c^x k\, dx\right) \tag{4.87}$$

Before matching this to (4.86), let us carry out the matching at d. The two wells being mirror images of each other, we can write ψ_{IV} as

$$\psi_{IV} = A_4 e^{i\varphi} k^{-\frac{1}{2}} \exp\left(i \int_d^x k\, dx\right) + B_4 e^{-i\varphi} k^{-\frac{1}{2}} \exp\left(-i \int_d^x k\, dx\right)$$

Region V $\psi_V = C_5 \kappa^{-\frac{1}{2}} \exp\left(-\int_d^x \kappa\, dx\right)$

so that from (4.75),

$$A_4 e^{i\varphi} = \vartheta C_5 \qquad B_4 e^{-i\varphi} = \vartheta^* C_5$$

Equation (4.87) is thus

$$\psi_{IV} = C_5 \vartheta e^{-i\varphi} k^{-\frac{1}{2}} \exp\left(i \int_c^x k\, dx\right)$$
$$+ C_5 \vartheta^* e^{i\varphi} k^{-\frac{1}{2}} \exp\left(-i \int_c^x k\, dx\right)$$

and this can be matched to (4.86) by means of (4.76). The result is

$$D_1 e^{-\sigma} \sin \varphi = 2C_5 \cos \varphi$$
$$2D_1 e^{\sigma} \cos \varphi = C_5 \sin \varphi \tag{4.88}$$

Taken together, these two relations impose a restriction on φ, since dividing the first by the second leads to

$$\tan \varphi = \pm 2e^{\sigma} \tag{4.89}$$

and putting this back into (4.88) shows that

$$C_5 = \pm D_1 \tag{4.90}$$

where the signs in (4.89) and (4.90) correspond. As in the case of (4.78) and (4.79), the possible wave functions are of symmetric or antisymmetric type, and this time their properties differ in a significant way. We shall restrict ourselves to the most important case, in which e^{σ} is a large number and φ is therefore, by (4.89), in the neighborhood of $\frac{1}{2}\pi$, $\frac{3}{2}\pi$, etc. To solve (4.89) we write

$$\varphi = (n + \tfrac{1}{2})\pi - \varphi_1$$

where n is any integer and φ_1 is small, so that (4.89) gives

$$\varphi_1 \approx \tan \varphi_1 = \pm \tfrac{1}{2} e^{-\sigma} \tag{4.91}$$

Case 1: Symmetric wave functions $(C_5 = D_1)$

The plus sign in (4.89) applies, and

$$\varphi \approx (n + \tfrac{1}{2})\pi - \tfrac{1}{2} e^{-\sigma} \qquad (n = 0, 1, 2, \ldots)$$

For a given n, let us compare this value of φ with the value $(n + \frac{1}{2})\pi$, which corresponds to wells which are infinitely separated, that is, for which $\sigma = \infty$. Since the energy is the only variable, we must have a slight difference of energy in the two cases:

$$\varphi \approx (n + \tfrac{1}{2})\pi + \frac{\partial \varphi}{\partial E} \Delta E$$

from which

$$\Delta E \approx -\frac{1}{2} \frac{e^{-\sigma}}{\partial \varphi / \partial E} \tag{4.92}$$

Comparison with (4.81) shows that this can also be written as

$$\Delta E \approx -\hbar \nu e^{-\sigma} \tag{4.93}$$

where ν is the number of vibrations per second, classically reckoned, executed by a particle having the given energy in one of the two potential wells.

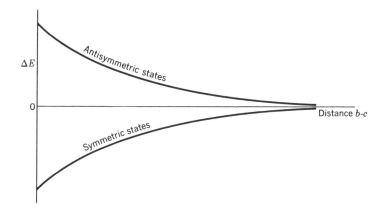

Fig. 4.17 Energy shift ΔE as a function of the separation of the potential wells for symmetric and antisymmetric states.

Case 2: Antisymmetric wave functions $(C_5 = -D_1)$

We find

$$\varphi \approx (n + \tfrac{1}{2})\pi + \tfrac{1}{2}e^{-\sigma}$$

and

$$\Delta E \approx \frac{1}{2}\frac{e^{-\sigma}}{\partial \varphi / \partial E} \approx \hbar \nu e^{-\sigma} \tag{4.94}$$

In Fig. 4.17 we have sketched the two values of ΔE as functions of the distance apart of the two centers of force, and Fig. 4.18 shows typical wave functions.

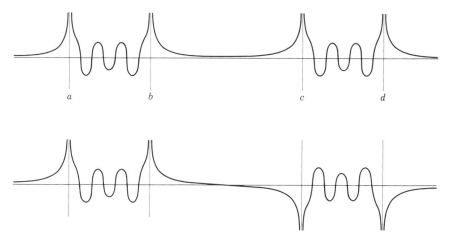

Fig. 4.18 Typical wave functions of (upper) symmetric and (lower) antisymmetric states. There are also states in which the wave function within each potential well is antisymmetric.

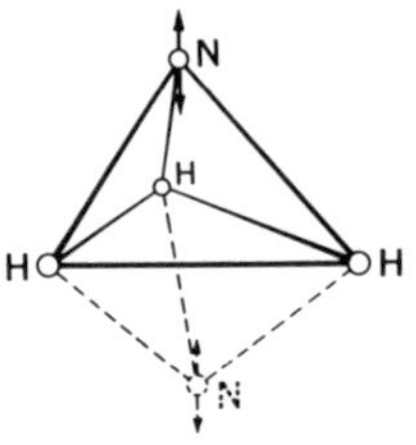

Fig. 4.19   The nitrogen atom in an ammonia molecule has two
positions of equilibrium around which it can oscillate.
It can tunnel from one to the other.

Problem 4.13   Show that the above expressions for φ can be
divided into two groups, analogous to (4.78) and (4.79), corresponding to different (approximate) symmetries of the wave function in
each well.

Consequences

Imagine, in the light of this calculation, two similar atoms being
brought together. As soon as they are close enough that they can
occasionally exchange electrons (in defiance of the laws of classical
physics), there will begin to exist two types of wave function for the
system as a whole, of which the symmetrical one will have the lower
energy. In the absence of disturbing influences, the system will
spontaneously go into the state of lower energy. Then the system
will further decrease its energy if the atoms come closer together.
There thus exists an attractive *exchange force*, of purely quantum-
mechanical nature, in the symmetric state and a repulsive one in the
antisymmetric state. This is the origin of the covalent bond of
chemistry.

   Another immediate application of these results is to clarify
the fact that the lines of the infrared spectra of certain molecules are
double. An example is the ammonia molecule, NH_3, in which the
four atoms lie roughly at the vertices of a tetrahedron (Fig. 4.19).
But for a given orientation of the three hydrogens, the nitrogen
atom has two positions of stability located symmetrically on
opposite sides of the plane formed by the hydrogens. The situation
is therefore similar to that considered here. Under the conditions of a
gas discharge tube the symmetric and antisymmetric states are about
equally populated, and to each mode of motion of the molecule
correspond two slightly different possible energies. This splitting
of energy levels results in a corresponding splitting of the spectral
lines.[14]

   Problem 4.14   Show that if the electron starts out in one of
the potential wells and loses no energy by radiation or otherwise,
it will oscillate back and forth from one well to the other.

   Solution.   It is clear from Fig. 4.18 that in the left-hand well

[14] D. M. Dennison and G. E. Uhlenbeck, Phys. Rev., **41**, 313 (1932).

the symmetric and antisymmetric wave functions are very nearly equal, whereas in the right-hand well they are very nearly opposite. In obvious notation, this is

$$\psi_s^{(L)} = \psi_a^{(L)} \qquad \psi_s^{(R)} = -\psi_a^{(R)}$$

Thus if we take the initial state to be the superposition $\psi = \psi_s + \psi_a$, it will be essentially zero in the right-hand well. If E_0 is the energy of the electron in an isolated well and $\Delta E = \hbar\nu e^{-\sigma}$, the time dependence of ψ in the left-hand well will be

$$\psi^{(L)}(t) = \psi_s^{(L)}e^{-i\hbar^{-1}(E_0-\Delta E)t} + \psi_a^{(L)}e^{-i\hbar^{-1}(E_0+\Delta E)t}$$

$$= 2\psi_s^{(L)}e^{-i\hbar^{-1}E_0 t}\cos(\hbar^{-1}\Delta E\, t)$$

$$|\psi^{(L)}(t)|^2 = 4|\psi_s^{(L)}|^2\cos^2(\hbar^{-1}\Delta E\, t)$$

and similarly,

$$|\psi^{(R)}(t)|^2 = 4|\psi_s^{(R)}|^2\sin^2(\hbar^{-1}\Delta E\, t)$$

The electron clearly oscillates back and forth between the two wells (this phenomenon is known as exchange) with a frequency

$$\omega_{\text{exch}} = 2\hbar^{-1}\Delta E = 2\nu e^{-\sigma}$$

In contrast with this composite state, the symmetric and antisymmetric states each share the electron evenly between the two wells, in the sense that at any moment it is equally likely to be found in either of them.

Problem 4.15 Prove in a perfectly general way that the probability of penetration of a potential barrier is independent of the direction from which it is approached. Hint: Derive equations analogous to (4.71) but referring to conditions on the two sides of the barrier considered as a whole.

4.8 The Harmonic Oscillator

One of the basic elementary problems of classical mechanics is the harmonic oscillator, consisting of a particle which is bound by a force proportional to its displacement. Not only are its properties of special simplicity, but there are also a large number of oscillating systems occurring in nature which may be represented at least approximately in terms of such oscillators. This system plays a similar role in quantum theory, with the added importance that the methods used in analyzing it are of paramount interest in the theory of fields. In this chapter we shall illustrate two essentially distinct ways of carrying out a quantum-mechanical calculation by applying them both to an exact solution of the same problem. The first method envisages only a differential equation which is to be solved subject to certain boundary conditions. In contrast with this, the second dispenses with the use of any particular representation and solves the problem by constructing a solution directly from the operators $\hat{p}$ and x with the use of the commutation relations (3.23). These are the two extremes of quantum-mechanical reckoning. We shall use them both in the course of this book, and modern practice frequently combines them.

4.9 Analytical Solution

We suppose that the restoring force of the spring is given by Kx, so that the potential energy would be $\frac{1}{2}Kx^2$, and, in the x representation,

$$\hat{H} = \frac{\hat{p}^2}{2m} + \frac{1}{2}Kx^2 \tag{4.95a}$$

The Schrödinger equation is $\hat{H}\psi = E\psi$, or

$$\frac{\partial^2\psi}{\partial x^2} + \frac{2m}{\hbar^2}(E - \frac{1}{2}Kx^2)\psi = 0 \tag{4.95b}$$

It will be convenient to introduce the frequency of the corresponding oscillator in classical physics,

$$\omega = \left(\frac{K}{m}\right)^{\frac{1}{2}} \tag{4.96a}$$

and, in terms of this, a new independent variable

$$y = \left(\frac{m\omega}{\hbar}\right)^{\frac{1}{2}} x \tag{4.96b}$$

Denoting differentiation with respect to y by a prime, we find

$$\psi'' + (\lambda - y^2)\psi = 0 \tag{4.97}$$

where the new eigenvalue λ is related to E by

$$E = \frac{1}{2}\lambda\hbar\omega \tag{4.98}$$

The eigenvalue λ is to be found, but its sign can at once be determined if we note that if we take the expectation value of $\hat{H}$ in the state ψ, we have

$$\langle\hat{H}\rangle = E = \frac{1}{2m}\langle\hat{p}^2\rangle + \frac{K}{2}\langle x^2\rangle$$

By (3.35), this gives

$$E \geqslant 0 \qquad \lambda \geqslant 0 \tag{4.99}$$

The procedure will be to solve this equation subject to the usual condition that ψ must satisfy if it is to be normalizable,

$$\lim_{y \to \pm \infty} \psi(y) = 0$$

Let us therefore first examine the limiting behavior of ψ. In the limit, (4.97) becomes

$$\lim_{y \to \infty} \frac{\psi''}{y^2 \psi} = 1$$

a solution of which is

$$\psi_\infty = e^{-\frac{1}{2}y^2} \qquad (4.100)$$

since

$$\psi_\infty'' = (y^2 - 1)e^{-\frac{1}{2}y^2}$$

Now that we have found the dominating asymptotic behavior of ψ, it is convenient to replace ψ by a new unknown function $f(y)$ according to

$$\psi(y) = f(y)\psi_\infty(y) \qquad (4.101)$$

Putting this into (4.97) gives an equation for $f(y)$:

$$f'' - 2yf' + (\lambda - 1)f = 0 \qquad (4.102)$$

and this is to be solved subject to the condition that

$$\lim_{y \to \infty} f(y) < e^{\frac{1}{2}y^2} \qquad (4.103)$$

(Actually, it must be enough less that the normalization integral will be sure to converge, but the condition given here will suffice.)

Series solution

We shall solve (4.102) by assuming that $f(y)$ can be expanded as a power series in y and then determining the coefficients of the series. Let

$$f(y) = \sum_{n=0}^{\infty} A_n y^n \qquad (4.104)$$

(Why does the assumed series contain no negative powers of y?) We find

$$yf' = \sum_0^\infty n A_n y^n$$

$$f'' = \sum_0^\infty n(n-1)A_n y^{n-2} = \sum_0^\infty (n+2)(n+1)A_{n+2}y^n$$

(The reader should verify the last step with care.) Substituting these into (4.102) and setting the coefficient of each power of y

equal to zero gives

$$A_{n+2} = \frac{2n + 1 - \lambda}{(n + 2)(n + 1)} A_n \qquad (4.105)$$

Thus if we take A_0 and A_1 to be the two arbitrary constants in the solution of the original equation, we can construct from them all the rest of the coefficients in two chains, one starting from A_0 and the other from A_1. To verify that it is consistent to restrict the series (4.104) to positive powers of y, we write (4.105) as

$$A_n = \frac{(n + 2)(n + 1)}{2n + 1 - \lambda} A_{n+2}$$

By (4.99) the denominator does not vanish for any $n < 0$, so that, starting from A_0 and A_1 and working downward, we find all the coefficients of negative powers of y to be zero.

The eigenvalue condition

Returning to (4.105), let us examine the convergence of the series (4.104). We find

$$\lim_{n \to \infty} \frac{A_{n+2}}{A_n} = \frac{2}{n} \qquad (4.106)$$

which is ample to secure convergence.[15] Thus the series converges for all values of λ, but we require in addition that it converge to a function f satisfying (4.103), and this does not happen in general. The fact would be easy to prove if we had a general expression for the coefficients A_n, since with it we could write the series for f and the series for $e^{\frac{1}{2}y^2}$ and show that for sufficiently large values of n the terms of the first series are all larger than those of the second. This is not hard to do, but we need not bother; for we can show the same thing by considering the *ratios* of successive terms. For f, the limiting value of the ratio is $2/n$, by (4.106), and for $e^{\frac{1}{2}y^2}$ it is easily seen to be $1/2n$. After a certain point, therefore, the terms of the first series will exceed those of the second, and it is easy to see that f will violate (4.103).

The violation can be avoided only if the series for f terminates, that is, if all the A_n's beyond a certain value of n are zero. According to (4.105), this can be achieved as follows: Let λ be equal to $2m + 1$ for some integer m in one of the two chains. Then A_{m+2}, A_{m+4}, etc., are all zero. The termination of the other chain can be secured if we require that *all* its members, starting with A_0 or A_1 as the case may be, must vanish. The energy levels are thus given by (4.98) as

$$E_m = \hbar\omega(m + \tfrac{1}{2}) \qquad (4.107)$$

---

[15] See, for example, T. M. Apostol, *Calculus*, Blaisdell Publishing Co., New York, 1961, vol. 1, p. 435.

Proceeding in this way we can construct the following table:

m	ψ_m	λ_m	E_m
0	$A_0 e^{-\frac{1}{2}y^2}$	1	$\frac{1}{2}\hbar\omega$
1	$A_1 y e^{-\frac{1}{2}y^2}$	3	$\frac{3}{2}\hbar\omega$
2	$A_0(1 - 2y^2)e^{-\frac{1}{2}y^2}$	5	$\frac{5}{2}\hbar\omega$
3	$A_1(y - \frac{2}{3}y^3)e^{-\frac{1}{2}y^2}$	7	$\frac{7}{2}\hbar\omega$
4	$A_0(1 - 4y^2 + \frac{4}{3}y^4)e^{-\frac{1}{2}y^2}$	9	$\frac{9}{2}\hbar\omega$

the first four of which are sketched in Fig. 4.20. Like the wave functions we have studied previously, they alternate between symmetry and antisymmetry in y. We shall see in the next chapter that this is a general property. Finally, in order to find the A_0's and A_1's, it is necessary to square and integrate the ψ's and subject them to the normalization condition. We shall see in the next section that there is a much neater way to do it.

Problem 4.16 Formulate the same problem in terms of the momentum representation of Sec. 3.2, using the results of Prob. 3.6. Sketch the solution of the resulting equation, with special attention to physical content, and show that the same energy levels are obtained.

Problem 4.17 Show that the first two wave functions obtained in the last problem correspond, in the sense of Eqs. (2.12) and (2.13), to those obtained in this chapter.

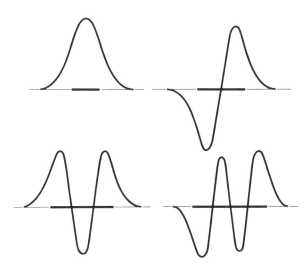

Fig. 4.20 The first four harmonic-oscillator wave functions. The heavy lines indicate the allowed regions of the x axis.

4.10 Algebraic Solution

In this section we shall show how the energy levels and normalized wave functions of the harmonic oscillator can be determined in a form which is independent of any particular representation, but at the end we shall write the results in the x representation to compare them with those of the preceding section.

The problem is to find eigenfunctions and eigenvalues satisfying

$$\hat{H}\psi = E\psi \qquad \hat{H} = \frac{\hat{p}^2}{2m} + \tfrac{1}{2}K\hat{x}^2 \tag{4.108}$$

where $\hat{p}$ and $\hat{x}$ are related by the algebraic rule

$$[\hat{p},\hat{x}] = -i\hbar \tag{4.109}$$

The device to be used centers around the introduction of two new *nonhermitian* operators

$$\hat{a} = \left(\frac{m\omega}{2\hbar}\right)^{\!\frac{1}{2}} \left(\hat{x} + \frac{i}{m\omega}\,\hat{p}\right)$$

$$\hat{a} = \left(\frac{m\omega}{2\hbar}\right)^{\!\frac{1}{2}} \left(\hat{x} - \frac{i}{m\omega}\,\hat{p}\right) \tag{4.110}$$

(We note that since $\hat{p}$ in the x representation involves an i, these two operators are actually free from i.) By the use of (4.109) they are easily seen to obey the commutation relation

$$[\hat{a},\hat{a}] = 1 \tag{4.111}$$

while $\hat{H}$ can be written in the form

$$\hat{H} = \tfrac{1}{2}\hbar\omega(\hat{a}\hat{a} + \hat{a}\hat{a})$$

$$= \hbar\omega(\hat{a}\hat{a} + \tfrac{1}{2})$$

Writing this formula as

$$\hat{H} = \hbar\omega(\hat{N} + \tfrac{1}{2}) \qquad \hat{N} = \hat{a}\hat{a} \tag{4.112}$$

we see that it is a sort of operator form of (4.107) and that the problem is reduced to determining the eigenvalues and eigenfunctions of the operator $\hat{N}$.

Suppose we have an eigenfunction of $\hat{N}$, ψ_n, belonging to the eigenvalue n,

$$\hat{N}\psi_n = n\psi_n \tag{4.113}$$

where n must be real and greater than $-\tfrac{1}{2}$ (why?). Let us now construct the function $\varphi = \hat{a}\psi_n$ and see what the operator $\hat{N}$ does to it.

$$\hat{N}\varphi = \hat{a}\hat{a}\varphi = \hat{a}\hat{a}\hat{a}\psi_n = \hat{a}(\hat{a}\hat{a} - 1)\psi_n$$

$$= \hat{a}(n-1)\psi_n = (n-1)\hat{a}\psi_n = (n-1)\varphi$$

Thus, φ is also an eigenfunction of $\hat{N}$, but it belongs to the eigenvalue $n - 1$. Omitting for a moment the matter of normalization, we write

$$\hat{a}\psi_n = \psi_{n-1} \qquad \hat{a}^2\psi_n = \psi_{n-2}, \; \ldots \tag{4.114}$$

Similarly, we find $\hat{N}\hat{a}\psi_n = (n + 1)\hat{a}\psi_n$ so that

$$\hat{a}\psi_n = \psi_{n+1} \qquad \hat{a}^2\psi_n = \psi_{n+2}, \; \ldots \tag{4.115}$$

Operators such as $\hat{a}$ and $\hat{a}$ are called *shift operators*.

Starting from any ψ_n we can by k successive operations with $\hat{a}$ form a ψ_{n-k} such that

$$\hat{N}\psi_{n-k} = (n - k)\psi_{n-k}$$

for any k, and here we run into a contradiction, since we have just seen that the eigenvalues of $\hat{N}$ must be greater than $-\frac{1}{2}$. There must therefore exist a wave function ψ_0 for which the shift process (4.114) fails, and this can happen only if

$$\hat{a}\psi_0 = 0 \tag{4.116}$$

Clearly,

$$\hat{N}\psi_0 = \hat{a}\hat{a}\psi_0 = 0 \tag{4.117}$$

which justifies the subscript zero, and if we now use (4.115) to go back up the ladder of states, we have

$$\psi_n = N_n\hat{a}^n\psi_0 \tag{4.118}$$

where N_n is an appropriate normalizing constant (not to be confused with the operator $\hat{N}$). Clearly, the first eigenvalue of $\hat{N}$ is zero and the rest are the positive integers, so (4.112) gives

$$\hat{H}\psi_n = \hbar\omega(n + \tfrac{1}{2})\psi_n \qquad (n = 0, 1, 2, \ldots) \tag{4.119}$$

just as in (4.107).

Normalization

It remains to find the eigenfunctions and the normalization constants N_n. The latter are defined by

$$\int \psi_n^*\psi_n = 1 \qquad (n = 0, 1, 2, \ldots) \tag{4.120}$$

where the integration is over whatever variable is used to specify the system, x or p. Using (4.118), let us put

$$\psi_n = \frac{N_n}{N_{n-1}}\,\hat{a}\psi_{n-1} \tag{4.121}$$

into (4.120) to get

$$\left|\frac{N_n}{N_{n-1}}\right|^2 \int \hat{a}^*\psi_{n-1}^*\hat{a}\psi_{n-1} = \left|\frac{N_n}{N_{n-1}}\right|^2 \int \psi_{n-1}^*\hat{a}\hat{a}\psi_{n-1}$$

by (4.110) and the hermiticity of $\hat{p}$

$$\left|\frac{N_n}{N_{n-1}}\right|^2 \int \psi^*_{n-1} \hat{a} \hat{a} \psi_{n-1} = \left|\frac{N_n}{N_{n-1}}\right|^2 \int \psi^*_{n-1} (\hat{N} + 1)\psi_{n-1}$$

by (4.111) and (4.112)

$$= \left|\frac{N_n}{N_{n-1}}\right|^2 \int \psi^*_{n-1}(n - 1 + 1)\psi_{n-1}$$

by (4.113)

$$= n \left|\frac{N_n}{N_{n-1}}\right|^2 = 1 \qquad \text{by (4.120)} \qquad (4.122)$$

We can choose ψ_0 in (4.118) to be such that $N_0 = 1$ and the phases of the other N's so that they are real. Then (4.122) gives a recurrence relation between the N's,

$$N_n = n^{-\frac{1}{2}} N_{n-1} \qquad N_0 = 1$$

the solution of which is

$$N_n = (n!)^{-\frac{1}{2}} \qquad (0! = 1) \tag{4.123}$$

so that the nth normalized eigenfunction is

$$\psi_n = (n!)^{-\frac{1}{2}} \hat{a}^n \psi_0 \tag{4.124}$$

The Rodrigues formula

To go further, we must choose a representation. In the x representation, (4.116) is

$$\left(x + \frac{\hbar}{m\omega}\frac{\partial}{\partial x}\right)\psi_0 = 0$$

whose normalized solution is

$$\psi_0 = \left(\frac{m\omega}{\pi\hbar}\right)^{\frac{1}{4}} e^{-(m\omega/2\hbar)x^2}$$

It will be convenient at this point to introduce again the variable y of (4.96b), in terms of which (4.124) becomes

$$\psi_n(y) = \left(\frac{m\omega}{\pi\hbar}\right)^{\frac{1}{4}} (2^n n!)^{-\frac{1}{2}} \left(y - \frac{\partial}{\partial y}\right)^n e^{-\frac{1}{2}y^2} \tag{4.125}$$

This formula can be simplified for computational purposes if we note that

$$\left(y - \frac{\partial}{\partial y}\right) e^{-\frac{1}{2}y^2} = 2ye^{-\frac{1}{2}y^2} = -e^{\frac{1}{2}y^2}\frac{\partial}{\partial y} e^{-y^2}$$

A second application of $y - \partial/\partial y$ gives

$$-\left(y - \frac{\partial}{\partial y}\right) e^{\frac{1}{2}y^2} \frac{\partial}{\partial y} e^{-y^2}$$

$$= -\left(y - \frac{\partial}{\partial y}\right) e^{\frac{1}{2}y^2} \frac{\partial}{\partial y} e^{-y^2} + e^{\frac{1}{2}y^2} \frac{\partial^2}{\partial y^2} e^{-y^2}$$

$$= e^{\frac{1}{2}y^2} \frac{\partial^2}{\partial y^2} e^{-y^2}$$

since the first term vanishes identically. Successive terms go in the same way, so that the general expression for the nth normalized wave function can be written as

$$\psi_n = \left(\frac{m\omega}{\pi\hbar}\right)^{\frac{1}{4}} (2^n n!)^{-\frac{1}{2}} H_n(y) e^{-\frac{1}{2}y^2} \tag{4.126}$$

where

$$y = \left(\frac{m\omega}{\hbar}\right)^{\frac{1}{2}} x \quad \text{and} \quad H_n(y) = (-1)^n \left(e^{y^2} \frac{\partial^n}{\partial y^n} e^{-y^2}\right) \tag{4.127}$$

and comparison with (4.101) shows that $H_n(y)$ is essentially the same as $f(y)$. $H_n(y)$ is clearly a polynomial of degree n (why?), and it is referred to as a Hermite polynomial[16] after the first man who studied its properties. (Note that Hermite polynomials and hermitian operators are not to be confused.) The first three Hermite polynomials are

$$H_0(y) = 1 \qquad H_1(y) = 2y \qquad H_2(y) = 4y^2 - 2 \tag{4.128}$$

These are to be compared with the wave functions as already given after (4.107).

Differential formulas like (4.127) exist for many of the special functions of mathematics and are known as Rodrigues formulas. They lead to another useful way of characterizing a function. Consider, for example, the quantity $e^{-(y-t)^2}$. By Taylor's theorem this is

$$e^{-(y-t)^2} = \sum_{n=0}^{\infty} \frac{(-1)^n t^n}{n!} \frac{\partial^n}{\partial y^n} e^{-y^2} = e^{-y^2} \sum_{n=0}^{\infty} \frac{H_n(y)}{n!} t^n$$

or

$$e^{2yt - t^2} = \sum_{n=0}^{\infty} \frac{H_n(y)}{n!} t^n \tag{4.129}$$

The function on the left is called a *generating function* for the Hermite polynomials, and it is useful because it effectively summarizes the properties of all of them in a single formula.

[16] The reader should be warned that there is not unanimity in the literature as to just how H_n is defined.

Problem 4.18   Starting from (4.123), construct the normalized wave functions in the momentum representation and verify that the first three are the same as those obtained in the solution of Prob. 4.16.

Orthogonality

We shall now evaluate an important integral involving the ψ_n's,

$$\int_{-\infty}^{\infty} \psi_m(y)\psi_n(y)\, dy \qquad (m \neq n)$$

We let m be greater than n and write the integral asymmetrically as

$$\int_{-\infty}^{\infty} \psi_m\psi_n\, dy = \int_{-\infty}^{\infty} \left(e^{y^2}\frac{\partial^m}{\partial y^m}\, e^{-y^2} \cdot e^{-\frac{1}{2}y^2} \right) (H_n(y)e^{-\frac{1}{2}y^2})\, dy$$

multiplied by various numerical factors which we need not write down. This is the same as

$$\int_{-\infty}^{\infty} \frac{\partial^m}{\partial y^m}\, e^{-y^2} \cdot H_n(y)\, dy$$

which, on integrating m times by parts, becomes

$$\int_{-\infty}^{\infty} e^{-y^2} \frac{\partial^m}{\partial y^m} H_n(y)\, dy = 0$$

since $H_n(y)$ is a polynomial of degree lower than m. Thus, returning to the variable x and remembering that ψ is normalized, we have

$$\int_{-\infty}^{\infty} \psi_m\psi_n\, dx = \begin{cases} \cdot 0 & (m \neq n) \\ 1 & (m = n) \end{cases}$$

It is customary to write this in terms of a symbol known as the *Kronecker delta*, δ_{mn}, a function of the integers m and n whose possible values are 0 and 1:

$$\delta_{mn} = \begin{cases} 0 & (m \neq n) \\ 1 & (m = n) \end{cases} \tag{4.130}$$

so that

$$\int_{-\infty}^{\infty} \psi_m\psi_n\, dx = \delta_{mn} \tag{4.131}$$

The property that the integral of the product of any two different members of the set of functions ψ_n vanishes is called *orthogonality*, and we shall see in the next chapter that it is exhibited in one way or another by all sets of eigenfunctions. The reader will already have encountered a special case of it in his study of Fourier series. Functions satisfying (4.131) are said to be *orthonormal*.

Problem 4.19   It follows from (4.121) and (4.123) that

$$\hat{a}^\dagger\psi_n = (n + 1)^{\frac{1}{2}}\psi_{n+1}$$

Prove that $\hat{a}\psi_n = n^{\frac{1}{2}}\psi_{n-1}$.

Problem 4.20   Evaluate the integral

$$x_{mn} = \int_{-\infty}^{\infty} \psi_m x \psi_n \, dx \tag{4.132}$$

This can be done easily if one notes that according to (4.110),

$$x = \left(\frac{\hbar}{2m\omega}\right)^{\frac{1}{2}} (\hat{a}^\dagger + \hat{a}) \tag{4.133}$$

and then uses the results of the preceding problem.

Problem 4.21   Derive the differentiation formula

$$H'_n(y) = 2nH_{n-1}(y) \tag{4.134}$$

and the recurrence relation

$$H_{n+1}(y) = 2yH_n(y) - 2nH_{n-1}(y) \tag{4.135}$$

Use this last relation to solve Prob. 4.20 in a purely analytical way.

Problem 4.22   Use the generating function to prove that the functions ψ_m form an orthonormal set.

Solution.   Start by writing the generating function relation twice:

$$e^{2ys-s^2}e^{2yt-t^2} = \sum_{m,n=0}^{\infty} \frac{s^m t^n}{m!n!} H_m(y) H_n(y)$$

Then multiply each side by e^{-y^2} and integrate over y. Finally, compare the coefficients of corresponding terms in $s^m t^n$.

Problem 4.23   Solve Prob. 4.20 by the use of the generating function.

Problem 4.24   What is the expectation value of the potential energy of a simple harmonic oscillator in the nth energy state?

Problem 4.25   What is $\Delta p \, \Delta x$ for the nth state?

Problem 4.26   Calculate the energy levels of a harmonic oscillator according to the WKB approximation. Denoting the oscillator's classical frequency by ω, compare the resulting energies and the symmetries of the associated wave functions with those calculated exactly, Eq. (4.107) and the subsequent table.

5

Hermitian Operators
and Angular Momentum

Before going on to the study of more complex physical systems it will be helpful to develop some more theorems on hermitian operators; for the reader will by now have seen that these play a special role not only in the formulation of quantum mechanics but also in its practical working out. The reader may have encountered some of these theorems (for example, the orthogonality theorem) in the study of calculus; others (for example, Section 5.4) have profound analogies in classical mechanics, and taken together they constitute some of the basic mathematical apparatus of the theory. The main reason for going into these abstract matters in some detail is their utility in computation. This will be shown in exploring some of the intricacies of the quantum theory of angular momentum in the latter part of this chapter, and the same approach provides the central theorem for the study of the wave functions of electrons in a (one-dimensional) crystal in Chap. 13.

5.1 The Orthogonality Theorem

We say that two functions f and g are *orthogonal* over a certain region if the integral $\int f^*g$ over this region is zero. In this and following chapters we shall often use an integral sign with no dx. The reader is reminded that as in Sec. 3.4, where the notation was first introduced, we do this for generality. The wave functions may be written in either coordinate or momentum space, and as we shall see later, the number of variables of integration may be more than 3.

THEOREM.   If ψ_1 and ψ_2 are eigenfunctions of a hermitian operator $\hat{Q}$ corresponding to different eigenvalues q_1 and q_2, then they are

116

orthogonal over $\hat{Q}$'s region of hermiticity.

Proof. $\int \psi_1^* \hat{Q} \psi_2 = \int (\hat{Q}\psi_1)^* \psi_2$

$\qquad\quad \| \qquad\qquad \|$

$\qquad q_2 \int \psi_1^* \psi_2 = q_1 \int \psi_1^* \psi_2$

where we have used the fact that the eigenfunctions of hermitian operators are real (Sec. 3.4). If $q_1 \neq q_2$, then

$$\int \psi_1^* \psi_2 = 0 \qquad\qquad (5.1)$$

Equation (4.131) is an example of this fact.

It can happen that ψ_1 and ψ_2 are different functions but both belong to the same eigenvalue q. This eigenvalue is then said to be *degenerate*, and the theorem no longer holds. But if ψ_1 and ψ_2 are eigenfunctions, then for any linear combination $\alpha\psi_1 + \beta\psi_2$ we have

$$\hat{Q}(\alpha\psi_1 + \beta\psi_2) = \alpha q\psi_1 + \beta q\psi_2 = q(\alpha\psi_1 + \beta\psi_2)$$

and so the linear combination is again an eigenfunction belonging to the same eigenvalue. From any normalized ψ_1 and ψ_2 which do not happen to be orthogonal we can now easily form another pair that is, for example

$$\psi_1 \qquad \text{and} \qquad \frac{\psi_2 - \psi_1 \int \psi_1^* \psi_2}{[1 - |\int \psi_1^* \psi_2|^2]^{1/2}} \qquad\qquad (5.2)$$

which is both normalized and orthogonal, *orthonormal* for short. This is only one of many such orthonormal pairs which can be found. (The reader should verify these statements.) Equation (5.2) is an example of the *Schmidt orthogonalization procedure*,[1] and though it grows somewhat cumbersome, it may be carried out for any number of degenerate eigenfunctions. Thus the orthogonality theorem can be extended: All eigenfunctions of a hermitian operator are either mutually orthogonal or, if degenerate and not orthogonal, may be replaced by others which are.

Problem 5.1 Let $\hat{Q} = d^2/dx^2$ and let the region of hermiticity be the line from $x = 0$ to $x = \pi$. What are the normalized eigenfunctions of $\hat{Q}$ for which $\hat{Q}$ is hermitian? What are the corresponding eigenvalues? Show by direct integration that any two of the eigenfunctions are orthogonal.

Problem 5.2 Show that if any set of ψ's are orthogonal, then the relation

$$\Sigma d_i \psi_i = 0$$

cannot hold unless all the d's are zero.

---

[1] P. M. Morse and H. Feshbach, *Methods of Theoretical Physics*, McGraw-Hill Book Company, Inc., New York, 1953, vol. 1, p. 928.

Problem 5.3   With $\hat{Q} = d^2/dx^2$ as in Prob. 5.1 but the region of hermiticity now taken as a closed loop of length L, show that for suitable values of k, two normalized eigenfunctions of Q belonging to the same eigenvalue are

$$\psi_1 = \left(\frac{2}{L}\right)^{\frac{1}{2}} \sin\left(kx + \vartheta_1\right) \qquad \psi_2 = \left(\frac{2}{L}\right)^{\frac{1}{2}} \sin\left(kx + \vartheta_2\right)$$

where ϑ_1 and ϑ_2 are constants. Show that ψ_1 and ψ_2 are not in general orthogonal, and construct a pair of ψ's which belong to the same eigenvalue of $\hat{Q}$ and which are orthogonal.

5.2 Eigenfunction Expansions

Suppose we wish to represent a given function ψ as a linear combination of the normalized eigenfunctions ψ_i of a certain hermitian operator $\hat{Q}$. Writing ψ as

$$\psi = \Sigma C_i \psi_i \tag{5.3}$$

we multiply both sides of the equation by the complex conjugate of one of the ψ_i's, say ψ_n, and integrate it over $\hat{Q}$'s region of hermiticity. Because of the orthogonality of the ψ_i's, all terms but the nth drop out, and we have

$$C_n = \int \psi_n^* \psi \tag{5.4}$$

These are (for real ψ's) the familiar steps of Fourier analysis, and they follow from the assumption (5.3). But the assumption is rather a large one; for it must be shown, first, that the series (5.3) converges and, second, that it converges to the function ψ. Suppose, for example, that one were to omit some of the nonzero terms in a convergent Fourier series. The remaining series might still converge, but it would converge to the wrong function. Clearly, it is necessary to use the *complete* set of sines and cosines in Fourier analysis, and one must investigate the set of eigenfunctions of any hermitian operator to see whether it is complete. The investigation of the general case has not been made (this is essentially because the idea of a hermitian operator is such a general one), but many special cases are known,[2] and we are led to conjecture that any function for which the operator $\hat{Q}$ is hermitian can be expanded as a convergent series of eigenfunctions of $\hat{Q}$. This will be assumed to be true, even where it has not been proved, throughout the book.

The difficulties, both in proving the postulate and in applying it, come when the region of hermiticity is infinite. This is true for the

[2] R. Courant and D. Hilbert, *Methods of Mathematical Physics*, Interscience Publishers, Inc., New York, 1953, vol. 1, chap. 2. It is particularly necessary when generating a set of eigenfunctions by means of shift operators to be sure that the set is complete.

Fig. 5.1   To illustrate Prob. 5.4.

momentum operator and for many others. What happens is that the successive eigenvalues form a continuum (the eigenvalues of $\hat{p}$ are $\hbar k$, where k is any real number), so that both normalization and orthogonalization become difficult to define and the sum in (5.3) is replaced by an integral. For the most part in this book we shall avoid difficulties when they arise by making the region finite to start with and then afterward letting it become infinite as a limit.

Problem 5.4   Expand $f(x)$ of Fig. 5.1 in terms of the normalized eigenfunctions of $\hat{Q}$ found in Prob. 5.1.

We now turn our attention to the expansion coefficients C_n. First, we prove that if ψ is normalized, then

THEOREM. $$\sum_n |C_n|^2 = 1 \tag{5.5}$$

Proof. $$\int |\psi|^2 = \sum_{m,n} C_m^* C_n \int \psi_m^* \psi_n$$

$$= \sum_n |C_n|^2 = 1$$

(This relation can be used as a criterion of the completeness of the set of ψ_n's, since if any of the nonvanishing C's are omitted, the sum will be less than 1.)

Problem 5.5   Complete the steps leading to Eq. (5.5).

The expansion coefficients C_n have, further, a definite and very important physical significance, as can be seen if we calculate the expectation value of an operator $\hat{Q}$ in the state ψ by expanding ψ in a series of eigenfunctions of $\hat{Q}$.

$$\langle \hat{Q} \rangle = \int \psi^* \hat{Q} \psi = \sum_{m,n} C_m^* C_n \int \psi_m^* \hat{Q} \psi_n$$

$$= \sum_{m,n} C_m^* C_n q_n \int \psi_m^* \psi_n$$

or

$$\langle \hat{Q} \rangle = \sum_n |C_n|^2 q_n \tag{5.6}$$

This relation is exactly of the form (2.3), from which it follows at once that if a system is known to be in the state described by ψ and then a measurement is made of the dynamical variable Q, the number $|C_n|^2$ is the probability that the number q_n will result, or, in other words, it is the probability that the system will be found in the state ψ_n. We have already seen an example in (2.15).

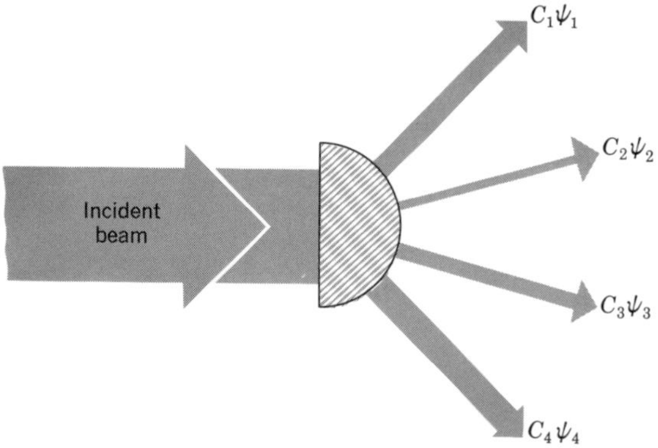

$C_1\psi_1$

$C_2\psi_2$

$C_3\psi_3$

$C_4\psi_4$

Fig. 5.2 Apparatus for analyzing a beam of particles by physically separating its components.

The content of (5.6) can be visualized very easily. The states ψ_n must differ from each other by some physical property which depends on Q, and we imagine that an instrument which will sort out an incident beam of electrons according to this property (Fig. 5.2) has been constructed. The electrons in the emerging beams have had their Q's measured, and they will be present in whatever recording devices are used proportionally to their amplitude in the original mixture, $\psi = \Sigma C_i\psi_i$. The probability density of an electron in the nth beam, for example, is $|C_n|^2|\psi_n|^2$. Now let the incident beam be turned off, as in Fig. 5.3. The probability that the electron finds itself somewhere in the nth beam is $|C_n|^2\int|\psi_n|^2$, that is, $|C_n|^2$ if ψ_n is correctly normalized, and this is what was concluded above.

Problem 5.6   A particle in an infinitely deep potential well has a wave function which is initially as sketched in Fig. 5.4. Find the probability that the particle's energy, when measured, is exactly $(\hbar^2/2m)(n\pi/L)^2$. How does this probability change with time?

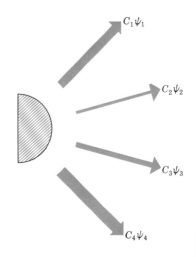

$C_1\psi_1$

$C_2\psi_2$

$C_3\psi_3$

$C_4\psi_4$

Fig. 5.3 Apparatus of Fig. 5.2 after the incident beam has been turned off.

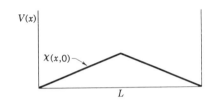

Fig. 5.4   To illustrate Prob. 5.6.

The reader should guard himself with great care from thinking of the superposition $\psi = \Sigma C_i \psi_i$ as representing a mixture of groups of electrons with different values for Q. This is not the case. The different groups appear only *after* the sorting operation illustrated in Fig. 5.2 has been carried out. Before it, ψ is a superposition, not a mixture. We have discussed a conceptual experiment in terms of beams of particles only in order to make it easier to visualize, since this is the way in which such measurements are normally made. Actually, each individual electron is described by the superposition $\psi = \Sigma C_i \psi_i$. Suppose, for example, that the wave function has two components, $\psi = C_1 \psi_1 + C_2 \psi_2$, and that we evaluate the expectation value of a dynamical variable A in this state. The result (if $\hat{A}$ is hermitian) is

$$\langle A \rangle = |C_1|^2 \int \psi_1^* \hat{A} \psi_1 + |C_2|^2 \int \psi_2^* \hat{A} \psi_2 + 2 \operatorname{Re} C_1^* C_2 \int \psi_2^* \hat{A} \psi_1 \tag{5.7}$$

where Re denotes that one takes the real part of what follows. The first two terms fall into the pattern (2.3), but the third is perfectly inexplicable from a classical point of view. This is to be contrasted with the situation in Sec. 3.7 where the component ψ's are superposed incoherently with random phases and the last term averages to zero. Equation (5.6) takes its simple form as a sum of independent contributions only because ψ_n is assumed an eigenfunction of Q.

If the functions ψ_1 and ψ_2 are energy eigenfunctions belonging to different eigenvalues and if A does not involve the time explicitly, then the last term in (5.7) fluctuates in time proportionally to $e^{i(E_2 - E_1)t/\hbar}$, at a rate which is ordinarily far too rapid to be followed experimentally. Thus the result of a measurement of A will ordinarily be the time average

$$\overline{\langle A \rangle} = |C_1|^2 \int \psi_1^* \hat{A} \psi_1 + |C_2|^2 \int \psi_2^* \hat{A} \psi_2$$

in which probabilities are once more superposed in the classical way. Comparison with Sec. 3.7 shows that in this respect, coherent superposition is effectively the same as incoherent superposition. In almost all interesting cases, the states to be superposed have exactly the same energy.

5.3   Simultaneous Observables

We are now in a position to answer a question that has no analogue in Newtonian mechanics but is of great importance in the quantum theory: "Under what circumstances is it possible to know simultaneously the exact numerical values of two different observables?" In experimental terms, a measurement of the first quantity, say, P, will leave a system in a certain state in which P has the value p. After the second measurement, of some other property Q, the system will be in a state in which Q has the measured value q. Now, will a remeasurement of P again give the value p? If so, we can say that it is possible to know the values of P and Q simultaneously. Comparison with the uncertainty principle in its general form (3.41) suggests that for this to be possible, the operators P and Q must commute. Let us now examine the question mathematically. We say that P and Q are known simultaneously if any eigenfunction of $\hat{P}$ is at the same time an eigenfunction of $\hat{Q}$:

$$\hat{P}\psi_i = p_i\psi_i \quad \text{and} \quad \hat{Q}\psi_i = q_i\psi_i$$

Clearly,

$$\hat{P}\hat{Q}\psi_i = \hat{P}q_i\psi_i = q_i\hat{P}\psi_i = q_ip_i\psi_i$$

and also

$$\hat{Q}\hat{P}\psi_i = p_iq_i\psi_i$$

Subtracting, we have $[\hat{P},\hat{Q}]\psi_i = 0$. Since any arbitrary function ψ for which $\hat{P}$ (or $\hat{Q}$) is hermitian can be expanded in terms of the ψ_i, it follows that

$$[\hat{P},\hat{Q}]\psi = 0$$

We have previously adopted the convention that an operator which gives zero when applied to any arbitrary function can itself be called zero, and so we see that $\hat{P}$ and $\hat{Q}$ must indeed commute if at least one of them is hermitian.

But just because the commutator $\hat{C}$ in (3.41) is zero, it does not follow that Δp and Δq are both zero. We are therefore led to the more profound question: If two operators $\hat{P}$ and $\hat{Q}$ commute, are the eigenfunctions of one also eigenfunctions of the other? If at least one of the two operators is nondegenerate, that is, does not have degenerate eigenvalues, the answer is easily arrived at. Suppose that $[\hat{P},\hat{Q}] = 0$ and

$$\hat{Q}\psi = q\psi \tag{5.8}$$

where $\hat{Q}$ is the nondegenerate operator. Now form the product $\hat{P}\hat{Q}\psi$. Since $\hat{P}\hat{Q} = \hat{Q}\hat{P}$, it is equal to $\hat{Q}\hat{P}\psi$. But by (5.8) it is also $q\hat{P}\psi$. Thus

$$\hat{Q}\hat{P}\psi = q\hat{P}\psi$$

and so $\hat{P}\psi$ is an eigenfunction of $\hat{Q}$ belonging to the eigenvalue q. But we have assumed that there is only one eigenfunction ψ belonging to q. Thus $\hat{P}\psi$ can only be a numerical multiple of ψ:

$$\hat{P}\psi = p\psi$$

and we see that ψ is simultaneously an eigenfunction of $\hat{P}$ and $\hat{Q}$. Note that in this case neither $\hat{P}$ nor $\hat{Q}$ need be assumed hermitian.

If both operators are degenerate, then one has to take more pains. As with the orthogonality theorem, it is necessary to find a particular set of ψ's corresponding to any degenerate eigenvalue of $\hat{Q}$ which shall at the same time be eigenfunctions of $\hat{P}$. It is straightforward, though somewhat tedious, to show that this can always be done.[3] Further, the argument can be extended to situations in which there are more than two operators which commute. We can summarize all this in the

THEOREM ON SIMULTANEOUS OBSERVABLES.   Let $\hat{P}, \hat{Q}, \hat{R}, \ldots$ be a set of hermitian operators which commute among each other. Then a set of eigenfunctions which are simultaneously eigenfunctions of all the operators can be found.

The great importance of this theorem is that it enables one to know, in advance of carrying out a quantum-mechanical calculation, how precisely it is possible to specify the system under discussion. It is customary in discussing atomic and nuclear states, for example, to make use of several *quantum numbers* (n, l, m, etc.) in order to characterize certain exactly knowable constant properties of the system. The theorem just given enables one to know how many different quantum numbers there may be, by finding what operators commute with $\hat{H}$, and how many of them may be assigned values at one time, by finding a set which commute among each other. We shall see in Sec. 5.5, for example, that the operators representing the different components of the angular momentum $\mathbf{P}$ do not commute among each other. Thus it is possible to specify at most one of them; the others must be left indeterminate. This at once clarifies the paradox of Bohr's theory mentioned in Sec. 1.3, in which the component P_z, introduced in order to characterize an atom in a magnetic field parallel to the z axis, continues to play a special role even when the magnetic field is removed and any one direction seems as good as any other.

A set of dynamical variables represented by operators which commute among themselves, and which is maximal in the sense that no more dynamical variables can be found to enlarge the set, is called by Dirac a *complete set of commuting observables*. A state

---

[3] H. A. Kramers, *Quantum Mechanics*, Interscience Publishers, Inc., New York, 1957, p. 139, or E. Merzbacher, *Quantum Mechanics*, John Wiley & Sons, Inc., New York, 1961, p. 153.

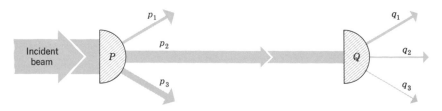

Fig. 5.5 Measurement of P followed by a measurement of Q.

specified by the eigenvalues of the corresponding set of operators is specified as completely as possible.

We can represent the content of the theorem on simultaneous observables by a diagram in the spirit of Fig. 5.2. Figure 5.5 shows a measurement of P giving the value p_2 and being followed by a measurement of Q. (P and Q are any two dynamical variables.) The beams issuing from the second instrument have definite values of Q; the question is whether they all still have the same value p_2. (For example, if measuring Q involves only a static magnetic field, it will change the momentum of an incident beam but not its energy.) The theorem implies that if $\hat{P}$ commutes with $\hat{Q}$, then the measurement of Q can be so carried out as to leave P unchanged. We have already referred to this possibility in Sec. 2.3.

The theorem finds its most important applications in systems in more than one dimension and, in particular, in systems composed of several particles. But even in very simple cases, if our idea of what kinds of operators to use is broad enough, it yields interesting and significant results.

5.4 Transformations as Dynamical Variables

It is intuitively clear that if we know that a dynamical system has certain symmetries, we already know a good deal about the way it will behave. The Hamilton-Jacobi theory of classical dynamics exploits this fact to simplify the solution of mechanical problems. To see how analogous simplifications can be made in quantum mechanics, let us look for a moment at how the idea of a dynamical system with symmetries can be expressed mathematically.

Let x represent all the coordinates of a system and let T represent a transformation which changes them to some different values, x_T. Thus in one dimension, T might represent a displacement D,

$$x_\mathrm{D} = x + l \tag{5.9}$$

or a reflection in the origin P,

$$x_\mathrm{P} = -x \tag{5.10}$$

and in two (or more) dimensions it might represent a rotation R in the xy plane

$$x_R = x \cos \vartheta - y \sin \vartheta$$
$$y_R = x \sin \vartheta + y \cos \vartheta$$

(5.11)

Applied to a scalar function $f(x)$, we define the transformation operator $\hat{T}$ by writing

$$\hat{T} f(x) = f(x_T)$$

(5.12)

[If $f(x)$ represents a vector, the operation of $\hat{T}$ is more complicated, since it involves in general a shuffling of the different components, as with the vector whose components are x and y in (5.11). We shall not need to consider this case.] Now suppose that the value of $f(x)$ is unchanged by this change of x. Then $f(x)$ is said to be *invariant*, or *symmetrical* with respect to the transformation. For example, if $f(x)$ depends only on x^2, then

$$\hat{P}f(x^2) = f(x_P{}^2) = f((-x)^2) = f(x^2)$$

and a graph of f is symmetrical with respect to right and left. Because symmetry of various sorts is of common occurrence in physics, this notion turns out to be very useful. Since it is supposed that a physical system is described by its hamiltonian $\hat{H}$, it is here that one normally looks for symmetries to occur. For example, for a free particle,

$$\hat{H}(x) = -\frac{\hbar^2}{2m} \frac{\partial^2}{\partial x^2}$$

and we readily see that $\hat{H}$ is symmetrical under D and P.

Suppose now that the hamiltonian is invariant under some T. For any function $f(x)$, we have, since $H(x_T) = H(x)$,

$$\hat{T}\hat{H}(x)f(x) = \hat{H}(x_T)f(x_T) = \hat{H}(x)f(x_T)$$
$$= \hat{H}(x) \hat{T} f(x)$$

and since $f(x)$ is arbitrary, we can express this as a relation between operators,

$$[\hat{H},\hat{T}] = 0$$

(5.13)

This equation has three different implications. First, it implies that $\hat{H}$ is invariant under the transformation T. Second, according to the last section, it means that all eigenfunctions ψ_i of $\hat{H}$ can be simultaneously eigenfunctions of $\hat{T}$, that is, they can be so chosen that

$$\hat{H}\psi_i = E_i\psi_i \quad \text{and} \quad \hat{T}\psi_i = t_i\psi_i$$

(5.14)

The integer which numbers the different values of E_i will be the energy quantum number; that which numbers the t_i will be some

other quantum number. Because there may be several different t's
for one value of E, and vice versa, these quantum numbers are not
in general the same, and a given state must be specified by giving
both of them. Third, according to (3.19) the relation (5.13) means
that if $\hat{T}$ does not contain the time variable explicitly (and these
are almost the only cases of interest), then in any state whatever the
expectation value of T is constant in time. We shall now give
some examples.

Finite displacements

The eigenfunctions of $\hat{D}$ satisfy

$$\hat{D}\psi(x) = \psi(x + l) = d\psi(x) \tag{5.15}$$

where d is the eigenvalue. A little thought shows that the most
general ψ satisfying this equation is of the form[4]

$$\psi(x) = e^{\alpha x}v(x) \tag{5.16}$$

where α is any complex number and $v(x)$ is periodic with period l:

$$v(x + l) = v(x) \tag{5.17}$$

This example is of great interest in the theory of the motion of
electrons in a crystalline material, either metal, insulator, or semiconductor; for here the field of force in which the electrons move,
and hence the hamiltonian which describes this motion, has regular
spatial periodicities. Let us consider a one-dimensional lattice in
the form of a closed loop that is N atoms in circumference. Unique-
ness of the wave function requires that

$$\psi(x + Nl) = \psi(x) \quad \text{or} \quad e^{\alpha(x+Nl)} = e^{\alpha x}$$

This is possible only if $e^{\alpha Nl} = 1$, or

$$\alpha = \frac{2\pi ni}{Nl} \qquad (n = 0, \pm 1, \pm 2, \ldots)$$

The possible wave functions in this case must have the form

$$\psi(x) = e^{2\pi nix/Nl}v(x) \tag{5.18}$$

and the corresponding eigenvalues of $\hat{D}$ are $e^{2\pi ni/N}$. Since there is an
infinite variety of choices for the periodic function $v(x)$, the eigenfunctions of $\hat{D}$ belonging to a given eigenvalue are infinitely degenerate. Equation (5.18) is a one-dimensional form of what is called
Bloch's theorem.[5] It forms the starting point for the study of electronic conduction in solids, as is shown in more detail in Chap. 13.

----

[4] This result is known as Floquet's theorem. See E. T. Whittaker and G. N.
Watson, *Modern Analysis*, 4th ed., Cambridge University Press, London, 1927,
sec. 19.4.

[5] F. Bloch, Z. Physik, **52**, 555 (1928).

Problem 5.7 Is $\hat{D}$ hermitian? Does it satisfy (3.33)?

Problem 5.8 Suppose that $[\hat{T},\hat{H}] = 0$ and that the eigenfunctions of $\hat{H}$ are doubly degenerate, whereas $\hat{T}$ is arbitrary. Are there simultaneous eigenfunctions of $\hat{H}$ and $\hat{T}$?

Solution.   Let ψ_1 and ψ_2 be two known eigenfunctions of $\hat{H}$, each belonging to the eigenvalue E. Then

$$\hat{H}\hat{T}\psi_1 = \hat{T}\hat{H}\psi_1 = \hat{T}E\psi_1 = E\hat{T}\psi_1$$

so that $\hat{T}\psi_1$ is an eigenfunction of $\hat{H}$ belonging to the eigenvalue E and must be some combination of ψ_1 and ψ_2, say,

$$\hat{T}\psi_1 = a\psi_1 + b\psi_2$$

and similarly,

$$\hat{T}\psi_2 = c\psi_1 + d\psi_2$$

We now wish to find a linear combination $\lambda\psi_1 + \mu\psi_2$ which is an eigenfunction of both $\hat{H}$ and $\hat{T}$. Clearly, any such combination is automatically an eigenfunction of $\hat{H}$. For it to be an eigenfunction of $\hat{T}$, we must have

$$\hat{T}(\lambda\psi_1 + \mu\psi_2) = t(\lambda\psi_1 + \mu\psi_2)$$

or

$$\lambda(a\psi_1 + b\psi_2) + \mu(c\psi_1 + d\psi_2) = t(\lambda\psi_1 + \mu\psi_2)$$

and this can be satisfied if the coefficients of ψ_1 and ψ_2 vanish separately:

$$(a - t)\lambda + c\mu = 0$$
$$b\lambda + (d - t)\mu = 0$$

These have solutions for λ and μ only if the determinant of the coefficients vanishes, and this gives an equation for t whose roots are

$$t = \tfrac{1}{2}\{a + d \pm [(a - d)^2 + 4bc]^{\frac{1}{2}}\}$$

If this is satisfied, values for λ and μ can readily be found. There are thus two eigenfunctions of $\hat{H}$ belonging to the eigenvalue E which are at the same time eigenvalues of $\hat{T}$, but they belong to two eigenvalues of $\hat{T}$ which in general are different. (It should be noted that $\hat{T}$ has not been assumed hermitian.)

Problem 5.9 A force-free particle moves in a one-dimensional region which is closed in a ring of length L (see Prob. 5.3). Two degenerate independent eigenfunctions of $\hat{H}$ are e^{ikx} and e^{-ikx}, with k suitably restricted, corresponding to particles moving in either direction around the loop. Using the results of the preceding problem, find simultaneous eigenfunctions of $\hat{H}$ and the reflection operator $\hat{P}$ and the corresponding eigenvalues of $\hat{P}$.

Infinitesimal displacements

If l is infinitesimal (we shall call it ε in this case), the operator $\hat{D}$ which changes $f(x)$ to $f(x + \varepsilon) = f(x) + \varepsilon\, \partial f(x)/\partial x$ can be represented as

$$\hat{D} = 1 + \varepsilon\frac{\partial}{\partial x} = 1 + \frac{i\varepsilon}{\hbar}\,\hat{p}_x$$

If now $\hat{H}(x)$ is invariant under such displacements, we have

$$[\hat{H},\hat{D}] = \left[\hat{H},\, 1 + \frac{i\varepsilon}{\hbar}\,\hat{p}_x \right] = 0$$

or

$$[\hat{H},\hat{p}_x] = 0 \tag{5.19}$$

whence we conclude the constancy of the momentum p_x in this case. This is quite natural, since $\hat{H}$ can be independent of x only if the potential energy V is independent of x, that is, if there is no force in that direction.

Problem 5.10 One of Hamilton's equations in classical dynamics states that if H is the hamiltonian function and p is the momentum corresponding to any coordinate q, then $dp/dt \doteq -\partial H/\partial q$. Discuss the form taken by this relation in quantum mechanics in the light of the example just given.

Reflection in the origin

If $\hat{H}(x)$ is an even function of x, then

$$[\hat{H},\hat{P}] = 0$$

where for any $f(x)$,

$$\hat{P}f(x) = f(-x)$$

The eigenfunctions ψ of $\hat{H}$ are therefore (or may be chosen to be) eigenfunctions of $\hat{P}$. To see what they are, let

$$\hat{P}\psi(x) = \psi(-x) = p\psi(x)$$

and

$$\hat{P}^2\psi(x) = \psi(+x) = p^2\psi(x)$$

Thus, $p^2 = 1$ and the only possible eigenvalues are

$$p = +1 \qquad \psi(-x) = \psi(x)$$
$$p = -1 \qquad \psi(-x) = -\psi(x)$$

Functions satisfying these conditions are called *even* and *odd*, respectively; all nondegenerate eigenfunctions of a symmetrical $\hat{H}$ must therefore be either even or odd. The reader should verify that the harmonic oscillator wave functions are, and should be, an example of this property.

Problem 5.11   Is $\hat{P}$ hermitian? Are its eigenfunctions belonging to different eigenvalues orthogonal?

Problem 5.12   Show that the WKB wave functions belonging to the bound states of a system described by a symmetrical hamiltonian are all either even or odd.

Time reversal

Let us look at the effect of interchanging i with $-i$ everywhere it occurs in quantum mechanics. This can be done by introducing an operator $\hat{K}$ which takes the complex conjugate: $\hat{K}f = f^*$ for any f. Since i does not appear in any of the final results of the theory, this change, which replaces ψ with ψ^* and $\hat{p}$ by $-\hat{p}$ but leaves x and $\hat{H}$ unchanged, yields a new form of quantum mechanics which is fully equivalent with the old. The new wave function, which we shall call ψ_K, satisfies the wave equation

$$-i\hbar\,\frac{\partial\psi_K}{\partial t} = \hat{H}\psi_K$$

which is the same as

$$i\hbar\,\frac{\partial\psi_K}{\partial t_K} = \hat{H}\psi_K \qquad t_K = -t \tag{5.20}$$

That is, if we replace ψ by ψ^* and simultaneously replace t by $-t$, we get back to the usual form of Schrödinger's equation. Thus the operation of $\hat{K}$ is equivalent to reversing the direction of the time variable in the usual theory. The fact that $\hat{H}$ is real, which makes it possible to derive (5.20), means that a system whose wave function is ψ_K behaves as the exact time-reversed image of that whose wave function is ψ; and both forms of behavior are physically possible. This is the expression of the well-known fact that to every possible process on the atomic scale (and therefore on any scale) there corresponds a process which is the exact reverse of the first and which, however improbable it may be owing to external circumstances, is also possible. Thus, an atom which absorbs a quantum and changes to a state of higher energy can change back again and re-emit an identical quantum. On the other hand, if a hot kettle placed on the ground cools off, a cool kettle placed on the ground could begin to boil. That it does not do so is an effect of statistics explained by the second law of thermodynamics (see Chap. 18).

Suppose that $\psi(t)$ is a solution of Schrödinger's equation which evolves from a specified initial state $\psi(0)$. The time-reversed image of this state, by (5.20), is $\psi_K(-t)$ or $\psi_K(t_K)$, and we shall choose ψ_K to be that solution of (5.20) which starts at $t_K = 0$ exactly equal to $\psi^*(0)$,

$$\psi_K(0) = \psi^*(0) \tag{5.21}$$

Suppose, for example, that the initial state is $\psi = e^{i(kx-\omega t)}$, describing a free particle moving toward the right. By (5.21), $\psi_{\mathrm{K}}(0) = e^{-ikx}$, and so

$$\psi_{\mathrm{K}}(t_{\mathrm{K}}) = e^{i(-kx-\omega t_{\mathrm{K}})}$$

Thus, the time-reversed picture represents the particle moving toward the left.

There is no point here in trying to imagine a system which "moves backward in time." We are talking, rather, of a reversed image. A motion picture is taken of the system in operation and it is run through backwards. This reversed image of the system's development is described by the coordinate t_{K}.

Let us now examine the behavior of an arbitrary hermitian operator $\hat{Q}$ in the time-reversed state at the instant $t = t_{\mathrm{K}} = 0$, which may, of course, be any instant.

$$\langle \hat{Q} \rangle_{\mathrm{K}} = \int \psi_{\mathrm{K}}^* \hat{Q} \psi_{\mathrm{K}} = \int \psi \hat{Q} \psi^*$$
$$= \int (\hat{Q}^* \psi)^* \cdot \psi = \int \psi^* \hat{Q}^* \psi$$

or

$$\langle \hat{Q} \rangle_{\mathrm{K}} = \langle \hat{Q}^* \rangle \qquad (5.22)$$

Thus linear and angular momenta, having factors of i, are reversed by time reversal, whereas real operators such as the hamiltonian are not. This fact lies at the bottom of the explicit occurrence of i in operators representing physical quantities which have to do with the flow of charge.

Problem 5.13 Discuss the eigenfunctions and eigenvalues of $\hat{\mathrm{K}}$. Is $\hat{\mathrm{K}}$ hermitian? Are its eigenfunctions degenerate?

Problem 5.14 Show that if ψ is an eigenfunction of $\hat{H}$, then ψ^* is also an eigenfunction. Give an example.

Problem 5.15 Find a formula analogous to (5.22) for the time derivative of $\langle \hat{Q} \rangle_{\mathrm{K}}$. Is the result reasonable?

Problem 5.16 Starting from the initial condition (5.21), what is the relation of ψ_{K} to ψ at values of t_{K} and t different from zero?

Problem 5.17 The operator $\hat{\mathrm{K}}$ is of quite a different kind from others we have discussed, since, for example, it does not commute with ordinary complex numbers. Is it governed by any of the theorems proved earlier in this chapter?

Transformed coordinates

When one writes down a transformation of coordinates such as (5.9), (5.10), or (5.11), there is always an ambiguity in its meaning. Mathematicians tend to regard it as the passage to a new description of the original system; physicists are generally more interested in a

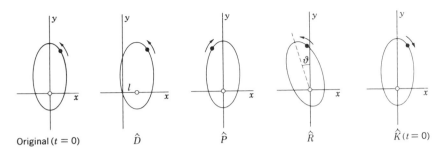

Fig. 5.6   An orbiting particle classically represented and its transforms under displacement in the x direction, reflection in the
y axis, rotation in the xy plane, and time reversal.

change in the physical system, still described in terms of the original
variables. Figure 5.6 shows a simple Newtonian system and its transformations considered as copies which are changed in different ways:
the second is displaced as a whole toward the right, the third is a
mirror image of the first, etc. Note that the coordinates x_D, x_P, x_R
have exactly the same meaning as the original x and that t_K is the
same thing as t; their numerical values differ from x and t only
because the systems they describe are different.[6]

Problem 5.18   Express the Newtonian principle of relativity
in words, symbols, and a diagram analogous to the diagrams used
here.[7]

It should by now be clear what is the principal importance of
these considerations in carrying out calculations in quantum
mechanics. It is that one is enabled to solve the central equation
$\hat{H}\psi = E\psi$ by stages, instead of having to do it all at once. For ψ
will be an eigenfunction of all the operators which commute with $\hat{H}$
and each other, and these will usually be of far simpler structure
than $\hat{H}$ itself. One can thus narrow down the possible choices for ψ
by requiring it first to be an eigenfunction of all the operators one
can find which commute with $\hat{H}$ and with each other before embark-
ing on the solution of the central equation. We shall make use of this
procedure several times in the rest of this book.

Problem 5.19   Discuss the part played by constants of the
motion in integrating the equations of *classical* dynamics. Show

[6] Very interesting applications of parity symmetry (invariance under $\hat{P}$)
are given by H. Zocher and C. Török, Proc. Natl. Acad. Sci. U.S., **39**, 681 (1953).
With regard to the importance of symmetry arguments in fundamental physics
the following articles may be read: P. Morrison, Am. J. Phys., **26**, 358 (1958);
D. Park, Am. J. Phys., **26**, 210, 349 (1958); T.-Y. Wu, Am. J. Phys., **26**, 568
(1958).

[7] The formulation of this principle in quantum mechanics is given in Appendix 3.

how the solution of the Kepler problem can be simplified by build-
ing into it the conservation of energy and angular momentum.
Discuss also the integration of the same problem by the use of
Hamilton's vectorial integral.[8]

Problem 5.20 Do all of the constants of the motion discussed
above have classical analogues?

5.5 Angular Momentum

The angular momentum plays an important part in the solution of
problems in the dynamics of particles and rigid bodies because in
many cases it satisfies a conservation law; this is the case either
when the system under discussion is isolated in space or when (as
with a planet) its external interaction is symmetrical about a fixed
point. We have already seen in Prob. 2.7 that the same is true in
quantum mechanics, but in quantum mechanics the fact gains
added significance because the possible values of the angular
momentum turn out to be restricted by a quantum principle; and
this, as in Bohr's theory, has a profound effect on the structure of
atomic (and nuclear) energy states.

In order to illustrate the techniques of this chapter, let us investigate the consequences of making a simple statement about a physical system: that its physical environment shows perfect spherical
symmetry. Since the dynamical specification of a system is supposed to lie in its hamiltonian function, we shall express this fact
mathematically by asserting that the hamiltonian operator describing the system is invariant under rotations of the coordinate axes.
Equation (5.11) defines what we can call $R_z(\vartheta)$, a rotation through
an angle ϑ about the z axis. If $\hat{H}$ is invariant under this transformation, then it commutes with the operator which performs this rota-
tion, as well as with those which rotate about the x and y axes.

Problem 5.21 Show, by carrying out the transformation
directly, that

$$\hat{H}(x,y,z,\hat{p}_x,\hat{p}_y,\hat{p}_z) = \hat{H}(x_R,y_R,z_R,\hat{p}_{xR},\hat{p}_{yR},\hat{p}_{zR})$$

where

$$\hat{p}_{xR} = \frac{\hbar}{i}\frac{\partial}{\partial x_R}, \text{ etc.}$$

Calculate $\hat{p}_{xR}$ and $\hat{p}_{yR}$ in terms of $\hat{p}_x$ and $\hat{p}_y$ and compare with (5.11).

It will be sufficient to consider only infinitesimal rotations,
that is, rotations for which the angle ϑ is some quantity ε whose

---

[8] E. A. Milne, *Vectorial Mechanics*, Methuen & Co., Ltd., London, 1948,
p. 268. See also E. Madelung, *Die Mathematischen Hilfsmittel des Physikers*,
Dover Publications, Inc., New York, 1943, appendix 9, where Hamilton's
integral is denoted by **a**.

square and higher powers can be neglected, since any finite rotation may be regarded as the result of a sequence of infinitesimal ones. Thus, (5.11) becomes

$$x_R = x - \varepsilon y \qquad y_R = \varepsilon x + y \tag{5.23}$$

and for an arbitrary function $f(x,y)$ we have

$$f(x_R, y_R) = f(x - \varepsilon y, y + \varepsilon x) = f(x,y) - \varepsilon y \frac{\partial f(x,y)}{\partial x} + \varepsilon x \frac{\partial f(x,y)}{\partial y}$$

$$= f(x,y) + \varepsilon \left(x \frac{\partial}{\partial y} - y \frac{\partial}{\partial x} \right) f(x,y)$$

plus terms of higher order in ε. The operator which performs the infinitesimal rotation about the z axis may be written as

$$\hat{R}_z = 1 + \frac{i}{\hbar} \varepsilon (x \hat{p}_y - y \hat{p}_x)$$

which with

$$\hat{P}_z = x \hat{p}_y - y \hat{p}_x \tag{5.24}$$

becomes

$$\hat{R}_z = 1 + \frac{i}{\hbar} \varepsilon \hat{P}_z \tag{5.25}$$

By hypothesis, $\hat{H}$ is invariant under the rotation R_z, and therefore, as in (5.13), it commutes with $\hat{R}_z$. Dropping the inessential terms, we therefore have

$$[\hat{H}, \hat{P}_z] = 0 \tag{5.26}$$

so that $\hat{P}_z$ emerges as the operator corresponding to some dynamical variable which is numerically a constant and which according to Sec. 5.3 may be exactly specified at the same time as the energy. We have now only to guess what the interpretation of this operator may be, that is, to see how it can be related to the ideas of Newtonian mechanics. This is very easy to do, for we expect from the latter that in the situation under discussion the angular momentum, defined vectorially by $\mathbf{P} = \mathbf{r} \times \mathbf{p}$, will be conserved, and now we see that the operator which we have invented from considerations of invariance is just the operator form of the z component of this vector. Clearly, then, we must call the operator

$$\hat{\mathbf{P}} = \mathbf{r} \times \hat{\mathbf{p}} \tag{5.27}$$

the *angular-momentum operator*.

Problem 5.22 The foregoing considerations have been expressed in terms of the x picture. Is it valid to write $\hat{\mathbf{P}} = \hat{\mathbf{r}} \times \mathbf{p}$ in the p picture?

In the solution of problems in classical dynamics, the constancy of all three components of **P** is an important fact. In quantum mechanics the situation is somewhat similar, in that $\langle P_x \rangle$, $\langle P_y \rangle$, and $\langle P_z \rangle$ are all constant, but there is here the new feature that no two components of the operator commute with each other. Since the dimensions of Planck's constant are those of angular momentum, we shall economize writing by introducing a dimensionless operator $\hat{\mathbf{L}}$ such that

$$\hat{\mathbf{P}} = \hbar\hat{\mathbf{L}} \tag{5.28}$$

and in terms of $\hat{\mathbf{L}}$ the commutation relations among the different components of angular momentum may be written as

$$[\hat{L}_x, \hat{L}_y] = i\hat{L}_z \tag{5.29a}$$
$$[\hat{L}_y, \hat{L}_z] = i\hat{L}_x \tag{5.29b}$$
$$[\hat{L}_z, \hat{L}_x] = i\hat{L}_y \tag{5.29c}$$

in which the cyclic arrangement of the indices in the order

$$(.\,.\,.\ yzxyzxyzx\ .\,.\,.)$$

should be noted and remembered. This means that if we assign a definite value to one component (usually chosen as $\hat{L}_z$), we cannot do so for the others. But at the same time they are not completely indeterminate, because it can be shown that each component of $\hat{\mathbf{L}}$ also commutes with the operator representing the square of $\hat{\mathbf{L}}$,

$$[\hat{L}_i, \hat{L}^2] = 0 \qquad (i = x,y,z) \tag{5.30}$$

where

$$\hat{L}^2 = \hat{L}_x{}^2 + \hat{L}_y{}^2 + \hat{L}_z{}^2$$

One can therefore specify simultaneously the exact values of H, L^2, and one component of **L**.

Problem 5.23   Derive the relations (5.29).

Problem 5.24   Show that $[\hat{H}, \hat{L}^2] = 0$.

Problem 5.25   Prove Eq. (5.30). [The relations (3.24) to (3.28) will be invaluable in carrying out these calculations.]

Problem 5.26   Prove that any function $f(r)$ involving only $r = (x^2 + y^2 + z^2)^{1/2}$ is an eigenfunction of $\hat{L}_z$ and $\hat{L}^2$ with eigenvalue zero in each case and that any function $g(z,r)$ is an eigenfunction of $\hat{L}_z$ with eigenvalue zero.

Simple precession

To obtain some idea of the dynamical content of the relations (5.29), let us look at the equation of motion of a spherically symmetrical one-particle system immersed in a magnetic field, assuming that the system has a (vectorial) magnetic moment proportional to its angular momentum,

$$\hat{\mathbf{M}} = \gamma \hat{\mathbf{P}}$$

where γ is called the *gyromagnetic ratio*. The energy of a magnet in a field $\mathbf{B}$ is given by $-\mathbf{M} \cdot \mathbf{B}$, so that we would expect the total hamiltonian of the system to be given by[9]

$$\hat{H} = \hat{H}_0 - \gamma \mathbf{B} \cdot \hat{\mathbf{P}}$$

where $\hat{H}_0$ is the spherically symmetrical hamiltonian function including the particle's kinetic and potential energies which we have denoted by $\hat{H}$ heretofore. The equation of motion for the expectation value of $\hat{\mathbf{P}}$ is

$$\frac{\partial}{\partial t} \langle \hat{\mathbf{P}} \rangle = \frac{i}{\hbar} \langle [\hat{H}, \hat{\mathbf{P}}] \rangle$$

$$= -\frac{i\gamma}{\hbar} \langle [\mathbf{B} \cdot \hat{\mathbf{P}}, \hat{\mathbf{P}}] \rangle$$

since, as in (5.26), $\hat{H}_0$ commutes with $\hat{\mathbf{P}}$. Evaluating the commutators gives a set of relations which may be written as

$$\frac{\partial}{\partial t} \langle \hat{\mathbf{P}} \rangle = -\gamma \mathbf{B} \times \langle \hat{\mathbf{P}} \rangle \qquad (5.31)$$

The equation describes a precessional motion of the vector $\langle \hat{\mathbf{P}} \rangle$ about the direction of the field $\mathbf{B}$. To see that this is so, we note first that the magnitude of $\langle \hat{\mathbf{P}} \rangle$ remains constant,

$$\frac{\partial}{\partial t} (\langle \hat{\mathbf{P}} \rangle)^2 = 2\langle \hat{\mathbf{P}} \rangle \cdot \frac{\partial}{\partial t} \langle \hat{\mathbf{P}} \rangle = 0$$

Thus the motion of the vector is a rotation. The particular kind of rotation is illustrated in Fig. 5.7, which shows the change of a vector precessing rigidly about an axis with an angular velocity ω. Comparison with (5.31) shows that

$$\omega = -\gamma \mathbf{B}$$

The magnitude of ω is called the Larmor precessional frequency, and the result which we have just proved is an example of the more general phenomenon of Larmor precession.

Problem 5.27 Derive the equations of motion (5.31) and prove that $\frac{\partial}{\partial t} (\mathbf{B} \cdot \langle \mathbf{P} \rangle) = 0$. What does this relation imply?

---

[9] We shall see in Sec. 6.6 that this form of hamiltonian is correct, with $\gamma = e/2m$, if B is not too large.

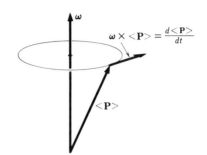

Fig. 5.7 Precession of angular momentum.

Problem 5.28 Derive the classical analogue of (5.31) for an electron moving subject to an arbitrary central force and a static magnetic field, and show that the classical value of γ is $e/2m$.

Larmor's theorem

In classical mechanics, the equation of motion for a particle subject to an arbitrary force $\mathbf{F}$ and a uniform magnetic field $\mathbf{B}$ is

$$m\ddot{\mathbf{r}} = \mathbf{F} + e\dot{\mathbf{r}} \times \mathbf{B}$$

If $\mathbf{B}$ is parallel to the z axis, this is

$$m\ddot{x} = F_x + eB\dot{y} \qquad m\ddot{y} = F_y - eB\dot{x} \qquad m\ddot{z} = F_z$$

Let us transform these equations to a new set of axes x' and y', rotating clockwise with respect to x and y with angular velocity ω,

$$x' = x \cos \omega t - y \sin \omega t$$
$$y' = x \sin \omega t + y \cos \omega t$$
$$z' = z$$

From the first of these we find

$$\ddot{x}' = \ddot{x} \cos \omega t - \ddot{y} \sin \omega t - 2\omega\dot{x} \sin \omega t - 2\omega\dot{y} \cos \omega t$$

plus terms in ω^2 which we shall neglect. Let us consider the instant $t = 0$ at which the two sets of axes momentarily coincide: $x' = x$, etc., so that $F_{x'} = F_x$, etc.,

$$\ddot{x}' = \ddot{x} - 2\omega\dot{y}$$

and similarly,

$$\ddot{y}' = \ddot{y} + 2\omega\dot{x} \qquad \ddot{z}' = \ddot{z}$$

In the rotating system, the equations of motion become

$$m\ddot{x}' = F_{x'} + eB\dot{y} - 2m\omega\dot{y}$$
$$m\ddot{y}' = F_{y'} - eB\dot{x} + 2m\omega\dot{x}$$
$$m\ddot{z}' = F_{z'}$$

If we choose $\omega = eB/2m$, the effects of B and ω cancel, and we are left only with the effects of $\mathbf{F}$ and of terms in ω^2 representing centripetal actions which we can neglect for small B. To this approximation, the system in the field B behaves the same as one without B except that it rotates clockwise with angular velocity ω. This is Larmor's theorem.[10] Since the value of γ calculated from classical mechanics (Prob. 5.28) is $e/2m$, we see that the Larmor precessional frequency can be written as γB.

5.6 The Eigenvalues of $\hat{L}_z$ and $\hat{L}^2$

The most direct way to determine the allowed values of $\hat{L}_z$ and $\hat{L}^2$ is to proceed in analogy with the discussion of the simple harmonic oscillator in Sec. 4.10, where we constructed operators designed to raise and lower the eigenvalues of the hamiltonian. In this case we shall assume that we have an eigenfunction ψ_m such that

$$\hat{L}_z\psi_m = m\psi_m \tag{5.32}$$

(where m will turn out to be the usual azimuthal quantum number) and try to find an operator $\hat{\Omega}$ which will produce a ψ corresponding to a different value of m. That is, we wish to satisfy a relation of the form

$$\hat{L}_z\hat{\Omega}\psi_m = (m + \lambda)\hat{\Omega}\psi_m \tag{5.33}$$

Multiplying (5.32) by $\hat{\Omega}$ and subtracting it from (5.33) gives

$$[\hat{L}_z,\hat{\Omega}]\psi_m = \lambda\hat{\Omega}\psi_m$$

for any m, and so we must require that $\hat{\Omega}$ and λ satisfy the operator equation

$$[\hat{L}_z,\hat{\Omega}] = \lambda\hat{\Omega} \tag{5.34}$$

The operator $\hat{\Omega}$ can be constructed using only L_x and L_y. Choosing for convenience the coefficient of L_x to be unity, we write

$$\hat{\Omega} = \hat{L}_x + \alpha\hat{L}_y$$

so that (5.34) and (5.29) give

$$i\hat{L}_y - i\alpha\hat{L}_x = \lambda(\hat{L}_x + \alpha\hat{L}_y)$$

from which, by matching the coefficients of $\hat{L}_x$ and $\hat{L}_y$, we get

$$-i\alpha = \lambda \qquad i = \lambda\alpha$$

These are compatible when $\lambda = \pm 1$, and we find

$$\lambda = +1: \quad \alpha = +i \qquad \hat{\Omega} = \hat{L}_x + i\hat{L}_y$$
$$\lambda = -1: \quad \alpha = -i \qquad \hat{\Omega} = \hat{L}_x - i\hat{L}_y$$

---

[10] For an interesting special case, see A. P. French, *Principles of Modern Physics*, John Wiley & Sons, Inc., New York, 1958, appendix II.

To distinguish these shift operators, we shall denote them as $\hat{L}_+$ and $\hat{L}_-$:

$$\hat{L}_\pm = \hat{L}_x \pm i\hat{L}_y \qquad (5.35)$$

and (5.33) now reads

$$\hat{L}_z\hat{L}_+\psi_m = (m+1)\hat{L}_+\psi_m \qquad \hat{L}_z\hat{L}_-\psi_m = (m-1)\hat{L}_-\psi_m \qquad (5.36)$$

so that, except for normalization,

$$\hat{L}_+\psi_m = \psi_{m+1} \qquad \hat{L}_-\psi_m = \psi_{m-1} \qquad (5.37)$$

By repeating this process, we can arrive at a whole series of ψ's corresponding to different values of m at unit intervals from the original one. But, remembering that ψ_m may also be chosen to be an eigenfunction of $\hat{L}^2$, let us now ask how the eigenvalue of $\hat{L}^2$ is changed by this process. If

$$\hat{L}^2\psi_m = K^2\psi_m$$

we have

$$\hat{L}^2\hat{L}_\pm\psi_m = \hat{L}_\pm\hat{L}^2\psi_m = K^2\hat{L}_\pm\psi_m$$

so that $\hat{L}_\pm\psi_m$ belongs to the same eigenvalue of $\hat{L}^2$ as did ψ_m.

Problem 5.29 Fill in the details of the last step.

We are thus led to a seeming contradiction; for it appears that without changing the length of a vector, one can increase its z component without limit! That the contradiction is a real one is seen from the fact that

$$\langle L^2 \rangle = \langle L_x^2 \rangle + \langle L_y^2 \rangle + \langle L_z^2 \rangle$$

and evaluating the expectation values in the state ψ_m gives

$$K^2 = \langle L_x^2 \rangle + \langle L_y^2 \rangle + m^2 \geqslant m^2$$

by (3.35), since each component of $\hat{\mathbf{L}}$ is a hermitian operator. Therefore, for a given value of K^2, m must be bounded above and below; and from this we conclude, as with the harmonic oscillator, that the ladder process must fail, so there must exist a ψ_{max} and a ψ_{min} such that

$$\hat{L}_z\psi_{max} = m_{max}\psi_{max} \qquad \hat{L}_+\psi_{max} = 0 \qquad (5.38a)$$
$$\hat{L}_z\psi_{min} = m_{min}\psi_{min} \qquad \hat{L}_-\psi_{min} = 0 \qquad (5.38b)$$

To specify further the states ψ_{max} and ψ_{min}, let us calculate the corresponding values of K^2, which are, of course, equal. Using the identities

$$\hat{L}_-\hat{L}_+ = \hat{L}^2 - \hat{L}_z^2 - \hat{L}_z \qquad (5.39a)$$
$$\hat{L}_+\hat{L}_- = \hat{L}^2 - \hat{L}_z^2 + \hat{L}_z \qquad (5.39b)$$

we see that, from (5.38a) and (5.39a)

$$\hat{L}^2\psi_{max} = K^2\psi_{max} = (\hat{L}_-\hat{L}_+ + \hat{L}_z^2 + \hat{L}_z)\psi_{max}$$
$$= m_{max}(m_{max} + 1)\psi_{max}$$

and similarly,

$$\hat{L}^2\psi_{min} = K^2\psi_{min} = m_{min}(m_{min} - 1)\psi_{min}$$

and these are compatible only if $m_{min} = -m_{max}$. Denoting m_{max} by the letter l, as is customary in spectroscopy, we see by (5.36) that the possible values of m go in integer steps from $-l$ to $+l$ and that $K^2 = l(l+1)$. We have seen in Prob. 5.26 that it is possible to construct eigenfunctions of $\hat{L}_z$ with eigenvalue zero. This suggests that zero will be one of a chain of eigenvalues going from $-l$ to $+l$, and we can summarize the foregoing results by stating that there exists a set of ψ's, which we shall call ψ_{lm}, such that

$$\hat{L}^2\psi_{lm} = l(l+1)\psi_{lm} \tag{5.40}$$

and

$$\hat{L}_z\psi_{lm} = m\psi_{lm} \tag{5.41}$$

where

$$m = -l, -l+1, \ldots, -1, 0, 1, \ldots, l-1, l \tag{5.42}$$

taking on $(2l+1)$ values in all.

In situations involving spinning electrons, zero may not be a possible eigenvalue for m. There is one other possibility: that l is half an odd integer and

$$m = -l, -l+1, \ldots, -\tfrac{3}{2}, -\tfrac{1}{2}, \tfrac{1}{2}, \tfrac{3}{2}, \ldots, l-1, l \tag{5.43}$$

We shall come back to this case in the next chapter.

Let us compare the foregoing results with the assumptions of Bohr's theory mentioned in Sec. 1.3. We see that (5.41) is in fact just the same as (1.17). We see also that the situation may be represented by a vector diagram similar to Fig. 1.2 but not exactly the same, since an L vector pointing straight up or down has its x and y components exactly zero and its z component of definite size, in conflict with our previous result that they cannot all be determined simultaneously. The situation is explained by the fact that, by (5.40), the L vector is of length $[l(l+1)]^{\frac{1}{2}}$, a little longer than l, so that the vector diagram must look as in Fig. 5.8, drawn for $l = 2$, with the position of the vector on each of its circles unspecified.

In Sec. 1.3 it was pointed out how the peculiar role of the z axis in spatial quantization is something of a puzzle; we see here what the answer is: the single component of **L** which one chooses to take on a definite value is in fact distinguished from the others by this choice, even though in the absence of external forces the choice may be made arbitrarily.

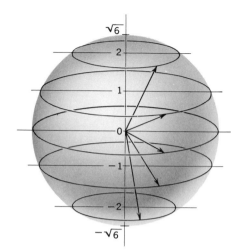

Fig. 5.8   Quantum-mechanical revision of Fig.
1.2, showing the possible orientations
of an angular-momentum vector
corresponding to $l = 2$.

It is quite possible to go on and construct the normalized eigen-functions of $\hat{L}^2$ and $\hat{L}_z$ as was done in Chap. 4 for the harmonic oscillator, but for computational purposes it is more convenient to go over to polar coordinates, and this will be done in Appendix 4.

Problem 5.30   If ψ_m in (5.37) is normalized, ψ_{m+1} and ψ_{m-1} will not be. What normalizing constants should be inserted? That is, writing

$$\hat{L}_\pm \psi_{l,m} = N_{l,m}^{(\pm)} \psi_{l,m\pm 1}$$

with both $\psi_{l,m}$ and $\psi_{l,m\pm 1}$ normalized, what are the constants $N_{l,m}^{(\pm)}$? The general approach leading to (4.122) will be useful here.

Answer. $N_{l,m}^{(+)} = [(l - m)(l + m + 1)]^{1/2}$ (5.44)

$\qquad\quad N_{l,m}^{(-)} = [(l + m)(l - m + 1)]^{1/2}$ (5.45)

6

The Spinning Electron

Except for effects of indeterminacy arising from the fact that the various components of $\hat{\mathbf{L}}$ do not commute among themselves, the results of the quantum theory of angular momentum can at least qualitatively be understood from an acquaintance with the classical theory. This is hardly true of the phenomenon of spin. The angular-momentum quantum numbers here take their smallest values, and so the theory is as far as possible from its approach to classical physics via the correspondence theory. The subject is also of great interest in the study of elementary particles; and though it is a somewhat narrow one, we shall here devote a chapter to it, paying particular attention to correspondences with classical theory, in order to give the reader some mathematical practice and to help sharpen his quantum-mechanical sense of reality.

6.1 The Phenomenon of Spin

The principles of quantum mechanics as we have developed them thus far account qualitatively for a host of atomic phenomena, but the facts, as we know, require that the electron be endowed with a new property, "a peculiar kind of double-valuedness, not describable in classical terms,"[1] whose existence Pauli inferred from his failure to explain the Zeeman effect of even simple atomic spectra

---

[1] "Die Dublettstruktur der Alkalispektren, sowie die Durchbrechung des Larmortheorems kommt gemäss diesen Standpunkt durch eine eigentumliche, klassisch nicht beschreibbare Art von Zweideutigkeit der quantentheoretischen Eigenschaften des Leuchtelektrons zustande." W. Pauli, Z. Physik, **31**, 373 (1925).

by Bohr's theory. Earlier, Compton had argued qualitatively from the anomalous gyromagnetic ratios and other properties of ferromagnetic materials that the electron must possess a significant magnetic moment,[2] and in 1925, shortly after the paper containing Pauli's remark, Goudsmit and Uhlenbeck[3] gave a simple physical model which included Compton's magnetic moment and Pauli's double-valuedness by proposing that the electron rotates about its axis with an invariable angular momentum of $\frac{1}{2}\hbar$. According to (5.43) there should be only two possible orientations for this vector. The electron was further endowed with a gyromagnetic ratio of e/m, double the value associated with orbital motion,[4] so that its magnetic moment is $e\hbar/2m$. This anomalous value was required in order to explain the doublet spectral lines of the alkali metals, which were imagined to originate in the two possible orientations of the spin of an orbiting electron. This mechanical model has been immensely successful in explaining atomic spectra, and in particular their Zeeman effects, but it tends to suggest to the mind notions such as the electron's diameter, structure, moment of inertia, and angular velocity which have no place in the theory as worked out below and for which the explanation of experiments shows no need. The reader may finally find that Pauli's cautious characterization will enlighten him as much as the mechanical model.

The main ideas of the sections on hermitian operators are very well exemplified in the theory of the spinning electron, and the mathematics is in this case so simple that most of the purely computational difficulties disappear. The theory is a direct generalization of that of orbital angular momentum developed in the preceding sections.[5] There we wrote down an operator $\hat{\mathbf{P}} = \hbar\hat{\mathbf{L}}$ in (5.28) and found that $\hat{\mathbf{L}}$ satisfies the commutation relations (5.29). The rest of the argument was based entirely on the commutation relations and not at all on the formula (5.27), and we found in (5.42) and (5.43) that there are two non-overlapping sets of eigenvalues possible for $\hat{L}_z$. The possible values of orbital angular momentum are comprised in the first set. We shall now look at the second.

We shall say that a set of three operators represents an angular momentum if it satisfies (5.29) and in addition transforms like a

[2] A. H. Compton, J. Franklin Inst., **192**, 144 (1921).

[3] Naturwiss., **13**, 953 (1925); Nature, **127**, 264 (1926). The same model occurred earlier in unpublished work by Kronig. See R. Kronig in the Pauli memorial volume, *Theoretical Physics in the Twentieth Century*, Interscience Publishers, Inc., New York, 1960, for the history of the idea of spin.

[4] This anomalous value, at first postulated from experiment by Goudsmit and Uhlenbeck, is justified by the theory of relativity, either on classical grounds as a result of the Thomas precession (Ruark and Urey, *Atoms, Molecules and Quanta*, McGraw-Hill Book Company, Inc., New York, 1932) or, in quantum mechanics, by the completely relativistic theory of Dirac, of which it is an immediate consequence.

[5] W. Pauli, Z. Physik, **43**, 601 (1927).

vector [that is, like the pair (x,y) in (5.11) under a rotation of the coordinate system]. The emphasis here is on the relations between the operators rather than on the operators themselves. If one can write down explicitly a set of operators which satisfy a certain set of rules, these operators are said to form a *realization* of the set of rules; (5.27) representing an orbital angular momentum, is (except for a factor of $\hbar$) a realization of the commutation rules (5.29), but it is not the only one. (For example, a representation in terms of matrices is possible and is to be found in almost any detailed text on quantum mechanics.)

In order to describe the spin, we shall introduce operators $\hat{\mathbf{S}}$ which satisfy

$$[\hat{S}_x,\hat{S}_y] = i\hat{S}_z$$
$$[\hat{S}_y,\hat{S}_z] = i\hat{S}_x \tag{6.1}$$
$$[\hat{S}_z,\hat{S}_x] = i\hat{S}_y$$

and eigenfunctions χ such that

$$\hat{S}_z\chi = m_s\chi \tag{6.2}$$

and

$$\hat{S}^2\chi = s(s + 1)\chi \tag{6.3}$$

Spectra and the evidence of the Stern-Gerlach experiment show that m_s takes only two values. By (5.43), they must be $\pm\frac{1}{2}$, so that $s = \frac{1}{2}$ and we have only two different spin eigenfunctions, which we shall call χ_+ and χ_-, with

$$\hat{S}_z\chi_+ = \frac{1}{2}\chi_+ \qquad \hat{S}_z\chi_- = -\frac{1}{2}\chi_- \qquad \hat{S}^2\chi_\pm = \frac{3}{4}\chi_\pm \tag{6.4}$$

Further, we have relations between χ_+ and χ_-, since as in (5.37) and (5.38)

$$(\hat{S}_x - i\hat{S}_y)\chi_+ = \chi_- \qquad (\hat{S}_x + i\hat{S}_y)\chi_- = \chi_+$$
$$(\hat{S}_x + i\hat{S}_y)\chi_+ = 0 \qquad (\hat{S}_x - i\hat{S}_y)\chi_- = 0 \tag{6.5}$$

where the factors $N^{(\pm)}_{\frac{1}{2},\pm\frac{1}{2}}$ introduced in Prob. 5.30 both turn out equal to 1. From these we can fill out a multiplication table which tells the result of operating on either χ with any component of $\hat{\mathbf{S}}$. Including (6.4) we have

$$\hat{S}_x\chi_+ = \frac{1}{2}\chi_- \qquad \hat{S}_x\chi_- = \frac{1}{2}\chi_+$$
$$\hat{S}_y\chi_+ = \frac{1}{2}i\chi_- \qquad \hat{S}_y\chi_- = -\frac{1}{2}i\chi_+ \tag{6.6}$$
$$\hat{S}_z\chi_+ = \frac{1}{2}\chi_+ \qquad \hat{S}_z\chi_- = -\frac{1}{2}\chi_-$$

This table itself forms a realization of $\hat{\mathbf{S}}$, since it tells exactly what each component of $\hat{\mathbf{S}}$ does to each kind of spin function. It is customary, and very useful, to express this realization in terms of matrices, but for our purposes they are quite unnecessary, and it seems best to omit them.[6]

Problem 6.1   The assignment (6.5) is actually a special case. Show that the top two equations could as well have been written

$$(\hat{S}_x - i\hat{S}_y)\chi_+ = e^{i\lambda_+}\chi_- \qquad (\hat{S}_x + i\hat{S}_y)\chi_- = e^{i\lambda_-}\chi_+$$

where λ_+ and λ_- are phases. Can λ_+ and λ_- be chosen arbitrarily? (That is, are these two equations automatically consistent with each other?)

We must now investigate how to handle questions of hermiticity, normalization, and expectation value in this case where a realization in conventional analytical terms is lacking. The clue to how to proceed is that there are only two different eigenfunctions, χ_+ and χ_-, instead of the infinite variety usually encountered. Thus an arbitrary spin function χ may be expressed in the manner of (5.3) as

$$\chi = a_+\chi_+ + a_-\chi_- \tag{6.7}$$

We further *define* the process which we have previously denoted by the sign $\int$ by the four relations

$$\int\chi_+^*\chi_+ = \int\chi_-^*\chi_- = 1 \qquad \int\chi_+^*\chi_- = \int\chi_-^*\chi_+ = 0 \tag{6.8}$$

Thus for example, the normalization of χ in (6.7) requires that

$$\int\chi^*\chi = \int(a_+^*\chi_+^* + a_-^*\chi_-^*)(a_+\chi_+ + a_-\chi_-)$$
$$= |a_+|^2 + |a_-|^2 = 1 \tag{6.9}$$

According to the general principles of quantum mechanics, $|a_+|^2$ and $|a_-|^2$ represent the probabilities of finding a spin respectively up or down, and (6.9), which is analogous to (5.5), implies merely that it must be one or the other.

We can also use the relations (6.8) to find the a's in (6.7) exactly as in (5.4),

$$a_+ = \int\chi_+^*\chi \qquad a_- = \int\chi_-^*\chi \tag{6.10}$$

These relations are merely identities, however, since we have not defined any "integrals" save those listed in (6.8), and χ must therefore be given in the form (6.7).

Problem 6.2   Verify that hermiticity can still be expressed in the usual way (3.33). That is, show that

$$\int(\hat{S}_i\chi)^* \cdot \varphi = \int\chi^*\hat{S}_i\varphi \qquad (i = x, y, z)$$

where χ and φ are two arbitrary spin functions expressed as in (6.7).

---

[6] The interested reader will find a very clear introduction to matrices in V. Rojansky, *Introductory Quantum Mechanics*, Prentice-Hall, Inc., Englewood Cliffs, N.J., 1938, where the theory of spin also is presented in matrix form.

Geometrical interpretation

Equation (6.7) above represents the spin state of a particle in a convenient and economical way, but it has little to do with one's intuitive idea of spin as a vector which points in a particular direction. This vector is represented quantum-mechanically by the operator whose components are $\hat{S}_x$, $\hat{S}_y$, and $\hat{S}_z$, operating on the function χ which describes the spin state. Further, we have seen in (5.31), which by its derivation is immediately applicable here, that the vector $\langle \mathbf{S} \rangle$ will gyrate in an external field in a way which answers to our intuitive notion of a spin. Note that (5.31), referring only to averages, says nothing about how "the spin has to point either up or down"; the latter statement applies to the result of an individual spin determination on an individual electron, which is quite different. The thing which is missing in our two characterizations of spin, one in terms of $a_\pm$ and the other in terms of $\langle \mathbf{S} \rangle$, is the point of contact between them, but this can readily be found if we resort to a slightly artificial strategem. If a_+ and a_- are restricted only by the normalization relation (6.9), then they can have an arbitrary phase, which we shall call δ, and an arbitrary relative phase, which we shall call φ. Thus we can write

$$a_+ = e^{i\delta} \cos \tfrac{1}{2}\vartheta \qquad a_- = e^{i(\delta+\varphi)} \sin \tfrac{1}{2}\vartheta \tag{6.11}$$

(the reason for the $\tfrac{1}{2}$ will be clear in a moment) where δ, φ, and ϑ are arbitrary real parameters. Now let us calculate the expectation values of the components of $\mathbf{S}$. We find

$$\langle S_x \rangle = \tfrac{1}{2} \sin \vartheta \cos \varphi$$
$$\langle S_y \rangle = \tfrac{1}{2} \sin \vartheta \sin \varphi \tag{6.12}$$
$$\langle S_z \rangle = \tfrac{1}{2} \cos \vartheta$$

and we see that the parameters ϑ and φ have an immediate physical interpretation as the polar angles giving the direction of $\langle \mathbf{S} \rangle$, Fig. 6.1. The disappearance of the third parameter, δ, reflects the fact that the absolute phase of a wave function is unobservable.

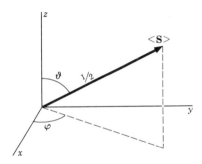

Fig. 6.1 Geometrical interpretation
of spin parameters.

Problem 6.3   Derive Eqs. (6.12).

We see also that a_+ and a_- contain more information than just the relative probabilities of finding that the spin points "up" or "down." These probabilities are contained in the absolute magnitudes of a_+ and a_-; their relative phase enables one to specify the statistical results of measurements to tell whether the spin is toward the right or the left, back or front.

6.2   Spin in a Constant Magnetic Field

We have already mentioned that for an electron in a magnetic field the vector representing the expectation value of **S** moves according to the classical formula

$$\frac{d}{dt} \langle \mathbf{S} \rangle = -\gamma \mathbf{B} \times \langle \mathbf{S} \rangle \tag{6.13}$$

where

$$\gamma = \frac{e}{m} \tag{6.14}$$

In this section we shall carry out analogous calculations quantum-mechanically. We shall first find the stationary states of a spin of $\frac{1}{2}$ in a constant magnetic field, and we shall then solve the time-dependent Schrödinger equation to find how a spin behaves if it is immersed in a constant magnetic field with an arbitrary initial state. The result will be a spin function which is a linear combination of the spin eigenfunctions with varying coefficients. In the next section we shall study the situation when the applied field is a function of time. The spin to be studied may be thought of as belonging to an atom, such as a sodium atom in its ground state. Here the closed shells, whose orbital and spin angular momenta and magnetic moments add up to zero, are orbited by a single electron in an *s* state. This electron has no orbital magnetic moment, and all its magnetic properties reside in its spin. The situation in which the magnetic moment comes from more than one spin, or from orbital motion as well as spin, will be discussed briefly in Secs. 6.4 and 6.5.

The spin may also be thought of as belonging to a free electron in a beam of electrons. Although this picture is simple and satisfactory for many purposes, it is to some extent an idealization, since it cannot be discussed in terms of the conventional procedure for making measurements in microphysics in which one analyzes the beam into physically separated components having different values of the spin and measures the counting rate for each component. It turns out that the uncertainty principle makes it impossible to perform this separation if the particles in the beam are as light as electrons.[7] This is one of the ways in which the spin of an

[7] N. F. Mott and H. S. W. Massey, *The Theory of Atomic Collisions*, 2d ed., Clarendon Press, Oxford, 1949, chap. 4.

electron is "classically undescribable." (On the other hand, it is possible to polarize a beam of electrons partially by scattering it from a suitable target and to measure its polarization by scattering from a second target.)

Stationary states

Let us suppose for generality that the applied magnetic field **B** is arbitrary in direction. The equation to be solved is

$$\hat{H}\chi = E\chi \tag{6.15}$$

where $\hat{H}$ is the potential energy of a magnet of moment $\mathbf{M} = \gamma\hbar\mathbf{S}$,

$$\hat{H} = -\gamma\hbar\mathbf{B}\cdot\hat{\mathbf{S}} \tag{6.16}$$

As we have seen, the situation here is simpler than usual in quantum mechanics in that there are only two possible basic eigenfunctions, χ_+ and χ_-, in terms of which any arbitrary χ may be written as in (6.7). Writing everything out in longhand gives

$$-\gamma\hbar(B_x\hat{S}_x + B_y\hat{S}_y + B_z\hat{S}_z)(a_+\chi_+ + a_-\chi_-) = E(a_+\chi_+ + a_-\chi_-)$$

the left-hand side of which can be evaluated by means of (6.6) in terms of χ_+ and χ_-. This gives

$$[Ea_+ + \tfrac{1}{2}\gamma\hbar(B_x - iB_y)a_- + \tfrac{1}{2}\gamma\hbar B_z a_+]\chi_+$$
$$+ [Ea_- + \tfrac{1}{2}\gamma\hbar(B_x + iB_y)a_- - \tfrac{1}{2}\gamma\hbar B_z a_-]\chi_- = 0$$

The coefficients of χ_+ and χ_- must equal zero separately (why?) so that

$$(E + \tfrac{1}{2}\gamma\hbar B_z)a_+ + \tfrac{1}{2}\gamma\hbar(B_x - iB_y)a_- = 0$$
$$\tfrac{1}{2}\gamma\hbar(B_x + iB_y)a_+ + (E - \tfrac{1}{2}\gamma\hbar B_z)a_- = 0$$

For these to be consistent, their determinant must vanish; and this condition on E leads at once to two solutions:

$$E = \pm\tfrac{1}{2}\gamma\hbar B \tag{6.17}$$

These correspond to two possible orientations of the spin, and we must now see what they are. Let us use polar coordinates, with

$$B_x = B\sin\vartheta\cos\varphi \qquad B_y = B\sin\vartheta\sin\varphi \qquad B_z = B\cos\varphi$$

Returning to the first of the equations for a_+ and a_-, we find

$$\frac{a_+}{a_-} = -\frac{B_x - iB_y}{\pm B + B_z} = -\frac{\sin\vartheta e^{-i\varphi}}{\pm 1 + \cos\vartheta}$$

Using trigonometry and putting the phase factor into the denominator gives

$$\frac{a_+}{a_-} = -\frac{\sin\tfrac{1}{2}\vartheta}{\cos\tfrac{1}{2}\vartheta e^{i\varphi}} \quad (E > 0) \qquad \frac{\cos\tfrac{1}{2}\vartheta}{\sin\tfrac{1}{2}\vartheta e^{i\varphi}} \quad (E < 0)$$

in the two cases. The first one can be written

$$\frac{a_+}{a_-} = \frac{\cos \tfrac{1}{2}(\pi - \vartheta)}{\sin \tfrac{1}{2}(\pi - \vartheta)e^{i(\pi+\varphi)}} \qquad (E > 0)$$

and comparison with (6.11) and (6.12) shows that the expectation value of **S** associated with the two stationary states is parallel to **B**, that is, has the same polar angles, when $E < 0$ and that it is anti-parallel when $E > 0$. (These signs are for positive γ. An electron has e and γ negative, and the roles of positive and negative energies are reversed.) The reader will easily verify that if one starts by taking the z axis parallel to **B**, the above calculation becomes trivial.

Problem 6.4 Find a_+, a_-, $|a_+|^2$, and $|a_-|^2$ for each of the two states determined above. What is the exact physical meaning of the last two quantities? Show by simple arguments that the results are qualitatively reasonable.

Time-dependent states

If a spin is introduced into a magnetic field to which it is neither parallel nor antiparallel (in the sense used above), then from the classical viewpoint expressed by (6.13) it will begin to process. Let us analyze this motion by solving the time-dependent Schrödinger equation

$$i\hbar \frac{\partial \chi}{\partial t} = \hat{H}\chi \qquad (6.18)$$

subject to the given initial conditions. We write the spin function $\chi(t)$ as in (6.7), with fixed χ_+ and χ_-, so that its entire time variation is expressed in terms of variations in the coefficients a_+ and a_-.[8] To find them, we start with (6.10) written compactly as

$$a_\pm(t) = \int \chi_\pm^* \chi(t)$$

and use (6.16), together with our assumption that $\chi_\pm$ are fixed, to find

$$i\hbar \dot{a}_\pm(t) = \int \chi_\pm^* i\hbar \dot{\chi}(t)$$
$$= -\gamma \hbar \mathbf{B} \cdot \int \chi_\pm^* \hat{\mathbf{S}} \chi(t) \qquad (6.19)$$

Writing χ on the right again in the form (6.7) and evaluating the integrals, we find a pair of equations

$$i\dot{a}_+ = -\tfrac{1}{2}\gamma[(B_x - iB_y)a_- + B_z a_+]$$
$$i\dot{a}_- = -\tfrac{1}{2}\gamma[(B_x + iB_y)a_+ - B_z a_-] \qquad (6.20)$$

These equations are the quantum-mechanical counterpart of (6.13).

---

[8] This calculation will serve later as a prototype for the more complicated theory of time-dependent perturbations in Sec. 8.7.

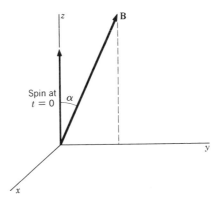

Fig. 6.2   Spin introduced into an inclined magnetic field.

Problem 6.5   Derive Eqs. (6.20).

Problem 6.6   Consider an electron with arbitrary initial values of a_+ and a_-, placed at $t = 0$ in a magnetic field B in the z direction. Show that $|a_+(t)|^2$ and $|a_-(t)|^2$ remain constant in time and interpret this result in the light of (6.13).

As an example of the physical content of (6.20) let us consider the following problem. An electron whose spin is known to be upward is introduced at time $t = 0$ into a magnetic field inclined at an angle α to the vertical, Fig. 6.2, so that its components are

$$B_x = 0 \qquad B_y = B \sin \alpha \qquad B_z = B \cos \alpha$$

We are to find the spin's subsequent motion. The coupled equations for a_+ and a_- are

$$i\dot{a}_+ = -\tfrac{1}{2}\gamma B(a_+ \cos \alpha - ia_- \sin \alpha)$$
$$i\dot{a}_- = \tfrac{1}{2}\gamma B(a_- \cos \alpha - ia_+ \sin \alpha)$$

(6.21)

To solve these, let a_+ and a_- each be proportional to the same time factor

$$a_+ = A_+ e^{i\lambda t} \qquad a_- = A_- e^{i\lambda t}$$

(6.22)

so that the equations become

$$(-\lambda + \tfrac{1}{2}\gamma B \cos \alpha)A_+ - \tfrac{1}{2}i\gamma B \sin \alpha\, A_- = 0$$
$$\tfrac{1}{2}i\gamma B \sin \alpha\, A_+ - (\lambda + \tfrac{1}{2}\gamma B \cos \alpha)A_- = 0$$

These equations are soluble for A_+ and A_- if their determinant vanishes, and this gives for λ the equation $\lambda^2 = \tfrac{1}{4}\gamma^2 B^2$, or

$$\lambda = \pm\omega \qquad \omega = \tfrac{1}{2}\gamma B$$

(6.23)

Thus the λ in (6.22) can be either positive or negative, and a_-, for example, can be written as

$$a_-(t) = A_- e^{i\omega t} + B_- e^{-i\omega t}$$

(6.24)

But according to the initial conditions of the experiment, $a_-(0) = 0$, so that (6.24) becomes

$$a_-(t) = A \sin \omega t \tag{6.25}$$

where A is an arbitrary amplitude. Already we see a remarkable feature of the situation, which is that a_- periodically returns to zero. To find a_+, we can put a_- back into the second of Eqs. (6.20) to get

$$a_+(t) = -\frac{A}{\sin \alpha}(\cos \omega t + i \cos \alpha \sin \omega t)$$

We now use (6.9) to find the magnitude of A:

$$|a_+|^2 + |a_-|^2 = \frac{A^2}{\sin^2 \alpha}(\cos^2 \omega t + \cos^2 \alpha \sin^2 \omega t + \sin^2 \alpha \sin^2 \omega t)$$
$$= 1$$

so that except for a phase factor, $A = \sin \alpha$, and

$$a_+(t) = -(\cos \omega t + i \cos \alpha \sin \omega t) \qquad a_-(t) = \sin \alpha \sin \omega t \tag{6.26}$$

The probabilities of finding the spin up and down after a time t are respectively

$$|a_+(t)|^2 = 1 - \sin^2 \alpha \sin^2 \omega t \qquad |a_-(t)|^2 = \sin^2 \alpha \sin^2 \omega t$$

The frequency with which the state of upward spin recurs is the frequency of $\sin^2 \omega t$, or 2ω, which is γB, the Larmor frequency. The behavior of the spin after the initial moment shown in Fig. 6.2 may be represented in classical terms as a precession in a cone of aperture α, Fig. 6.3.

Problem 6.7   Find $\langle S_x \rangle$, $\langle S_y \rangle$, and $\langle S_z \rangle$ from (6.26) and verify that they satisfy the classical equations of motion for the spin precession.

The device of Figs. 6.2 and 6.3 is closely analogous to an analyzer of polarized light, for if the field B is made inhomogeneous, it

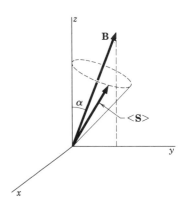

Fig. 6.3   Precession of the spin after $t = 0$.

can be used to separate out atoms whose spin is parallel to the B axis from those antiparallel. Let us suppose that the antiparallel spins are rejected. The "analyzer" thus resembles a Nicol prism, which passes light of one polarization and rejects the other. As an analyzing Nicol is rotated away from the direction of initial polarization, the intensity of the transmitted beam follows the law of Malus,

$$I = I_0 \cos^2 \alpha \qquad \text{light} \tag{6.27}$$

In the next problems it will be shown that the analogous formula for spin $\frac{1}{2}$ is

$$I = I_0 \cos^2 \tfrac{1}{2}\alpha \qquad \text{spin } \tfrac{1}{2} \tag{6.28}$$

Problem 6.8 We have assumed above that the three components of the operator **S** transform under rotations of coordinates like the components of a vector. Show that the component of **S** parallel to B in Fig. 6.2 is $S_B = S_z \cos \alpha + S_y \sin \alpha$.

Problem 6.9 What is the expectation value of S_B in the state given by (6.26)? Has the result a simple physical interpretation?

Problem 6.10 What are the eigenvalues and eigenfunctions of S_B? Calculate them by setting

$$S_B X = \lambda X \qquad X = C_+ \chi_+ + C_- \chi_-$$

and solving for λ, C_+, and C_-. Show that (6.28) and the result of Prob. 6.9 follow from this calculation.

Problem 6.11 Work out a theory analogous to the above for particles of spin 1, for which there will be three spin states, χ_+, χ_0, and χ_-. This can be done by a choice of methods, either by constructing a realization of the spin operators analogous to (6.6) or by using their analytical realization as $\mathbf{r} \times \mathbf{p}$. Following the approach of the preceding problem, find $\langle S_B \rangle$ and the intensities in the beams polarized parallel, perpendicular, and antiparallel to B.

6.3 Magnetic Resonance

Most modern experimental determinations of nuclear moments involve one form or another of magnetic resonance. We shall not here give any detailed description of the methods used, but the underlying mathematics of the resonance phenomenon is quite simple and can be illustrated with the formulas for the motion of a spin of $\frac{1}{2}\hbar$. Suppose we subject the particle simultaneously to a fixed, strong magnetic field B in the z direction and a rotating field b, of angular frequency ν, in the xy plane, so that the total field has components

$$B_x = b \cos \nu t \qquad B_y = -b \sin \nu t \qquad B_z = B \tag{6.29}$$

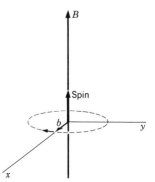

Fig. 6.4 Situation at $t = 0$ for a spin placed in a fixed magnetic field B and a rotating field b.

as shown in Fig. 6.4. Further, we assume that the electron's spin is initially upward, so that

$$a_+ = 1 \qquad a_- = 0 \qquad \text{at } t = 0 \tag{6.30}$$

The equations (6.20) become

$$i\dot{a}_+ = -\tfrac{1}{2}\gamma(be^{i\nu t}a_- + Ba_+) \tag{6.31}$$

$$i\dot{a}_- = -\tfrac{1}{2}\gamma(be^{-i\nu t}a_+ - Ba_-) \tag{6.32}$$

These equations can be solved rather simply if we make the substitutions

$$a_+ = A_+ e^{i\lambda_+ t} \qquad a_- = A_- e^{i\lambda_- t} \tag{6.33}$$

This gives

$$(\lambda_+ - \omega)A_+ - \tfrac{1}{2}\gamma b e^{i(\lambda_- - \lambda_+ + \nu)t}A_- = 0$$

$$-\tfrac{1}{2}\gamma b e^{i(\lambda_+ - \lambda_- - \nu)t}A_+ + (\lambda_- + \omega)A_- = 0$$

where we have introduced the free-field frequency ω from (6.23). The time-dependent terms become constant if we choose

$$\lambda_+ = \lambda_- + \nu \tag{6.34}$$

Making this substitution in the first equation, we set the determinant of the coefficients of A_+ and A_- equal to zero and find an equation for λ_- whose roots are

$$\lambda_- = -\tfrac{1}{2}\nu \pm \Delta \qquad \Delta = [(\omega - \tfrac{1}{2}\nu)^2 + \beta^2]^{\frac{1}{2}}$$

where

$$\beta = \tfrac{1}{2}\gamma b$$

Thus,

$$a_- = A_-^{(1)} e^{-i(\frac{1}{2}\nu - \Delta)t} + A_-^{(2)} e^{-i(\frac{1}{2}\nu + \Delta)t}$$

and the solution which satisfies (6.30) is therefore

$$a_- = A \sin \Delta t \, e^{-\frac{1}{2}i\nu t}$$

To find A, we first find $a_+(0)$ from (6.31), (6.33), and (6.34) and then set it equal to unity,

$$a_+(0) = -\frac{iA\Delta}{\beta} = 1 \qquad A = \frac{i\beta}{\Delta}$$

so that the final solution for a_- is

$$a_- = \frac{i\beta}{\Delta} \sin \Delta t \; e^{-\frac{1}{2}i\nu t}$$

and the probability of finding the spin pointing downward is

$$|a_-|^2 = \left(\frac{\beta}{\Delta}\right)^2 \sin^2 \Delta t \tag{6.35}$$

Thus, a fraction of the spins equal to

$$|a_-|^2_{\text{max}} = \left(\frac{\beta}{\Delta}\right)^2 \tag{6.36}$$

oscillates up and down with a frequency 2Δ, where in terms of the fields

$$2\Delta = [(\gamma B - \nu)^2 + (\gamma b)^2]^{\frac{1}{2}} \tag{6.37}$$

$|a_-|^2_{\text{max}}$ is sketched as a function of the circular frequency ν of the rotating field for different values of b in Fig. 6.5. Suppose now that the driving field b is made quite weak compared with the fixed field B. Then as ν is swept through the resonance frequency γB, $|a_-|^2_{\text{max}}$ passes through a very narrow maximum at which there is periodically a 100 percent probability of finding the spin inverted. It is the sharpness of the maximum that contributes most to the accuracy of the various experimental techniques based on this phenomenon. If δ is the width between the points where a curve in Fig. 6.5 takes on half its maximum value, then it is easy to see that $\delta/\gamma B = 2b/B$. On the other hand, the value of the resonant frequency ω is independent of b. Thus a careful measurement of ω and a calibration of B, usually by some system whose magnetic moment

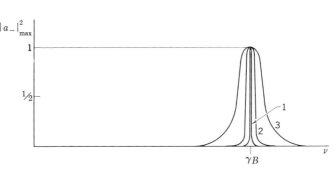

Fig. 6.5 Plot of $|a_-|^2_{\text{max}}$ giving the probability of spin flip as a function of the strength and frequency of the rotating field. Curves 1, 2, and 3 are for successively increasing values of b.

is known, enables one to measure experimental values of γ, notably for nuclei, with great precision.[9]

Problem 6.12   Analyze the above experiment in terms of the classical equations of motion and exhibit the corresponding resonance phenomenon.[10]

6.4   Addition of Two Spins

A helium atom has many possible quantum states, including the ground state, in which both electrons are in s states (that is, neither has any orbital angular momentum), and their entire angular momentum arises from their spins. The spins are not dynamically independent of each other, since they interact to exert a mutual torque through their magnetic moments. Therefore, if we seek to describe the system by quantum numbers representing conserved quantities, it is clear that any such numbers must be taken to refer to the two-spin system as a whole, since all components of the total angular momentum are surely constant. There is a further reason for adding the spins, which operates even in the presence of effects of orbital motion: that the vector model of atomic spectra[11] deals with the spin and orbital properties of several electrons by assigning a total spin $\mathbf{S}$ and a total orbital angular momentum $\mathbf{L}$ to the electrons and then treating the mutual interaction of $\mathbf{S}$ with $\mathbf{L}$.

Let us write the two spin operators as $\hat{\mathbf{S}}_1$ and $\hat{\mathbf{S}}_2$ and the basic spin functions of the two electrons as $\chi_\pm(1)$ and $\chi_\pm(2)$. $\hat{\mathbf{S}}_1$ operates only on $\chi(1)$ and $\hat{\mathbf{S}}_2$ only on $\chi(2)$; and therefore the two operators commute. The total spin is represented by

$$\hat{\mathbf{S}} = \hat{\mathbf{S}}_1 + \hat{\mathbf{S}}_2 \tag{6.38}$$

and its square by

$$\begin{aligned}
\hat{S}^2 &= \hat{S}_1{}^2 + \hat{S}_2{}^2 + 2\hat{\mathbf{S}}_1 \cdot \hat{\mathbf{S}}_2 \\
&= \tfrac{3}{2} + 2\hat{\mathbf{S}}_1 \cdot \hat{\mathbf{S}}_2
\end{aligned} \tag{6.39}$$

by (6.4). Since each spin can be directed either up or down independently of the other, there are four different spin states which we can take to be

$$\begin{aligned}
&\chi_a = \chi_+(1)\chi_+(2) \uparrow\uparrow &\quad &\chi_c = \chi_-(1)\chi_+(2) \downarrow\uparrow \\
&\chi_b = \chi_+(1)\chi_-(2) \uparrow\downarrow &\quad &\chi_d = \chi_-(1)\chi_-(2) \downarrow\downarrow
\end{aligned} \tag{6.40}$$

---

[9] See, for example, N. F. Ramsay, Nuclear Moments, sec. 3D in E. Segré (ed.), *Experimental Nuclear Physics*, John Wiley & Sons, Inc., New York, 1953, reprinted in enlarged form as *Nuclear Moments*, John Wiley & Sons, Inc., New York, 1953.

[10] *Ibid.* and also F. Bloch, Phys. Rev., **70**, 460 (1946).

[11] F. K. Richtmyer, E. H. Kennard, T. Lauritsen, *Introduction to Modern Physics*, 5th ed., McGraw-Hill Book Company, Inc., New York, 1955, chap. 7.

where the arrows illustrate the configurations represented. Clearly,

$$\hat{S}_z\chi_a = (\hat{S}_{1z} + \hat{S}_{2z})\chi_+(1)\chi_+(2)$$
$$= [\hat{S}_{1z}\chi_+(1)]\chi_+(2) + \chi_+(1)\hat{S}_{2z}\chi_+(2)$$
$$= \tfrac{1}{2}\chi_+(1)\chi_+(2) + \tfrac{1}{2}\chi_+(1)\chi_+(2)$$
$$= \chi_a \tag{6.41}$$

and similarly for the others. Further, we can evaluate the result of operating on χ_a with $\hat{S}^2$; though since $\hat{S}^2$ differs from $\hat{S}_1 \cdot \hat{S}_2$ only by constants, we shall first use the latter. We easily fill out the following table:

Spin function χ	$\hat{S}_z\chi$	$\hat{S}_1 \cdot \hat{S}_2\chi$	$\hat{S}^2\chi$
χ_a ↑↑	χ_a	$\tfrac{1}{4}\chi_a$	$2\chi_a$
χ_b ↑↓	0	$-\tfrac{1}{4}\chi_b + \tfrac{1}{2}\chi_c$	$\chi_b + \chi_c$
χ_c ↓↑	0	$-\tfrac{1}{4}\chi_c + \tfrac{1}{2}\chi_b$	$\chi_b + \chi_c$
χ_d ↓↓	$-\chi_d$	$\tfrac{1}{4}\chi_d$	$2\chi_a$

Problem 6.13   Calculate the values of $\hat{S}_1 \cdot \hat{S}_2\chi$ given above.

Not only are χ_a and χ_d eigenfunctions of $\hat{S}^2$; the eigenvalues are just what one would expect, for two parallel spins of $\tfrac{1}{2}$ should be equivalent to one spin of $s = 1$, and the formula $s(s + 1)$ for the eigenvalues of $\hat{S}^2$ gives 2. The other two functions, while eigenfunctions of $\hat{S}_z$, are not eigenfunctions of $\hat{S}^2$. To find the correct eigenfunctions, let us simplify the problem by finding a simpler operator which commutes with $\hat{S}_z$ and $\hat{S}^2$. Such a one is the permutation operator $\hat{P}$, which interchanges the labels 1 and 2 on operators and spin functions:

$$\hat{P}\hat{S}\chi(1,2) = \hat{P}(\mathbf{S}_1 + \mathbf{S}_2)\chi(1,2)$$
$$= (\mathbf{S}_2 + \mathbf{S}_1)\chi(2,1) = \hat{S}\hat{P}\chi(1,2)$$

where χ is any two-spin function. Thus $[\hat{P},\hat{S}] = 0$, and we now look at the eigenvalues p of $\hat{P}$. The trick has already been used in Sec. 5.4: if

$$\hat{P}\chi(1,2) = \chi(2,1) = p\chi(1,2)$$

then

$$\hat{P}^2\chi(1,2) = \chi(1,2) = p^2\chi(1,2)$$

so that $p = \pm 1$, corresponding to symmetric and antisymmetric spin functions, respectively. It is possible to form linear combinations of χ_b and χ_c which are symmetric and antisymmetric in the indices 1 and 2. They are

$$\chi_0^{(s)} = 2^{-\frac{1}{2}}(\chi_c + \chi_d) \qquad (6.42)$$

$$\chi_0^{(a)} = 2^{-\frac{1}{2}}(\chi_c - \chi_d) \qquad (6.43)$$

where the subscript zero means that they belong to the eigenvalue zero of S_z and the $2^{-\frac{1}{2}}$ is for normalization. We can then easily find the following results:

Spin function	Eigenvalues of $\hat{P}$	$\hat{S}_z$	$\hat{S}_1 \cdot \hat{S}_2$	$s(s+1)$	s
$\chi_1^{(s)} = \chi_a$	1	1	$\frac{1}{4}$	2	1
$\chi_0^{(s)} = 2^{-\frac{1}{2}}(\chi_b + \chi_c)$	1	0	$\frac{1}{4}$	2	1
$\chi_{-1}^{(s)} = \chi_d$	1	-1	$\frac{1}{4}$	2	1
$\chi_0^{(a)} = 2^{-\frac{1}{2}}(\chi_b - \chi_c)$	-1	0	$-\frac{3}{4}$	0	0

where χ_a and χ_d have been renamed with superscripts (s) because they are symmetric in the two spins. This completes the task of finding the eigenfunctions and eigenvalues of the total spin operators.

Problem 6.14 Calculate the new entries in the table above.

Problem 6.15 Find the same results without the use of $\hat{P}$ by forming an arbitrary linear combination of χ_b and χ_c and then so choosing the coefficients as to make it an eigenfunction of $\hat{S}_1 \cdot \hat{S}_2$.

Problem 6.16 Show that the factors of $2^{-\frac{1}{2}}$ are correct for normalizing $\chi_0^{(s)}$ and $\chi_0^{(a)}$.

The 2×2 spin functions χ_a to χ_d have been replaced by the $3 + 1$ functions $\chi^{(s)}$ and $\chi^{(a)}$, where the antisymmetric one evidently belongs in a class by itself. To see what is the difference between the two eigenfunctions with $S_z = 0$, let us look at a simple-minded picture of a spin vector in the state $S_z = +\frac{1}{2}$. Figure 6.6 shows it with its dimensions labeled. Only the z component of the vector is fixed; the other two components fluctuate at random. Its length is given as $\frac{1}{2}\sqrt{3}$ because the eigenvalue of S^2 is $\frac{3}{4}$. But suppose we have two spins rigidly coupled as in Fig. 6.7. Their resultant is easily found to be of length $\sqrt{2}$ with no z component, corresponding to

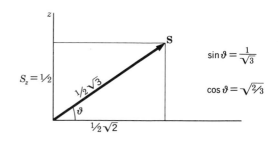

$$\sin \vartheta = \frac{1}{\sqrt{3}}$$

$$\cos \vartheta = \sqrt{\frac{2}{3}}$$

Fig. 6.6 Spin vector whose length is $\frac{1}{2}\sqrt{3}$ and whose z component is $\frac{1}{2}$.

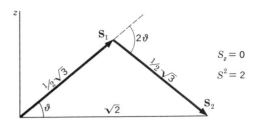

Fig. 6.7 Spin vectors rigidly coupled to
give $S_z = 0$, $S^2 = 2$.

$S_z = 0$ and the eigenvalue 2 of S^2. The scalar product is

$$\mathbf{S}_1 \cdot \mathbf{S}_2 = S_1 S_2 \cos 2\vartheta = \left(\frac{\sqrt{3}}{2}\right)^2 (\cos^2 \vartheta - \sin^2 \vartheta) = \tfrac{1}{4}$$

as in the table.

Now imagine an upward and a downward spin coupled rigidly
the other way, as in Fig. 6.8. Here $S_z = 0$ and the resultant is also
zero. The scalar product is

$$\mathbf{S}_1 \cdot \mathbf{S}_2 = -S_1 S_2 = -\left(\frac{\sqrt{3}}{2}\right)^2 = -\tfrac{3}{4}$$

again as in the table.

Problem 6.17   Draw three-dimensional diagrams in the spirit
of Figs. 6.7 and 6.8 to explain the other two spin states.

At first these results may seem strange, as though any two electrons in the universe that one might choose to consider as a pair at
once became rigidly coupled together. The point is, of course, that
this coupling is characteristic only of angular-momentum eigenstates, and a pair of electrons chosen at random is very unlikely to
be in such a state. The only significant physical effects arise when the
electrons are bound into a system whose energy depends on the relative spin orientations. Let us say for simplicity that the hamiltonian
contains a spin-dependent term equal to $-\alpha \hat{\mathbf{S}}_1 \cdot \hat{\mathbf{S}}_2$, with $\alpha > 0$. The
spin contributions to the energy in the symmetrical and antisym-
metrical states will be $-\tfrac{1}{4}\alpha$ and $\tfrac{3}{4}\alpha$, respectively. If now there is
nothing else affecting the spin orientations, they will make a transi-
tion from whatever mixed state they start with to the symmetrical
state, in which they are coupled together. Following through the
same process in the imagination from a classical point of view, one
arrives at a similar result.

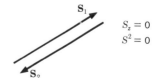

Fig. 6.8   Spin vectors rigidly coupled to give $S_z = S^2 = 0$.

6.5   Addition of Spin and Orbital Angular Momenta

In an atom there are two kinds of angular momentum: orbital ($\mathbf{L}$) and spin ($\mathbf{S}$), and the total angular momentum $\mathbf{J}$ is in general made up of both. We have, therefore, a number of variables which can be used to describe the compound system, for example L^2, L_z, S^2, S_z, J^2, and J_z, where

$$\mathbf{J} = \mathbf{L} + \mathbf{S} \tag{6.44}$$

and S^2 has in all cases the eigenvalue $\frac{1}{2}(\frac{1}{2} + 1) = \frac{3}{4}$. But we are limited in the use of such variables by the fact that usually no function is simultaneously an eigenfunction of two operators which do not commute. If we examine the set just mentioned, we find that $\hat{J}^2$ does not commute with $\hat{L}_z$ or $\hat{S}_z$, but that all other pairs commute. Thus two essentially distinct modes of description are possible, one based on the set L^2, L_z, S^2, and S_z, and the other on the set L^2, S^2, J^2, and J_z. Their physical nature is quite clear: in the first we regard the orbital and spin motions as dynamically independent and consider them separately, and in the second we regard them as components of a resultant vector $\mathbf{J}$ and concentrate our attention on that. It is sometimes indifferent which mode of description we use, but one is generally more convenient than the other, and we must study both.

The LS scheme

The first set of eigenfunctions is very simple to construct. Suppose we have a single electron in an orbital state Ω_{l,m_l} such that

$$\hat{L}^2 \Omega_{l,m_l} = l(l + 1)\Omega_{l,m_l} \tag{6.45}$$

and

$$\hat{L}_z \Omega_{l,m_l} = m_l \Omega_{l,m_l} \tag{6.46}$$

where l and m_l are integers. The functions Ω_{l,m_l} are functions of x, y, and z (or r, ϑ, and φ) but it will not be necessary to specify them any further, any more than it was necessary to say what the spin functions $\chi_\pm$ are. (It is shown in Appendix 4 that Ω_{l,m_l} has the form of an arbitrary function of r multiplied by a spherical harmonic in ϑ and φ.) The combination of orbit and spin is given by the product

$$\psi_{l,m_l,m_s} = \Omega_{l,m_l}\chi_{m_s} \tag{6.47}$$

where $m_s = \pm\frac{1}{2}$, and χ_{m_s} is the $\chi_\pm$ used earlier.

Problem 6.18   Show that ψ_{l,m_l,m_s} is an eigenfunction of $\hat{J}_z$ belonging to the eigenvalue $m_l + m_s$.

Problem 6.19   Show that $\hat{J}^2$ commutes with $\hat{L}^2$ and $\hat{S}^2$ but not with $\hat{L}_z$ or $\hat{S}_z$.

Problem 6.20   What is the expectation value of $\hat{J}^2$ in the state ψ_{l,m_l,m_s}? It is convenient to start by writing

$$\hat{J}^2 = \hat{L}^2 + \hat{S}^2 + 2\hat{\mathbf{L}} \cdot \hat{\mathbf{S}}$$

The J scheme

We now turn to the other mode of description, in terms of simultaneous eigenfunctions of $\hat{L}^2$, $\hat{J}^2$, and $\hat{J}_z$ (we omit $\hat{S}^2$ because it is always equal to $\frac{3}{4}$). First of all, $\hat{\mathbf{J}}$ is itself an angular momentum, obeying the usual commutation rules, so we can conclude at once that eigenfunctions φ_{j,m_j} can be found such that

$$\hat{J}^2 \varphi_{j,m_j} = j(j+1)\varphi_{j,m_j} \tag{6.48}$$

and

$$\hat{J}_z \varphi_{j,m_j} = m_j \varphi_{j,m_j} \tag{6.49}$$

where

$$m_j = -j, -j+1, \ldots, j-1, j \tag{6.50}$$

making $2j + 1$ values in all. We have now to relate these quantities to **L**, **S**, and their eigenfunctions. We shall illustrate the procedure with a simple case, that in which the orbital part has $l = 1$. Here, since m_l has three values and m_s has two, there are altogether six states of the form (6.47). Our purpose is to find a set of six states φ_{j,m_j} which are linear combinations of the ψ_{l,m_l,m_s} and which are also eigenfunctions of $\hat{J}^2$ and $\hat{J}_z$.

To start with, it is clear that the ψ_{l,m_l,m_s} are all eigenfunctions of $\hat{J}_z$ belonging to the eigenvalues $m_j = m_l + m_s$. Some of them are degenerate, as can be seen from the following table corresponding to $l = 1$:

m_j	m_l	m_s
$\frac{3}{2}$	1	$\frac{1}{2}$
$\frac{1}{2}$	$\left\{\begin{array}{c}1\\0\end{array}\right.$	$\begin{array}{c}-\frac{1}{2}\\\frac{1}{2}\end{array}$
$-\frac{1}{2}$	$\left\{\begin{array}{c}0\\-1\end{array}\right.$	$\begin{array}{c}-\frac{1}{2}\\\frac{1}{2}\end{array}$
$-\frac{3}{2}$	-1	$-\frac{1}{2}$

Of these the first and last are also eigenfunctions of $\hat{J}^2$. To show this we write

$$\hat{J}^2 = \hat{L}^2 + \hat{S}^2 + \hat{L}_+\hat{S}_- + \hat{L}_-\hat{S}_+ + 2\hat{L}_z\hat{S}_z \tag{6.51}$$

and note that for any l,

$$\hat{J}^2 \psi_{l,l,\frac{1}{2}} = [l(l+1) + \tfrac{3}{4} + 0 + 0 + 2l \times \tfrac{1}{2}]\psi_{l,l,\frac{1}{2}}$$
$$= (l^2 + 2l + \tfrac{3}{4})\psi_{l,l,\frac{1}{2}}$$
$$= (l + \tfrac{1}{2})(l + \tfrac{3}{2})\psi_{l,l,\frac{1}{2}}$$

which is of the form (6.48) with

$$j = l + \tfrac{1}{2} \tag{6.52}$$

Thus in general,

$$\psi_{l,l,\frac{1}{2}} = \varphi_{l+\frac{1}{2},l+\frac{1}{2}} \tag{6.53}$$

and by an obvious symmetry

$$\psi_{l,-l,-\frac{1}{2}} = \varphi_{l+\frac{1}{2},-l-\frac{1}{2}} \tag{6.54}$$

We can now construct more eigenfunctions of $\hat{J}^2$ by the use of operators which shift m_j. It follows from (5.44) that

$$\hat{J}_+ \varphi_{l+\frac{1}{2},-l-\frac{1}{2}} = (2l+1)^{\frac{1}{2}} \varphi_{l+\frac{1}{2},-l+\frac{1}{2}}$$

so that when $l = 1$,

$$\varphi_{\frac{3}{2},-\frac{1}{2}} = \sqrt{\tfrac{1}{3}}\, \hat{J}_+ \varphi_{\frac{3}{2},-\frac{3}{2}} \tag{6.55}$$

On the other hand, $\hat{J}_+ = \hat{L}_+ + \hat{S}_+$, so that using (5.44) again, we have

$$\begin{aligned}
\hat{J}_+ \varphi_{\frac{3}{2},-\frac{3}{2}} &= (\hat{L}_+ + \hat{S}_+) \Omega_{1,-1} \chi_{-\frac{1}{2}} \\
&= (\hat{L}_+ \Omega_{1,-1}) \chi_{-\frac{1}{2}} + \Omega_{1,-1} \hat{S}_+ \chi_{-\frac{1}{2}} \\
&= \sqrt{2}\, \Omega_{1,0} \chi_{-\frac{1}{2}} + \Omega_{1,-1} \chi_{\frac{1}{2}} \\
&= \sqrt{2}\, \psi_{1,0,-\frac{1}{2}} + \psi_{1,-1,\frac{1}{2}}
\end{aligned}$$

showing the combination of eigenfunctions degenerate in m_j given in the table above. Comparison with (6.55) gives

$$\varphi_{\frac{3}{2},-\frac{1}{2}} = \sqrt{\tfrac{2}{3}}\, \psi_{1,0,-\frac{1}{2}} + \sqrt{\tfrac{1}{3}}\, \psi_{1,-1,\frac{1}{2}}$$

By another application of $\hat{J}_+$, we can find $\varphi_{\frac{3}{2},\frac{1}{2}}$ and fill out the following table of eigenfunctions with $j = \tfrac{3}{2}$:

$$\left.\begin{aligned}
\varphi_{\frac{3}{2},\frac{3}{2}} &= \psi_{1,1,\frac{1}{2}} \\
\varphi_{\frac{3}{2},\frac{1}{2}} &= \sqrt{\tfrac{1}{3}}\, \psi_{1,1,-\frac{1}{2}} + \sqrt{\tfrac{2}{3}}\, \psi_{1,0,\frac{1}{2}} \\
\varphi_{\frac{3}{2},-\frac{1}{2}} &= \sqrt{\tfrac{2}{3}}\, \psi_{1,0,-\frac{1}{2}} + \sqrt{\tfrac{1}{3}}\, \psi_{1,-1,\frac{1}{2}} \\
\varphi_{\frac{3}{2},-\frac{3}{2}} &= \psi_{1,-1,-\frac{1}{2}}
\end{aligned}\right\} \tag{6.56}$$

These are four of the six eigenfunctions of $\hat{J}_z$ and $\hat{J}^2$ which were to be found. The other two must belong to two of these same values of m_j, and it is clear that they correspond to $j = \tfrac{1}{2}$, $m_j = \pm\tfrac{1}{2}$. The easiest way to find $\varphi_{\frac{1}{2},\frac{1}{2}}$, for example, is to note that it must be formed from the same ψ's as $\varphi_{\frac{3}{2},\frac{1}{2}}$ but be orthogonal to it (why?). Writing

$$\varphi_{\frac{1}{2},\frac{1}{2}} = \alpha \psi_{1,1,-\frac{1}{2}} + \beta \psi_{1,0,\frac{1}{2}}$$

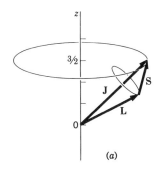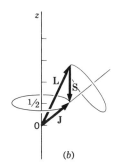

Fig. 6.9 Vector diagrams of $\mathbf{J} = \mathbf{L} + \mathbf{S}$ with $l = 1$ and $s = \frac{1}{2}$. (a) $j = \frac{3}{2}$, (b) $j = \frac{1}{2}$.

(a)

(b)

we easily find α and β to make it orthogonal (there is a choice of sign which is made conventionally) and similarly for $\varphi_{\frac{1}{2}, -\frac{1}{2}}$:

$$\varphi_{\frac{1}{2},\frac{1}{2}} = \sqrt{\tfrac{2}{3}}\,\psi_{1,1,-\frac{1}{2}} - \sqrt{\tfrac{1}{3}}\,\psi_{1,0,\frac{1}{2}}$$
$$\varphi_{\frac{1}{2},-\frac{1}{2}} = \sqrt{\tfrac{1}{3}}\,\psi_{1,0,-\frac{1}{2}} - \sqrt{\tfrac{2}{3}}\,\psi_{1,-1,\frac{1}{2}}$$

(6.57)

Vector diagrams of $\varphi_{\frac{3}{2},\frac{1}{2}}$ and $\varphi_{\frac{1}{2},\frac{1}{2}}$ are shown in Fig. 6.9.

The numerical coefficients in (6.56) and (6.57) are known as *normalized Clebsch-Gordan* coefficients. They can be calculated for higher values of l (see Prob. 6.25 and Table 6.1), and indeed for the combination of any two angular momenta, but for this purpose more advanced methods are easier.[12]

Problem 6.21   Show that the φ_{j,m_j} are correctly normalized.

Problem 6.22   Show that $\varphi_{\frac{1}{2},\frac{1}{2}}$ and $\varphi_{\frac{1}{2},-\frac{1}{2}}$ in (6.57) are eigenfunctions of $\hat{J}^2$.

Problem 6.23   In a system for which $l = 1$, $j = \frac{3}{2}$, $m_j = \frac{1}{2}$, what is the probability of finding the electron with its spin pointing upward?

Problem 6.24   Apply the method used here to give another derivation of the addition of two angular momenta corresponding to spin $\frac{1}{2}$.

Problem 6.25   Show that when l is any integer, the formulas analogous to (6.56) and (6.57) are

$$\varphi_{j=l+\frac{1}{2},m_j} = \left(\frac{j - m_j}{2j}\right)^{\frac{1}{2}} \psi_{l,m_l,-\frac{1}{2}} + \left(\frac{j + m_j}{2j}\right)^{\frac{1}{2}} \psi_{l,m_l-1,\frac{1}{2}}$$

(6.58)

$$\varphi_{j=l-\frac{1}{2},m_j} = \left(\frac{j + 1 + m_j}{2(j + 1)}\right)^{\frac{1}{2}} \psi_{l,m_l,-\frac{1}{2}} - \left(\frac{j + 1 - m_j}{2(j + 1)}\right)^{\frac{1}{2}} \psi_{l,m_l-1,\frac{1}{2}}$$

(6.59)

Problem 6.26   Derive the entries in Table 6.1.

[12] Details, and tables of the coefficients, are found in A. R. Edmonds, *Angular Momentum in Quantum Mechanics*, Princeton University Press, Princeton, N.J., 1957; E. P. Wigner, *Group Theory*, Academic Press Inc., New York, 1959; E. U. Condon and G. R. Shortley, *The Theory of Atomic Spectra*, Cambridge University Press, London, 1935.

Table 6.1

Description	$\hat{L}^2$	$\hat{L}_z$	$\hat{S}^2$	$\hat{S}_z$	$\hat{L}\cdot\hat{S}$	$\hat{J}^2$	$\hat{J}_z$
L^2, L_z, S^2, S_z	$l(l+1)$	m_l	$\tfrac{3}{4}$	m_s	$\langle m_l m_s\rangle$	$\langle l(l+1) +$ $2m_l m_s + \tfrac{3}{4}\rangle$	$m_l + m_s$
L^2, S^2, J^2, J_z $(j = l + \tfrac{1}{2})$	$l(l+1)$	$\left\langle \dfrac{2lm_j}{2l+1}\right\rangle$	$\tfrac{3}{4}$	$\left\langle \dfrac{m_j}{2l+1}\right\rangle$	$\tfrac{1}{2}l$	$j(j+1)$	m_j
L^2, S^2, J^2, J_z $(j = l - \tfrac{1}{2})$	$l(l+1)$	$\left\langle \dfrac{2(l+1)m_j}{2l+1}\right\rangle$	$\tfrac{3}{4}$	$\left\langle \dfrac{-m_j}{2l+1}\right\rangle$	$-\tfrac{1}{2}(l+1)$	$j(j+1)$	m_j

Eigenvalues and expectation values of the principal angular-momentum variables in the descriptions discussed above. Values in brackets are expectation values; the others are eigenvalues. In addition, when $m_j = j$, the expectation values in the second and third rows become eigenvalues. (See Prob. 6.25.)

Addition of angular momenta

Generalized to angular momenta of arbitrary size, the construction which has just been carried out forms the basis of the vector model of the atom, in which the **L**'s of individual electrons are combined to form a resultant **L** and similarly with the spins to form an **S**, and finally **L** and **S** are combined to form a **J**. If $\mathbf{J}_1$ and $\mathbf{J}_2$ are any two angular momenta whose sum is **J**, choose $\mathbf{J}_1$ to be the larger one (or either, if they are equal), and let it determine a direction in space. Then $\mathbf{J}_2$ may assume $2j_2 + 1$ different orientations with respect to it, each giving rise to a different resultant **J**. The j values of these **J**'s run from $j_1 - j_2$ to $j_1 + j_2$. For each j value, there are $2j + 1$ orientations of the whole diagram. The total number of states is thus

$$\sum_{j=j_1-j_2}^{j_1+j_2} (2j + 1) = (2j_1 + 1)(2j_2 + 1)$$

exactly the same as the number one would get by choosing the states according to the $2j_1 + 1$ possible eigenfunctions of $\hat{\mathbf{J}}_1$ taken together with the $2j_2 + 1$ possible eigenfunctions of $\hat{\mathbf{J}}_2$. The formulas giving the eigenfunctions of $\hat{J}^2$ and $\hat{J}_z$ in terms of those of $\hat{J}_1{}^2$, $\hat{J}_2{}^2$, $\hat{J}_{1z}$, and $\hat{J}_{2z}$ are similar to (6.56) and (6.57) but have more terms, and the coefficients in the formulas are available in tables.

7
Systems in Two and Three Dimensions

7.1 Degeneracy

There is no significant difference between calculations in one dimension and in more than one, and indeed we shall see that in most soluble cases the latter can be reduced to the former. There are, however, differences in detail, and probably the chief of these is the greatly increased occurrence of degeneracy. The reason for this is obvious, and it is illustrated in Fig. 5.8. The five states with $l = 2$ do not differ from each other in any way except their orientation in space. From an internal point of view they are (in the absence of external forces and torques) exactly equivalent, and their energies thus being equal, they will be degenerate. We shall often encounter degenerate wave functions in the remainder of this book, and we must remember always to note whether or not the degeneracy has its origin in the simple possibility of different spatial orientations. We shall now work out two examples of two-dimensional systems to show how the degeneracy arises.

The square box

In Chap. 1, in order to illustrate the occurrence of stationary states, we wrote down and solved in parallel columns the eigenvalue problems for a stretched spring and a particle confined to move in a bounded segment of a line. Here we shall illustrate the occurrence of degeneracy by analyzing the corresponding systems in two dimensions: a square drumhead and a particle which moves freely within a square enclosure, with coordinates as shown in Fig. 7.1. The equations to be solved are

Vibrating membrane	Schrödinger's equation

$$\frac{\partial^2 u}{\partial x^2} + \frac{\partial^2 u}{\partial y^2} = \frac{1}{v^2}\frac{\partial^2 u}{\partial t^2} \qquad\qquad \frac{\partial^2 \psi}{\partial x^2} + \frac{\partial^2 \psi}{\partial y^2} = -i\,\frac{2m}{\hbar}\frac{\partial \psi}{\partial t}$$

where v is the velocity of waves in the membrane and u is the displacement of the membrane from equilibrium. The normal modes of the vibration of the membrane and the corresponding stationary states of the particle have

$$u \propto \cos \omega t \qquad\qquad\qquad \psi \propto e^{-iEt/\hbar}$$

so that

$$\frac{\partial^2 u}{\partial x^2} + \frac{\partial^2 u}{\partial y^2} = -\left(\frac{\omega}{v}\right)^2 u \qquad\qquad \frac{\partial^2 \psi}{\partial x^2} + \frac{\partial^2 \psi}{\partial y^2} = -\frac{2mE}{\hbar^2}\psi$$

We solve these equations by separation of variables (this procedure will be explained in detail in connection with the next example). Writing

$$u = \sin ax \sin by \qquad\qquad\qquad \psi = \sin cx \sin dy$$

we find by substituting back that the equations are satisfied provided that

$$a^2 + b^2 = \left(\frac{\omega}{v}\right)^2 \qquad\qquad\qquad c^2 + d^2 = \frac{2mE}{\hbar^2}$$

while the boundary conditions

$$u(x,y) = 0 \qquad\qquad\qquad \psi(x,y) = 0$$

around the periphery of a square of side L imply that

$$a = \frac{m\pi}{L} \qquad b = \frac{n\pi}{L} \qquad c = \frac{m\pi}{L} \qquad d = \frac{n\pi}{L}$$

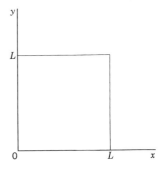

Fig. 7.1   Square region defining an eigenvalue problem with degeneracies.

where m and n are positive integers (why not negative or zero?). Thus, the eigenvalue conditions are

$$\left(\frac{\omega}{v}\right)^2 = (m^2 + n^2)\left(\frac{\pi}{L}\right)^2 \qquad \frac{2mE}{\hbar^2} = (m^2 + n^2)\left(\frac{\pi}{L}\right)^2$$

or

$$\frac{\omega}{v} = (m^2 + n^2)^{\frac{1}{2}}\frac{\pi}{L} \qquad E = (m^2 + n^2)\frac{\hbar^2}{2m}\frac{\pi^2}{L^2}$$

The occurrence of degeneracy is plain in the last pair of formulas; any two pairs of numbers whose squares add up to the same sum define states degenerate with one another. We see also that there are two essentially different types of degeneracy which occur. The first is what we shall call *symmetry degeneracy:* since the boundary is square, one can interchange the labels x and y, which is the same as exchanging m and n; and since $m^2 + n^2 = n^2 + m^2$, one obtains again the same energy. Thus whenever m and n are different, each energy level is at least doubly degenerate. In Fig. 7.2 we illustrate the configuration of the membrane for $m = 1$, $n = 2$ and for $m = 2$, $n = 1$.

But there is another type of degeneracy, occurring more rarely, which is termed *accidental degeneracy.* This is when two different pairs of integers give the same sum of squares, as, for example,

$$4^2 + 13^2 = 8^2 + 11^2$$

This degeneracy is inherent in the structure of the system and is independent of its spatial orientation.

Problem 7.1 Show that if the boundary is rectangular and not square, the symmetry degeneracy disappears though accidental degeneracy may still occur.

Problem 7.2 Show that both the symmetry-degenerate and the accidentally degenerate states are mutually orthogonal.

Finally, there are yet other states degenerate with those we have mentioned and not in general orthogonal to them, formed by

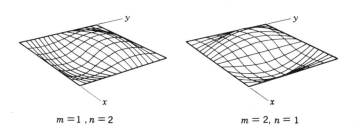

$$m = 1, n = 2 \qquad\qquad m = 2, n = 1$$

Fig. 7.2 Two symmetry-degenerate
eigenstates of a square membrane.

taking linear combinations. For example, the symmetry-degenerate pair mentioned above are, when normalized,

$$u_{1,2} = 2L^{-\frac{1}{2}} \sin \frac{\pi x}{L} \sin \frac{2\pi y}{L}$$

$$u_{2,1} = 2L^{-\frac{1}{2}} \sin \frac{2\pi x}{L} \sin \frac{\pi y}{L}$$

and from them we can form normalized linear combinations of the form

$$u_\vartheta = (\cos \vartheta)u_{1,2} + (\sin \vartheta)u_{2,1}$$

where ϑ is any real number (why real?) and the cosine and sine are used for purposes of normalization. The vibration patterns corresponding to several values of ϑ are shown in Fig. 7.3.

Fig. 7.3   Nodal lines of the linear combination u_ϑ corresponding to different values of ϑ.

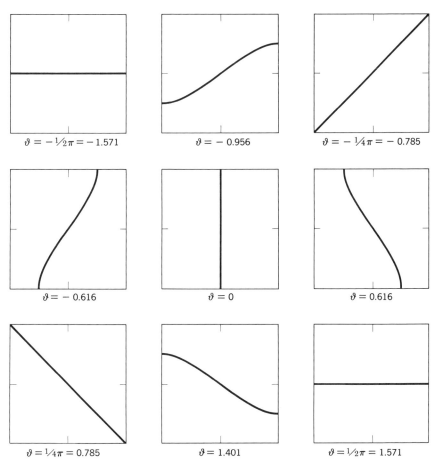

$\vartheta = -\frac{1}{2}\pi = -1.571$ $\vartheta = -0.956$ $\vartheta = -\frac{1}{4}\pi = -0.785$

$\vartheta = -0.616$ $\vartheta = 0$ $\vartheta = 0.616$

$\vartheta = \frac{1}{4}\pi = 0.785$ $\vartheta = 1.401$ $\vartheta = \frac{1}{2}\pi = 1.571$

Problem 7.3 Using the Schmidt orthogonalization procedure, find another wave function degenerate with u_9 and orthogonal to it.

Which of the different degenerate states occurs in any given situation depends, of course, on how the system is excited. For definiteness, let us first discuss the square membrane. It is a little difficult to make and activate such a thing, but closely analogous results can be observed with a Chladni plate, which is a thin sheet of metal, in this case square, supported at the center and set into vibration with a violin bow. Nodal patterns can be observed by sprinkling on the plate a little sand, which tends to collect along the nodes. The reader should spend a little time with this apparatus if he can find one. He will discover that with practice a wide variety of figures can be produced, and that the best way to select a particular one is to introduce a *perturbation*, a subject which will occupy the next chapter, by touching the plate at one point or another while it is being bowed. It will go into vibration in a pattern in which a nodal line crosses the point where the finger touches, and an antinode appears at the edge near where the bow is applied. The importance in quantum mechanics of perturbations in selecting out a particular eigenfunction from a degenerate set will be discussed in Chap. 8.

The two-dimensional oscillator

A second example, somewhat more involved mathematically, is a harmonic oscillator free to move in a plane, with the restoring force always directed toward a point on the plane which we shall take to be the origin.

Problem 7.4 What, in classical physics, is the motion of such a system? Is this motion degenerate?

The potential energy is

$$V = \tfrac{1}{2}Kr^2 = \tfrac{1}{2}K(x^2 + y^2) \tag{7.1}$$

and we shall first write the wave equation for the system in cartesian coordinates:

$$-\frac{\hbar^2}{2m}\left(\frac{\partial^2}{\partial x^2} + \frac{\partial^2}{\partial y^2}\right)\psi(x,y) + \tfrac{1}{2}K(x^2 + y^2)\psi(x,y) = E\psi(x,y) \tag{7.2}$$

As in the preceding example, this equation can be solved by the method of separation of variables. We *assume* that a solution can be written in the form

$$\psi(x,y) = \psi_1(x)\psi_2(y) \tag{7.3}$$

and see whether it is possible to satisfy the equation with it. Substituting (7.3) into (7.2) gives

$$-\frac{\hbar^2}{2m}(\psi_1''\psi_2 + \psi_1\psi_2'') + \tfrac{1}{2}K(x^2 + y^2)\psi_1\psi_2 = E\psi_1\psi_2 \tag{7.4}$$

where the primes denote differentiation with respect to whichever independent variable the function depends on. The next step is to divide the equation by $\psi_1\psi_2$ and rearrange it.

$$\left(-\frac{\hbar^2}{2m}\frac{\psi_1''}{\psi_1} + \tfrac{1}{2}Kx^2\right) + \left(-\frac{\hbar^2}{2m}\frac{\psi_2''}{\psi_2} + \tfrac{1}{2}Ky^2\right) = E \tag{7.5}$$

The point of the procedure is now that the first expression in brackets is a function only of x and the second only of y. If the equation is to be satisfied for all values of x and of y, then obviously each bracketed expression must be a constant, so that

$$-\frac{\hbar^2}{2m}\psi_1'' + \tfrac{1}{2}Kx^2\psi_1 = E_1\psi_1 \qquad -\frac{\hbar^2}{2m}\psi_2'' + \tfrac{1}{2}Ky^2\psi_2 = E_2\psi_2 \tag{7.6}$$

where E_1 and E_2 are constants connected by

$$E_1 + E_2 = E \tag{7.7}$$

Each of the equations of (7.6) is of the familiar type already encountered in Sec. 4.9 for the one-dimensional case, and its solution is of the form (4.125). To avoid confusion in notation, we introduce two new variables

$$\xi = \left(\frac{m\omega}{\hbar}\right)^{\!\frac{1}{2}} x = \left(\frac{Km}{\hbar^2}\right)^{\!\frac{1}{4}} x \qquad \eta = \left(\frac{Km}{\hbar^2}\right)^{\!\frac{1}{4}} y \tag{7.8}$$

so that (omitting the normalization) we have

$$\psi_1 = H_{n_1}(\xi)e^{-\frac{1}{2}\xi^2} \qquad \psi_2 = H_{n_2}(\eta)e^{-\frac{1}{2}\eta^2}$$
$$(n_1, n_2 = 0, 1, 2, \ldots) \tag{7.9}$$

$$E = (n_1 + n_2 + 1)\hbar\omega \qquad (n_1, n_2 = 0, 1, 2, \ldots) \tag{7.10}$$

and for the entire wave function

$$\psi_{n_1n_2}(\xi,\eta) = H_{n_1}(\xi)H_{n_2}(\eta)e^{-\frac{1}{2}(\xi^2+\eta^2)} \tag{7.11}$$

This gives a distinct solution for every pair of values (n_1,n_2). We do not claim, of course, that *all* solutions of (7.2) can be written in this product form, any more than was the case in the preceding example. But it can be shown that they can all be written as linear combinations of product solutions, each provided with its appropriate factor of $e^{-iEt/\hbar}$.

Problem 7.5 Let the state of the system at time $t = 0$ be $\Psi(x,y)$, an arbitrary function of x and y satisfying the boundary conditions. Write down the time-dependent wave function for a two-dimensional harmonic oscillator which reduces to $\Psi(x,y)$

at $t = 0$. What has this to do with the last sentence of the preceding paragraph?

Solution. Assume that $\psi(x,y,t)$ can be expressed in the form

$$\psi(x,y,t) = \sum_{n_1,n_2} C_{n_1 n_2} \psi_{n_1 n_2}(\xi,\eta) \exp\left[-\frac{i}{\hbar}(E_{n_1} + E_{n_2})t \right]$$

Its initial value is

$$\psi(x,y,0) = \Sigma C_{n_1 n_2} \psi_{n_1}(x)\psi_{n_2}(y) = \Psi(x,y)$$

where we shall assume that the ψ_n's are normalized one-dimensional oscillator eigenfunctions written in terms of x and y. To find C_{kl}, we multiply by $\psi_k(x)\psi_l(y)$ and integrate over x and y.

$$C_{kl} = \int\int \psi_k(x)\psi_l(y)\Psi(x,y)\,dx\,dy$$

The remaining question can be answered by remarking that the ψ_n's form a complete set of orthogonal functions.

The existence of degeneracy in (7.10) is, of course, clear. Any pair of numbers (n_1,n_2) having a given sum, $n_1 + n_2 = n$, will correspond to the same energy. The degree of degeneracy is given by the number of ways in which one can add two positive integers, including zeros, to get n. The reader will readily convince himself that this number is $n + 1$. To examine the degeneracy in more detail, let us start with a state $(n_1 = 0, n_2 = 1)$, given by

$$\psi_{0,1} = \eta e^{-\frac{1}{2}(\xi^2+\eta^2)} \tag{7.12}$$

if we ignore normalization. The general form of this wave function can be seen in Fig. 7.4, where the value of the "intensity" $|\psi|^2$ is indicated by the intensity of the shading.

Suppose now that we express this same wave function with respect to rotated axes, as in Fig. 7.5. We have

$$\xi = \xi_R \cos \vartheta - \eta_R \sin \vartheta \qquad \eta = \xi_R \sin \vartheta + \eta_R \cos \vartheta$$

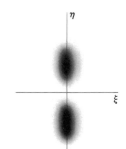

Fig. 7.4 State $(n_1 = 0, n_2 = 1)$ of a two-dimensional oscillator. The intensity of $|\psi|^2$ is indicated by the depth of the shading.

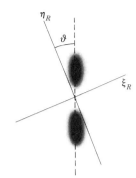

Fig. 7.5   The same state described in terms of rotated axes.

and in these new coordinates, (7.12) becomes

$$\psi_{0,1}(\xi,\eta) = (\xi_R \sin \vartheta + \eta_R \cos \vartheta) \exp [\tfrac{1}{2}(\xi_R{}^2 + \eta_R{}^2)]$$

or

$$\psi_{0,1}(\xi,\eta) = \cos \vartheta\psi_{0,1}(\xi_R,\eta_R) + \sin \vartheta\psi_{1,0}(\xi_R,\eta_R)$$

which is a linear combination of two states of equal energy.

Problem 7.6   Express the normalized $\psi_{1,1}(\xi,\eta)$ in terms of normalized wave functions of (ξ_R,η_R) and show that the latter all belong to the same energy. Is the degeneracy of $\psi_{0,2}$, $\psi_{1,1}$, and $\psi_{2,0}$ of the accidental or the symmetry kind?

We shall end this section by solving the same problem again in polar coordinates, which will illustrate in a simple way how one uses angular variables in quantum mechanics. Let us return to (7.2) and note that, with

$$x = r \cos \vartheta \qquad y = r \sin \vartheta$$

we have[1]

$$\frac{\partial^2}{\partial x^2} + \frac{\partial^2}{\partial y^2} = \frac{\partial^2}{\partial r^2} + \frac{1}{r}\frac{\partial}{\partial r} + \frac{1}{r^2}\frac{\partial^2}{\partial \vartheta^2} \tag{7.13}$$

Schrödinger's equation is

$$-\frac{\hbar^2}{2m}\left(\frac{\partial^2}{\partial r^2} + \frac{1}{r}\frac{\partial}{\partial r} + \frac{1}{r^2}\frac{\partial^2}{\partial \vartheta^2}\right)\psi(r,\vartheta) + \tfrac{1}{2}Kr^2\psi(r,\vartheta) = E\psi(r,\vartheta) \tag{7.14}$$

and we carry out a separation of variables exactly as before. Writing

$$\psi(r,\vartheta) = R(r)\Theta(\vartheta) \tag{7.15}$$

[1] Expressions for the laplacian operator in other coordinate systems are tedious to derive. In practice one uses trick methods or general formulas (G. Joos, *Theoretical Physics*, Hafner Publishing Company, Inc., New York, 1950, 1958) or looks up the desired result in a calculus book.

we find

$$-\frac{\hbar^2}{2m}\left(\frac{R''}{R} + \frac{1}{r}\frac{R'}{R} + \frac{1}{r^2}\frac{\Theta''}{\Theta}\right) + \tfrac{1}{2}Kr^2 = E$$

But the terms in r and ϑ are still not separated; we must multiply through by r^2 to get

$$\left\{-\frac{\hbar^2}{2m}r^2\left(\frac{R''}{R} + \frac{1}{r}\frac{R'}{R}\right) + \tfrac{1}{2}Kr^4 - Er^2\right\} - \left\{\frac{\hbar^2}{2m}\frac{\Theta''}{\Theta}\right\} = 0$$

Each bracketed expression involves only one variable, and so each must be independent of both r and ϑ. If we write

$$\frac{\Theta''}{\Theta} = -l^2 \tag{7.16}$$

where l is a constant, we have

$$-\frac{\hbar^2}{2m}r^2\left(\frac{R''}{R} + \frac{1}{r}\frac{R'}{R}\right) + \tfrac{1}{2}Kr^4 - Er^2 = -\frac{\hbar^2}{2m}l^2 \tag{7.17}$$

From (7.16), neglecting normalization, we have

$$\Theta = e^{\pm il\vartheta} \tag{7.18}$$

and this is a properly single-valued function only if l is an integer. Returning to (7.17), we now have

$$-\frac{\hbar^2}{2m}\left(R'' + \frac{1}{r}R' - \frac{l^2}{r^2}R\right) + \tfrac{1}{2}Kr^2R = ER \tag{7.19}$$

and this must be solved for the eigenvalues E and the corresponding R's.

Problem 7.7 What is the physical interpretation of l in (7.18)?

Problem 7.8 Following the procedure of Sec. 4.9, show that the eigenvalues are of the form

$$E = (n + 1)\hbar\omega \qquad (n = 0, 1, 2, \ldots) \tag{7.20}$$

independent of l, and that for a given value of n, l can range only from 0 to n. Compare the degeneracy thus obtained with that found in the cartesian solution.

Problem 7.9 Write down all the polar eigenfunctions corresponding to $n = 0$ and $n = 1$. These should be representable in terms of linear combinations of the cartesian eigenfunctions obtained above. Are they?

We have presented the solution in polar coordinates to show how angular variables are handled. Three-dimensional systems can be analyzed in the same way, but the process is considerably more complicated. In Sec. 7.3 we shall discuss a few simple states of the

hydrogen atom, reserving a general solution in polar coordinates
for Chap. 14.

7.2 Systems of Several Particles

Just as in classical mechanics, a many-particle system in quantum
mechanics is described by adopting a separate, labeled set of coordinates for each particle. Thus the wave function of a two-particle system is of the form $\psi(x_1,y_1,z_1,x_2,y_2,z_2,t)$, and its hamiltonian operator
can be written as

$$\hat{H} = \hat{H}_1 + \hat{H}_2 + H_{int} \tag{7.21}$$

where

$$\hat{H}_1 = -\frac{\hbar^2}{2m_1}\left(\frac{\partial^2}{\partial x_1{}^2} + \frac{\partial^2}{\partial y_1{}^2} + \frac{\partial^2}{\partial z_1{}^2}\right) + V_1(x_1,y_1,z_1) \tag{7.22a}$$

$$\hat{H}_2 = -\frac{\hbar^2}{2m_2}\left(\frac{\partial^2}{\partial x_2{}^2} + \frac{\partial^2}{\partial y_2{}^2} + \frac{\partial^2}{\partial z_2{}^2}\right) + V_2(x_2,y_2,z_2) \tag{7.22b}$$

and

$$H_{int} = V(x_1 - x_2,\; y_1 - y_2,\; z_1 - z_2) \tag{7.23}$$

The first represents the kinetic and potential energies of a particle
at the point (x_1,y_1,z_1) and similarly for the second, while H_{int} represents the energy of interaction which exists when one particle is at
the point (x_1,y_1,z_1) and the other is simultaneously at (x_2,y_2,z_2).
The wave equation for the two-particle system is

$$i\hbar \frac{\partial \psi}{\partial t} = \hat{H}\psi \tag{7.24}$$

or

$$\hat{H}\psi = E\psi \tag{7.25}$$

as the case may be. Consistently with the axioms which we have
laid down for the one-particle system, we adopt the interpretation
that

> $|\psi(x_1,y_1,z_1,x_2,y_2,z_2,t)|^2\, dx_1\, dy_1\, dz_1\, dx_2\, dy_2\, dz_2$ is the joint prob-
> ability that, at time t, particle 1 lies in the volume element
> $dx_1\, dy_1\, dz_1$ at (x_1,y_1,z_1) *and* particle 2 lies in $dx_2\, dy_2\, dz_2$ at
> (x_2,y_2,z_2). $\tag{7.26}$

It is a striking feature of quantum mechanics that an N-particle
system inhabits an essentially $3N$-dimensional world. As we have
seen, this fact arises naturally out of the transcription from classical
mechanics, but in attempting to imagine or to draw such a ψ, we
realize how far we have come from a wave which can easily be
visualized in a classical way.

In order to gain some insight into the structure of the equations, let us first look at the special and uninteresting case in which $H_{int} = 0$ and the particles proceed without interacting with each other. The energy eigenfunctions satisfy the equation

$$(\hat{H}_1 + \hat{H}_2)\psi(\mathbf{r}_1,\mathbf{r}_2) = E\psi(\mathbf{r}_1,\mathbf{r}_2) \tag{7.27}$$

where for convenience we have represented the arguments (x_1,y_1,z_1) by the symbol $\mathbf{r}_1$, and similarly with $\mathbf{r}_2$. Since $\hat{H}_1$ depends only on x_1,y_1,z_1 and similarly with $\hat{H}_2$, the equation can be solved by separation of variables. We write

$$\psi(\mathbf{r}_1,\mathbf{r}_2) = \psi_1(\mathbf{r}_1)\psi_2(\mathbf{r}_2) \tag{7.28}$$

where ψ_1 and ψ_2 are in general two different eigenfunctions, so that

$$\psi_2(\mathbf{r}_2)\hat{H}_1\psi_1(\mathbf{r}_1) + \psi_1(\mathbf{r}_1)\hat{H}_2\psi_2(\mathbf{r}_2) = E\psi_1(\mathbf{r}_1)\psi_2(\mathbf{r}_2)$$

As before, we find

$$\hat{H}_1\psi_1(\mathbf{r}_1) = E_1\psi_1(\mathbf{r}_1) \quad \text{and} \quad \hat{H}_2\psi_2(\mathbf{r}_2) = E_2\psi_2(\mathbf{r}_2) \tag{7.29}$$

with

$$E_1 + E_2 = E \tag{7.30}$$

The significance of this is obvious: each particle behaves as though the other were not present and the energy of the system is the sum of the individual energies. Further, comparing (7.28) with (7.26), we see that the joint probability in (7.26) is

$$|\psi(\mathbf{r}_1,\mathbf{r}_2)|^2\, dv_1\, dv_2 = |\psi_1(\mathbf{r}_1)|^2\, dv_1\, |\psi_2(\mathbf{r}_2)|^2\, dv_2 \tag{7.31}$$

where dv_1 and dv_2 are the two elements of volume. The splitting of the joint probability into the product of the probabilities of the individual events is exactly what one expects if the two particles do not interact; they are dynamically independent, and so their joint probability is formed by multiplying the probabilities of the two independent events. If, for example, a die is thrown, the chance of throwing a 6 is $\frac{1}{6}$. If two dice are thrown, the chance of a double 6 is $(\frac{1}{6})^2$, but only if they fall independently (and not, for example, if they are stuck together). And if the component parts of a system do interact, then the wave function of the system will not factor in the manner of (7.28).

Problem 7.10   Given the wave function $\psi(\mathbf{r}_1,\mathbf{r}_2)$, what is the probability of finding particle 1 in the volume element dv, regardless of the location of particle 2?

Problem 7.11   Given the wave function $\psi(\mathbf{r}_1,\mathbf{r}_2)$, what is the probability of finding a particle (either one) in the volume element $dx\, dy\, dz$ at the point (x,y,z), regardless of where the other may be?

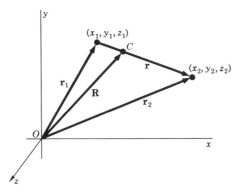

Fig. 7.6 Introduction of center-of-mass coordinates.

The center of mass

In the next section we are going to find some of the states of the hydrogen atom. This two-particle system has to be described by a wave function in six variables, but we know from classical mechanics that three of them are unnecessary if one separates out the motion of the center of mass and considers only the motion of the two bodies relative to each other. Three variables then describe the motion of the center of mass (motion in a straight line at constant velocity), and the remaining three describe the internal motion. Let us see whether the same can be done in quantum mechanics. Figure 7.6 shows the position vectors of the two particles and of their center of mass C relative to an arbitrary fixed origin O. We now introduce two new sets of coordinates: $\mathbf{R}$, which locates the center of mass, and $\mathbf{r}$, which gives the position of particle 2 relative to particle 1. They are given in terms of the old coordinates by

$$\mathbf{R} = \frac{m_1\mathbf{r}_1 + m_2\mathbf{r}_2}{M} \qquad \mathbf{r} = \mathbf{r}_2 - \mathbf{r}_1 \tag{7.32}$$

where $M = m_1 + m_2$. Assuming now that the wave function ψ depends only on $\mathbf{r}$ with components (x,y,z) and $\mathbf{R}$ with components (X,Y,Z), we have, for example,

$$\frac{\partial\psi(\mathbf{r},\mathbf{R})}{\partial x_1} = \frac{\partial\psi}{\partial x}\frac{\partial x}{\partial x_1} + \frac{\partial\psi}{\partial X}\frac{\partial X}{\partial x_1}$$

$$= -\frac{\partial\psi}{\partial x} + \frac{m_1}{M}\frac{\partial\psi}{\partial X}$$

$$\frac{\partial^2\psi(\mathbf{r},\mathbf{R})}{\partial x_1{}^2} = \frac{\partial^2\psi}{\partial x^2} - \frac{2m_1}{M}\frac{\partial^2\psi}{\partial x\,\partial X} + \frac{m_1{}^2}{M^2}\frac{\partial^2\psi}{\partial X^2}$$

Similarly,

$$\frac{\partial^2\psi(\mathbf{r},\mathbf{R})}{\partial x_2{}^2} = \frac{\partial^2\psi}{\partial x^2} + \frac{2m_2}{M}\frac{\partial^2\psi}{\partial x\,\partial X} + \frac{m_2{}^2}{M^2}\frac{\partial^2\psi}{\partial X^2}$$

and similarly also for the other four variables. The atom being isolated from its surroundings, the terms $V_1(x_1,y_1,z_1)$ and $V_2(x_2,y_2,z_2)$ are absent from (7.22a,b), and (7.25) becomes after a few steps

$$\left[-\frac{\hbar^2}{2\mu}\left(\frac{\partial^2}{\partial x^2} + \frac{\partial^2}{\partial y^2} + \frac{\partial^2}{\partial z^2}\right) - \frac{\hbar^2}{2M}\left(\frac{\partial^2}{\partial X^2} + \frac{\partial^2}{\partial Y^2} + \frac{\partial^2}{\partial Z^2}\right)\right.$$

$$\left. + V(\mathbf{r}) - E\right]\psi(\mathbf{r},\mathbf{R}) = 0 \qquad (7.33)$$

where μ is the *reduced mass* familiar from classical mechanics, given by

$$\frac{1}{\mu} = \frac{1}{m_1} + \frac{1}{m_2} \qquad (7.34)$$

and M, as before, is the total mass. The kinetic energy has been split into two parts which represent the kinetic energy associated with the particles' relative velocity and that associated with the motion of the center of mass. Now the variables may be separated. Writing

$$\psi(\mathbf{r},\mathbf{R}) = \psi(\mathbf{r})\Psi(\mathbf{R}) \qquad (7.35)$$

we find

$$\left[-\frac{\hbar^2}{2\mu}\nabla_r^2 + V(\mathbf{r})\right]\psi(\mathbf{r}) = E_1\psi(\mathbf{r}) \qquad (7.36)$$

and

$$-\frac{\hbar^2}{2M}\nabla_R^2\Psi(\mathbf{R}) = E_2\Psi(\mathbf{R}) \qquad (7.37)$$

where

$$E_1 + E_2 = E \qquad (7.38)$$

The subscripts on the laplacians denote differentiation with respect to different variables in the two equations.

Problem 7.12 Fill in the steps leading to (7.33), (7.36), and (7.37). If (7.26) defines the content of $|\psi(\mathbf{r}_1,\mathbf{r}_2)|^2$, what are those of (a) $|\psi(\mathbf{r},\mathbf{R})|^2$, (b) $\int|\psi(\mathbf{r},\mathbf{R})|^2\,dv$, (c) $\int|\psi(\mathbf{r},\mathbf{R})|^2\,dV$, where the last two denote integration over x,y,z and X,Y,Z? Evaluate $\int|\psi(\mathbf{r},\mathbf{R})|^2\,dv\,dV$ if $\int|\psi(\mathbf{r}_1,\mathbf{r}_2)|^2\,dv_1\,dv_2$ is known.

Problem 7.13 Show that if $\hat{\mathbf{p}}_r$ and $\hat{\mathbf{p}}_R$ are the operators whose x components are $(\hbar/i)\,\partial/\partial x$ and $(\hbar/i)\,\partial/\partial X$, respectively, the angular momentum of a two-particle system is equal to $\mathbf{r}\times\hat{\mathbf{p}}_r + \mathbf{R}\times\hat{\mathbf{p}}_R$.

Problem 7.14 Show how the analogous separation of variables is performed in classical mechanics.

The significance of the two wave equations is clear. Equation (7.37) describes the motion of the entire system considered as a single free particle of mass M. It predicts that the system as a whole will exhibit diffraction phenomena analogous to those for a single particle, and we have seen in Chap. 1 that such phenomena are in fact observed. Equation (7.36), except for the appearance of the reduced mass μ, is precisely of the one-particle form with potential $V(\mathbf{r})$. The total energy is the sum of the kinetic energy associated with the motion of the center of mass and the internal energy, E_1. Clearly, only the latter is of interest, and so we shall in the next section consider only (7.36).

The variables in a system of more than two particles can be combined analogously in several different ways;[2] we shall encounter one of them later in discussing the energy levels of helium.

7.3 The Hydrogen Atom

Every branch of exact science has a physical system with which it specially likes to deal—complex enough that it exhibits most of the characteristic features of the subject under discussion and simple enough to avoid the worst technical difficulties. Such are the hydrogen atom in atomic theory, the NaCl lattice in crystallography, the deuteron in nuclear physics, and the virus in microbiology. In this section we shall consider a few low-energy states of the hydrogen atom in some detail, reserving a more complete discussion for Chap. 14. There also we shall discuss some refinements of the simple theory presented here that are required when phenomena of relativity and of electron spin are taken into account.

The hydrogen atom consists of an electron of mass m and a proton of mass $(1836.12 \pm 0.02)m$, so that the reduced mass is very close to m,

$$\mu = \frac{1836m}{1 + 1836} = m(1 - \tfrac{1}{1837})$$

The Coulomb potential is

$$V(r) = -e'^2/r$$

where, since we are squarely within the province of electrostatics, it is unnecessary to bother about electrical units and we have written

$$\frac{e^2}{4\pi\varepsilon_0} = e'^2 \tag{7.39}$$

Or, if one prefers, one can read the following equations in the electrostatic system with e' in statcoulombs, m in grams, and lengths in centimeters. The mks system has no special advantages until one begins to discuss interrelations between electricity and magnetism.

[2] See J. O. Hirschfelder and J. S. Dahler, Proc. Natl. Acad. Sci. U.S., **42**, 363 (1956); D. W. Jepsen and J. O. Hirschfelder, *ibid.*, **45**, 249 (1959).

Schrödinger's equation is

$$-\frac{\hbar^2}{2\mu}\nabla^2\psi(\mathbf{r}) - \frac{e'^2}{r}\psi(\mathbf{r}) = E\psi(\mathbf{r}) \qquad (7.40)$$

Finding the exact solutions to this equation is instructive mathematically but not otherwise very rewarding, since it is of little use in the analogous computations for other atoms. We shall therefore content ourselves here with guessing a few of the lowest states.

The wave function is, of course, a function of three variables: x, y, and z, or r, ϑ, and φ, or occasionally some other set. It must be normalizable, that is, the integral $\int|\psi|^2 r^2 \sin\vartheta\, dr\, d\vartheta\, d\varphi$ must converge. For unbound states this is not the case, and the integral must be made finite by imposing suitable boundary conditions, as we have seen above. For bound states there is no difficulty as $r \to \infty$, since ψ normally vanishes exponentially. For small r, suppose that ψ varies as r^α. Then the indefinite integral varies as $r^{2\alpha+3}$, and it will converge at the origin provided that

$$\alpha \geqslant -\tfrac{3}{2}$$

But normalizability is not the only requirement to be imposed in this respect, and it turns out that the hermiticity of $\hat{H}$ is more stringent. We have seen in Sec. 3.4 that an operator cannot be called hermitian in itself, but only with respect to a certain class of functions over a certain range of variables. Let f and g be two functions of this class (not necessarily eigenfunctions). This means that

$$\int[f^*\hat{H}g - (\hat{H}f)^*g]\, dv = 0$$

Writing (for one particle)

$$\hat{H} = -\frac{\hbar^2}{2m}\nabla^2 + V(\mathbf{r})$$

where $V(\mathbf{r})$ is real, we find

$$\int(f^*\nabla^2 g - g\nabla^2 f^*)\, dv = \int\nabla\cdot(f^*\nabla g - g\nabla f^*)\, dv = 0$$

Around the origin of coordinates let us cut out a small sphere and integrate over all space except the sphere. The functions may be assumed to vanish strongly at infinity, so that all that remains is

$$-\int\left(f^*\frac{\partial g}{\partial r} - g\frac{\partial f^*}{\partial r}\right)dS$$

integrated over the surface of the sphere, where the negative sign is because the normal direction on the sphere was inward. Suppose that f and g both belong to the most singular class of functions possible, say

$$f(r) = (a + br + \cdots)r^\alpha \qquad g(r) = (c + dr + \cdots)r^\alpha$$

in the neighborhood of the origin, where the coefficients a, etc. may be functions of ϑ and φ. The integral is equal to

$$-r^{2\alpha+2} \int (a^*d - b^*c) \, d\Omega$$

plus terms which vanish more strongly with r, where we have written dS as $r^2 \, d\Omega$, with r constant and $d\Omega$ an element of solid angle, and this vanishes with r if $2\alpha + 2 > 0$, or

$$\alpha > -1 \tag{7.41}$$

As we have said, this is a more restrictive condition than that imposed by normalizability. Functions which are normalizable and for which $\hat{H}$ is hermitian will be called *admissible functions*.

The ground state

First, we look for a solution of (7.40) with spherical symmetry. If ψ depends on r only, the laplacian operator becomes

$$\nabla^2 \psi(r) = \frac{d^2\psi}{dr^2} + \frac{2}{r}\frac{d\psi}{dr} \tag{7.42}$$

and we have

$$\frac{\hbar^2}{2\mu}\left(\frac{d^2\psi}{dr^2} + \frac{2}{r}\frac{d\psi}{dr}\right) + \left(\frac{e'^2}{r} + E\right)\psi = 0 \tag{7.43}$$

The simplest wave function which is finite at the origin and falls off rapidly for large r is

$$\psi = e^{-\alpha r} \tag{7.44}$$

Substitution of this into (7.43) shows that it is a solution if α and E satisfy the two relations

$$\alpha = \frac{\mu e'^2}{\hbar^2} \qquad E = -\frac{\hbar^2 \alpha^2}{2\mu} \tag{7.45}$$

Problem 7.15 The ions He$^+$, Li^{++}, etc. have the same one-electron structure as H. How will α and E depend on the atomic number Z? Can this dependence be understood on physical grounds?

Problem 7.16 Derive Eqs. (7.42) and (7.45). Exactly what does it mean that E is negative? (To what extent is this a convention; to what extent is it a physical result?)

Problem 7.17 To what values of L_z and L^2 does (7.44) correspond?

The energy of the eigenstate which we have found is

$$E = -\frac{1}{2}\frac{\mu e'^4}{\hbar^2} = -\frac{1}{2}\frac{\mu e^4}{(4\pi\varepsilon_0)^2\hbar^2} = -13.597 \text{ eV} \tag{7.46}$$

and except for the correction for reduced mass, this is the value given in (1.11) by Bohr's theory for the energy of the ground state of hydrogen. (Naturally, the Bohr theory can also be corrected for reduced mass.) Since the state is spherically symmetrical, there is no angular degeneracy of the kind discussed in Sec. 6.1, and a more complete treatment (Chap. 14) shows that in fact this level is not degenerate at all. We have thus found the ground-state energy and wave function of hydrogen.

Clearly, $1/\alpha = \hbar^2/\mu e'^2$ is the order of magnitude of the size of the electron cloud, and we have encountered it before as the radius of the smallest orbit in Bohr's theory. Two obvious and fundamental points of difference from that theory should, however, be noted. First, by (7.44), the electron is actually more likely to be found at the nucleus than anywhere else, and second, by Prob. 7.17, it has no angular momentum at all, whereas in Bohr's theory its angular momentum was $\hbar$.

There is a possible source of confusion in interpreting (7.44). The probability of finding the electron in a given element of volume dv is proportional to $e^{-2\alpha r}\, dv$. If we consider dv to be the volume of a spherical shell of radius r and thickness dr, it is

$$dv = 4\pi r^2\, dr \tag{7.47}$$

and the probability of finding the electron at a distance between r and $r + dr$ from the nucleus is accordingly proportional to

$$dP = r^2 e^{-2\alpha r}\, dr \tag{7.48}$$

When plotted, as in Fig. 7.7, the function is seen to have a maximum. This maximum does not, however, correspond to a maximum in the probability per unit volume of finding the electron at a given distance from the origin; for we have just seen that this is greatest at the origin. In no sense, therefore, is Fig. 7.7 a spread-out representation of the first Bohr orbit.

Problem 7.18 What is the normalized wave function for the ground state of hydrogen?

Problem 7.19 Find $\langle r \rangle$, $\langle r^2 \rangle$, and Δr for the ground state and compare $\langle r \rangle$ with the value at which dP/dr in Fig. 7.7 goes through its maximum.

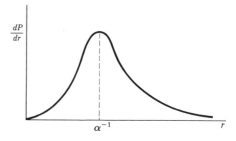

Fig. 7.7 Radial probability distribution function for the electron in a hydrogen atom in its ground state. The height of the curve is proportional to the probability of finding the electron at a distance between r and $r + dr$ from the nucleus.

Excited states

Let us now try to construct a slightly more complicated wave function which will satisfy (7.41), and in particular, one which will not have spherical symmetry. The higher states of one-dimensional systems have wave functions with nodes. Suppose, for example, that we try something of the form

$$\psi_z = zf(r) \tag{7.49}$$

which has a node at the origin. The laplacian of this quantity can readily be evaluated in cartesian coordinates, with the result

$$\nabla^2\psi_z = z\left(\frac{d^2f}{dr^2} + \frac{4}{r}\frac{df}{dr}\right) \tag{7.50}$$

so that the equation for $f(r)$ is

$$\frac{\hbar^2}{2\mu}\left(\frac{d^2f}{dr^2} + \frac{4}{r}\frac{df}{dr}\right) + \left(\frac{e'^2}{r} + E\right)f = 0 \tag{7.51}$$

and this is of exactly the same form as (7.43), so that the same trial solution can be used. We write

$$f(r) = e^{-\beta r} \qquad \psi_z = ze^{-\beta r} \tag{7.52}$$

and find that

$$\beta = \frac{\mu e'^2}{2\hbar^2} = \tfrac{1}{2}\alpha$$

$$E = \frac{-\hbar^2\beta^2}{2\mu} = -\tfrac{1}{4}\,\text{Ry}_\text{H}$$

where we have again used the pair of letters Ry to denote the ground-state energy and the subscript H refers to the correction of (1.11) for the effective mass appropriate to hydrogen. Comparison with (1.10) shows that we have here the first excited state of hydrogen, but this state is clearly degenerate, for there is nothing special about the direction z, and two other wave functions

$$\psi_x = xe^{-\beta r} \qquad \psi_y = ye^{-\beta r} \tag{7.53}$$

will have exactly the same energy. Thus we have three degenerate eigenfunctions of $\hat{H}$, and for some purposes they are very convenient, but they do not fit into the general scheme we have set up in Chap. 5 for classifying states according to their eigenvalues for a given set of operators. Indeed, according to Prob. 5.26, ψ_z is an eigenfunction of $\hat{L}_z$, but it is not an eigenfunction of $\hat{L}_x$ or $\hat{L}_y$, and analogous statements hold for ψ_x and ψ_y.

Problem 7.20   The first line of the principal series of hydrogen, the so-called Lyman α line, results when an atom makes a transition from one of the states just identified down to the ground state.

Compute the wavelength of this line in angstroms. Evaluate the same quantity for deuterium. Is the difference detectable by optical spectroscopy?

Problem 7.21 Show that $\hat{L}_x\psi_z = -i\psi_y$, $\hat{L}_y\psi_z = i\psi_x$, and $\hat{L}_z\psi_z = 0$, and fill in the remaining six products. Using the multiplication table thus obtained, show that $\hat{L}^2\psi_x = 2\psi_x$ and similarly for ψ_y and ψ_z, so that each of them is an eigenfunction of $\hat{L}^2$ corresponding to $l \doteq 1$.

In Chap. 5 we have set up a general program whereby we try to carry out calculations in quantum mechanics by constructing wave functions which are at the same time eigenfunctions of $\hat{H}$ and of operators which commute with $\hat{H}$ and with each other. We have seen that one of these operators may be chosen to be $\hat{L}_z$ (or $\hat{L}_x$ or $\hat{L}_y$) and another to be $\hat{L}^2$. Now we are going to see how this program can be carried through for the lowest states of hydrogen.

Let us denote by ψ_{nlm} the eigenfunction belonging to the nth energy level in (1.11) and also such that

$$\hat{L}_z\psi_{nlm} = m\psi_{nlm} \qquad \hat{L}^2\psi_{nlm} = l(l+1)\psi_{nlm}$$

Fig. 7.8 Probability distributions corresponding to hydrogen atoms in states with $n = 1$ and $n = 2$. The state $\psi_{2,0,0}$ has a central cloud like that of $\psi_{1,0,0}$, enveloped by a concentric spherical cloud.

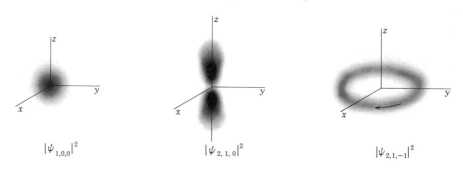

$|\psi_{1,0,0}|^2$ $|\psi_{2,1,0}|^2$ $|\psi_{2,1,-1}|^2$

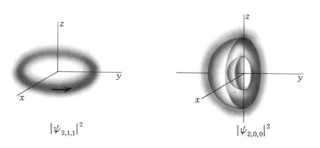

$|\psi_{2,1,1}|^2$ $|\psi_{2,0,0}|^2$

We have seen in Prob. 7.21 that ψ_z is $\psi_{2,1,0}$. To find $\psi_{2,1,-1}$ and $\psi_{2,1,1}$ we can apply $\hat{L}_-$ and $\hat{L}_+$ or else use the result of Prob. 5.21 to get the unnormalized eigenfunctions

$$\psi_{2,1,-1} = (x - iy)e^{-\beta r} \qquad \psi_{2,1,0} = ze^{-\beta r}$$
$$\psi_{2,1,1} = (x + iy)e^{-\beta r} \tag{7.54}$$

We see that $\psi_{2,1,-1}$ and $\psi_{2,1,1}$ are linear combinations of ψ_x and ψ_y, so that the set (7.54) is merely a rearrangement of the set ψ_x, ψ_y, ψ_z in a form more suitable for our general purposes of classification. The charge densities of $\psi_{2,1,-1}$ and $\psi_{2,1,1}$ are proportional to $(x^2 + y^2)e^{-2\beta r}$, and the charge density of $\psi_{2,1,0}$ is proportional to $z^2e^{-2\beta r}$. The former vanish on the z axis, and the latter vanishes on the xy plane. They are illustrated in Fig. 7.8, together with a fourth state degenerate with them which is found in Prob. 7.22.

Orbital magnetic moment

The wave functions $\psi_{2,1,-1}$ and $\psi_{2,1,1}$ clearly represent circulating currents, and a circulating current gives rise to a magnetic moment, whose value is characteristic of the atom in this state and which determines the atom's behavior in a magnetic field. If a circular current di flows in a ring of radius ρ, the magnetic moment produced is equal to the current multiplied by the area of the ring,

$$dM = \pi\rho^2 \, di$$

Since the current is uniform around the ring, let us calculate its value in the state $\psi_{2,1,-1}$ as it passes through the yz plane (see Fig. 7.9). It will be convenient to neglect entirely the motion of the nucleus, which contributes little to the magnetic properties. This amounts to taking the proton's mass to be infinite, so that the reduced mass μ is replaced by the electron mass m. With e denoting the electron's charge (and remembering that it is negative), we have for the current density

$$s_x = \frac{e\hbar}{2mi}\left(\psi^* \frac{\partial \psi}{\partial x} - \psi \frac{\partial \psi^*}{\partial x}\right)$$

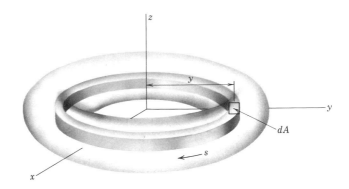

Fig. 7.9 Calculation of the magnetic moment corresponding to the state $\psi_{2,1,-1}$.

and with $\psi = N(x - iy)e^{-\beta r}$ this is

$$s_x = \frac{e\hbar}{m} |N|^2 y e^{-2\beta r}$$

Let dA be an element of area in the yz plane. The current element is $i = s_x \, dA$ and $\rho = y$, so that

$$dM = \pi y^2 \frac{e\hbar}{m} |N|^2 y e^{-2\beta r} \, dA$$

We note that, in the yz plane, $x = 0$ and so $|N|^2 y^2 e^{-2\beta r} = |\psi|^2$. Further, $2\pi y \, dA$ is the volume element of a circular tube around the z axis, which we shall call dv, so that dM becomes

$$dM = \frac{e\hbar}{2m} |\psi|^2 \, dv$$

and integration over all space gives for the total magnetic moment

$$M = \frac{e\hbar}{2m} \quad \text{Am}^2 \tag{7.55}$$

This is the basic unit of orbital magnetic moment, and it is known as a *Bohr magneton*. We shall see later, in Sec. 7.6, how it is possible to arrive at this result without resorting to such an explicit construction.

Problem 7.22 Look for a spherically symmetric state whose wave function is of the form

$$\psi = (1 - cr)e^{-\gamma r}$$

Find c, γ, and the energy, and show that $\psi_{2,0,0}$ is an appropriate designation for the state. Check your calculation by showing that your $\psi_{2,0,0}$ is orthogonal to $\psi_{1,0,0}$.

Problem 7.23 Find the normalization constants for the states $\psi_{2,l,m}$, thereby verifying the following table.

Normalized hydrogen eigenfunctions

$$\psi_{1,0,0} = \pi^{-1/2} a_0^{-3/2} e^{-r/a_0} \qquad\qquad\qquad E = -1 \text{ Ry}$$

$$\psi_{2,0,0} = (8\pi)^{-1/2} a_0^{-3/2} \left(1 - \frac{r}{2a_0}\right) e^{-r/2a_0} \qquad E = -\tfrac{1}{4} \text{ Ry}$$

$$\psi_{2,1,-1} = (64\pi)^{-1/2} a_0^{-5/2} (x - iy)e^{-r/2a_0} \qquad E = -\tfrac{1}{4} \text{ Ry} \tag{7.56}$$

$$\psi_{2,1,0} = (32\pi)^{-1/2} a_0^{-5/2} z e^{-r/2a_0} \qquad\qquad E = -\tfrac{1}{4} \text{ Ry}$$

$$\psi_{2,1,1} = (64\pi)^{-1/2} a_0^{-5/2} (x + iy)e^{-r/2a_0} \qquad E = -\tfrac{1}{4} \text{ Ry}$$

Here a_0 denotes the radius of the first Bohr orbit (1.9), and we ignore the distinction between the electron's inertial mass, used in Chap. 1, and its reduced mass, encountered above. We shall several times have occasion to refer to these expressions again, and it will be useful to introduce a standard nomenclature. States of different l are denoted by names which survive from the early days of spectroscopy.

l	0	1	2	3	4	etc.
Name	sharp	principal	diffuse	fine	—	
Abbreviation	s	p	d	f	g	etc.

To the letter denoting the angular-momentum value is prefixed the value of n as defined above; thus in table (7.56) we have exhibited the $1s$, $2s$, and $2p$ states. The notation is further elaborated to take account of spin states and their associated multiplicities. It is described in all books where the elements of spectroscopy are discussed, and we shall develop it below as it is needed.

The energies we have obtained are exceedingly accurate, thanks to the dynamical simplicity of the system considered. There are, however, small corrections to be made for the effect of spin and for the relativistic variation of mass with velocity. These will be evaluated in Chap. 14.

At this point the reader who skipped Prob. 6.11 may wish to reconsider his decision, for the problem is essentially that of calculating the relative intensities in a beam of atoms prepared in the state $\psi_{2,1,1}$ and split into three by the action of an oblique magnetic field.

Problem 7.24   One would perhaps conclude from the lack of angular momentum in the $1s$ state that the electron it describes is stationary. To show that this is not so, calculate the probability that the electron, if measured, would be found to lie in a momentum element $dp_x\, dp_y\, dp_z$ at the end of the vector $\mathbf{p}$. What are the electron's mean kinetic and potential energies? Verify that they add up to the appropriate value.

A singular potential

We have seen that even though the coefficient $V(r)$ in Schrödinger's equation for the hydrogen atom becomes infinite at the origin, still the wave function is perfectly regular there. If the potential is more singular at the origin than $1/r$, however, the situation changes. The subject of singular potentials is a complex one, and it is still not entirely understood; we shall confine ourselves here to a single, rather academic example in which the mathematical difficulties and their physical origin can easily be observed. The example is that of a hydrogen atom in which the nucleus exerts an inverse-cube force (of unspecified origin) in addition to the Coulomb force. Writing the energy E as $-\hbar^2\kappa^2/2m$, where κ is yet to be determined, we have for a spherically symmetrical state

$$\left[-\frac{\hbar^2}{2m}\left(\frac{d^2}{dr^2} + \frac{2}{r}\frac{d}{dr}\right) - \frac{e'^2}{r} + \frac{g}{r^2} \right]\psi(r) = -\frac{\hbar^2\kappa^2}{2m}\psi(r)$$

or

$$\left[-\left(\frac{d^2}{dr^2} + \frac{2}{r}\frac{d}{dr}\right) - \frac{2}{a_0 r} + \frac{\gamma}{r^2} \right]\psi(r) = -\kappa^2\psi(r) \tag{7.57}$$

where a_0 is the first Bohr radius and, for convenience, $\gamma = 2mg/\hbar^2$. If γ is positive, the inverse-cube force is repulsive. The ground state wave function is of the form

$$\psi(r) = r^\alpha e^{-\beta r} \tag{7.58}$$

Inserting this into (7.57) and equating to zero the coefficients of different powers of r gives

$$\alpha(\alpha + 1) = \gamma \qquad (\alpha + 1)\beta = a_0^{-1} \qquad \kappa^2 = \beta^2$$

whence

$$\alpha = \tfrac{1}{2}[-1 \pm (1 + 4\gamma)^{\frac{1}{2}}] \tag{7.59}$$

$$\beta = \frac{2}{a_0[1 \pm (1 + 4\gamma)^{\frac{1}{2}}]}$$

$$E = -\frac{\hbar^2\kappa^2}{2m} = -\frac{2}{1 + 2\gamma \pm (1 + 4\gamma)^{\frac{1}{2}}}\,\text{Ry}$$

If $\gamma > 0$, Eq. (7.41) dictates that the upper sign must be chosen in (7.59). If $\gamma < 0$, it must not be less than $-\frac{1}{4}$, for that would make E a complex number. There is no admissible solution in this case, and Probs. 7.25 and 7.26 will show why. For $-\frac{1}{4} < \gamma < 0$, one can argue from a principle of continuity. If $\gamma = 0$, we have a hydrogen atom and $\alpha = 0$. This requires the upper sign. If now γ is varied gradually from zero, ψ will also vary gradually, and so the upper sign is kept. This argument gains some force from the adiabatic theorem (Chap. 8), but it is not based on first principles and cannot be regarded as definitive.

A number of attempts have been made to discriminate between the two solutions, but they all involve more or less arbitrary assumptions, and it appears that the last word still remains to be spoken.

Problem 7.25 It has been noted that when $\gamma < -\frac{1}{4}$, the value of E becomes complex and the stable solution therefore fails. To explain this failure, calculate s_r, the (radial) current density for small values of $\mathbf{r}$ and integrate it, showing that there is a net flow inward toward the nucleus.

Problem 7.26 Show that a stable state with a strong, attractive inverse-cube potential would violate the uncertainty principle.

Solution. If there is an uncertainty Δp in the size of p, then p cannot be specified to be smaller than Δp, and similarly with r and Δr, so that

$$p \geqslant \Delta p \qquad r \geqslant \Delta r$$

To keep the signs straight, write $-g = g' > 0$, so that the energy classically calculated is

$$E = \frac{p^2}{2m} - \frac{e'^2}{r} - \frac{g'}{r^2} \geqslant \frac{(\Delta p)^2}{2m} - \frac{e'^2}{\Delta r} - \frac{g'}{(\Delta r)^2}$$

Now $\Delta p\, \Delta r \geqslant \tfrac{1}{2}\hbar$, so

$$E \geqslant \frac{\hbar^2}{8m(\Delta r)^2} - \frac{e'^2}{\Delta r} - \frac{g'}{(\Delta r)^2}$$

The minimum of this expression occurs for

$$\Delta r = \frac{2}{e'^2}\left(\frac{\hbar^2}{8m} - g'\right) = \tfrac{1}{2}a_0(1 - 4\gamma')$$

where $\gamma' = -\gamma$. If γ' increases from zero, Δr becomes smaller as the particle is sucked in toward the center until when $\gamma' = \tfrac{1}{4}$ $(\gamma = -\tfrac{1}{4})$, Δr becomes zero. Negative values of Δr are meaningless; the orbiting particle is swallowed up by the nucleus. The energy can now be calculated and compared with the exact value, with which it agrees qualitatively if the upper sign is chosen.

Problem 7.27 Show that the unwanted solution of (7.57) arises from the behavior of $V(r)$ in the neighborhood of the origin by solving the equation again for the potential

$$V_1(r) = \begin{cases} -\dfrac{e'^2}{r_0} + \dfrac{g}{r_0{}^2} & (0 < r < r_0) \\[2ex] -\dfrac{e'^2}{r} + \dfrac{g}{r^2} & (r_0 < r) \end{cases}$$

where $\beta r_0 \ll 1$. Sketch $V_1(r)$ for positive and negative values of g. Construct a solution in each region and match them at r_0 in the usual way. (That in the inner region is unique except for scale, while in the outer region a linear combination of ψ's formed with the two values of α is required.) Show that as $r_0 \to 0$ and $V_1(r) \to V(r)$, the solution so obtained is that formed by using the upper sign in (7.59).[3]

Problem 7.28 Discuss the p states corresponding to this singular potential.

The study of singular potentials slopes rapidly from here into deep water. There are certain special circumstances under which the wave equation may be said to have a solution in these cases,[3] but in

---

[3] K. Case, Phys. Rev., **80**, 797 (1950).

general the situation is somewhat unclear. Fortunately, these questions rarely occur in practice, and the only singular potential which will interest us in this book is a centrifugal force term arising in the study of the hydrogen atom. The equation in this case is of the form (7.57) with

$$\gamma = l(l + 1)$$

where l, the angular-momentum quantum number, is zero or a positive integer. Solving $\alpha(\alpha + 1) = l(l + 1)$ we find

$$\alpha = l \quad \text{or} \quad -l - 1 \quad (l = 0, 1, 2, \ldots)$$

and we see that all negative values of α are excluded by (7.41). The singular potential in this case presents no difficulties.

7.4 The Deuteron

We have found four out of the infinite number of bound states of the hydrogen atom. At the other extreme is another bound system, almost equally simple, which has only one. This is the deuteron, composed of a neutron and a proton in interaction with each other through a force whose most important property is that it has a very short range. In this section we shall consider the properties of two models of the deuteron, one highly artificial and the other slightly less so, but we shall reserve a quantitative discussion of the relation between the model and experiment for Chap. 17.

The square well

The first model is bound by the short-range potential shown in Fig. 7.10, which has a depth V_0 and a range r_0. The equation to be solved is (7.36) and, profiting from the discussion of the hydrogen atom, we shall assume that the ground state is an s state, that is, that it is spherically symmetrical. In this case the laplacian operator is given by (7.42), which we shall write in a simpler form,

$$\nabla^2\psi(r) = \frac{d^2\psi}{dr^2} + \frac{2}{r}\frac{d\psi}{dr} = \frac{1}{r}\frac{d^2}{dr^2}(r\psi) \tag{7.60}$$

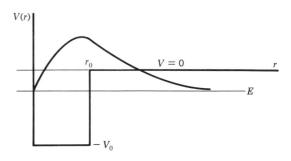

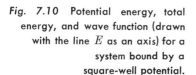

Fig. 7.10 Potential energy, total energy, and wave function (drawn with the line E as an axis) for a system bound by a square-well potential.

as is easily verified by carrying out the differentiation on the right. Assuming that the neutron and proton masses are each equal to M, we see from (7.34) that $\mu = \frac{1}{2}M$, so that (7.36) becomes

$$\frac{1}{r}\frac{d^2}{dr^2}(r\psi) + \frac{M}{\hbar^2}[E - V(r)]\psi = 0$$

This takes a simpler form if we introduce a new radial wave function

$$u = r\psi \tag{7.61}$$

which satisfies

$$u'' + \frac{M}{\hbar^2}[E - V(r)]u = 0 \qquad u(0) = u(\infty) = 0 \tag{7.62}$$

the first boundary condition following from (7.61) and (7.41). The situation here is somewhat different from that in the last section in that the binding energy $-E$, which must be supplied in order to take a deuteron apart, is experimentally known to be 2.23 Mev, whereas V_0 is not directly measurable. It will be convenient to write

$$-\frac{M}{\hbar^2}E = \kappa^2 \tag{7.63}$$

where κ has the dimensions of a reciprocal length and is analogous to the quantity designated by the same letter in Chap. 4 and in the preceding section. The characteristic unit of nuclear size is 10^{-13} cm, which we shall call one fermi (F), and in terms of it we find from (7.63) that

$$\kappa^{-1} = 4.32 \text{ F} \tag{7.64}$$

The range r_0 is not directly measurable, but it is known from various evidence to be in the neighborhood of 1.7 F, so that

$$\kappa r_0 \approx 0.40 \tag{7.65}$$

We introduce also the notation

$$\frac{M}{\hbar^2}(E + V_0) = K^2 \tag{7.66}$$

and separate (7.62) into two equations corresponding to the two ranges of r:

inside $u'' + K^2u = 0 \qquad (0 \leqslant r \leqslant r_0)$ 　　　　(7.67a)

outside $u'' - \kappa^2u = 0 \qquad (r_0 \leqslant r < \infty)$ 　　　　(7.67b)

The solution of the first can at once be written down from the fact that u must vanish at the origin,

$$u_{in} = A \sin Kr \qquad (0 \leqslant r \leqslant r_0) \tag{7.68a}$$

Similarly, the solution with the right asymptotic behavior in the outside region is

$$u_{\text{out}} = Be^{-\kappa r} \qquad (r_0 \leqslant r) \tag{7.68b}$$

For u and its derivative to be continuous at r_0 we must have

$$A \sin Kr_0 = Be^{-\kappa r_0} \tag{7.69a}$$

and

$$AK \cos Kr_0 = -B\kappa e^{-\kappa r_0} \tag{7.69b}$$

Dividing the first by the second gives

$$\tan \dot{K}r_0 = -\frac{K}{\kappa} = -\frac{Kr_0}{\kappa r_0} \tag{7.70}$$

We shall solve this equation by a graphical method. Figure 7.11 shows a plot of both sides of (7.70). Clearly, in order to have just one bound state, it is necessary to have

$$\tfrac{1}{2}\pi < Kr_0 < \pi \tag{7.71}$$

In view of (7.65), the straight line in the figure is relatively steep and the intersection occurs at

$$Kr_0 \gtrsim \tfrac{1}{2}\pi \tag{7.72}$$

What this implies becomes plain if we divide both sides by κr_0 and use the definitions of κ and K:

$$\left(\frac{V_0}{|E|} - 1\right)^{\frac{1}{2}} \gtrsim \frac{\pi}{2\kappa r_0} \approx 4$$

by (7.65), or

$$V_0 \gtrsim 17|E| \approx 38 \text{ MeV} \tag{7.73}$$

The content of (7.72) and (7.73) should be clearly noted, since it is vital for understanding the physical behavior of the deuteron.

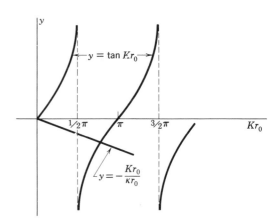

Fig. 7.11 Graphical solution of Eq. (7.70).

It is that the deuteron is just barely stable. The horizontal line E in Fig. 7.10 is about $16/17$ of the way to the top of the well, and (7.72) says that the wave function has barely turned over and started down at the edge of the well; its tangent is still almost flat.

Problem 7.29 Find the next approximation beyond the inequality (7.72) by using the fact that, if $x \gtrsim \frac{1}{2}\pi$,

$$\tan x = -\cot (\tfrac{1}{2}\pi - x) \approx -(\tfrac{1}{2}\pi - x)^{-1}$$

Show that, neglecting terms in κ^2,

$$Kr_0 \approx \frac{\pi}{2} + \frac{2}{\pi}\kappa r_0 \approx 105°$$

and that

$$V_0 \approx \frac{\hbar^2}{M}\left[\left(\frac{\pi}{2r_0}\right)^2 + \frac{2\kappa}{r_0}\right] \approx 41 \text{ MeV} \qquad (7.74)$$

The normalization of the square-well wave function is somewhat tricky, so we shall sketch it here. Integration of (7.68a,b) gives

$$4\pi\left(A^2\int_0^{r_0}\sin^2 Kr\,dr + B^2\int_{r_0}^\infty e^{-2\kappa r}\,dr\right) = 1$$

where we have used (7.61), and this is

$$4\pi\left[\frac{A^2}{2K}(Kr_0 - \sin Kr_0\cos Kr_0) + \frac{B^2}{2\kappa}e^{-2\kappa r_0}\right] = 1$$

Eliminate B by means of (7.69a):

$$4\pi\frac{A^2}{2K}\left[Kr_0 - \sin Kr_0\cos Kr_0 + \frac{K}{\kappa}\sin^2 Kr_0\right] = 1$$

By (7.70), this is

$$\frac{2\pi A^2}{K}[Kr_0 - \sin Kr_0\cos Kr_0 - \tan Kr_0\sin^2 Kr_0] = 1$$

or

$$\frac{2\pi A^2}{K}(Kr_0 - \tan Kr_0) = 1$$

so that using (7.70) again,

$$\frac{2\pi A^2}{\kappa}(1 + \kappa r_0) = 1$$

Thus, except for an arbitrary phase factor,

$$A = \left(\frac{\kappa}{2\pi}\right)^{1/2}(1 + \kappa r_0)^{-1/2}$$

and

$$B = \left(\frac{\kappa}{2\pi}\right)^{1/2}\frac{e^{\kappa r_0}}{(1 + \kappa r_0)^{1/2}}\left(1 + \frac{\kappa^2}{K^2}\right)^{-1/2}$$

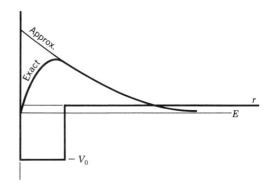

Fig. 7.12   Deuteron wave function and its zero-range approximation.

This exact relation can be simplified further if we remember that κ^2/K^2 is small and that κr_0 is about 0.4. We then have

$$B \approx \left(\frac{\kappa}{2\pi}\right)^{\frac{1}{2}} (1 + \tfrac{1}{2}\kappa r_0)$$

For purposes of rough calculation, it is often possible to neglect entirely the inner part of the wave function and write

$$u \approx \left(\frac{\kappa}{2\pi}\right)^{\frac{1}{2}} (1 + \tfrac{1}{2}\kappa r_0)e^{-\kappa r} \qquad (0 \leqslant r \leqslant \infty) \tag{7.75}$$

Exact and approximate wave functions are compared in Fig. 7.12.

Problem 7.30   To assess the accuracy of (7.75), calculate the fraction of time during which the neutron and proton in a deuteron are outside the range of each other's forces.

Hulthén's potential

The wave function of Fig. 7.10 has a simple form, and the complications of the square-well model arise mainly from the division of the potential function into two ranges. Here we shall adopt a different procedure. The neutron-proton potential is not in fact a square well and we do not know exactly what it is, except that it is complex in form and depends on the spins and charges of the particles in a very involved way. For purposes of the elementary theory, therefore, it should suffice to guess a reasonable wave function with simple analytic properties and then try to find the potential which would result in such a wave function. Solving (7.62) for $V(r)$ gives

$$V(r) - E = \frac{\hbar^2}{M} \frac{u''}{u} \tag{7.76}$$

Let us write a trial wave function in the form

$$u(r) = (1 - e^{-\alpha r})e^{-\kappa r} \tag{7.77}$$

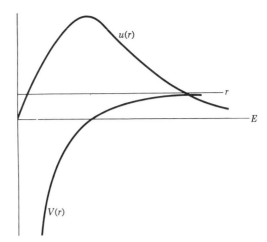

Fig. 7.13   Hulthén potential and
wave function.

This is zero at the origin, as required, and like (7.68b) it falls off as $e^{-\kappa r}$ for large r. Substitution into (7.76) gives

$$V(r) - E = \frac{\hbar^2}{M} \frac{\kappa^2 - (\alpha + \kappa)^2 e^{-\alpha r}}{1 - e^{-\alpha r}}$$

To evaluate E, we let $r \to \infty$ in this expression, and find that $-E = \hbar^2 \kappa^2 / M$, exactly as in (7.63). With this, we have

$$V(r) = -\frac{\hbar^2}{M} \frac{\alpha^2 + 2\alpha\kappa}{e^{\alpha r} - 1} \tag{7.78}$$

Introducing the abbreviation

$$\frac{\hbar^2}{M}(\alpha^2 + 2\alpha\kappa) = V_h \tag{7.79}$$

we have

$$V(r) = -\frac{V_h}{e^{\alpha r} - 1} \qquad E = -\frac{\hbar^2 \alpha^2}{4M}\left(\frac{M V_h}{\hbar^2 \alpha^2} - 1\right)^2 \tag{7.80}$$

This is an attractive potential of short range, first written down by Hulthén, and is shown together with its wave function in Fig. 7.13. It satisfies

$$\lim_{r \to 0} V(r) = \frac{V_h}{\alpha r} \qquad \lim_{r \to \infty} V(r) = V_h e^{-\alpha r}$$

Clearly, the range of the force is of the order of $1/\alpha$, and V_h plays roughly the role of V_0 in the square-well calculation.[4] It can be shown

[4] It should be noted that (7.74) and (7.79) are of the same general form. It can be shown that for any short-range force with loose binding, the three quantities well depth, range, and binding energy are always related in this same general way.

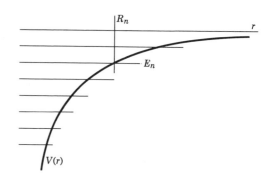

Fig. 7.14   Asymptotic distribution
of energy levels.

by more advanced methods[5] that the nth s-state energy level for a
Hulthén potential is

$$E_n = -\frac{\hbar^2\alpha^2}{4M}\left(\frac{MV_h}{n\hbar^2\alpha^2} - n\right)^2$$

where n starts at 1 and stops when the second term in the parentheses becomes greater than the first. The number of stationary s
states is thus given by the next integer smaller than $(MV_h)^{1/2}/\hbar\alpha$.

The number of bound s states

If a Hulthén potential is weak enough so that $V_h < \hbar^2\alpha^2/M$, there
will be no bound states. This leads to a rather fundamental question:
which potential functions produce an infinite number of bound states
and which a finite number? Of course, any potential which, like that
of the harmonic oscillator, increases without limit at large distances
will produce an infinite number of bound states. Such systems, however, are not met with in nature except as approximations to actual
situations, and so we shall consider only the case in which $V(r)$ goes
to zero for large r.

The question can easily be answered by using the WKB approximation, which we know to be good for large quantum numbers.
We shall see in Prob. 7.32 that the condition for the nth bound s
state is

$$\varphi = \int_0^{R_n} \left\{\frac{2m}{\hbar^2}\left[V(r) - E_n\right]\right\}^{1/2} dr = (n + \tfrac{1}{4})\pi \tag{7.81}$$

where R_n is the value of r at which the turning point occurs (Fig.
7.14). If the number of stationary states is infinite, then n must increase without limit as E approaches zero or, what is the same thing,

$$\lim_{E \to 0} \varphi = \infty$$

[5] L. Rosenfeld, *Nuclear Forces*, Interscience Publishers, Inc., New York,
1948, p. 77.

Clearly, only the asymptotic behavior of $V(r)$ for large r is of interest here. Let us write $E = -B$ $(B > 0)$ and suppose that $V(r)$ behaves asymptotically as $-Cr^{-a}$. Then $R_n = (C/B)^{1/a}$ and

$$\varphi = \left(\frac{2m}{\hbar^2}\right)^{1/2} \int^{(C/B)^{1/a}} (Cr^{-a} - B)^{1/2} \, dr$$

where the lower limit is omitted because the asymptotic behavior is all that matters. To simplify the integral, let $(B/C)r^a = x^a$, so that

$$\varphi = \left(\frac{2m}{\hbar^2}\right)^{1/2} B^{(1/2 - 1/a)} C^{1/a} \int^1 (1 - x^a)^{1/2} x^{-a/2} \, dx$$

The integral is a finite number, so that φ increases indefinitely as B approaches zero only if the exponent of B is negative, or $a < 2$. This result is conveniently expressed in the following form:

If $\lim\limits_{r \to \infty} r^2 V(r) = 0$, the number of bound s states is finite; otherwise, it is infinite.

The unshielded Coulomb potential—an idealization, of course—is the only commonly encountered potential in microphysics that produces an unlimited number of bound states.

In Chap. 9 we shall study the properties of short-range interactions as they are manifested in the scattering of one particle by another. Chapter 17 is devoted specifically to the neutron-proton interaction.

Problem 7.31   Show that the wave function 7.77 is normalized by

$$|N| = \left[\frac{\kappa}{2\pi}\left(1 + \frac{\kappa}{\alpha}\right)\left(1 + \frac{2\kappa}{\alpha}\right)\right]^{1/2}$$

Problem 7.32   Derive Eq. (7.81) and use it to determine the energy levels of the s states of hydrogen.[6]

Problem 7.33   Find the WKB energy levels of the s states of a system bound by a Hulthén potential. (The integral can be reduced to elementary forms by suitable changes of variable. Special attention should be paid to showing why there is a maximum value of n.)

7.5 The Diatomic Molecule

As a final example of systems in three dimensions, we shall briefly discuss the spectrum of a diatomic molecule. The energy levels are of three different sorts; they arise from the electronic energy states, the vibration of the two atoms, and the rotation of the molecule as a whole.

[6] How to improve the accuracy of this approximation is discussed by R. E. Langer, Phys. Rev., **51**, 669 (1937).

Electronic energy states

The electrons in a molecule are responsible for its mechanical stability. As was shown in a simplified calculation in Sec. 4.7, the sharing of electrons between two attractive centers can, for suitable electronic states, give rise to an attractive force between them. The electrons thus furnish the glue that holds a molecule together, but at the same time they can exist in a number of stable energy states. The electronic ground state in any molecule is, of course, one which produces binding; otherwise, the molecule would not exist. Excited states may or may not produce binding (that in Sec. 4.7 does not), and accordingly, excitation of the electrons to a higher energy level may lead to a dissociation of the molecule. Where the molecule remains stable, transitions among electronic energy levels will give rise to a spectrum much resembling atomic spectra and, like them, lying mostly in the visible and the ultraviolet range. To estimate the energies involved in such transitions, we note that as in (7.45), for example, if a represents a typical linear dimension of the molecule,

$$E_{el} \approx \frac{\hbar^2}{ma^2} \tag{7.82}$$

Problem 7.34 Derive (7.82) from the indeterminacy principle.

Vibrational energy states

At least for small departures from equilibrium, the vibrations of the two atoms under their mutual field of force will be approximately harmonic. If K is the elastic constant of this vibration and M the reduced mass of the two atoms, the vibrational energy states have energies given by

$$E_{vib} = (n + \tfrac{1}{2})\hbar\omega = (n + \tfrac{1}{2})\hbar\left(\frac{K}{M}\right)^{1/2} \tag{7.83a}$$

To estimate K, we remember that the molecular binding is produced by the action of electrons in their stable states, so that $\tfrac{1}{2}Ka^2$, the potential energy of a molecule distorted through a distance a and therefore strained to its maximum, is of the order of the electronic energy E_{el}. Thus for small values of n,

$$K \approx a^{-2}E_{el}$$

and

$$E_{vib} \approx \hbar\left(\frac{K}{M}\right)^{1/2} \approx \hbar\left(\frac{\hbar^2}{ma^4}\cdot\frac{1}{M}\right)^{1/2} \approx \left(\frac{m}{M}\right)^{1/2}E_{el} \tag{7.83b}$$

The vibrational energy levels are approximately equally spaced, and since the atomic masses M are commonly of the order of 10^4 times the electronic mass, the energies are of the order of 10^{-2} times the electronic energies. This puts the radiation associated with transitions among these energies into the infrared.

Rotational energy states

Let J be the molecule's moment of inertia. Then the operator giving its rotational kinetic energy is

$$\hat{H}_{\text{rot}} = \frac{\hat{P}^2}{2J}$$

where P represents the angular momentum. The eigenvalues of this quantity are of the form

$$E_{\text{rot}} = \frac{k(k+1)\hbar^2}{2J} \qquad (k = 0, 1, 2, \ldots) \tag{7.84a}$$

where k is the rotational quantum number. J is, of course, of the order of Ma^2, and so

$$E_{\text{rot}} \approx \frac{\hbar^2}{2J} \approx \frac{\hbar^2}{2Ma^2} \approx \frac{m}{M} E_{\text{el}} \tag{7.84b}$$

which is another factor of 10^2 smaller than E_{vib}, and the associated radiations are in the far infrared.[7]

We shall see in Chap. 10 that there is a selection rule in rotational transitions according to which l generally decreases by only one unit when a photon is given off. In the transition from k to $k - 1$, therefore, the photon energy is

$$\Delta E = \frac{[k(k+1) - (k-1)k]\hbar^2}{2J}$$

$$= \frac{k\hbar^2}{J} \qquad (k = 1, 2, 3, \ldots) \tag{7.85}$$

This means that, since k can take on all values up to some large number where the molecule flies apart, there will occur a great variety of (almost) evenly spaced photon energies. This is the origin of the bands of closely spaced lines which are characteristic of molecular spectra.

Problem 7.35 Roughly how many rotational states will a molecule have?

---

[7] The reader will perhaps have surmised that E_{el}, E_{vib}, and E_{rot} are the first three terms in an approximation to the exact energy which is expressed as a power series in the small quantity $(m/M)^{1/2}$. This is, in fact, the case; and the approximation amounts to assuming that, owing to their small mass, the electrons move so much faster than the atoms that at any point in the atoms' motion the electron orbits are nearly the same as they would be if the atoms were at rest in the same position. The details, worked out by Born and Oppenheimer in 1927, lead to quantum-mechanical formulas for the three types of process which we have discussed here.

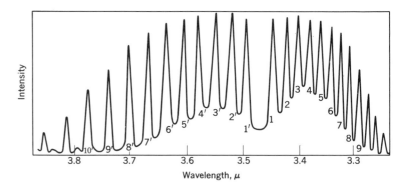

Fig. 7.15   Near infrared absorption spectrum of HCl. [From E. S.
Imes, Astrophys. J., **50**, 251 (1919). By permission of the
University of Chicago Press.]

Problem 7.36   Show that the moment of inertia about the center of mass of two atoms of masses M_1 and M_2 separated by a distance a is Ma^2, where M is the reduced mass.

The infrared spectra of diatomic molecules arise from transitions which are at once vibrational and rotational. The selection rule for an oscillator is that its quantum number may change by one unit. Since the electrons in an ordinary discharge tube are energetic enough to cause dissociation, molecular spectroscopy is done chiefly by measurement of absorption spectra. In absorbing a quantum, a molecule will increase its vibrational quantum number by one unit and either increase or decrease its angular momentum by one unit. The energy of the absorbed quantum is thus

$$\Delta E_{\text{abs}} = \Delta E_{\text{vib}} + \frac{\hbar^2}{2J} \begin{cases} k(k+1) - (k+1)(k+2) & \\ & (k \to k+1) \\ k(k+1) - (k-1)k & \\ & (k \to k-1) \end{cases}$$

$$= \Delta E_{\text{vib}} + \frac{\hbar^2}{2J} \begin{cases} -(2k+1) & (k = 0, 1, 2, \ldots) \\ +2k & (k = 1, 2, 3, \ldots) \end{cases} \tag{7.86}$$

where ΔE_{vib} is $\hbar\omega$ by (6.38a) and the value $k = 0$ is excluded in the second line of (7.86) because k cannot decrease if it is already zero.

As an example, let us look at the absorption spectrum of HCl in the near infrared, Fig. 7.15. The numbers under the absorption maxima give the value of k; primes distinguish the transitions $k \to k+1$. The gap in the center marks the missing value of k in (7.86). Careful measurements enable one to deduce that

$$\Delta E_{\text{vib}} = \hbar\omega = 6.47 \times 10^{-20} \text{ J} = 0.404 \text{ eV} \tag{7.87a}$$

$$\frac{\hbar^2}{2J} = 2.05 \times 10^{-22} \text{ J} = 1.28 \times 10^{-3} \text{ eV} \tag{7.87b}$$

leading to

$$a = 1.29\text{Å} \qquad (7.87c)$$

We note that the ratio of the lowest rotational energy to the lowest vibrational energy is

$$\frac{2\hbar^2/2J}{\frac{1}{2}\hbar\omega} = \frac{1}{79}$$

in rough agreement with the estimate of $(m/M)^{\frac{1}{2}}$ made earlier. Further, the small value of $\hbar^2/2J$ shows how it is that lines corresponding to all different values of k can be seen in the absorption spectrum; for the lowest rotational state is far lower than the thermal energy at room temperature, and so many rotational states will normally be excited.

Problem 7.37 The absorption cell in the measurements shown in Fig. 7.15 was at room temperature. The thermal energy kT per degree of freedom is 0.025 eV at room temperature. How many degrees of freedom has a rotating diatomic molecule? (We are not concerned here with vibration or with spinning about the symmetry axis.) Roughly how would you expect the occupation of rotational states to be distributed at thermal equilibrium? Does this explain the intensities in Fig. 7.15?

It can be seen from Fig. 7.15 that the theory is not perfect, for the bands are not evenly spaced. Three principal approximations have been made: one effect of rotation is to stretch the molecule and change its moment of inertia; this has been ignored. Also, the binding does not, of course, follow Hooke's law exactly; and, finally, a more exact treatment takes account of the Coriolis force on a molecule which is both rotating and vibrating. What one can in fact do is to carry out the calculations more exactly and then use them to deduce from the band spacing what must be the form of the intermolecular potential.[8] More complex polyatomic molecules may also be treated, though the mathematics becomes rather difficult, and it is also possible, for still larger molecules, to compute special spectral frequencies corresponding to the oscillation of certain bonds and the vibration or rotation of certain radicals. These techniques are of use in spectroscopically identifying compounds of high molecular weight.

7.6 Electron in a Magnetic Field

In this section we shall discuss the question of how to put a magnetic field into Schrödinger's equation, neglecting the effects which

---

[8] See G. Herzberg, *Spectra of Diatomic Molecules*, D. Van Nostrand Company, Inc., Princeton, N.J., 1950.

arise from the spin. In classical physics the effect of a magnetic field **B** is to exert a force at right angles to the particle's velocity **v** equal to

$$\mathbf{F}_{mag} = e\mathbf{v} \times \mathbf{B} \tag{7.88}$$

where e is the particle's charge. Such a force causes the particle to move in a curved path, but it does no work on it, leaving the velocity unchanged. It is therefore not obvious how to put **B** into the hamiltonian function of Schrödinger's theory, since the latter designates an energy which must be independent of **B**. It turns out that the way to do this is to use the vector potential $\mathbf{A}(\mathbf{r},t)$, defined in Appendix 5, and replace the momentum operator $\hat{\mathbf{p}}$, whenever it occurs in the hamiltonian, by $\hat{\mathbf{p}} - e\mathbf{A}$. This recipe can be deduced, somewhat artificially, from a study of hamiltonian dynamics, and that is how it was first done by K. Schwarzschild in 1903,[9] but the entire process is so much simpler and more natural in the framework of relativistic mechanics that we shall leave it for the reader's later study.[10] It is, however, easy to verify that the recipe gives the right results. We shall do so after the manner of Ehrenfest's theorem of Sec. 3.4, starting with the hamiltonian operator

$$\hat{H} = \frac{1}{2m} (\hat{\mathbf{p}} - e\mathbf{A})^2 + eV \tag{7.89}$$

Let us consider for simplicity a wave packet which is small compared with the distance over which **A** and V vary appreciably. Its velocity will be given by

$$\frac{d}{dt} \langle \mathbf{r} \rangle = \frac{i}{\hbar} \langle [\hat{H}, \mathbf{r}] \rangle$$

and this works out to be

$$\frac{d}{dt} \langle \mathbf{r} \rangle = \frac{1}{m} \langle \hat{\mathbf{p}} - e\mathbf{A} \rangle = \frac{1}{m} (\langle \hat{\mathbf{p}} \rangle - e\mathbf{\mathfrak{A}}) \tag{7.90}$$

where $\mathbf{\mathfrak{A}}$ in the last expression is the value of **A** at the position of the wave packet. It will be convenient to introduce a velocity operator

$$\hat{\mathbf{v}} = \frac{1}{m} (\hat{\mathbf{p}} - e\mathbf{A}) \tag{7.91}$$

so that the hamiltonian can still be written

$$\hat{H} = \tfrac{1}{2}m\hat{\mathbf{v}}^2 + eV$$

It is the significance of the quantity $\hat{\mathbf{p}}$ which has changed here.

[9] K. Symon, *Mechanics*, Addison-Wesley Publishing Company, Inc., Reading, Mass., 1953, chap. 9.

[10] L. Landau and E. Lifschitz, *The Classical Theory of Fields*, Addison-Wesley Publishing Company, Inc., Reading, Mass., 1951, 1962, chap. 3; W. Panofsky and M. Phillips, *Classical Electricity and Magnetism*, Addison-Wesley Publishing Company, Inc., Reading, Mass., 1955, 1962, chap. 23.

To find the acceleration, we have

$$\frac{d}{dt}\langle \hat{p}_x \rangle = \frac{i}{\hbar}\left\langle \frac{1}{2m}[(\hat{\mathbf{p}} - e\mathbf{A})^2, \hat{p}_x] + e[V, \hat{p}_x] \right\rangle$$

$$= \frac{e}{2m}\left\langle (\hat{\mathbf{p}} - e\mathbf{A})\cdot\frac{\partial \mathbf{A}}{\partial x} + \frac{\partial \mathbf{A}}{\partial x}\cdot(\hat{\mathbf{p}} - e\mathbf{A}) \right\rangle - e\left\langle \frac{\partial V}{\partial x} \right\rangle$$

Assuming that $\partial \mathbf{A}/\partial x$ and $\partial V/\partial x$ are essentially constant over the wave packet, we can take them outside the brackets and write

$$\frac{d}{dt}\langle \hat{p}_x \rangle = e\langle \hat{\mathbf{v}} \rangle\cdot\frac{\partial \mathbf{\mathcal{G}}}{\partial x} - e\frac{\partial \mathcal{V}}{\partial x} \tag{7.92}$$

and similarly for the y and z components. Introducing the number $\mathbf{v}$ to denote the expectation value $\langle \hat{\mathbf{v}} \rangle$, we can infer from (7.92) that

$$\frac{d}{dt}\langle \hat{\mathbf{p}} \rangle = e\mathbf{\nabla}[(\mathbf{v}\cdot\mathbf{\mathcal{G}}) - \mathcal{V}]$$

where it is understood that $\mathbf{v}$, the particle's velocity, is to be regarded as a function of t and not explicitly of x, y, and z. Going back to (7.90), we have

$$\frac{d}{dt}(m\mathbf{v} + e\mathbf{\mathcal{G}}) = e\mathbf{\nabla}[(\mathbf{v}\cdot\mathbf{\mathcal{G}}) - \mathcal{V}] \tag{7.93}$$

To reduce this to a more familiar form, we note that $\mathbf{\mathcal{G}}$, which is evaluated at the particle's position, has a time derivative arising from two sources: $\mathbf{A}$ itself is in general a function of time and also, even if it is not, the particle in moving from place to place encounters new values of $\mathbf{A}$ that change at a rate

$$\frac{\partial \mathbf{\mathcal{G}}}{\partial x}\frac{dx}{dt} + \frac{\partial \mathbf{\mathcal{G}}}{\partial y}\frac{dy}{dt} + \frac{\partial \mathbf{\mathcal{G}}}{\partial z}\frac{dz}{dt}$$

We shall write this, using a notation which is reasonable but which must be carefully noted, as $(\mathbf{v}\cdot\mathbf{\nabla})\mathbf{\mathcal{G}}$. The total time derivative which appears in (7.93) is thus

$$\frac{d\mathbf{\mathcal{G}}}{dt} = \frac{\partial \mathbf{\mathcal{G}}}{\partial t} + (\mathbf{v}\cdot\mathbf{\nabla})\mathbf{\mathcal{G}} \tag{7.94}$$

and (7.93) can be written as

$$m\frac{d\mathbf{v}}{dt} = e\left[-\mathbf{\nabla}\mathcal{V} - \frac{\partial \mathbf{\mathcal{G}}}{\partial t} + \mathbf{\nabla}(\mathbf{v}\cdot\mathbf{\mathcal{G}}) - (\mathbf{v}\cdot\mathbf{\nabla})\mathbf{\mathcal{G}}\right] \tag{7.95}$$

The first pair of terms on the right give just the electric field $\mathbf{\mathcal{E}}$ (see Appendix 5), and the second pair can be rewritten by the use of the vector identity

$$\mathbf{a} \times [\mathbf{b} \times \mathbf{c}] = \mathbf{b}(\mathbf{a}\cdot\mathbf{c}) - (\mathbf{a}\cdot\mathbf{b})\mathbf{c}$$

There is no inconsistency here if **b** is taken to be the gradient operator acting on **c**, the vector potential, but not on **a**, the velocity. The second pair of terms is therefore

$$\mathbf{v} \times [\nabla \times \mathbf{\mathfrak{C}}]$$

which by Appendix 5 is $\mathbf{v} \times \mathbf{\mathfrak{B}}$, and so the equation of motion (7.95) takes its final form

$$m \frac{d\mathbf{v}}{dt} = e[\mathbf{\mathcal{E}} + \mathbf{v} \times \mathbf{\mathfrak{B}}] \tag{7.96}$$

which is the well-known equation for a particle in an electric and magnetic field. We have thus shown that if in quantum mechanics we use the hamiltonian (7.89), then a wave packet whose limits are small compared with the distance over which **A** and V change appreciably has the behavior that classical physics attributes to a particle in the same situation.

The electromagnetic potentials were first introduced by Lorentz in 1867, and from the relatively simple structure of Maxwell's equations when expressed in terms of them one can see how they lead to great mathematical simplification of the theory. They remain somewhat nonphysical, however, since their magnitudes are not uniquely determined by the values of the classically observable force functions **B** and **E**. Still, quantum mechanics does not cavil at quantities which have no direct physical significance; for this is true even of the wave function itself. The reader should therefore not be surprised to find a quantity appearing in the equation of motion whose value is to a certain extent arbitrary. Equation (7.96) shows that the arbitrariness disappears in the classical limit, and he will get a chance in Prob. 7.39 to show that it actually has no effect at all on the results of the theory.

Problem 7.38   Derive (7.90) and (7.92).

Problem 7.39   Let $X(\mathbf{r},t)$ be a function of **r** and t which is arbitrary except that it satisfies the homogeneous wave equation

$$\nabla^2 X - \frac{1}{c^2} \ddot{X} = 0$$

and let $\psi(\mathbf{r},t)$ be a solution of the equation

$$i\hbar \frac{\partial \psi}{\partial t} - \frac{1}{2m} (\hat{\mathbf{p}} - e\mathbf{A})^2 \psi - eV\psi = 0$$

Consider a new ψ, given by $\psi_1 = e^{-ieX/\hbar}\psi$, and show that ψ_1 satisfies the equation

$$i\hbar \frac{\partial \psi_1}{\partial t} - \frac{1}{2m} [\hat{\mathbf{p}} - e(\mathbf{A} + \nabla X)]^2 \psi_1 - e(V - \dot{X})\psi_1 = 0 \tag{7.97}$$

This is the wave equation for a particle moving in fields whose potentials are $\mathbf{A} + \nabla X$ and $V - \dot{X}$. Calculate the corresponding values of $\mathbf{E}$ and $\mathbf{B}$. Show that in describing a particle moving in an electric and magnetic field a transformation of $\mathbf{A}$ and V which leaves $\mathbf{E}$ and $\mathbf{B}$ unchanged does not alter the value of $\langle x \rangle$ or $d\langle x \rangle/dt$ or, by extension, any other measurable dynamical quantity. Comment on the complementary roles played by arbitrariness in $\mathbf{A}$, V, and the phase of ψ in quantum mechanics.

Problem 7.40   As a special case of (7.97), show how the wave function of a particle in an electrostatic field is changed by a change in the zero level with respect to which the electrostatic potential is measured. Will this change any experimentally verifiable results given by the theory? We have seen that the wavelength of a de Broglie wave can be measured by diffraction. What is the outlook for the measurement of its frequency?

Problem 7.41   Find $[\hat{v}_x, \hat{v}_y]$ for a charged particle in a magnetic field and write down the corresponding indeterminacy relation. Can you devise a conceptual experiment by which it can be understood?

The Zeeman effect

As an example of the use of (7.89), let us calculate the energy levels of a hydrogen atom immersed in a uniform magnetic field B in the positive z direction. First we must find a vector potential which describes such a field; the reader can easily verify that

$$A_x = -\tfrac{1}{2}By \qquad A_y = \tfrac{1}{2}Bx \qquad A_z = 0$$

does so (though it is not unique). Now we can write out $\hat{H}$. It will be seen that $\hat{p}_x$ commutes with A_x, $\hat{p}_y$ with A_y, and $\hat{p}_z$ with A_z, so that the order in which these factors appear is unimportant; and approximating the reduced mass μ by the electronic mass m, we have

$$\hat{H} = \frac{1}{2m} (\hat{p}^2 - 2e\mathbf{A} \cdot \hat{\mathbf{p}} + e^2 A^2) + eV$$

$$= \frac{\hat{p}^2}{2m} - \frac{eB}{2m} (x\hat{p}_y - y\hat{p}_x) + \frac{e^2 B^2}{8m} (x^2 + y^2) + eV \tag{7.98}$$

$$\hat{H} = \frac{\hat{p}^2}{2m} - \frac{eB}{2m} \hbar \hat{L}_z + \frac{e^2 B^2}{8m} (x^2 + y^2) + eV \tag{7.99}$$

In most atomic situations the term in B^2 is quite unimportant. To see this, consider the expectation values of the terms in B and B^2. They are equal if B is equal to

$$B_0 = \frac{4\langle L_z \rangle \hbar}{e \langle x^2 + y^2 \rangle}$$

If $\langle L_z \rangle$ is of the order of 1 and $\langle x^2 + y^2 \rangle$ is of the order of a few square angstroms, then $B_0 \approx 10^5$ Wb/m² or 10^9 G, which is far larger than anything produced in the laboratory. If we neglect the term in B^2, then the remainder is usually easy to deal with. Consider, for example, the eigenstates of hydrogen found earlier in this chapter. They are at the same time eigenfunctions of $\hat{L}_z$ belonging to the eigenvalue m_l. They are therefore (omitting the small term) eigenfunctions of (7.99) with the added energy

$$E' = -\frac{e\hbar}{2m} m_l B \qquad (m_l = 0, \pm 1, \pm 2, \ldots) \tag{7.100}$$

(The neglect of the proton's motion will be remedied in Prob. 7.45, below.) But the potential energy of a magnet of moment $\mathbf{M}$ in the field B is given by $-\mathbf{M} \cdot \mathbf{B}$, from which we deduce that the atom as a whole acts (to this approximation) as though it had a magnetic moment whose z component is

$$M_z = \frac{e\hbar}{2m} m_l \tag{7.101}$$

in agreement with (7.55), which was calculated for the state with $m_l = 1$. Equation (7.101) can also be written

$$M_z = \frac{e}{2m} \langle P_z \rangle \tag{7.102}$$

where P is the angular momentum. The factor $e/2m$ is the gyromagnetic ratio for orbital motion, agreeing with the value calculated from classical mechanics in Prob. 5.28.

Problem 7.42 If $V = 0$ in (7.99), the hamiltonian begins to resemble that for a two-dimensional oscillator considered at the beginning of this chapter. Exploit this resemblance to find the energy levels of an electron in a uniform magnetic field. Note that $\hat{H}$, $\hat{p}_z$, and $\hat{L}_z$ commute with each other and can therefore take on definite values simultaneously. Evaluate and sketch the wave functions for the three lowest states.

Effects of spin

A very important group of calculations centered around the Zeeman effect and its nuclear analogue requires the evaluation of the magnetic moment in a situation in which the intrinsic magnetic moment connected with the particle's spin is added to the orbital contribution. Restricting ourselves to the case of a single electron, we shall give here an easily visualized graphical procedure which leads to the correct answer, reserving its rigorous justification for Prob. 7.42.

The difficulty of the calculation arises from the fact that the spin gyromagnetic ratio is twice as large as that for orbital motion.

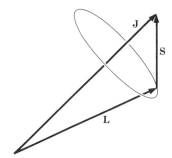

Fig. 7.16 The vector addition $\mathbf{J} = \mathbf{L} + \mathbf{S}$.

This fact was deduced by Goudsmit and Uhlenbeck from spectroscopic data at the time they proposed the existence of spin; it turns out to be a relativistic effect which is most easily understood from Dirac's electron theory. Accepting these gyromagnetic ratios, we then assume that the vector magnetic moment $\mathbf{M}$ is given by

$$\mathbf{M} = \frac{e\hbar}{2m} \langle \mathbf{L} + 2\mathbf{S} \rangle \tag{7.103}$$

where e must be taken negative for an electron. The relation between $\mathbf{L}$, $\mathbf{S}$, and the constant vector $\mathbf{J}$ is shown in Fig. 7.16, in which the circle marks the locus of the tip of the $\mathbf{L}$ vector. The $\mathbf{M}$ vectors (drawn as though $e\hbar/2m$ were positive) are shown in Fig. 7.17, where it is seen that, because of the difference in gyromagnetic ratios, $\mathbf{M}$ is not parallel to $\mathbf{J}$ but precesses around it. Since an expectation value in quantum mechanics corresponds to a time average in classical physics, and since the classical time average of the precessing $\mathbf{M}$ is just its projection on $\mathbf{J}$, we evaluate (7.103) as

$$\mathbf{M} = \frac{e\hbar}{2m} \left\langle \frac{\hat{\mathbf{J}} \cdot \hat{\mathbf{L}}}{\hat{J}^2} \hat{\mathbf{J}} + 2 \frac{\hat{\mathbf{J}} \cdot \hat{\mathbf{S}}}{\hat{J}^2} \hat{\mathbf{J}} \right\rangle$$

$$= \frac{e\hbar}{2m} \left\langle [\hat{\mathbf{J}} \cdot \hat{\mathbf{L}} + 2\hat{\mathbf{J}} \cdot \hat{\mathbf{S}}] \frac{\hat{\mathbf{J}}}{\hat{J}^2} \right\rangle$$

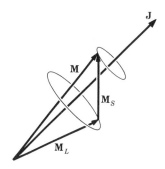

Fig. 7.17 The vector addition $\mathbf{M} = \mathbf{M}_L + \mathbf{M}_S$.

To evaluate the two scalar products, we write

$$\hat{\mathbf{S}} = \hat{\mathbf{J}} - \hat{\mathbf{L}} \qquad\qquad \hat{\mathbf{L}} = \hat{\mathbf{J}} - \hat{\mathbf{S}}$$

and

$$\hat{S}^2 = \hat{J}^2 + \hat{L}^2 - 2\hat{\mathbf{J}} \cdot \hat{\mathbf{L}} \qquad \hat{L}^2 = \hat{J}^2 + \hat{S}^2 - 2\hat{\mathbf{J}} \cdot \hat{\mathbf{S}}$$

whence

$$\mathbf{M} = \frac{e\hbar}{2m} \left\langle [\hat{J}^2 + \hat{L}^2 - \hat{S}^2 + 2(\hat{J}^2 + \hat{S}^2 - \hat{L}^2)] \frac{\hat{\mathbf{J}}}{2\hat{J}^2} \right\rangle$$

$$= \frac{e\hbar}{2m} \left\langle (3\hat{J}^2 - \hat{L}^2 + \hat{S}^2) \frac{\hat{\mathbf{J}}}{2\hat{J}^2} \right\rangle$$

and evaluating the expectation values in the one-electron case gives

$$\mathbf{M} = \frac{e\hbar}{2m} \left[1 + \frac{j(j+1) - l(l+1) + \frac{3}{4}}{2j(j+1)} \right] \langle \hat{\mathbf{J}} \rangle \tag{7.104}$$

from which we have the two special cases, analogous to those studied in Sec. 6.5,

$$\mathbf{M} = \frac{e\hbar}{2m} \frac{j + \frac{1}{2}}{j} \langle \hat{\mathbf{J}} \rangle \qquad (j = l + \frac{1}{2}) \tag{7.105a}$$

$$\mathbf{M} = \frac{e\hbar}{2m} \frac{j + \frac{1}{2}}{j + 1} \langle \hat{\mathbf{J}} \rangle \qquad (j = l - \frac{1}{2}) \tag{7.105b}$$

Suppose now that the entire system is immersed in a weak magnetic field B in the z direction. The $\mathbf{J}$ vector will begin to precess slowly about the z axis, and just as in (7.100) and (7.101), it is only the z component of $\mathbf{J}$ that will appear in the energy expression and hence in the effective magnetic moment. This gives finally

$$M_z = \frac{e\hbar}{2m} \frac{j + \frac{1}{2}}{j} m_j \qquad (j = l + \frac{1}{2}) \tag{7.106a}$$

$$M_z = \frac{e\hbar}{2m} \frac{j + \frac{1}{2}}{j + 1} m_j \qquad (j = l - \frac{1}{2}) \tag{7.106b}$$

It is customary to write formulas like this in the form

$$M_z = g_j \frac{e\hbar}{2m} m_j \tag{7.107}$$

where g_j, which measures the combined magnetic effects of orbit and spin, is known as the *Landé g factor*.

Problem 7.43 The evaluation of (7.103) is a perfectly straightforward problem if one knows the wave functions with respect to which the expectation value is to be taken. In the case considered just above, these are given exactly by (6.58) and (6.59). Evaluate M_z by using these wave functions or Table 6.1 and verify (7.106a,b). This validates the heuristic vector argument presented above.

Problem 7.44   The vector model of the atom, which is rather complex to justify theoretically and will not be discussed here, makes use of the scheme of LS coupling, in which the total **J** of the radiating electrons of an atom is compounded by first summing all the orbital momenta to get a single **L** and then all the spins to get a single **S**; then finally **J** = **L** + **S**. What is the general formula for the Landé g factor in this case? It is convenient to start by writing Eq. (7.103) as

$$\mathbf{M} = \frac{e\hbar}{2m} \langle \mathbf{J} + \mathbf{S} \rangle$$

As an example of the use of (7.106a,b) let us look at the Zeeman effect in the D lines of sodium. This spectrum is produced by a single radiating electron, and the D lines arise from the transitions from the first excited ^2P level to the ground state, which is ^2S. In these term designations, the prefixed number indicates the multiplicity. For example, ^2P means that the spin vector has two possible orientations relative to the angular-momentum vector. In the absence of an external magnetic field the ^2P level is split according to the two possibilities, $j = l \pm \frac{1}{2}$, into $^2P_{3/2}$ and $^2P_{1/2}$. The ^2S level is called a doublet only for uniformity with the other levels with spin $\frac{1}{2}$; since there is no **L**, there is no question of **S** having two possible orientations with respect to **L**, and the level is not split. The three levels are shown in Fig. 7.18a. In Fig. 7.18b the same levels are shown split by an external field.

Fig. 7.18   The lowest S and P levels of sodium. The splittings are greatly exaggerated relative to the level displacements. In (a), the D lines result from transitions from the pair of ^2P levels to the ^2S level. In (b), a magnetic field has been applied and the levels are further split.

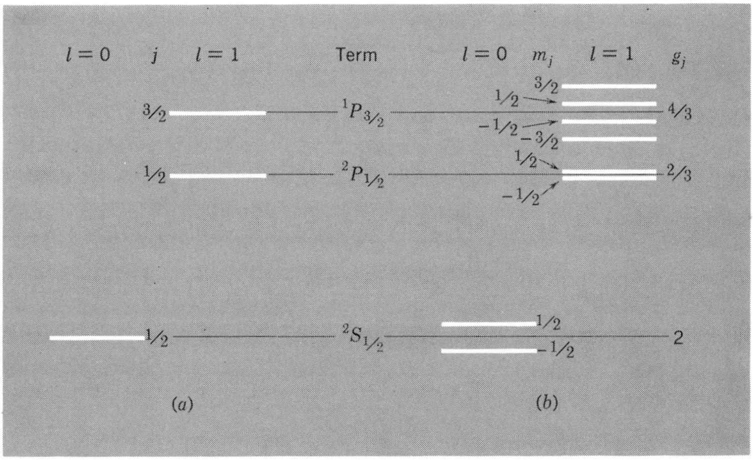

Problem 7.45   The selection rules governing transitions from one Zeeman level to another vary according as the spectrum is viewed from a direction parallel or perpendicular to the applied field. They are derived in Sec. 10.4:

$$\Delta m_j = \pm 1 \qquad \text{viewed parallel to } \mathbf{B}$$

$$\Delta m_j = 0, \pm 1 \qquad \text{viewed normal to } \mathbf{B}$$

Enumerate the lines which will be visible in each direction and calculate their wavelength displacements from those visible at zero field. Let $B = 5000$ G $(0.5$ Wb/m$^2)$. The wavelengths of the undisplaced lines are about 5890 Å.

Two-particle systems

The reader may wonder what happens to relations like (7.99) to (7.102) in a two-particle system in which both particles are considered movable, as in the argument leading up to (7.33). Let us consider a system whose center of mass is at rest in a uniform magnetic field of induction $\mathbf{B}$. It can then be shown with a little trouble that the two-particle hamiltonian is

$$\hat{H} = \frac{\hat{p}^2}{2\mu} - \frac{e_1 m_2{}^2 + e_2 m_1{}^2}{(m_1 + m_2)^2} \frac{\hbar B}{2\mu} \hat{L}_z + \frac{e_1{}^2 m_2{}^3 + e_2{}^2 m_1{}^3}{(m_1 + m_2)^3} \frac{B^2}{8\mu} (x^2 + y^2) \\ + eV \qquad (7.108)$$

where μ is the reduced mass and $\hat{p}$ is the operator whose x component is $(\hbar/i)\, \partial/\partial x$, x being the relative coordinate defined by (7.32). This is to be compared with (7.99). If the charges are equal and opposite, $e_1 = -e_2 = -e$, then

$$\hat{H} = \frac{\hat{p}^2}{2\mu} - \frac{m_1 - m_2}{m_1 + m_2} \frac{e\hbar B}{2\mu} \hat{L}_z + \frac{m_1{}^3 + m_2{}^3}{(m_1 + m_2)^3} \frac{e^2 B^2}{8\mu} (x^2 + y^2) + eV \qquad (7.109)$$

from which we see as in (7.102) that the reduced gyromagnetic ratio of the system is

$$\gamma_{\text{red}} = \frac{m_1 - m_2}{m_1 + m_2} \frac{e}{2\mu} \qquad (7.110)$$

which can be written as $e/2\mu'$, with

$$\frac{1}{\mu'} = \frac{1}{m_2} - \frac{1}{m_1}$$

The striking thing about this result is that γ_{red} vanishes if the two masses are equal. This can be understood qualitatively if we picture a positive and a negative particle with equal masses circling about their common center of mass. They revolve at the same rate in the same orbit, and since their charges are opposite, the magnetic moments which they produce cancel exactly.

Problem 7.46   Derive (7.110) classically for the case of circular motion of two particles of unequal mass about their common center of gravity.

Problem 7.47   Derive (7.108).

The quantization of flux

We can use these methods to prove an interesting and experimentally verifiable result: that the magnetic flux enclosed by a current loop is quantized. Let us first give an elementary derivation which has one foot in classical physics. Suppose that a magnetic flux Φ is built up from zero inside a ring of orbiting particles whose circumference is L, kept fixed by some combination of fields which does not vary. The electromotive force around the loop is $d\Phi/dt$ (we do not worry about the sign) and this gives the work done on a particle as it goes once around the loop,

$$\text{force} \times \text{distance} = \frac{dp}{dt}\, L = e\, \frac{d\Phi}{dt}$$

so that the change in momentum as the field is established is

$$\Delta p = \frac{e}{L}\, \Phi \tag{7.111}$$

But (cf. Prob. 3.14) the change in momentum of a particle must be restricted to the values $\Delta p = (2\pi\hbar/L)\,\Delta n$ where Δn is an integer, so that

$$\Phi = \frac{2\pi\hbar}{e}\, \Delta n \qquad (\Delta n = \ldots, \, -2, \, -1, \, 0, \, 1, \, 2, \, \ldots) \tag{7.112}$$

This result was first given by F. London in 1950. Note that one cannot speak of a universal quantum of flux, because the larger e is, the smaller are the steps in Φ. In superconductors, for example, where the effect has been observed,[11] the electrons move in pairs whose momenta are strongly correlated, and e in (7.112) is twice the electronic charge.

The quantum-mechanical argument we shall give[12] is quite different. We imagine a particle enclosed in a circular tube of length L. The tube lies entirely outside the region of flux. The one-dimensional equation of motion is

$$-\frac{\hbar^2}{2m}\left(\frac{d}{dx} - \frac{ie}{\hbar}\, A\right)^2 \psi(x) = E\psi(x) \tag{7.113}$$

where A is the vector potential, independent of x (see Prob. 7.48). The solutions are of the form

$$\psi = e^{ikx} \tag{7.114}$$

---

[11] B. S. Deaver, Jr. and W. F. Fairbank, Phys. Rev. Letters, **7**, 43 (1961); R. Doll and M. Näbauer, *ibid.*, 51.

[12] E. Merzbacher, Am. J. Phys., **30**, 237 (1962).

with

$$\frac{\hbar^2}{2m}\left(k - \frac{e}{\hbar}A\right)^2 = E \qquad (7.115)$$

We must now remember that the particle encounters no flux at all in its path, so that the presence of the field should not affect its behavior. Still, the value of k defined by (7.115) depends on A. There is no paradox here because the phase of ψ is not an observable, but E is an observable and must not depend on A. If ψ is single-valued, then k must be of the form $2\pi n/L$. Let us write (7.115) as

$$E = \frac{\hbar^2}{2m}\left(\frac{2\pi}{L}\right)^2\left(n - \frac{eL}{2\pi\hbar}A\right)^2$$

Suppose now that

$$A = \frac{2\pi\hbar}{eL}\Delta n \qquad (7.116)$$

where Δn is an integer. Then the value of E depends only on the integer $n - \Delta n$ and a measurement of E tells us nothing about A, since we do not know n. From (7.116) we easily recover (7.112) (see Prob. 7.48).

This argument raises the question whether electrons which pass through a region in which $B = 0$ but $A \neq 0$ can ever have their behavior influenced by the field they do not feel.[13] The answer, surprisingly, is yes,[14] and the effect can be explained as a consequence of the principle of indeterminacy.[15]

Problem 7.48   Show that an A can be found to describe a magnetic field B, uniform in a circle of radius $L/2\pi$, such that A is constant around the circle. Find the relationship between A and B.

Problem 7.49   In a region empty of charges and currents, a changing B induces an electric field given by

$$E_x = \tfrac{1}{2}\alpha t y \qquad E_y = -\tfrac{1}{2}\alpha t x \qquad E_z = 0$$

where α is a constant. Sketch the electric lines of force of this field, and use Maxwell's equations to find out the B which induced it. Are all of Maxwell's equations satisfied? What if the components of E are not linear in t?

Problem 7.50   Does either the phase velocity or the group velocity of the wave described by (7.114) and (7.115) depend on A?

[13] Y. Aharonov and D. Bohm, Phys. Rev., **115,** 485 (1959).
[14] R. G. Chambers, Phys. Rev. Letters, **5,** 3 (1960).
[15] W. H. Furry and N. F. Ramsay, Phys. Rev., **118,** 623 (1960). See also V. F. Weisskopf, in Brittin, Downs, and Downs (eds.), *Lectures in Theoretical Physics,* vol. 3, Interscience Publishers, New York, 1961, p. 63.

8

Approximate Methods of Calculation

8.1 Introduction

There are only a few computations in quantum mechanics which can be done exactly in finite form. Therefore, the most important part of the theory, for practical purposes, is the technique of calculating approximately. The general scheme of almost all approximate methods is this: first one finds a problem, as closely as possible resembling the one in hand, for which an exact solution is available, and then one finds a way of modifying and correcting this trial solution in the desired direction. Only the WKB approximation described in Chap. 4 does not answer this description, but it is of limited use because it is one-dimensional and because the phase integral usually cannot be evaluated in a convenient way. In this chapter we shall discuss the *perturbation theory*, a method of systematically constructing successively closer approximations to the calculation of both stationary and time-dependent states, and also the *variational theory*, in which one constructs the best possible approximation under specific limitations of form. We begin with the perturbation theory, which we present first of all in an exact form, without making any approximations.

8.2 Perturbation Theory for Stationary States

Suppose that the problem to be solved is of the form

$$\hat{H}\psi_n = E_n\psi_n \tag{8.1}$$

subject to the usual boundary conditions. Suppose further that one is able to solve exactly and completely the related problem

$$\hat{H}^{(0)}\psi_n{}^{(0)} = E_n{}^{(0)}\psi_n{}^{(0)} \tag{8.2}$$

in which $\hat{H}^{(0)}$ is hermitian and differs from the exact $\hat{H}$ by a quantity $\hat{H}'$, which one believes does not have a very large effect,

$$\hat{H} = \hat{H}^{(0)} + \hat{H}' \tag{8.3}$$

Correspondingly, let

$$\psi_n = \psi_n{}^{(0)} + \psi'_n \tag{8.4}$$

where both ψ_n and $\psi_n{}^{(0)}$ are normalized, and

$$E_n = E_n{}^{(0)} + E'_n \tag{8.5}$$

E'_n and ψ'_n are called *perturbations* of E_n and ψ_n due to $\hat{H}'$. In writing the subscript n on both energies and both wave functions we are assuming that they correspond to each other in the sense that $\psi_n{}^{(0)}$ is the state which ψ_n would become if the perturbing energy were gradually turned off. [This assumption is not necessary for the exact equation (8.6) which follows, but it underlies the later, approximate calculations.] In order to explain the perturbation approach, we shall give first an exact formula for E' and then show how it can be approximated. We rewrite (8.1) as

$$(\hat{H}^{(0)} + \hat{H}')(\psi_n{}^{(0)} + \psi'_n) = (E_n{}^{(0)} + E'_n)(\psi_n{}^{(0)} + \psi'_n)$$

and, in order to separate out the unperturbed part, expand and rearrange it as follows:

$$(\hat{H}^{(0)} - E_n{}^{(0)})\psi_n{}^{(0)} + (\hat{H}^{(0)} - E_n{}^{(0)})\psi'_n + (\hat{H}' - E'_n)\psi_n = 0$$

The first term of this vanishes by (8.2); next we multiply what remains by $\psi_n{}^{(0)*}$ and integrate it.

$$\int\psi_n{}^{(0)*}(\hat{H}^{(0)} - E_n{}^{(0)})\psi'_n + \int\psi_n{}^{(0)*}\hat{H}'\psi_n - E'_n\int\psi_n{}^{(0)*}\psi_n = 0$$

Again the first term vanishes, this time because $\hat{H}^{(0)}$ is hermitian, and we are left with

$$E'_n = \frac{\int\psi_n{}^{(0)*}\hat{H}'\psi_n}{\int\psi_n{}^{(0)*}\psi_n} \tag{8.6}$$

This is an exact expression for E'_n, but it is not immediately useful because in order to know ψ_n to put into the formula one would have to solve the whole problem anyhow. We must therefore seek a systematic method by which E'_n and ψ'_n can together be approximated in stages.

To do this, we make explicit the premise that $\hat{H}'$ is in some sense "small" and express it as

$$\hat{H}' = \lambda\hat{H}^{(1)} \tag{8.7}$$

where λ is an arbitrary parameter which we shall take to be real and as small as desired. In this case, it is plausible to suppose that ψ_n and E_n can be expanded in powers of λ:

$$\psi_n = \psi_n^{(0)} + \lambda\psi_n^{(1)} + \lambda^2\psi_n^{(2)} + \cdots \tag{8.8}$$

$$E_n = E_n^{(0)} + \lambda E_n^{(1)} + \lambda^2 E_n^{(2)} + \cdots \tag{8.9}$$

Substituting the last three equations into (8.1) and equating coefficients of equal powers of λ gives

$$(\hat{H}^{(0)} - E_n^{(0)})\psi_n^{(0)} = 0 \tag{8.10a}$$

$$(\hat{H}^{(0)} - E_n^{(0)})\psi_n^{(1)} = -(\hat{H}^{(1)} - E_n^{(1)})\psi_n^{(0)} \tag{8.10b}$$

$$(\hat{H}^{(0)} - E_n^{(0)})\psi_n^{(2)} = -(\hat{H}^{(1)} - E_n^{(1)})\psi_n^{(1)} + E_n^{(2)}\psi_n^{(0)} \tag{8.10c}$$

etc. The first of these is automatically satisfied. The second, since we know $\psi_n^{(0)}$, is of the form of a differential equation for $\psi_n^{(1)}$ provided that we can find the value of $E_n^{(1)}$ to put into it, and similarly for the third and higher equations. To find $E_n^{(1)}$, we proceed as in the exact theory, multiplying (8.10b) by $\psi_n^{(0)*}$ and integrating:

$$\int\psi_n^{(0)*}(\hat{H}^{(0)} - E_n^{(0)})\psi_n^{(1)} = -\int\psi_n^{(0)*}\hat{H}^{(1)}\psi_n^{(0)} + E_n^{(1)}$$

or

$$E_n^{(1)} = \langle\hat{H}^{(1)}\rangle_n^{(0)} \tag{8.11}$$

which is the expectation value of $\hat{H}^{(1)}$ evaluated in the nth *unperturbed* state. Thus we can in fact find $E_n^{(1)}$ without a knowledge of $\psi_n^{(1)}$. Equation (8.11) is quite easy to understand in the light of the exact formula (8.6); for it states that we can get an approximation to E' by assuming that ψ_n does not greatly differ from $\psi_n^{(0)}$ and by writing $\psi_n^{(0)}$ in (8.6). Here, however, we have derived $E_n^{(1)}$ as the first term of a series whose higher terms can also, at least in principle, be written down.

Equation (8.11) is one of the most important practical formulas in quantum mechanics.

To proceed, we assume that it has been possible to solve the differential equation (8.10b) for $\psi_n^{(1)}$; now let us find $E_n^{(2)}$. The same process as before gives

$$E_n^{(2)} = \int\psi_n^{(0)*}\hat{H}^{(1)}\psi_n^{(1)} - E_n^{(1)}\int\psi_n^{(0)*}\psi_n^{(1)} \tag{8.12}$$

This can be simplified if for a moment we consider the normalization of ψ_n. With (8.8), we have

$$\int|\psi_n|^2 = \int|\psi_n^{(0)}|^2 + \lambda[\int\psi_n^{(0)*}\psi_n^{(1)} + \int\psi_n^{(1)*}\psi_n^{(0)}]$$
$$+ \lambda^2[\int|\psi_n^{(1)}|^2 + \int\psi_n^{(0)*}\psi_n^{(2)} + \int\psi_n^{(2)*}\psi_n^{(0)}]$$
$$+ \cdots = 1$$

We assume that ψ_n and $\psi_n^{(0)}$ are normalized. Separating out powers of λ gives

$$\text{Re} \int \psi_n^{(0)*} \psi_n^{(1)} = 0 \tag{8.13a}$$

$$\text{Re} \int \psi_n^{(0)*} \psi_n^{(2)} + \tfrac{1}{2} \int |\psi_n^{(1)}|^2 = 0 \qquad \text{etc.} \tag{8.13b}$$

Returning to (8.12), we note that $E_n^{(2)}$ is real (why?) and so is equal to its own real part,

$$E_n^{(2)} = \text{Re} \int \psi_n^{(0)*} \hat{H}^{(1)} \psi_n^{(1)} \tag{8.14a}$$

by (8.13a), and similarly, using (8.13b), we find[1]

$$E_n^{(3)} = \text{Re} \int \psi_n^{(0)*} \hat{H}^{(1)} \psi_n^{(2)} + \tfrac{1}{2} E_n^{(2)} \int |\psi_n^{(1)}|^2 \tag{8.15}$$

Problem 8.1   Prove Eq. (8.15).

Problem 8.2   Prove that the exact formula (8.6) can be written

$$E_n' = \frac{\text{Re} \int \psi_n^{(0)*} \hat{H}' \psi_n}{1 - \tfrac{1}{2} \int |\psi_n'|^2} = \frac{E_n^{(1)} + \text{Re} \int \psi_n^{(0)*} \hat{H}' \psi_n'}{1 - \tfrac{1}{2} \int |\psi_n'|^2}$$

Knowing $\psi_n^{(1)}$ and $E_n^{(2)}$, one can attempt to solve (8.10c) and proceed in the same way. In practice, however, the successive approximations to ψ grow rapidly more difficult to obtain, and one generally contents oneself with the first or second term.

At this point the parameter λ has fulfilled its function of allowing us to separate out consecutive orders of magnitude. From here on it would merely get in the way, so we shall banish it by setting it equal to 1. $\hat{H}^{(1)}$ is therefore the exact perturbing energy, denoted earlier by $\hat{H}'$.

We must now say a few words about the criterion that $\hat{H}^{(1)}$ be "small." Physically this is clearly desirable in order that the perturbations be as small as possible. The only mathematical criterion for the correctness of our theory is that the infinite series in (8.8) and (8.9) converge. But of course in most cases we cannot say anything

---

[1] It is convenient for many purposes to choose $\psi_n^{(1)}$ to be that solution of (8.10b) which is exactly orthogonal to $\psi^{(0)}$, that is,

$$\int \psi_n^{(0)*} \psi_n^{(1)} = 0 \tag{8.16}$$

so that (8.13a) is then identically satisfied and (8.12) reduces to

$$E_n^{(2)} = \int \psi_n^{(0)*} \hat{H}^{(1)} \psi_n^{(1)} \tag{8.14b}$$

This is done by noting that if $\psi_n^{(1)}$ is any solution of (8.10b), then $\psi_n^{(1)} + \gamma \psi_n^{(0)}$ is an equally good solution for any (complex) value of γ. The reason for the arbitrariness is that there is more than one exact wave function which reduces to $\psi^{(0)}$ as λ approaches zero. For example, if ψ is one such, then $e^{i\lambda^2 \pi} \psi$ is another. Considered as a power series in λ it is very different, but physically it is just the same.

It is a simple matter to choose γ so that (8.16) is satisfied. The same could be done to $\psi_n^{(2)}$ except that here we run head-on into difficulties of normalization in (8.13b). One usually prefers to have ψ_n normalized and therefore $\psi_n^{(2)}$ not orthogonal to $\psi_n^{(0)}$.

about convergence because the higher terms of the series are not known. All we can do is examine the terms we can calculate and see whether $E_n{}^{(0)}$, $E_n{}^{(1)}$, $E_n{}^{(2)}$, etc., for example, are successively smaller in absolute magnitude. And in practice even this may be very difficult. We must therefore be content if $|E_n{}^{(1)}|$ is small compared with $|E_n{}^{(0)}|$ or, if $E_n{}^{(1)}$ equals zero, as it often does, if $|E_n{}^{(2)}|$, or in general the first nonvanishing term, is small compared with $|E_n{}^{(0)}|$. The small amount of research that has been done on this matter suggests that the above criterion, though hazy, is reasonable and that in applying it one will seldom be disappointed.

In the next two sections we shall study some examples of the first-order perturbation of energy levels and then return to the general theory in Sec. 8.5.

8.3   First-order Perturbations

The most elementary type of perturbation calculation is illustrated by the following example: Suppose that we have a simple harmonic oscillator of mass m and spring constant K and that the oscillator is in its ground state with energy

$$E_0{}^{(0)} = \tfrac{1}{2}\hbar\omega_0 \qquad \omega_0 = \left(\frac{K}{m}\right)^{\!1/2} \tag{8.17}$$

Let a second spring, whose constant is b, be added alongside the original one. By how much is the energy of the ground state increased? To solve this by perturbations, we use (8.11), writing for the potential energy of the added spring

$$H^{(1)} = \tfrac{1}{2}bx^2 \tag{8.18}$$

Using the ground-state wave function, we form

$$E^{(1)} = \langle H^{(1)}\rangle_0{}^{(0)} = \frac{1}{2}\left(\frac{m\omega_0}{\pi\hbar}\right)^{\!1/2} b \int_{-\infty}^{\infty} x^2 e^{-(m\omega_0 x^2/\hbar)}\, dx$$

$$= \frac{\hbar b}{4m\omega_0}$$

so that, to a first approximation,

$$E_0 = E_0{}^{(0)} + E_0{}^{(1)} = \tfrac{1}{2}\hbar\omega_0 + \frac{1}{4}\frac{\hbar b}{m\omega_0} \tag{8.19}$$

The calculation just performed is actually quite unnecessary, because we can write down the exact solution to the original problem without difficulty. If the second spring merely adds to the stiffness of the first, then one needs only to change K to $K + b$ in (8.17) in order to get the exact result. If $|b|$ is smaller than K (for generality, we envisage also a negative b), we can use the binomial theorem to expand the exact value of ω as

$$\left(\frac{K+b}{m}\right)^{\frac{1}{2}} = \left(\frac{K}{m}\right)^{\frac{1}{2}}\left(1 + \frac{b}{2K} - \frac{b^2}{8K^2} + \cdots\right)$$

Thus, the ground-state energy is

$$E_0 = \frac{1}{2}\hbar\left(\frac{K}{m}\right)^{\frac{1}{2}}\left(1 + \frac{b}{2K} - \frac{b^2}{8K^2} + \cdots\right)$$

or, in terms of ω_0,

$$E = \frac{1}{2}\hbar\omega_0\left(1 + \frac{b}{2m\omega_0^2} - \frac{b^2}{8m^2\omega_0^4} + \cdots\right) \qquad (8.20)$$

the first two terms of which are the same as (8.19). The third term will be computed in Prob. 8.20. We see, therefore, that the successive terms of perturbation theory are the series expansion of the exact energy (and we shall see later that this applies to the wave function also) in powers of the small parameter b. The expansion diverges if $|b| > K$. Physically, this is because if b is negative and $|b| > K$, the potential is negative, the net force is repulsive, and there is no bound state at all.

Problem 8.3   Find the first-order perturbation of the nth state of a simple harmonic oscillator by the added potential considered above, and compare with the result of an exact calculation.

Problem 8.4   Calculate the perturbation of the ground state of a simple harmonic oscillator by a potential

$$H^{(1)} = \frac{1}{4} dx^4 \qquad (8.21)$$

corresponding to a restoring force which follows a cubic law.

Problem 8.5   At the end of Sec. 7.3 we calculated the ground-state energy of a hydrogen atom perturbed by a potential g/r^2. There an ambiguity of sign was resolved by appeal to the principle of continuity. Show that the choice made gives an answer in agreement with the result of a perturbation calculation.

8.4 Perturbation of Degenerate States

If the initial, unperturbed state of a system is degenerate, some essentially new considerations come into play. This is because there is now an ambiguity: unless one is careful, the perturbed state may be very different from the unperturbed one. How this happens in a simple case can easily be seen if one imagines that the square membrane of Fig. 7.3 has been set vibrating in one of its modes, say, that shown in Fig. 8.1a, and that one then applies pressure at the point P. Until the pressure is applied, there is an infinite variety of nodal patterns available with the same frequency as that shown in Fig.

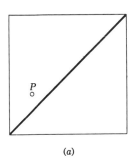
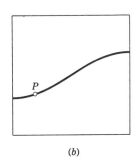

Fig. 8.1 The square membrane originally vibrating as in (a) changes to mode (b), degenerate with (a), when force is applied at P. A very small force can produce a large change of state.

(a)   (b)

8.1(*a*). A slight touch at P, however, converts the pattern to that shown in (*b*). Then when further pressure is applied, there will be a perceptible shift in frequency. The point is that a perturbing force selects out of all the possible degenerate modes one whose form is determined by the nature of the perturbation, and it is on this mode that the perturbation must be considered to act.[2] We shall now set up and solve the purely algebraic problem posed by the perturbation of a doubly degenerate quantum-mechanical state, and then we shall see that the answer is to some extent determined by the symmetry of the perturbing $H^{(1)}$ in the same sense that the nodal pattern of Fig. 8.1*b* is determined by the location of the point P.

Suppose that $\psi_1^{(0)}$ and $\psi_2^{(0)}$ are an orthogonal pair of unperturbed states corresponding to the energy $E^{(0)}$. We assume that there exists some linear combination

$$\psi^{(0)} = c_1\psi_1^{(0)} + c_2\psi_2^{(0)} \tag{8.22}$$

with $\psi_1^{(0)}$ orthogonal to $\psi_2^{(0)}$, from which the exact eigenfunction differs only slightly. This function is called a *stabilized eigenfunction* or, more dogmatically, the *right linear combination*. We write

$$(\hat{H}^{(0)} + \hat{H}^{(1)})(\psi^{(0)} + \psi^{(1)}) = (E^{(0)} + E^{(1)})(\psi^{(0)} + \psi^{(1)})$$

and from this, neglecting the small quantities $H^{(1)}\psi^{(1)}$ and $E^{(1)}\psi^{(1)}$, we find as in (8.10*b*),

$$(\hat{H}^{(0)} - E^{(0)})\psi^{(1)} + (\hat{H}^{(1)} - E^{(1)})\psi^{(0)} = 0$$

or, with (8.22),

$$(\hat{H}^{(0)} - E^{(0)})\psi^{(1)} + (\hat{H}^{(1)} - E^{(1)})(c_1\psi_1^{(0)} + c_2\psi_2^{(0)}) = 0$$

Multiply this equation by $\psi_1^{(0)*}$ and integrate, and then do the same with $\psi_2^{(0)*}$. Using the abbreviations

$$\int \psi_1^{(0)*}\hat{H}^{(1)}\psi_2^{(0)} = W_{12} \qquad \text{etc.}$$

---

[2] This process of selecting out the right mode can be watched if the reader has access to a Chladni plate, mentioned in the preceding chapter. Owing to the rigidity of the plate, one does not observe degenerate modes like those of Fig. 7.3, but they are easy to create and shift about if a circular plate is used.

we find

$$(W_{11} - E^{(1)})c_1 + W_{12}c_2 = 0$$
$$W_{21}c_1 + (W_{22} - E^{(1)})c_2 = 0$$

(8.23)

Problem 8.6   Derive Eqs. (8.23).

This pair of equations is compatible only if the determinant of the coefficients vanishes,

$$\begin{vmatrix} W_{11} - E^{(1)} & W_{12} \\ W_{21} & W_{22} - E^{(1)} \end{vmatrix} = 0$$

and on evaluating it, and noting that $W_{21} = W_{12}^*$, we find

$$E^{(1)} = \tfrac{1}{2}\{W_{11} + W_{22} \pm [(W_{11} - W_{22})^2 + 4|W_{12}|^2]^{\frac{1}{2}}\}$$

(8.24)

To interpret this formula, let us first suppose that W_{12} is zero. Then

$$E^{(1)} = \tfrac{1}{2}\{W_{11} + W_{22} \pm |W_{11} - W_{22}|\}$$

so that to the upper sign corresponds whichever is the greater of W_{11} and W_{22} and to the lower sign, whichever is the lesser. This is what one might at first sight have anticipated, since it corresponds to taking the expectation value of $H^{(1)}$ in each of the two unperturbed states $\psi_1^{(0)}$ and $\psi_2^{(0)}$. In general, as we see in (8.24), the situation is more complicated than this, but the most significant feature is seen at once: the perturbed state is usually no longer degenerate; for unless things happen to be so that $W_{11} = W_{22}$ and $W_{12} = 0$, there will always be two different solutions $E^{(1)}$. This *removal of degeneracy* by a small perturbation is a most important and characteristic feature of quantum mechanics. Perturbed wave functions and higher-order approximations to the energy can be developed in much the same way as we have done earlier in this chapter, but it turns out that (8.24), with the corresponding c_1 and c_2, answers most of the questions encountered in practice.

Problem 8.7   Evaluate c_1 and c_2 (except for an undetermined phase factor) for each value of $E^{(1)}$ and show that the two stabilized eigenfunctions so obtained are orthogonal to each other.

Problem 8.8   Prove that if $\psi_1^{(0)}$ and $\psi_2^{(0)}$ are replaced by the two linear combinations (8.22) with coefficients as found in the preceding problem, then the expression corresponding to W_{12} vanishes identically. Conversely, show that if $W_{12} = 0$, then $\psi_1^{(0)}$ and $\psi_2^{(0)}$ are a pair of stabilized eigenfunctions.

It often happens, as in (3.35), that $\hat{H}^{(1)}$ is an operator whose expectation value cannot be negative. If so, W_{12} satisfies an important inequality,

$$|W_{12}|^2 \leqslant W_{11}W_{22} \qquad \text{if } \langle \hat{H}^{(1)} \rangle \geqslant 0$$

(8.25)

To prove this, note that $E^{(1)}$ is the expectation value of $\hat{H}^{(1)}$ in a certain state and is therefore necessarily positive. Taking the smaller value for $E^{(1)}$, we find

$$W_{11} + W_{22} - [(W_{11} - W_{22})^2 + 4|W_{12}|^2]^{1/2} \geqslant 0$$

or

$$(W_{11} + W_{22})^2 \geqslant (W_{11} - W_{22})^2 + 4|W_{12}|^2$$

from which follows (8.25). This has an immediate application to (8.24), where it gives

$$0 \leqslant E^{(1)} \leqslant W_{11} + W_{22} \qquad \text{if } \langle \hat{H}^{(1)} \rangle \geqslant 0$$

(What happens if $\langle \hat{H}^{(1)} \rangle$ cannot be positive?)

One way of characterizing (8.24) is to say that it shows we chose the wrong pair of states to start with. An infinite variety of orthogonal pairs of degenerate states is available; if we could just choose a pair such that W_{12} vanishes, then there would, as we have noted above, be no difficulty at all, and the perturbations in the energy would be merely W_{11} and W_{22}. We shall now show that the correct choice can be determined by the symmetry properties of the perturbing hamiltonian $\hat{H}^{(1)}$. This fact is contained in the

THEOREM. Let $\hat{T}$ be a hermitian operator which commutes with $\hat{H}^{(1)}$ and let $\psi_1^{(0)}$ and $\psi_2^{(0)}$ be two eigenfunctions of $\hat{T}$ belonging to different eigenvalues, t_1 and t_2. Then W_{12} is zero.

The proof is simple. We start with $[\hat{T}, \hat{H}^{(1)}] = 0$ and form

$$\int \psi_1^{(0)*}(\hat{T}\hat{H}^{(1)} - \hat{H}^{(1)}\hat{T})\psi_2^{(0)} = 0$$

Using the hermiticity of $\hat{T}$ gives at once

$$(t_1 - t_2)W_{12} = 0 \tag{8.26}$$

and if $t_1 - t_2$ is not zero, then W_{12} must be.   Q.E.D.

Since $W_{12} = 0$, we see by Prob. 8.8 that $\psi_1^{(0)}$ and $\psi_2^{(0)}$ are the stabilized eigenfunctions, and since almost any physical situation which one is likely to encounter has at least one symmetry, the choice of the right linear combination can often be made by inspection, as the following examples will show.

An electron trap

The simplest kind of degenerate system is an electron free to move in a one-dimensional region of length L which is closed upon itself (see Sec. 3.2). The normalized wave functions are of the form e^{ikx} with the requirement that $\psi(L) = \psi(0)$, and this restricts k to the values $2n\pi/L$, with $n = 0, \pm 1, \pm 2, \ldots$. A double degeneracy exists, of course, because waves of a given energy may travel around the loop in either direction. Suppose that into this uniform

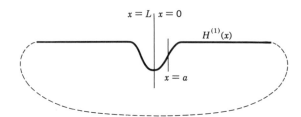

Fig. 8.2 Symmetric potential well in a closed one-dimensional system.

region is introduced a "trap" (the term is suggested by solid-state physics) consisting of a local dip in potential of the form

$$\hat{H}^{(1)}(x) = -V_0 e^{-x^2/a^2} \qquad (a \ll L)$$

as in Fig. 8.2. The trapping potential has been centered at the origin, and it is symmetric between x and $-x$. It therefore commutes with the spatial parity operator $\hat{P}$ of Sec. 5.4. According to the theorem we have just proved, the stabilized eigenfunctions for this problem will be eigenfunctions of $\hat{P}$ corresponding to different eigenvalues; as we have seen, there are only two eigenvalues, ± 1, and the corresponding eigenfunctions are even and odd in x. The point of this discussion is that such eigenfunctions can be formed from linear combinations of the e^{ikx} by inspection; they are

$$\psi_1^{(0)} = \left(\frac{2}{L}\right)^{1/2} \cos kx \qquad \psi_2^{(0)} = \left(\frac{2}{L}\right)^{1/2} \sin kx \qquad (8.27)$$

where now only the positive values of k need be considered, since each $\psi^{(0)}$ contains the corresponding negative value as well,

$$k = \frac{2n\pi}{L} \qquad (n = 0, 1, 2, \ldots) \qquad (8.28)$$

Problem 8.9 Verify that $\psi_1^{(0)}$ and $\psi_2^{(0)}$ are orthonormal and that they make $W_{12} = 0$.

We can now write down at once the perturbations in energy produced by $\hat{H}^{(1)}$. They are

$$W_{11} = -\frac{2V_0}{L} \int_{-L/2}^{L/2} \cos^2 kx e^{-x^2/a^2} \, dx$$

$$W_{22} = -\frac{2V_0}{L} \int_{-L/2}^{L/2} \sin^2 kx e^{-x^2/a^2} \, dx$$

which we can combine in the simpler form

$$E^{(1)} = -\frac{V_0}{L} \int_{-\infty}^{\infty} (1 \pm \cos 2kx) e^{-x^2/a^2} \, dx$$

where the upper sign belongs to $\psi_1^{(0)}$ and the lower to $\psi_2^{(0)}$ and we have replaced the limits of integration by $\pm \infty$ because $a \ll L$.

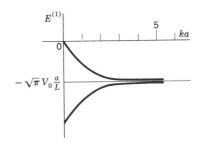

Fig. 8.3 Perturbation of the energy levels of the
system of Fig. 8.2. The lower curve belongs to
the symmetric states.

The integration gives

$$E^{(1)} = - \sqrt{\pi} \, V_0 \frac{a}{L} (1 \pm e^{-a^2 k^2}) \qquad (8.29)$$

which is plotted in Fig. 8.3 for fixed a as a function of ka. The
result is quite characteristic of this kind of calculation: a general
depression of the energy together with a splitting, symmetric above
and below, of the originally degenerate levels.

We should notice the limits of applicability of the result;
for the perturbation must be small compared with the unperturbed
energy. Neglecting unimportant constants, this is

$$\frac{\hbar^2 k^2}{2m} \gg V_0 \frac{a}{L} \qquad \text{or} \qquad k^2 a^2 \gg \frac{a}{L} \frac{V_0}{\hbar^2 / 2ma^2}$$

The second factor is the ratio between the well depth and the
(approximate) kinetic energy of an electron in a low bound state in
the well. This may be taken in the solid-state analogy to be in the
general neighborhood of unity;[3] a/L is, however, very small, and
so correspondingly small values of ka are possible. With $k = 2\pi n/L$
and $V_0 \approx \hbar^2 / 2ma^2$, we find

$$n \gg \frac{1}{2\pi} \left(\frac{L}{a} \right)^{1/2}$$

States lower than this are too much perturbed by the potential
for the first-order theory to be valid.

Problem 8.10 Find the perturbed energy values and the stabilized eigenfunctions for the unsymmetric perturbation

$$V = - V_0 e^{-x/a} \qquad (x \geqslant 0, L \gg a)$$

shown in Fig. 8.4.

Problem 8.11 Analyze the effect of a perturbing potential γ/r^3
on the quadruply degenerate first excited state of hydrogen.

---

[3] The reader is cautioned against taking this analogy too seriously. It is out
of the question to ignore all the forces acting on the electron except the force
exerted by the trap.

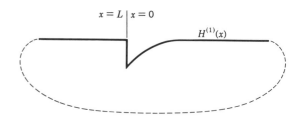

$x = L \mid x = 0$

$H^{(1)}(x)$

Fig. 8.4   Asymmetric potential well
in a closed
one-dimensional system.

Problem 8.12   What form is taken by the theorem on finding stabilized eigenfunctions if a symmetry operator is known, when the unperturbed state is n-fold instead of doubly degenerate?

Problem 8.13   What form does the same theorem take if there are several operators $\hat{T}$ which commute with $\hat{H}^{(1)}$?

Stark effect

If a radiating atom is immersed in a strong electric field, its energy levels, and consequently its spectrum, are thereby somewhat changed. In this section we shall see under what circumstances an electric field produces an energy shift in a hydrogen atom in the first order of perturbation theory, that is, a shift proportional to F. (We call the field F to avoid confusion.) We shall discuss the second-order perturbation (energy shift proportional to F^2) in Sec. 8.5. Let us choose the z axis parallel to the applied field, so that $\hat{H}^{(1)} = -eFz$. Then, looking at the hydrogen wave functions tabulated in (7.56), we see that the expectation value of $\hat{H}^{(1)}$ vanishes in the ground state and in each of the four excited states tabulated. Turning now to the possibility that the type of cross term which we have previously denoted by W_{12} may exist among the terms of the first excited state, we note that all the energy eigenfunctions are also eigenfunctions of $\hat{L}_z$, which commutes with $\hat{H}^{(1)}$ (why?), so that only $\psi_{2,0,0}$ and $\psi_{2,1,0}$, which belong to the same eigenvalue of $\hat{L}_z$, need be considered. We find easily that

$$\int \psi_{2,0,0} H^{(1)} \psi_{2,1,0} = 3eFa_0 \tag{8.30}$$

so that, by (8.24), the two levels are no longer degenerate, but are split by the perturbation

$$E^{(1)} = \pm 3eFa_0 \tag{8.31}$$

Correspondingly, we see by solving (8.23) that, corresponding to the two signs of (8.31), we have $c_1 = \pm c_2$, so that the stabilized eigenfunctions are

$$\psi_1 = 2^{-\frac{1}{2}}(\psi_{2,0,0} - \psi_{2,1,0}) \qquad E^{(1)} = +3eFa_0 \tag{8.32a}$$

$$\psi_2 = 2^{-\frac{1}{2}}(\psi_{2,0,0} + \psi_{2,1,0}) \qquad E^{(1)} = -3eFa_0 \tag{8.32b}$$

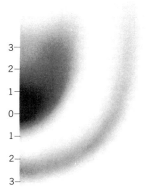

Fig. 8.5   Electron distribution in a hydrogen atom in a weak
electric field. The scale is in units of a_0, and the state
is that in which $<z> = 3a_0$.

Problem 8.14   Fill in the details of the calculation.

Immersed in the electric field, the atom in a state with $n = 2$
will have four possible states of definite energy, given by $\psi_{2,0,-1}$
and $\psi_{2,0,+1}$ with $E^{(1)} = 0$ and the ψ_1 and ψ_2 just found. Now an
object with an electric dipole moment $\mathbf{d}$ in a field $\mathbf{F}$ has an energy
$-\mathbf{d} \cdot \mathbf{F}$, which suggests that states ψ_1 and ψ_2 have dipole moments
of magnitude $3ea_0$ oriented respectively antiparallel and parallel
to the field. These are states of *permanent* electric dipole moment,
independent of the value of $\mathbf{F}$, which become spatially quantized
in the field. It is interesting to see what is the electronic distribution
of such a state. Choosing the more stable state, ψ_2, we can write it
from (7.56) as

$$\psi_2 = \tfrac{1}{4}\pi^{-\frac{1}{2}}a_0^{-\frac{3}{2}}\left(1 - \frac{r-z}{2a_0}\right)e^{-r/2a_0}$$

whence, with $z = r \cos \vartheta$, we get

$$|\psi_2|^2 = \frac{1}{16\pi a_0{}^3}\left(1 - \frac{r}{a_0}\sin^2 \tfrac{1}{2}\vartheta\right)^2 e^{-r/a_0} \tag{8.33}$$

The general behavior of this function is plotted in Fig. 8.5. To get
some intuitive notion of what is going on, we recall that in the
classical theory of motion of a particle under an inverse-square
force,[4] the orbits are in the form of ellipses having the attractive
center at one focus. Since the particle moves more slowly when it is
a farther from the center, it spends more time on one side of the
center than on the other, so that an atom viewed in this way is
effectively polarized. The linear combinations ψ_1 and ψ_2 are thus the
wave functions which correspond, at least roughly, to the classical
Keplerian orbits. It is well known that such stationary "polarizable"

[4] G. Joos, *Theoretical Physics*, Hafner Publishing Company, Inc., New
York, 1950, 1958.

orbits occur only for an inverse-square force and a few other cases. In quantum mechanics, as seen in Prob. 8.11 for example, the degeneracy between states of different l which makes the whole thing possible disappears as soon as the attractive force is no longer strictly inverse square. Thus the inverse-square force is an essential condition for the existence of a permanent electric moment in both theories, though for reasons which are at first sight a little difficult to relate to one another. The connection can in fact be established, but to do so would take us somewhat far afield.[5]

Magnetic fields

We have already seen in Sec. 7.6 how the effect of immersing a one-electron system in a weak magnetic field is to give it an extra energy proportional to the angular momentum. When the unperturbed state is an eigenstate of the angular momentum (and in simple cases it usually is), it is therefore unnecessary to use perturbation theory to calculate the shift in energy levels brought about by the field. But the ground state of many systems is without angular momentum, and for them the first-order Zeeman effect vanishes exactly. The term in B^2 remains, and it contributes an extra energy which is given in first approximation by

$$E^{(1)} = \frac{e^2 B^2}{8m} \langle x^2 + y^2 \rangle \tag{8.34}$$

an essentially positive quantity which has the same general order of magnitude for all atomic systems and which is, of course, always present, though it may be screened by the first-order splitting.

It is convenient to interpret the energy of the system in the external field in terms of an intrinsic property, its magnetic moment. The argument which relates the two quantities is a little long, and so it is relegated to Sec. 8.9 at the end of this chapter, but the result is simple. If the dependence of the system's energy E on the applied field B is known, the magnetic moment is given by

$$M = - \frac{\partial E}{\partial B} \tag{8.35}$$

Writing E, in our approximation, as $E^{(0)} + E^{(1)}$, we have

$$M = - \frac{e^2 B}{4m} \langle x^2 + y^2 \rangle \tag{8.36}$$

It is an induced moment, since it is proportional to B and vanishes in the absence of an applied field. The negative sign means that the moment is opposed to the inducing field, as one would expect from Lenz's law of electromagnetic induction. It therefore represents a

---

[5] There is no complete discussion of this topic in print, but the interested reader may start with H. V. McIntosh, Am. J. Phys., **27**, 620 (1959), from which the rest of the literature can be traced.

universal diamagnetism which is detectable experimentally in atoms or ions whose angular momentum is zero.[6] Such a diamagnetism is conveniently characterized in terms of a susceptibility χ. We set I, the magnetic moment per unit volume, equal to χH, where H is the magnetic field intensity, given closely enough by B/μ_0, and χ is a dimensionless number. We can calculate I for a gas by multiplying M by the number of molecules per cubic meter, which at 1 atm and $0°C$ is Loschmidt's number, $L_0 = 2.687 \times 10^{25}$. Thus we have

$$\chi = -\frac{\mu_0 L_0 e^2}{4m} \langle x^2 + y^2 \rangle \tag{8.37}$$

Problem 8.15 A helium atom may be regarded very crudely as a "double hydrogen atom" in which two electrons circle about a nucleus of charge 2 without interacting with each other. Calculate the diamagnetic susceptibility of helium on this model and compare it with the observed value of -1.05×10^{-9}. (A more accurate calculation will be made in Prob. 15.6.)

The effect which we have calculated has a close classical analogue in the Larmor precession executed by a system of electrons placed in a magnetic field. The precessional frequency is $-eB/2m$, and the orbital angular momentum is thus changed by

$$\Delta L = -JeB/2m$$

where J is the moment of inertia of the system. The corresponding change in the magnetic moment is given by (7.102) (see also Prob. 7.41) as

$$\Delta M = -\frac{Je^2}{4m^2} B \tag{8.38}$$

which, with J replaced by

$$J = m\langle x^2 + y^2 \rangle \tag{8.39}$$

for each electron, is exactly (8.36).

8.5 Calculation of Perturbed Wave Functions

In order to calculate $E^{(2)}$ or any higher approximation to the energy, it is necessary to find how the wave functions are altered by the perturbing forces. In the scheme of approximations we have set up, one must know $\psi^{(n)}$ in order to calculate either $E^{(n+1)}$ or $\psi^{(n+1)}$, and in practice the computations usually become rapidly more difficult with increasing order. (In fact, when this does not turn out to be the case, it is always because there is a way of solving the entire problem exactly which one has overlooked.) In this section we shall exhibit

---

[6] See C. Kittel, *Introduction to Solid State Physics*, 2d ed., John Wiley & Sons, Inc., New York, 1956, chap. 9.

two general approaches to the problem of finding a perturbed wave function: by solving a differential equation and by summing a series. Each has its uses. Recent interest in the first method dates from work by Dalgarno and collaborators[7] on the perturbation of atomic states; the second occurs in Schrödinger's early papers.

Hydrogen atom in an electric field

Suppose that a hydrogen atom in its ground state, centered at the origin, is subjected to an electric field in the z direction. Clearly, this will act so as to push the proton in one direction and the electron in the other, so that the atom will be distorted into an electric dipole parallel to the z axis. The calculation of the electric moment M_e proceeds like that of the magnetic moment in the preceding section. A system which when immersed in a uniform electric field F gains an added energy E' has an electric dipole moment equal to

$$M_e = -\frac{\partial E'}{\partial F} \tag{8.40}$$

Further, we define the *polarizability* α, which measures the ease with which the atom is deformed by the field,

$$\alpha = \frac{\partial M_e}{\partial F} = -\frac{\partial^2 E'}{\partial F^2} \tag{8.41}$$

We see from (8.31) that a hydrogen atom in the excited state ψ_1 or ψ_2 has an electric moment equal to

$$M_e = \pm 3ea_0 \tag{8.42}$$

and a polarizability of zero in the lowest approximation.

To carry out the analogous calculation for the ground state, we write the perturbing part of the hamiltonian as before,

$$\hat{H}^{(1)} = -eFz \tag{8.43}$$

We see at once that $E^{(1)}$ vanishes (why?). Thus the first-order perturbation formula is of no help; we have to find $E^{(2)}$, and this requires a knowledge of the first perturbed wave function, $\psi^{(1)}$. We therefore have to solve (8.10b), or

$$(\hat{H}^{(0)} - E^{(0)})\psi^{(1)} = -\hat{H}^{(1)}\psi^{(0)} \tag{8.44}$$

where

$$\hat{H}^{(0)} = -\frac{\hbar^2}{2m}\nabla^2 + \frac{e'^2}{r} \tag{8.45}$$

---

[7] Starting with A. Dalgarno and J. T. Lewis, Proc. Roy. Soc. (London), **A233**, 70 (1956). The method has been summarized and extended by C. Schwartz, Ann. Phys. (N.Y.), **6**, 156, 170, 178 (1959).

The equation can be simplified if we write $\psi^{(1)}$ as $\chi\psi^{(0)}$, where χ is to be determined. If we substitute this into (8.44), we find

$$-\frac{\hbar^2}{2m}[\psi^{(0)}\nabla^2\chi + 2\nabla\psi^{(0)}\cdot\nabla\chi] + \chi(\hat{H}^{(0)} - E^{(0)})\psi^{(0)} = eFz\psi^{(0)}$$

whence χ satisfies the relatively simple equation

$$\nabla^2\chi + 2\frac{\nabla\psi^{(0)}}{\psi^{(0)}}\cdot\nabla\chi = -\frac{2m}{\hbar^2}eFz \tag{8.46}$$

The χ satisfying this equation has a multiplying factor of z, as can be seen if we write

$$\chi = zf(r) \tag{8.47}$$

and substitute it into (8.46). Introducing ψ_0 from (7.56) and carrying out the differentiations gives

$$z\left[f'' + \frac{4}{r}f' - \frac{2}{a_0}\left(f' + \frac{1}{r}f\right)\right] = -\frac{2m}{\hbar^2}eFz \tag{8.48}$$

The remaining equation is extremely simple, and can be solved by

$$f(r) = \alpha + \beta r$$

with

$$\alpha = \frac{1}{2}\frac{2m}{\hbar^2}eFa_0{}^2 \qquad \beta = \frac{1}{4}\frac{2m}{\hbar^2}eFa_0 \tag{8.49}$$

Problem 8.16   Verify the steps from (8.46) to (8.49).

Problem 8.17   Show that all the other solutions of (8.48) are nonphysical [that is, cause the integral (8.50) to diverge].

The perturbed energy is given by (8.12) as

$$E^{(2)} = -eF\int\psi^{(0)*}z^2(\alpha + \beta r)\psi^{(0)}\,dv \tag{8.50}$$

which is easily evaluated if we note that the z^2 might as well be x^2 or y^2 or $\frac{1}{3}(x^2 + y^2 + z^2) = \frac{1}{3}r^2$ so that

$$E^{(2)} = -\frac{1}{3}eF\langle\alpha r^2 + \beta r^3\rangle^{(0)} = -9\pi\varepsilon_0 a_0{}^3 F^2$$

whence, by (8.41), the polarizability of atomic hydrogen is

$$\alpha = 18\pi\varepsilon_0 a_0{}^3 \text{ C-sec}^2/\text{kg} \tag{8.51}$$

It should be emphasized that this value, though obtained by perturbation theory, is in a sense exact. The higher approximations give contributions to E proportional to F^4, etc., and these correspond to a dependence of α on F for high fields. Equation (8.51) gives the exact value of the *initial polarizability*, that is, the limiting value of α in a weak field. The (unnormalized) ground state wave function distorted by the action of the electric field is

$$\psi \approx \left[1 + \frac{4\pi\varepsilon_0}{e} a_0 F z \left(1 + \frac{r}{2a_0} \right) \right] \psi^{(0)} \tag{8.52}$$

Problem 8.18 What is the probability of finding the distorted atom in the $2p$ state whose wave function is $\psi_{2,1,0}$? What (in magnitude and direction) is the expectation value of the distorted atom's angular momentum?

Problem 8.19 Calculate the dielectric constant of helium gas using the approximation of Prob. 8.15. The experimental value at 0°C and atmospheric pressure is 1.000068.

Schrödinger's perturbation theory

The success of the above approach depends on the possibility of solving the differential equation (8.46) or, in this case, its equivalent, (8.48). In many situations this is not at all easy to do, and we have need of another general method for constructing $\psi^{(1)}$ and the higher approximations without solving an equation. Such a method can be found, and it is the original form of perturbation theory developed by Schrödinger in his earliest papers from a method due to Lord Rayleigh for solving analogous problems in acoustics. We shall develop here only the lowest order, but the others can be developed similarly. Taking advantage of the fact [Eq. (8.16)] that $\psi^{(1)}$ can be chosen orthogonal to $\psi^{(0)}$, we write it as an expansion in the unperturbed eigenfunctions $\psi_n^{(0)}$, omitting the term in $\psi^{(0)}$. Let the unperturbed state be denoted by $\psi_a^{(0)}$. We now suppose that

$$\psi^{(1)} = \sum_{n \neq a} c_n \psi_n^{(0)} \tag{8.53}$$

and substitute this into (8.10b). Since

$$\hat{H}^{(0)} \psi_n^{(0)} = E_n^{(0)} \psi_n^{(0)}$$

where $E_n^{(0)}$ is the nth unperturbed eigenvalue, we have

$$\sum_{n \neq a} (E_n^{(0)} - E_a^{(0)}) c_n \psi_n^{(0)} = -(\hat{H}^{(1)} - E^{(1)}) \psi_a^{(0)}$$

If we multiply this by $\psi_a^{(0)*}$ and integrate, we get the first-order energy expression

$$E^{(1)} = \langle \hat{H}^{(1)} \rangle_a^{(0)}$$

whereas multiplying by some other $\psi_m^{(0)*}$ gives

$$(E_m^{(0)} - E_a^{(0)}) c_m = -\int \psi_m^{(0)*} \hat{H}^{(1)} \psi_a^{(0)}$$

or

$$c_m = -\frac{\int \psi_m^{(0)*} \hat{H}^{(1)} \psi_a^{(0)}}{E_m^{(0)} - E_a^{(0)}} \qquad (m \neq a) \tag{8.54}$$

The integral of an operator placed between two different wave functions has already been encountered in (8.23). Because of the way in which it occurs in the matrix form of quantum mechanics, it is called a *matrix element*.[8] We shall adopt the special notation

$$\int \psi_m^{(0)*} \hat{H}^{(1)} \psi_a^{(0)} = \langle m|\hat{H}^{(1)}|a \rangle \tag{8.55}$$

so that (8.54) is

$$c_m = -\frac{\langle m|\hat{H}^{(1)}|a \rangle}{E_m^{(0)} - E_a^{(0)}} \qquad (m \neq a) \tag{8.56}$$

To find $E^{(2)}$, we substitute (8.53) and (8.56) into (8.14b), which gives

$$E^{(2)} = -\sum_{m \neq a} \frac{\langle a|\hat{H}^{(1)}|m \rangle \langle m|\hat{H}^{(1)}|a \rangle}{E_m^{(0)} - E_a^{(0)}} \tag{8.57}$$

Since the second integral is the complex conjugate of the first, we can write this as

$$E^{(2)} = -\sum_{m \neq a} \frac{|\langle m|\hat{H}^{(1)}|a \rangle|^2}{E_m^{(0)} - E_a^{(0)}} \tag{8.58}$$

This construction of $\psi^{(1)}$ and $E^{(2)}$ depends only on the possibility of carrying out the integrations and performing the sum. The former is not usually difficult, and in some cases the latter involves only two or three terms. But often it involves an infinite sum or, what is more difficult, an integration; for there may be groups of states distributed in a continuous fashion. This was in fact the case in calculating the polarizability of hydrogen; for in addition to all the bound states of the electron-proton system there is an infinite set for which the particles are not bound. These states have positive energies and, since there is no eigenvalue condition to restrict them, all positive energies are possible. Though in this case we know the final answer, we have said nothing about such states or how the integrals are to be carried out. They will be treated in the next chapter, but in a somewhat different context. About all one can do with (8.58) in such a case is to use it to make estimates. If state a is the

---

[8] The reason for this name becomes clear from the following. Expand the quantity $\hat{B}\psi_b$ (we omit the superscripts $^{(0)}$) in terms of the ψ's,

$$\hat{B}\psi_b = \Sigma b_m \psi_m \qquad b_m = \int \psi_m^* \hat{B} \psi_b = \langle m|\hat{B}|b \rangle$$

Then consider the sum

$$\sum_m \langle a|\hat{A}|m \rangle \langle m|\hat{B}|b \rangle = \sum b_m \langle a|\hat{A}|m \rangle = \int \psi_a^* \hat{A} \sum b_m \psi_m = \int \psi_a^* \hat{A} \hat{B} \psi_b$$

or

$$\sum_m \langle a|\hat{A}|m \rangle \langle m|\hat{B}|b \rangle = \langle a|\hat{A}\hat{B}|b \rangle$$

where $\hat{A}$ and $\hat{B}$ are any two operators. Readers familiar with matrix notation will see that this relation follows the rule for multiplication of matrices.

normal ground state, then all the other states have higher energy and each term of (8.58) is zero or negative. Further, the denominators get successively larger and the numerators are often found to decrease, so that one or two terms will often give a valid estimate.

Problem 8.20 Use the first terms of (8.53) and (8.58) to estimate the perturbed wave function and the polarizability of the hydrogen atom in its ground state. How close is the polarizability to the exact value? With $a = 0$ in (8.58), find upper (and lower) bounds for $E^{(2)}$ by replacing the denominator by the largest (and smallest) values and factoring it out of the sum, which can then be evaluated by footnote 8. (Remember to exclude the term $m = 0$.) Compare these bounds with the exact value.

As an example of the use of (8.58) under favorable circumstances, let us consider the perturbation of a simple harmonic oscillator by a constant force of magnitude f in the positive x direction, analogous to the uniform field of the last section. Say that the oscillator is originally in its ath quantum state and that

$$\hat{H}^{(1)} = -fx$$

The first-order perturbed energy $E^{(1)}$ vanishes identically (why?), so that we must do a second-order calculation. To calculate $E^{(2)}$, we must evaluate integrals of the form

$$\int_{-\infty}^{\infty} \psi_m{}^{(0)} x \psi_a{}^{(0)} \, dx$$

where the $\psi^{(0)}$'s are ordinary harmonic oscillator wave functions, and these were evaluated in Prob. 4.20, with the result

$$\int_{-\infty}^{\infty} \psi_m{}^{(0)} x \psi_a{}^{(0)} \, dx = \left(\frac{\hbar}{2m\omega}\right)^{1/2} [a^{1/2}\delta_{m,a-1} + (a+1)^{1/2}\delta_{m,a+1}] \tag{8.59}$$

where $\delta_{m,a\pm1}$, the Kronecker delta, is defined in (4.130), the commas being inserted here to make it easier to read. The sum (8.57) thus consists of two terms only,

$$\psi^{(1)} = -f\left(\frac{\hbar}{2m\omega}\right)^{1/2}\left(\frac{a^{1/2}\psi_{a-1}^{(0)}}{E_a^{(0)} - E_{a-1}^{(0)}} + \frac{(a+1)^{1/2}\psi_{a+1}^{(0)}}{E_a^{(0)} - E_{a+1}^{(0)}}\right) \tag{8.60}$$

and if a happens to be the ground state 0, the first term of this expression is, of course, missing. Similarly, (8.58) is

$$E^{(2)} = \frac{\hbar}{2m\omega} f^2 \left(\frac{a}{E_a^{(0)} - E_{a-1}^{(0)}} + \frac{a+1}{E_a^{(0)} - E_{a+1}^{(0)}}\right)$$

or, since the energies are in steps of $\hbar\omega$,

$$E^{(2)} = \frac{\hbar}{2m\omega} f^2 \left(\frac{a}{\hbar\omega} - \frac{a+1}{\hbar\omega}\right)$$

$$= -\frac{f^2}{2m\omega^2} = -\frac{f^2}{2K} \qquad (a \geqslant 0) \tag{8.61}$$

since $m\omega^2 = K$, the spring constant. The energies are thus shifted by an amount which is independent of the oscillator's state.

Problem 8.21 Fill in the mathematical steps leading to (8.61).

Problem 8.22 The problem we have just treated approximately is one for which a simple exact solution is available. Insert into the original equation (4.95b) the new perturbing energy, and note that by changing x to a new variable $\xi + \lambda$, with a suitable value for λ, one can cancel the perturbing $\hat{H}^{(1)}$, leaving the whole problem substantially in its unperturbed form. Show that the new energy is exactly equal to (8.61), so that all higher-order perturbations must vanish exactly.

Problem 8.23 Find the perturbed energy and wave function for the oscillator in its ground state, using the method developed in the first part of this section.

Problem 8.24 Calculate the third term of the series (8.19) and compare the result with (8.20).

8.6 The Variation Principle

An entirely different approach to the problem of finding approximate wave functions and energies is suggested by the question: "If I can guess a wave function of reasonable form which contains one or two adjustable parameters, how can I choose the parameters so as to get the best fit?" First, we need to decide exactly what is meant by "the best fit," and this is most easily seen if for a moment we restrict attention to finding the ground state of the system (this is what one usually wants anyhow). Let us pose the following problem: If instead of the correct normalized wave function ψ_0 (the subscript referring to the lowest energy state) we use an erroneous, but still normalized function ψ, how does the energy of the state ψ compare with the true energy E_0? This question can be answered at once. Let ψ_n be the nth exact normalized eigenfunction of $\hat{H}$ (of course, we do not know what it is), and expand ψ in terms of the ψ_n,

$$\psi = \Sigma c_n \psi_n \tag{8.62}$$

where, because of the normalization of ψ, we have

$$\Sigma |c_n|^2 = 1 \tag{8.63}$$

by (5.5). The expectation value of $\hat{H}$ in the state ψ is, by (5.6),

$$W \equiv \langle \hat{H} \rangle_\psi = \Sigma |c_n|^2 E_n \tag{8.64}$$

If E_0 is the ground-state energy, we have the inequality

$$W \geqslant \Sigma |c_n|^2 E_0$$

or, by (8.63),

$$W \geqslant E_0 \qquad (8.65)$$

The approximate energy W is therefore always in excess, and a very natural criterion of best fit for a trial wave function suggests itself: the parameters of the trial wave function should be adjusted so as to minimize the expectation value of the energy. The mathematical content of this rule can be seen if we write ψ as $\psi_0 + \delta\psi$, where $\delta\psi$ represents the error, and W, using (8.63), as

$$W = E_0 + \Sigma|c_n|^2(E_n - E_0) \qquad (8.66)$$

where the sum is clearly over values of $n > 0$. The coefficients c_n are given by

$$c_n = \int\psi_n^*\psi = \int\psi_n^*(\psi_0 + \delta\psi)$$

or

$$c_n = \int\psi_n^* \delta\psi \qquad (n > 0)$$

so that if $\delta\psi$ is thought to be proportional to some parameter of smallness ε, then c_n is also proportional to ε and the sum in (8.66) representing the error in energy is proportional to ε^2. This is of a higher order of smallness, so that, to put it roughly, a good guess at ψ_0 gives a very good guess at E_0.

The connection of this principle with the first-order perturbation theory is immediate. Suppose that the total hamiltonian is of the form $\hat{H}^{(0)} + \hat{H}^{(1)}$, with $\hat{H}^{(1)}$ "small" relative to $\hat{H}^{(0)}$, and that we decide to use for a trial function the function $\psi^{(0)}$ such that

$$\hat{H}^{(0)}\psi^{(0)} = E^{(0)}\psi^{(0)}$$

Then the exact energy E satisfies

$$E \leqslant W^{(0)} = \langle\hat{H}^{(0)} + \hat{H}^{(1)}\rangle^{(0)} = E^{(0)} + E^{(1)} \qquad (8.67)$$

by (8.11), and we see that the first-order perturbation is always in excess of the exact value. But if $\psi^{(0)}$ differs from $\psi^{(1)}$ by something of the order of ε, the excess is of the order of ε^2.

An intuitive way to look at this situation is to note that a material system able to radiate will always lose energy until it arrives in the lowest state available to it. Imagine that an atomic system is formed with its electrons in some disordered state. It will lose energy until, subject to its constraints, it can lose no more, which leads to our characterization of the correct ground state as that having the least energy.

We can apply these same principles to states higher than the ground state if we can characterize them by their symmetry properties. Suppose, for example, that the first excited state ψ_1 is known to belong to some eigenvalue of a symmetry operator (such as angular momentum or parity) different from that of the ground state ψ_0. If we choose an approximate ψ with the same symmetry as ψ_1, then it will be orthogonal to ψ_0 (even though we do not know ψ_0!) and c_0 in (8.62) vanishes exactly (why?). The sum in (8.64) then starts at $n = 1$, and we can prove accordingly that $W \geqslant E_1$. The proof that the error in E_1 is of a lower order of magnitude than that in ψ_1 goes through as before.

Problem 8.25 Fill in the details of the above argument.

Examples

As a simple example which does not involve too much arithmetic, let us calculate the first two energy levels of the (one-dimensional) anharmonic oscillator discussed in Sec. 4.6, in which the potential function is

$$V(x) = \lambda x^4$$

The wave functions must decrease rapidly with increasing distance from the origin; for simplicity we choose them to be like those of the harmonic oscillator:

$$\psi_0 = \alpha^{\frac{1}{2}}\pi^{-\frac{1}{4}}e^{-\frac{1}{2}\alpha^2 x^2}$$
$$\psi_1 = 2^{\frac{1}{2}}\beta^{\frac{3}{2}}\pi^{-\frac{1}{4}}xe^{-\frac{1}{2}\beta^2 x^2}$$

(8.68)

Starting with the ground state, we form

$$W_0 = \alpha\pi^{-\frac{1}{2}}\int_{-\infty}^{\infty} e^{-\frac{1}{2}\alpha^2 x^2}\left(-\frac{\hbar^2}{2m}\frac{d^2}{dx^2} + \lambda x^4\right)e^{-\frac{1}{2}\alpha^2 x^2}\,dx$$

$$= \alpha\pi^{-\frac{1}{2}}\int_{-\infty}^{\infty}\left[-\frac{\hbar^2}{2m}(\alpha^4 x^2 - \alpha^2) + \lambda x^4\right]e^{-\alpha^2 x^2}\,dx$$

To evaluate this, we use the integral formula

$$\int_{-\infty}^{\infty} x^{2n}e^{-\alpha^2 x^2}\,dx$$
$$= \begin{cases} \dfrac{\pi^{\frac{1}{2}}}{\alpha} & (n = 0) \\[2mm] \dfrac{1 \times 3 \times 5 \times \cdots \times (2n-1)\pi^{\frac{1}{2}}}{2^n \alpha^{2n+1}} & (n = 1, 2, \ldots) \end{cases}$$

(8.69)

and get

$$W_0 = \frac{\hbar^2}{2m}\frac{\alpha^2}{2} + \frac{3}{4}\frac{\lambda}{\alpha^4}$$

The value of α which makes this a minimum is

$$\alpha = \left(\frac{6m\lambda}{\hbar^2}\right)^{\frac{1}{6}}$$

with which W_0 becomes

$$W_0 = \frac{3^{1/3}}{4}\left(\frac{\hbar^2}{2m}\right)^{2/3}\lambda^{1/3} = 1.082\left(\frac{\hbar^2}{2m}\right)^{2/3}\lambda^{1/3} \tag{8.70}$$

We have seen in Sec. 4.6 that the exact value of the coefficient, obtained by numerical integration, is 1.060. The error here is therefore only 2 percent, as compared with 18 percent for the WKB estimate. In exactly the same way, we find for the first excited state

$$\beta = \left(\frac{10m\lambda}{\hbar^2}\right)^{1/6}$$

and

$$W_1 = \frac{9 \times 5^{1/3}}{4}\left(\frac{\hbar^2}{2m}\right)^{2/3}\lambda^{1/3} = 3.847\left(\frac{\hbar^2}{2m}\right)^{2/3}\lambda^{1/3}$$

The correct value for the coefficient is 3.800; the error is 1.2 percent. Thus, with a wave function which has only a single variable parameter, and which we know to be adapted to a markedly different problem, we can come very close to the true value of the energy. This illustrates the remark, based on (8.66), that the error in energy is generally much smaller than the error in ψ.

Problem 8.26 How does ψ_1 satisfy the criteria developed above for an estimate of the wave function of the first excited state?

Problem 8.27 Solve Prob. 8.4 variationally and compare the answer with that obtained before.

Problem 8.28 Carry out the calculation of W_1.

Problem 8.29 Try to find a better approximation to W_0. (How will you know if it is better?)

As a second example let us again evaluate the polarizability of a hydrogen atom. The hamiltonian function is

$$\hat{H} = -\frac{\hbar^2}{2m}\nabla^2 - \frac{e'^2}{r} - eFz \tag{8.71}$$

and as trial wave function we take the ground state, slightly perturbed along the z axis,

$$\psi = N(1 + qFz)\psi_{1,0,0}^{(0)} \tag{8.72}$$

where the perturbation has been written as qFz in anticipation that it will turn out proportional to F. Our problem is to find the number q. First ψ must be normalized, and we find that

$$|N|^2 = (1 + q^2F^2a_0^2)^{-1} \approx 1 - q^2F^2a_0^2 \tag{8.73}$$

where we have approximated in the limit of small F. The expectation value of (8.71) in the state (8.72) turns out to be

$$\langle E \rangle = E^{(0)} - (2qe + q^2E^{(0)})F^2a_0^2 \tag{8.74}$$

and this has a minimum as a function of q because $E^{(0)}$ is negative. We find that at the minimum,

$$q = -\frac{e}{E^{(0)}} = \frac{8\pi\varepsilon_0 a_0}{e}$$

and

$$\langle E \rangle = E^{(0)} - 8\pi\varepsilon_0 a_0{}^3 F^2 \tag{8.75}$$

Comparison with (8.41) shows that the resulting value of α is

$$\alpha_{\text{appr}} = 16\pi\varepsilon_0 a_0{}^3$$

which is about 11 percent smaller than the exact value (8.51). The perturbed wave function is

$$\psi \approx N\left(1 + \frac{8\pi\varepsilon_0}{e} a_0 F z\right) \psi_{1,0,0}^{(0)} \tag{8.76}$$

with N given by (8.73). The general resemblance to the more exact wave function (8.52) is obvious.

Problem 8.30   Fill in the computational steps leading to (8.75).

Problem 8.31   Recalling that the standard deviation of the energy ΔE vanishes if the state with respect to which it is taken is an exact eigenstate of the hamiltonian, one would conjecture that the value of ΔE is a measure of the closeness of our variational estimate W to the correct eigenvalue E. Prove that if W is initially good enough that it is closer to the correct energy level than to the one above it, then ΔE is a limit for the error and E satisfies the double inequality

$$W - \Delta E \leqslant E \leqslant W \tag{8.77}$$

Problem 8.32   Show that for the ground state of the anharmonic oscillator discussed above,

$$\Delta E = 2^{-1/3} 3^{-1/6} \left(\frac{\hbar^2}{2m}\right)^{2/3} \lambda^{1/3}$$

and compare this estimate with the actual error.

A general form of the variational principle

As a final remark on the variational principle, we shall exhibit it in a somewhat different form applicable to the determination of higher energy values. Let ψ_n be an exact nth eigenfunction, which we shall not assume to be normalized, and suppose that a small error or change is made in it. We require to know the corresponding change in the energy E_n. First, we write E_n as

$$E_n \int \psi_n^* \psi_n = \int \psi_n^* \hat{H} \psi_n \tag{8.78}$$

and then we let ψ_n become $\psi_n + \delta\psi_n$ and, correspondingly, E_n become $E_n + \delta E_n$. Taking differentials of (8.78) gives

$$\delta E_n \int \psi_n^* \psi_n + E_n(\int \delta\psi_n^* \cdot \psi_n + \int \psi_n^* \, \delta\psi_n)$$
$$= \int \delta\psi_n^* \cdot \hat{H}\psi_n + \int \psi_n^* \hat{H} \, \delta\psi_n \qquad (8.79)$$

Using the hermiticity of $\hat{H}$ and the fact that ψ_n is an exact eigenfunction gives for the right-hand side

$$E_n(\int \delta\psi_n^* \cdot \psi_n + \int \psi_n^* \, \delta\psi_n)$$

so that (8.79) becomes

$$\delta E_n \int \psi_n^* \psi_n = 0 \qquad (8.80)$$

or $\delta E_n = 0$. Thus, to the first order in small quantities, an error in ψ in the neighborhood of any of the eigenfunctions ψ_n gives no error in the energy. This shows that if one can guess close enough to the correct wave function for any stationary state whatever, then the error in $\langle \hat{H} \rangle$ will always be of a higher order in small quantities than that of the wave function. This is the most general statement of the variational principle.

We shall not give any further examples of the variational method here because its principal usefulness lies in computing atomic wave functions in which several electrons are involved. We shall encounter it again in Chap. 15.

8.7   Perturbation Theory for Nonstationary States

When the probability of finding a physical system in any of its stationary states varies with time, the system is said to be in a nonstationary state. There are two essentially distinct ways in which such states occur. The first is if the system is influenced from outside in some way by a time-dependent force which changes its energy and thus causes it to make transitions from one energy state to another. An example of this is the excitation of an electron to a higher state by the absorption of a quantum of energy. The second is characteristic of a system in a degenerate state. Here even a perturbation which is constant in time and which therefore cannot affect the system's energy may cause it to make a transition out of its original state into another which is degenerate with it. An example of this is the scattering of a beam of particles by a fixed center of force such as an atomic nucleus, where the particles are deflected into another direction with no change in their energy. The mathematical apparatus which we are about to develop will be applicable to both purposes; the characteristic differences will appear later on. We shall, of course, have to work with time-dependent wave functions, and to avoid confusions in notation we shall distinguish them from the time-independent ψ's used so far in this chapter by calling them φ.

We now state the following problem: Suppose that the hamiltonian of a system is of the form

$$\hat{H} = \hat{H}^{(0)} + \hat{H}'$$ (8.81)

where $\hat{H}'$ may be a function of the time and we shall later (but not yet) wish to assume that it is small compared with $\hat{H}^{(0)}$. We are to solve the equation

$$i\hbar\dot{\varphi} = \hat{H}\varphi$$ (8.82)

under the assumption that we know how to solve the unperturbed equation

$$ih\dot{\varphi}^{(0)} = \hat{H}^{(0)}\varphi^{(0)}$$ (8.83)

We shall need only the solutions corresponding to stationary states,

$$i\hbar\dot{\varphi}_n^{(0)} = \hat{H}^{(0)}\varphi_n^{(0)} = E_n^{(0)}\varphi_n^{(0)}$$ (8.84)

where

$$\varphi_n^{(0)} = \psi_n^{(0)}e^{-iE_nt/\hbar}$$ (8.85)

the $\psi_n^{(0)}$ being the ordinary time-independent wave functions which we have used earlier in this chapter.

As in Sec. 8.1, we write the exact φ in terms of $\varphi^{(0)}$ and a correction,

$$\varphi = \varphi^{(0)} + \varphi'$$ (8.86)

Putting this into (8.82) gives

$$i\hbar(\dot{\varphi}^{(0)} + \dot{\varphi}') = (\hat{H}^{(0)}\varphi^{(0)} + \hat{H}^{(0)}\varphi' + \hat{H}'\varphi)$$

The use of (8.83) reduces this to

$$i\hbar\dot{\varphi}' - \hat{H}^{(0)}\varphi' = \hat{H}'\varphi$$ (8.87)

We now make the basic assumption characteristic of this approach, that φ' can be expanded in terms of the unperturbed $\varphi^{(0)}$'s with coefficients which vary with time,

$$\varphi' = \Sigma a_n(t)\varphi_n^{(0)} = \Sigma a_n(t)\psi_n^{(0)}e^{-iE_nt/\hbar}$$ (8.88)

We substitute this into (8.87) and carry out the differentiation

$$i\hbar\Sigma\dot{a}_n(t)\psi_n^{(0)}e^{-iE_nt/\hbar} + \Sigma a_n(t)E_n\psi_n^{(0)}e^{-iE_nt/\hbar} \\ - \Sigma a_n(t)\hat{H}^{(0)}\psi_n^{(0)}e^{-iE_nt/\hbar} = \hat{H}'\varphi$$

By (8.84), the second and third terms cancel each other. We then multiply both sides of the equation by some $\psi_m^{(0)*}$ and integrate over the spatial variables. All terms of the sum except one drop out, and we have

$$i\hbar\dot{a}_m(t)e^{-iE_mt/\hbar} = \int\psi_m^{(0)*}\hat{H}'\varphi$$

or, reinstating $\varphi_m{}^{(0)}$,

$$i\hbar\dot{a}_m(t) = \int\varphi_m{}^{(0)*}\hat{H}'\varphi \tag{8.89}$$

This equation is closely related to (6.19), but it is more general, since H' can now be a function of the time. It is, of course, exact, and since φ is unknown, it is not very useful as a computational tool; but we shall have occasion to use it in connection with the theory of scattering in Chap. 10.

To derive a systematic way of approximating to $a_m(t)$, we use the same method of series expansion as we used earlier in treating the stationary states. The treatment here will accordingly be brief. We write

$$\hat{H} = \hat{H}^{(0)} + \lambda\hat{H}^{(1)}$$

and assume for convenience that the unperturbed system is in its ath stationary state, so that φ can be expanded as

$$\varphi = \varphi_a{}^{(0)} + \lambda\varphi_a{}^{(1)} + \lambda^2\varphi_a{}^{(2)} + \cdots \tag{8.90}$$

Substituting into (8.82) and separating out coefficients of different powers of λ gives

$$i\hbar\dot{\varphi}_a{}^{(0)} - \hat{H}^{(0)}\varphi_a{}^{(0)} = 0 \tag{8.91a}$$

$$i\hbar\dot{\varphi}_a{}^{(1)} - \hat{H}^{(0)}\varphi_a{}^{(1)} = \hat{H}^{(1)}\varphi_a{}^{(0)} \tag{8.91b}$$

$$i\hbar\dot{\varphi}_a{}^{(2)} - \hat{H}^{(0)}\varphi_a{}^{(2)} = \hat{H}^{(1)}\varphi_a{}^{(1)} \tag{8.91c}$$

etc., after which, as before, we can set λ equal to 1 and forget about it. The first of these is satisfied automatically. In the second we write

$$\varphi_a{}^{(1)} = \Sigma c_n(t)\varphi_n{}^{(0)} = \Sigma c_n(t)\psi_n{}^{(0)} \exp\left(\frac{-iE_n{}^{(0)}t}{\hbar}\right) \tag{8.92}$$

where the c's are a first approximation to the a's used above and this expansion is exactly analogous to that in (8.53). The resulting equation is multiplied through by $\psi_b{}^{(0)*}$ and integrated, and the result, in the notation of (8.55) and (8.56), is

$$i\hbar\dot{c}_b = \langle b|\hat{H}^{(1)}|a\rangle e^{i\omega_{ba}t} \tag{8.93}$$

where the matrix element $\langle b|H^{(1)}|a\rangle$ depends on the time only through $\hat{H}^{(1)}$, and $\hbar\omega_{ba} = E_b{}^{(0)} - E_a{}^{(0)}$. The coefficients c_b can now be found by direct integration if their values are known at some initial instant t_0,

$$c_b(t) = c_b(t_0) - \frac{i}{\hbar}\int_{t_0}^{t} \langle b|\hat{H}^{(1)}|a\rangle e^{i\omega_{ba}t'}\, dt' \tag{8.94}$$

In order to show the content of this expression, we can illustrate it as follows. Suppose that at the initial instant t_0 the system is known to be in some unperturbed state $\varphi_a{}^{(0)}$. We ask the probability that later, at time t, it will be found in the state $\varphi_b{}^{(0)}$, where $b \neq a$. Clearly, all the c's except c_a are equal to zero at t_0, and the approximate wave function at later times is

$$\varphi(t) = \varphi_a{}^{(0)}(t) + \Sigma c_n(t)\varphi_n{}^{(0)}(t) \tag{8.95}$$

Clearly, the probability of finding the system in the bth state is

$$P_b(t) = |c_b(t)|^2 \qquad (b \neq a) \tag{8.96}$$

where

$$c_b(t) = -\frac{i}{\hbar}\int_{t_0}^{t} \langle b|\hat{H}^{(1)}|a\rangle e^{i\omega_{ba}t'}\, dt' \tag{8.97}$$

Let us evaluate this first under the assumption that $\hat{H}^{(1)}$ is independent of time. Also, it will save space to set $t_0 = 0$. Integration of (8.97) gives

$$c_b(t) = -\frac{\langle b|\hat{H}^{(1)}|a\rangle}{\hbar\omega_{ba}} (e^{i\omega_{ba}t} - 1) \tag{8.98}$$

and the probability P_b is

$$P_b = 2|\langle b|\hat{H}^{(1)}|a\rangle|^2 \frac{1 - \cos\omega_{ba}t}{(\hbar\omega_{ba})^2} \tag{8.99}$$

This is perhaps a rather surprising result. It states that a system which starts in a definite state $\varphi_a{}^{(0)}$ will thereafter continually be oscillating into and out of other states $\varphi_b{}^{(0)}(b \neq a)$ at a frequency which is proportional to the energy difference between the two levels. This effect is analogous to undamped transients in an electric circuit. It is clearly somewhat unphysical, since for optical levels, for example, the frequency of alternation is of the order of 10^{14} per sec. Moreover, in electric circuits the transient behavior is damped by resistance which dissipates the extra energy. In atomic systems this damping takes place through radiation of energy, as will be discussed in the next chapter.

It should be noted further that the fluctuating amplitudes occur only over a rather narrow range of energies. To show this, we plot in Fig. 8.6 the last factor in (8.99). The perturbing energy causes fluctuations into neighboring states, but they are slight unless ω_{ba} lies within the central maximum of the curve. Even this is striking, however, since a constant perturbation cannot change the energy of a system *after* it has been applied, so it is difficult to see how any such fluctuations could take place without violating the conservation of energy. But from Fig. 8.6 we see that the fluctuations are appreciable only if

$$|\hbar\omega_{ba}| = |E_b{}^{(0)} - E_a{}^{(0)}| \leqslant \frac{2\pi\hbar}{t}$$

or

$$|E_b{}^{(0)} - E_a{}^{(0)}|t \leqslant 2\pi\hbar \tag{8.100}$$

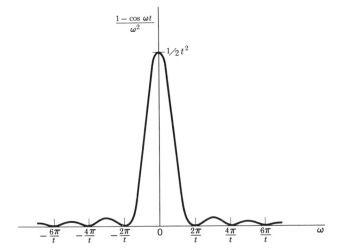

Fig. 8.6 Plot of the time-dependent factor in (8.99).

And here we come into conflict with the uncertainty principle; for according to (2.39), an energy measurement sufficiently accurate to tell whether or not the conservation of energy is being violated cannot be made within the time t at our disposal. The peak becomes narrower and higher as time goes on, and for intervals of laboratory size its height is effectively infinite and its width effectively zero. Thus the role played by the transient oscillations of the system turns out in practice to be a minor one.

But for a moment let us consider another question: is there any way of turning on a perturbation gradually, so that no transients will be excited?

Adiabatic transitions

Let us return to (8.97), making $\hat{H}^{(1)}$ a function of t which is zero at t_0 and slowly increases thereafter. It will be convenient to write t_0 as $-\infty$; clearly no loss of generality is involved. We thus have to integrate

$$c_b(t) = -\frac{i}{\hbar}\int_{-\infty}^{t} \langle b|\hat{H}^{(1)}(t')|a\rangle e^{i\omega_{ba}t'}\, dt' \tag{8.101}$$

and we do it by parts,

$$c_b(t) = -\frac{\langle b|\hat{H}^{(1)}(t)|a\rangle}{\hbar\omega_{ba}}\, e^{i\omega_{ba}t}$$
$$+\frac{1}{\hbar\omega_{ba}}\int_{-\infty}^{t}\left\langle b\left|\frac{d\hat{H}^{(1)}(t')}{dt'}\right|a\right\rangle e^{i\omega_{ba}t'}\, dt'$$

The point now is that if $\hat{H}^{(1)}$ is established slowly enough, the integral on the right may be made as small as desired. Such a process is termed *adiabatic*, and in this limit we have

$$c_b^{(ad)}(t) = -\frac{\langle b|\hat{H}^{(1)}(t)|a\rangle}{E_b^{(0)} - E_a^{(0)}} e^{i\omega_{ba}t} \qquad (b \neq a) \qquad (8.102)$$

If we remember that in the section on stationary states we omitted the time dependence of the wave functions and here included it, so that (8.92) differs from (8.53) by exponential factors, we see that (8.102) is exactly the same as (8.56), so that a junction has here been made between the two methods of approach. We have, in fact, solved two different problems and found that both have the same solution, and it will be convenient to compare them.

Stationary state	Nonstationary state
$\hat{H}^{(1)}$ is constant from the beginning.	$\hat{H}^{(1)}$ is turned on gradually.
The system is in an eigenstate of $\hat{H}^{(0)} + \hat{H}^{(1)}$ belonging to the energy $E_a^{(0)} + E_a^{(1)}$ from the beginning.	The system starts out in an eigenstate of $\hat{H}^{(0)}$ belonging to the energy $E_a^{(0)}$ and, as $\hat{H}^{(1)}$ increases, gradually changes its state.

What we have shown is that, in the adiabatic limit, the states end up the same in each case; that is, a system which starts out in the ith state of the unperturbed system will end up in the corresponding ith state of the perturbed system. Naturally, the final energies are the same in each case, and one can show directly that the expectation value of $\hat{H}$ in the state (8.95) is exactly equal to $E_a^{(0)}$ plus the first- and second-order energy perturbations calculated from stationary states. But the proof requires algebra that is long without being enlightening, and we shall leave it for the dedicated reader to work out for himself.

The result just proved is known as the *adiabatic theorem*. It was proved first by Ehrenfest on the basis of the old quantum theory, and we shall see in Chap. 18 that it is of great importance in elucidating the connection between atomic theory and thermodynamics.[9]

A striking example of adiabatic behavior is seen in the elastic collisions between molecules in a gas. As two molecules move into each other's fields of force, their electronic energy levels are continuously distorted and one might expect electronic transitions to occur. But since electrons move much faster than whole atoms, the distortion is essentially adiabatic; so that when the molecules

---

[9] The reader may be enlightened on this subject if he can experiment with a violin or its one-stringed laboratory equivalent. A little practice will enable him to produce the fundamental note or any of the first few overtones of the string. If now the string's tension is changed while a given harmonic is being bowed, it will be found that the string does not attempt to remain at its original frequency by changing overtones, but, rather, will keep on the same overtone and change its frequency. This is adiabatic behavior.

separate, their rotational or vibrational states may have been altered but their electronic states, which determine the molecular binding, have only rarely been changed.

Problem 8.33   Analyze classically the adiabatic behavior of a string of varying tension described in footnote 9.

Problem 8.34   Suppose that the perturbing energy $\hat{H}^{(1)}$ which occurs in (8.101) is turned on in an exponential way, starting at zero in the infinite past and arriving at the value $\hat{H}^{(1)}(t)$ at the time t. Evaluate $P_b(t)$ in terms of $\hat{H}^{(1)}(t)$ and the rate of increase, and show that the behavior is adiabatic if the rate of increase is infinitely small.

Problem 8.35   Let the perturbation be of the form

$$K(x)\tau^{-1}e^{-t^2/\tau^2}$$

Sketch this as a function of time for various values of τ. (Why is the factor of τ^{-1} written into the perturbation?) Evaluate the final probability of a transition from a to b in terms of τ and ω_{ba}. Under what circumstances is the probability appreciably different from zero? (This problem is suggested by the remarks on elastic collisions made above.)

Delta functions

To conclude this section, let us return to (8.99) and develop a convenient notation for it. We have already seen that the last factor of this equation (see Fig. 8.6) is, for intervals $t - t_0$ of laboratory duration, a curve with a very high, narrow maximum. Functions of this kind were mentioned briefly in Chap. 4; they are termed delta functions, and they are conveniently defined for our purposes in terms of the derivative of a step function. Let $s(x)$ (Fig. 8.7) be a step function of unit height. Then we define $\delta(x)$ as

$$\delta(x) = s'(x) \tag{8.103}$$

Clearly, this "function" is infinitely high and narrow. It has, however, a finite integral, for on integrating it from any $a < 0$ to any $b > 0$, we have

$$\int_a^b \delta(x)\,dx = \int_a^b s'(x)\,dx = s(b) - s(a) = 1$$

The delta function has a property which makes it very useful. It is that for any arbitrary function $f(x)$ continuous at $x = 0$,

$$\int_a^b f(x)\delta(x)\,dx = f(0) \tag{8.104}$$

or, more generally,

$$\int_{-\infty}^{\infty} f(x)\delta(x - x_0)\,dx = f(x_0) \tag{8.105}$$

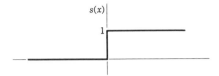

Fig. 8.7   A unit step function. Its derivative
is the function $\delta(x)$.

Problem 8.36   Without attempting to be mathematically rigorous, prove the last two equations from the definitions given.[10]

The function in (8.99) is of this kind. For large enough values of t it is nearly proportional to a delta function; and to find the constant of proportionality we need only evaluate its energy integral. Since $dE_b = \hbar\, d\omega_{ba}$, it is

$$I = \int_{-\infty}^{\infty} \frac{1 - \cos \omega_{ba}t}{(\hbar\omega_{ba})^2}\, \hbar\, d\omega_{ba}$$

First we let $\omega_{ba}t = x$, so that

$$I = \frac{t}{\hbar} \int_{-\infty}^{\infty} \frac{1 - \cos x}{x^2}\, dx$$

Integrating this by parts gives

$$I = \frac{t}{\hbar} \int_{-\infty}^{\infty} \frac{\sin x}{x}\, dx = \frac{2t}{\hbar} \int_{0}^{\infty} \frac{\sin x}{x}\, dx \tag{8.106}$$

and this is found in readily available tables such as *Dwight's* or the *Handbook of Chemistry and Physics* to be[11]

$$I = \frac{\pi t}{\hbar}$$

Therefore, in the limit of large t, we have

$$\lim_{t \to \infty} \frac{1 - \cos \omega_{ba}t}{(\hbar\omega_{ba})^2} = \frac{\pi t}{\hbar}\, \delta(E_b^{(0)} - E_a^{(0)}) \tag{8.107}$$

[10] The interested reader will find delta functions discussed briefly but clearly in D. Bohm, *Quantum Mechanics*, Prentice-Hall, Inc., Englewood Cliffs, N.J., 1951, pp. 212–214, and thoroughly in J. M. Lighthill, *Introduction to Fourier Series and Generalized Functions*, Cambridge University Press, London, 1958. See also G. Temple, Proc. Roy. Soc. (London), **A276**, 149, 168 (1963).

[11] To evaluate (8.106), we use the integral representation

$$\frac{1}{x} = \int_{0}^{\infty} e^{-ux}\, du \qquad (x > 0)$$

Putting this into I and interchanging the order of integration gives

$$I = \frac{2t}{\hbar} \int_{0}^{\infty} du \int_{0}^{\infty} e^{-ux} \sin x\, dx$$

$$= \frac{2t}{\hbar} \int_{0}^{\infty} \frac{du}{1 + u^2} = \frac{\pi t}{\hbar}$$

(Carrying out the exponential-trigonometrical integral is left as an exercise for the reader.)

and in (8.99), the probability of finding the system in state m is

$$P_b = \frac{2\pi t}{\hbar} |\langle b|\hat{H}^{(1)}|a\rangle|^2 \delta(E_b^{(0)} - E_a^{(0)}) \tag{8.108}$$

In using this expression it should be remembered that the delta function is not strictly a mathematical delta function, since the latter is infinitely high and narrow whereas this is always of finite width. Except under certain extreme circumstances, however, the replacement is permissible, and the resulting simplification makes it very convenient to use when the initial or final energy, or both, lie in a continuous range, so that states exist for which $E_b^{(0)} - E_a^{(0)}$ is arbitrarily small.

Problem 8.37   The oscillations in an expression like (8.99) correspond to transients suddenly excited in an electrical system. Imagine now that $\hat{H}^{(1)}(t)$ has grown proportionally to $e^{\varepsilon t}$, with ε very small, since $t = -\infty$. How is (8.108) obtained now?

Problem 8.38   Assuming that φ is an exact eigenstate of the full hamiltonian $\hat{H}^{(0)} + \hat{H}^{(1)}$ corresponding to the energy E, use (8.89) to derive an exact formula analogous to the approximation (8.108). State clearly exactly what physical quantity is given by this formula.

The second approximation

If the matrix elements $\langle b|\hat{H}^{(1)}|a\rangle$ connecting states of equal energy vanish, then the first-order transition probability as calculated above is zero, and we must go on to the second order. Writing $\varphi_a^{(2)}$ in (8.91c) as

$$\varphi_a^{(2)} = \Sigma d_n(t) \varphi_n^{(0)}$$

we find, exactly as above,

$$i\hbar \dot{d}_b = \int \varphi_b^{(0)*} \hat{H}^{(1)} \varphi_a^{(1)}$$

and substitution of (8.92) and (8.98) gives

$$i\hbar \dot{d}_b = -\sum_n \frac{\langle b|\hat{H}^{(1)}|n\rangle\langle n|\hat{H}^{(1)}|a\rangle}{\hbar \omega_{na}} \left(e^{i\omega_{ba}t} - e^{i\omega_{bn}t}\right)$$

whence

$$i\hbar \dot{d}_b = -\sum_n \frac{\langle b|\hat{H}^{(1)}|n\rangle\langle n|\hat{H}^{(1)}|a\rangle}{\hbar \omega_{na}} \left(\frac{e^{i\omega_{ba}t} - 1}{i\omega_{ba}} - \frac{e^{i\omega_{bn}t} - 1}{i\omega_{bn}}\right)$$

The two terms in the parentheses are quite different in their effects. The first is independent of the intermediate energy $E_n^{(0)}$ and has the same strong resonance as before when the final energy $E_b^{(0)}$ is close to the initial energy $E_a^{(0)}$. The second has no such maximum, since it contains the factor $\langle b|\hat{H}^{(1)}|n\rangle(e^{i\omega_{bn}t} - 1)/\omega_{bn}$ in which we are assuming that the matrix element vanishes when $E_n^{(0)}$ approaches

$E_b^{(0)}$. Thus only the first factor is effective in producing transitions, and in (8.108),

$$\langle b|\hat{H}^{(1)}|a\rangle \qquad \text{becomes} \qquad -\sum_n \frac{\langle b|\hat{H}^{(1)}|n\rangle\langle n|\hat{H}^{(1)}|a\rangle}{E_n^{(0)} - E_a^{(0)}}$$

This fact is known to Fermi's students as Golden Rule #1.

8.8 Perturbations Periodic in Time

We have treated in the preceding section two sorts of perturbing energy, those which are constant and those which are established in an adiabatic way. There is a third sort of perturbation, very common in physics, which is periodic in time. This would describe the action of a monochromatic beam of light falling on an atom, for example, or under certain circumstances the effect of a sound wave of high frequency.

We begin with (8.97), in which $\hat{H}^{(1)}$ is a periodic function of time,

$$\hat{H}^{(1)}(t) = \hat{H}_0^{(1)} \cos \omega t \tag{8.109}$$

To simplify matters, we take t_0 to be zero. Splitting the cosine into two exponentials and carrying out the time integration then gives

$$c_b(t) = -\frac{1}{2\hbar}\langle b|\hat{H}_0^{(1)}|a\rangle\left(\frac{e^{i(\omega_{ba}-\omega)t}-1}{\omega_{ba}-\omega} + \frac{e^{i(\omega_{ba}+\omega)t}-1}{\omega_{ba}+\omega}\right) \tag{8.110}$$

Each term of this expression is (except for the factor $\frac{1}{2}$) exactly like (8.98). Further, the two terms act in general quite independently of each other, since for any ω and t large enough that $\omega t \gg 1$, which is always the case of practice, any value of ω_{ba} which makes one of them large will make the other effectively zero. In squaring (8.110), therefore, the cross term will never be important, and we can write at once, copying from (8.108),

$$P_b = \frac{\pi t}{2\hbar}|\langle b|\hat{H}^{(1)}|a\rangle|^2[\delta(E_b^{(0)} - E_a^{(0)} - \hbar\omega) + \delta(E_b^{(0)} - E_a^{(0)} + \hbar\omega)] \tag{8.111}$$

The notation should not disguise the fact that we are here dealing with a resonance phenomenon very much like mechanical or electrical resonance. A periodic force is applied to a resonating system, which responds with a disturbance of large amplitude if the applied frequency corresponds to a natural frequency of the system; and in fact if the two frequencies coincide exactly, the resonance builds up proportionally to t, exactly as in (8.111).

Problem 8.39 Discuss the resonant behavior of a series LC circuit with negligible resistance under the influence of an alternating applied voltage and finally express the results in a form as closely resembling (8.111) as possible. Comment on the differences as well as the similarities.

The formula (8.111) is of great interest in atomic physics because it explains the origin of what is usually called the "quantum of energy." The first delta function in (8.111) is $\delta[E_b^{(0)} - (E_a^{(0)} + \hbar\omega)]$. It is equal to zero unless

$$E_b^{(0)} = E_a^{(0)} + \hbar\omega$$

and so we see that a disturbance of angular frequency ω will cause a system to make a transition only into a state whose energy is greater than that of the initial state by exactly $\hbar\omega$. This accounts for the "particle nature" of light which is apparent in so many phenomena, beginning with the photoelectric effect. The important thing, however, is that this explanation does *not* presuppose that the energy $\hbar\omega$ is concentrated at a point in space, that is, that the photon is a localized entity analogous to a very small bullet. A locally uniform plane wave will do just as well. This explains how "photons" can go through many slits of a diffraction apparatus at the same time and be diffracted. The same holds true of sound waves of high frequency. Solids emit and absorb sound (that is, vibrational) energy in units of $\hbar\omega$; these units are called *phonons*, and they play a major part in the discussion of transport phenomena in solids.

Returning to (8.111), we consider next the second term, which comes into play if

$$E_b^{(0)} = E_a^{(0)} - \hbar\omega$$

If, as is often the case, the state a is the ground state, then there is no such state of lower energy, and the term is zero. But if not, then we see that the perturbation is just as likely to cause a transition downward as a transition upward. This can be very simply understood, for if a vibrating system is acted upon by a periodic force, the system gains or loses energy according as the force is in or out of phase with the velocity of the system. If the force is applied at random, the probability that the phase difference is less than 90° is just equal to the probability that it is greater, and this accounts for the equal weights of the two terms in (8.111). Mathematically, they are of equal weight because they arise from the breaking up of $\cos \omega t$ in (8.109) into two exponentials. The $e^{i\omega t}$ is responsible for loss of energy and the $e^{-i\omega t}$ for gain.

Equations (8.108) and (8.111) are the fundamental formulas in atomic physics for calculating the rates at which transitions occur. The conservation of energy is built into them, though not to a degree of accuracy greater than that permitted by the indeterminacy principle. In the following chapters of this book these formulas will be applied to the determination of a number of rates: rates of absorption and emission of radiation, of scattering of particles by a center of force, and a few more.

Problem 8.40 A spin of $\frac{1}{2}$ with an associated magnetic moment is immersed in a magnetic field

$$B_x = B_0 \cos \omega t \qquad B_y = B_0 \sin \omega t \qquad B_z = B \text{ (const)}$$

If the hamiltonian is $-\gamma \hbar \mathbf{B} \cdot \hat{\mathbf{S}}$, find the transition produced by the rotating field and evaluate its probability. Explain the answer in elementary terms.

8.9 Electric and Magnetic Moments

In order to calculate physical properties of an atomic system, we often start by computing an energy. In this supplementary section we shall show how the electric and magnetic moments of a system can be calculated from a knowledge of the change in its energy when it is put into an external field. The arguments to be given first are rather intuitive; following them, we shall show how the formulas so derived can be understood rigorously.

Electric moment

When a system of charged particles is subject to an electric field F, it distorts until a dynamical equilibrium is set up between the external field tending to distort it and the internal field tending to resist the distortion. The potential energy of a dipole with respect to the external field is

$$E_{\text{ext}} = -M_e F$$

where M_e is the component of the system's electric moment in the direction of the field. Suppose now that the field is changed slightly so that a new dynamical equilibrium establishes itself. The change in energy is

$$dE_{\text{ext}} = -M_e \, dF - F \, dM_e$$

But there is also a change in the system's internal energy as it distorts. At equilibrium, the work done against the internal field is equal and opposite to that done against the external one,

$$dE_{\text{int}} = F \, dM_e$$

since the internal field does not change appreciably. (In classical mechanics this is essentially the principle of virtual work.) Thus the total change is

$$dE = dE_{\text{ext}} + dE_{\text{int}} = -M_e \, dF$$

and we can calculate the electric moment from the relation

$$M_e = -\frac{\partial E}{\partial F} \tag{8.112}$$

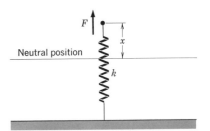

Fig. 8.8 A charge e on a spring at stiffness k is displaced a distance x by the action of an electric field F. At equilibrium, $eF = kx$. The total potential energy is $E = -eFx + \frac{1}{2}kx^2$. Thus,

$$dE = -ex\,dF - eF\,dx + kx\,dx$$
$$= -ex\,dF = -M_e dF$$

where M_e is the charge's electric moment.

where E is the total energy of the system in the external field. Figure 8.8 applies this argument to a simple example.

Magnetic moment

Here the situation is a little more complicated, since a static magnetic field does no work and so the meaning of a magnetic energy is not completely obvious. (The work comes from the electric field produced when the magnetic field *changes* from B to $B + dB$.)

Figure 8.9 shows the system at the center of a current loop, where the current I produces a field

$$B = \frac{\mu_0 I}{2a} \tag{8.113}$$

The loop's self-inductance without the system is L_0; the presence of the system adds an extra L_1. The potential energy of the magnetic dipole with respect to the external field is $-M_m B$, where M_m is the component of the magnetic moment in the direction of B. As the current is changed from I to $I + dI$ in a time dt, the total change in the system's energy is

$$dU = (L_0 + L_1)\frac{dI}{dt} I\,dt - d(M_m B)$$
$$= (L_0 + L_1)I\,dI - M_m\,dB - B\,dM_m$$

To calculate L_1 we start from its definition as the change in flux through the loop per unit change in current: $L = d\Phi_1/dI$, where Φ_1 is the flux produced by the system. The associated energy change is

$$L_1 I\,dI = I\,d\Phi_1$$

To calculate $d\Phi_1$ it is easiest to calculate the change in the amount of flux that does not pass through the loop. Since the field produced

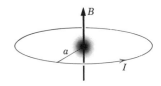

Fig. 8.9 System at the center of a current loop producing a magnetic field B.

by a dipole at a distance much greater than its size is

$$B_{\text{dip}} = \frac{\mu_0 M_m}{4\pi r^3}$$

the flux external to the loop is

$$\Phi_{\text{ext}} = \frac{\mu_0 M_m}{4\pi} \int_a^\infty \frac{2\pi r\, dr}{r^3} = \frac{\mu_0 M_m}{2a}$$

so that

$$I\, d\Phi_1 = \frac{\mu_0 I\, dM_m}{2a} = B\, dM_m$$

by (8.113). Thus,

$$dU = L_0 I\, dI + B\, dM_m - M_m\, dB - B\, dM_m$$

and the change in energy of the system itself is

$$dE = dU - L_0 I\, dI = -M_m\, dB$$

Thus, M_m can be calculated as

$$M_m = -\frac{\partial E}{\partial B} \tag{8.114}$$

Quantum-mechanical interpretation

The hamiltonian for a particle in uniform electric and magnetic fields, both parallel to the z axis, is given by (7.98) as

$$\hat{H} = \frac{\hat{p}^2}{2m} - \frac{eB}{2m}(x\hat{p}_y - y\hat{p}_x) + \frac{e^2 B^2}{8m}(x^2 + y^2) + eV_0 - eFz \tag{8.115}$$

where V_0 is the internal potential. The wave function satisfies

$$\hat{H}\psi = E\psi \tag{8.116}$$

but let us start from the formula

$$E = \langle \hat{H} \rangle = \int \psi^* \hat{H} \psi$$

We find

$$\frac{\partial E}{\partial F} = \int \frac{\partial \psi^*}{\partial F} \hat{H} \psi + \int \psi^* \frac{\partial \hat{H}}{\partial F} \psi + \int \psi^* \hat{H} \frac{\partial \psi}{\partial F}$$

$$= E \frac{\partial}{\partial F} \int \psi^* \psi + \left\langle \frac{\partial \hat{H}}{\partial F} \right\rangle$$

where we have used (8.116) and the hermiticity of $\hat{H}$. But if ψ is normalized, the first term is zero; and calculating the partial derivative from (8.115) gives

$$M_e = -\frac{\partial E}{\partial F} = \langle ez \rangle$$

which is the formula one would expect from classical physics. For the magnetic moment we find

$$
\begin{aligned}
M_m &= -\frac{\partial E}{\partial B} = -\left\langle \frac{\partial \hat{H}}{\partial B} \right\rangle \\
&= \left\langle \frac{e}{2m}\,(x\hat{p}_y - y\hat{p}_x) - \frac{e^2 B}{4m}\,(x^2 + y^2) \right\rangle \\
&= \left\langle \frac{e}{2m}\,[x(\hat{p}_y - \tfrac{1}{2}eBx) - y(\hat{p}_x + \tfrac{1}{2}eBy)] \right\rangle \\
&= \left\langle \frac{e}{2m}\,[x(\hat{p}_y - eA_y) - y(\hat{p}_x - eA_x)] \right\rangle \\
&= \left\langle \frac{e}{2}\,(x\hat{v}_y - y\hat{v}_x) \right\rangle
\end{aligned}
\tag{8.117}
$$

where $\hat{\mathbf{v}}$ is the velocity operator which occurs in (7.91). The classical analogue of the operator which occurs here is

$$
\frac{e}{2m}\,(xmv_y - ymv_x) = \frac{e}{2m}\,P_z
$$

where P_z is the angular momentum. Since $e/2m$ is the correct gyromagnetic ratio, (8.117) is recognized as the quantum-mechanical equivalent of the classical theory.

Most systems of interest contain a number of charged particles. The foregoing results are easily generalized by writing the hamiltonian as the sum of the hamiltonians of the individual particles.

Gauge Transformations

The above results are so simple and natural that we are apt to forget they were obtained by a particular choice of gauge. The beauty of (8.115) is that the term linear in B is clearly paramagnetic in its effect while the quadratic term is diamagnetic. But the vector potential used to derive (7.98) is not unique. We could have used

$$
A_x = -\tfrac{1}{2}B(y - y_0) \qquad A_y = \tfrac{1}{2}B(x - x_0) \qquad A_z = 0
$$

which corresponds to the same uniform B but shifts the origin of coordinates in (8.115).   Or we could have made many other choices, including $A_x = -By$, $A_y = A_z = 0$. With this the clear separation between paramagnetic and diamagnetic terms disappears. But we know from the result of Prob. 7.39 that changes of gauge make no difference to the result of any calculation. This can be understood only when we remember that the terms in B and B^2 are perturbations, and that the B^2 correction to the energy comes from the first order of the perturbation in B^2 plus the second order of that in B. It is the total perturbed E that is invariant, and a particular choice of gauge is made only in order to simplify calculation.

9

The Theory of Scattering

If one wants to learn about the forces between elementary particles, there are two principal experimental techniques available. One is the study of bound states, some of whose main features were outlined in Chap. 7; the other is the study of the scattering of a beam of particles from a stationary target. The second technique is more important than the first, for it is more under the experimenter's control. In studying bound states, one has to be content with the bound states there are (the neutron-proton system, for example, has only one), whereas in scattering one measures the angular distributions of the scattered particles at a variety of angles and over a range of energies which is limited only by the apparatus available. The quantity of data available from scattering experiments is potentially very great; in addition, the experimental energies available normally cover a far wider range than do the energies of bound states, so that at higher energies one has the added advantage of the greater resolving power provided by scattered particles whose de Broglie wavelengths can be made small in comparison with the ranges of the forces involved.

It is customary to establish contact between theory and experiment by considering the scattering cross section, a quantity which is susceptible of a reasonably direct experimental measurement and which at the same time, as we shall see, lends itself readily to calculation. We shall therefore begin with a discussion of this quantity.

9.1 The Scattering Cross Section

Suppose one had a particle detector whose aperture A was to be be determined. Short of measuring A directly with calipers, one

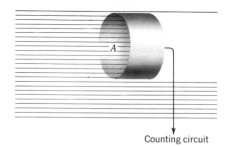

Fig. 9.1 Detector with effective area A.   Counting circuit

could also find it in the following way (Fig. 9.1). Produce a beam of particles of known intensity, say, I particles arriving per unit area per second. Then if the detector is introduced into the beam, its counting rate N, in counts per second, will obviously be given by IA, so that A is determined as

$$A = \frac{N \text{ (counts per second)}}{I \text{ (particles per unit area per second)}}$$ (9.1)

The reader will, of course, notice that a statistical assumption has been made here: the particles arrive strictly at random, and the detector receives the expected number of hits. A large range of answers for A is, of course, possible, and if only a few counts are received, the statistical uncertainty will be rather large. We therefore envisage an experimental situation in which enough counts are recorded that the statistical uncertainty does not dominate that arising from other quarters. The convenience of an experimental method based on these considerations is that the statistical point of view necessary for its interpretation is built into quantum mechanics, where again one calculates not where such-and-such a particle will hit, but only the average rate of counting in a given small region.

We shall now show how the angular distribution of particles scattered from a target can be described in terms of a cross section; for clarity, this will first be done in classical terms. Figure 9.2 shows a situation in which particles are scattered by a repulsive central force. The detector records all the particles which enter it, and these originate in a narrow prism of space shown shaded in the end view. The counting rate $dN(\vartheta)$ is equal to $Is\,ds\,d\varphi$, where s is called the *collision parameter* for a particle which ends up being scattered through ϑ, the *scattering angle*. Thus, the ratio $dN(\vartheta)/I$ gives the value of the effective area $s\,ds\,d\varphi$. We call this area $d\sigma$, remembering that its value depends in general not only on the scattering angle ϑ at which the detector is situated but also on the energy of the incoming particles. Thus,

$$d\sigma = \frac{dN(\vartheta)}{I}$$ (9.2)

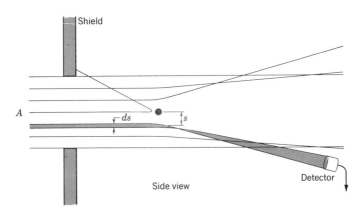

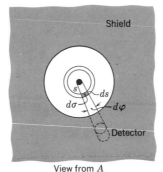

Fig. 9.2 The small part of the incident beam which ends up in the detector defines the element of cross section $d\sigma$.

and this is evaluated classically as

$$d\sigma = s\, ds\, d\varphi$$

But the value of $dN(\vartheta)$ varies proportionally with the size of the counter, or rather with the size of the solid angle $d\Omega$ which it subtends at the target. Thus a measure of the scattering which is independent of this size is the ratio

$$\frac{dN(\vartheta)}{d\Omega} = I\, \frac{d\sigma}{d\Omega} \tag{9.3}$$

where $d\sigma/d\Omega$ defined in this way is known as the *differential scattering cross section*. It should be noted that $d\sigma/d\Omega$ does not denote "differentiation with respect to Ω," for no such variable as Ω enters our calculation. Rather, it is the ratio of two small numbers. The value of $d\Omega$ can be written as

$$d\Omega = \sin\vartheta\, d\vartheta\, d\varphi \tag{9.4}$$

so that we can calculate

$$\frac{d\sigma}{d\Omega} = \frac{s}{\sin\vartheta} \frac{ds}{d\vartheta} \tag{9.5}$$

as soon as we know how, for the given law of force, s depends on ϑ.

A famous example is the scattering of particles of charge $z'e$ by the Coulomb field of a nucleus of charge ze; this is the α-particle experiment by which Rutherford was first led to the idea of the nuclear atom. In this case one can show by direct integration of the Newtonian equations of motion[1] that

$$s = \frac{zz'e'^2}{2E} \cot \tfrac{1}{2}\vartheta$$

where E is the (nonrelativistic) kinetic energy of the incident particle. Putting this into (9.5) gives the theoretical value

$$\frac{d\sigma}{d\Omega} = \left(\frac{zz'e'^2}{E}\right)^2 (2 \sin \tfrac{1}{2}\vartheta)^{-4} \tag{9.6}$$

This, in modern language, is Rutherford's formula. Comparison with the experimental value derived from (9.3) at various angles and energies leads to a verification that the law of force is what it was assumed to be, and hence to the Rutherford model.

The differential cross section as we have defined it is related to the amount of scattering into a given direction. We can also talk about the total scattering cross section, which we shall call σ and which is the same as the quantity defined in (9.1). It is clearly given by

$$\sigma = \int \frac{d\sigma}{d\Omega} \, d\Omega \tag{9.7}$$

integrated over all directions, and it is in general a function of the energy of the incident particles.

Problem 9.1 Suppose that the target is a smooth stationary sphere of radius a, from which incident particles of radius b bounce elastically. Show that

$$\frac{d\sigma}{d\Omega} = \tfrac{1}{4}(a + b)^2$$

independent of angle and energy. What is σ?

If we try to find the total cross section for Coulomb scattering by integrating (9.7), we find that the integral diverges at small values of ϑ. This corresponds to the fact that the Coulomb force, unlike the typical forces of atomic and nuclear interactions, falls off relatively slowly with increasing distances s. Therefore, a divergent number of particles experiences *some* deflection. In practice, this divergence is not observed, since the experimental angle ϑ cannot go to zero. This is because detectors are of finite angular width

[1] See for example H. Goldstein, *Classical Mechanics*, Addison-Wesley Publishing Company, Inc., Reading, Mass., 1951, sec. 3.7, or A. P. French, *Principles of Modern Physics*, John Wiley & Sons, Inc., New York, 1958, appendix 5.

and cannot be brought arbitrarily close to zero scattering angle without beginning to count the undeflected beam which passes straight through the target. Thus the integration in (9.7) must in practice be cut off at some small value of ϑ. (Another reason for this cutoff is that the particles deflected least have passed farthest from the center of force. If they pass too far away, they will be scattered by extraneous forces exerted by other parts of the system.)

9.2 Coordinate Systems

We have said that the idea of cross section is important because it is here that theory and experiment make contact. There is generally, however, a correction which must be made before the results of theory and experiment can be compared. This correction arises from the necessity of taking into account the recoil of the target particle; for scattering is essentially a two-body process rather than the one-body process which we have pictured in Fig. 9.2. The study of two-body interactions which we have made in Secs. 7.2 and 7.3 shows that no real difficulty arises here, for the two-body system is mathematically equivalent to a one-body system if we make use of the reduced mass and transform everything to a coordinate system in which the center of mass is at rest. The theory will therfore generally give its results in this center-of-mass system (*C.M. system*), whereas experiments are generally carried out so that one of the colliding particles is initially at rest. Data are therefore normally obtained in the *lab system*, and we must now see how to transform results from one to the other.

Let us first consider in classical physics a particle of mass m approaching a target particle of mass M with a velocity v (Fig. 9.3). The center of mass of the system is moving toward the right at a velocity

$$\bar{v} = \frac{m}{m + M} v \qquad (9.8)$$

The following relations are now easy to see:

	Lab system	C.M. system
Momentum of m	mv	μv
Momentum of M	0	$-\mu v$
Total kinetic energy	$\frac{1}{2}mv^2$	$\frac{1}{2}\mu v^2$

(9.9)

where μ is the reduced mass. Further, the total kinetic energy $\frac{1}{2}mv^2$ is divided into a part referring to the motion of the center of mass

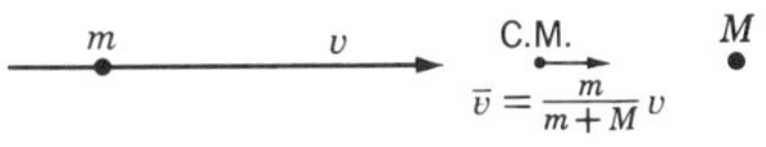

Fig. 9.3 The center of mass of m and M
and its motion.

and a part referring to motion with respect to the center of mass:

$$\tfrac{1}{2}mv^2 = \tfrac{1}{2}(m + M)\bar{v}^2 + \tfrac{1}{2}\mu v^2 \tag{9.10}$$

corresponding to the separation found in (7.36) to (7.38). In scattering calculations, this kinetic energy represents the total energy of the system; for the potential energy is effectively zero except in the very small region where interaction occurs, and there, of course, the kinetic energy so changes as to keep the total energy constant. In terms of the initial velocity v, therefore, we must distinguish two energies,

$$E_L = \tfrac{1}{2}mv^2 \qquad E_C = \tfrac{1}{2}\mu v^2 \tag{9.11}$$

Energies given in connection with experimental scattering data are nearly always laboratory energies, and so for input into the theoretical formulas we must use

$$E_C = \frac{\mu}{m} E_L = \frac{M}{m + M} E_L \tag{9.12}$$

Problem 9.2   Prove Equations (9.8) and (9.10) and show that E_C is the sum of the kinetic energies of the two particles with respect to the center of mass.

Let us now follow the collision process of Fig. 9.3 through to its conclusion, Fig. 9.4. It is at once apparent that the scattering process as viewed in the C.M. system is the simpler of the two, since at every instant the two particles have equal and opposite momenta. Since (for an elastic collision) the kinetic energy remains constant, it follows that all four momenta, incoming and outgoing, are equal in magnitude, so that each particle leaves the collision at the same velocity with which it arrived. These velocities are

$$v_C = \frac{M}{m + M} v = \frac{M}{m} \bar{v} \qquad V_C = \frac{m}{m + M} v = \bar{v} \tag{9.13}$$

Fig. 9.4   The same collision as viewed from lab and C.M. systems. The convenience of the C.M. system is illustrated by the fact that $v'_c = v_c$ and $V'_C = V_C$.

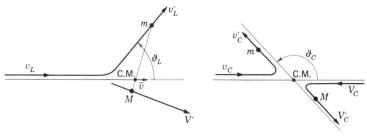

Lab system   C.M. system

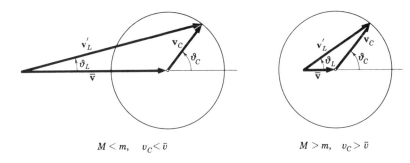

$$M < m, \quad v_C < \bar{v} \qquad\qquad M > m, \quad v_C > \bar{v}$$

Fig. 9.5   Kinematics of $\mathbf{v}'_L$, $\mathbf{v}_C$, and $\bar{\mathbf{v}}$ for $M < m$ and $M > m$.

Since the two systems are in relative motion with a (vectorial) velocity $\bar{\mathbf{v}}$, the velocities in Fig. 9.4 are related by

$$\mathbf{v}_L = \mathbf{v}_C + \bar{\mathbf{v}} \qquad \mathbf{V}_L = \mathbf{V}_C + \bar{\mathbf{v}} \tag{9.14}$$

If we restrict our attention to the trajectory of the bombarding particle, we can represent the possible scattering processes by a vector diagram of (9.14) as in Fig. 9.5, from which we see that if $M < m$, the largest laboratory scattering angle that can ever be observed is given by

$$\sin \vartheta_L{}^{\max} = \frac{v_C}{\bar{v}} = \frac{M}{m}$$

whereas for $M \geqslant m$, all angles are possible. The connection between the scattering angles in the two systems is readily seen from Fig. 9.5 to be

$$\tan \vartheta_L = \frac{v_C \sin \vartheta_C}{\bar{v} + v_C \cos \vartheta_C}$$

or

$$\tan \vartheta_L = \frac{\sin \vartheta_C}{m/M + \cos \vartheta_C} \tag{9.15}$$

in which we see that if $M \gg m$, the laboratory and C.M. descriptions are essentially the same. Another simple case is that encountered in neutron-proton scattering, in which $m \approx M$ and (9.15) gives $\tan \vartheta_L = \tan \frac{1}{2}\vartheta_C$ or

$$\vartheta_L = \frac{1}{2}\vartheta_C \qquad (m = M) \tag{9.16}$$

Finally, we must see how to transform scattering cross sections from one system to the other. We can do it if we note that the actual counting rate $I\, d\sigma$ is independent of which description is being used. Thus

$$\left(\frac{d\sigma}{d\Omega}\right)_L \sin \vartheta_L\, d\vartheta_L\, d\varphi = \left(\frac{d\sigma}{d\Omega}\right)_C \sin \vartheta_C\, d\vartheta_C\, d\varphi$$

where we note that the two φ's are the same. This can be written as

$$\left(\frac{d\sigma}{d\Omega}\right)_L = \left(\frac{d\sigma}{d\Omega}\right)_c \frac{d \cos \vartheta_C}{d \cos \vartheta_L}$$

To evaluate the derivative, we rewrite (9.15) as

$$\cos \vartheta_L = \frac{\gamma + \cos \vartheta_C}{(1 + 2\gamma \cos \vartheta_C + \gamma^2)^{1/2}} \qquad \left(\gamma = \frac{m}{M}\right) \tag{9.17a}$$

whence if $\gamma \leqslant 1$,

$$\cos \vartheta_C = (1 - \gamma^2 \sin^2 \vartheta_L)^{1/2} \cos \vartheta_L - \gamma \sin^2 \vartheta_L \tag{9.17b}$$

and

$$\left(\frac{d\sigma}{d\Omega}\right)_L = \left(\frac{d\sigma}{d\Omega}\right)_c \frac{[(1 - \gamma^2 \sin^2 \vartheta_L)^{1/2} + \gamma \cos \vartheta_L]^2}{(1 - \gamma^2 \sin^2 \vartheta_L)^{1/2}} \qquad (\gamma \leqslant 1) \tag{9.18a}$$

Again, in the special case of equal masses we have

$$\left(\frac{d\sigma}{d\Omega}\right)_L = 4\left(\frac{d\sigma}{d\Omega}\right)_c \cos \frac{1}{2}\vartheta_C \qquad (m = M) \tag{9.18b}$$

or, by (9.16),

$$\left(\frac{d\sigma}{d\Omega}\right)_L = 4\left(\frac{d\sigma}{d\Omega}\right)_c \cos \vartheta_L \tag{9.18c}$$

For any mass ratio, it is clear that the total cross section presented to the incident beam is the same in both systems,

$$\sigma = \int \left(\frac{d\sigma}{d\Omega}\right)_c d\Omega_C = \int \left(\frac{d\sigma}{d\Omega}\right)_L d\Omega_L \tag{9.19}$$

Finally, we should stress the reason why all these formulas, derived by classical reasoning, hold good quite generally. It is, of course, that the only aspects of classical physics we have used are the conservation laws of energy and momentum, and these, as far as anyone knows, are of general validity.

Problem 9.3 Prove that when the masses are equal, all scattering in the laboratory system is into the forward hemisphere of directions.

Problem 9.4 Sketch the form of $(d\sigma/d\Omega)_L$ in the laboratory system for the collisions of Prob. 9.1 if the target sphere is just as massive as the incident particles and is free to recoil.

Problem 9.5 If $\gamma > 1$, it would seem from (9.18a) that $(d\sigma/d\Omega)_L$ could become complex for certain values of ϑ_C. Prove that for such values of ϑ_C, one should just set $(d\sigma/d\Omega)_L$ equal to zero.

Problem 9.6 Prove Eq. (9.19) by direct integration, with special attention to the case $M < m$.

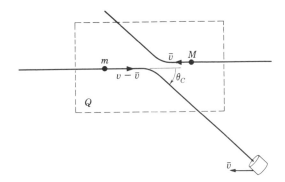

Fig. 9.6 To illustrate Prob. 9.7. The scattering process, including the detector, is viewed by an observer traveling with velocity $\bar{v}$ toward the right.

Problem 9.7 Figure 9.6 shows a classically imagined scattering process in the C.M. system. Let the density of the large target particles be D_t and that of the incident particles be D_i. Show that the defining relation analogous to (9.2) for this case is

$$d\sigma_C(\vartheta_C) = \frac{dN(\vartheta_C)}{Qv D_i D_t}$$

where $dN(\vartheta_C)$ is the number of incident particles issuing per second from the dotted region of volume Q.

Problem 9.8 Prove that if $m = M$, the angle between the scattered particle and the recoiling target particle for elastic collisions is always 90° in the lab system.

It is instructive to look again at the formula for the elastic scattering of particles off a movable hard sphere (cf. Prob. 9.1). The scattering cross section observed in the laboratory will be

$$\left(\frac{d\sigma}{d\Omega}\right)_L = \tfrac{1}{4}\pi(a+b)^2 \frac{[(1 - \gamma^2 \sin^2 \vartheta_L)^{\frac{1}{2}} + \gamma \cos \vartheta_L]^2}{(1 - \gamma^2 \sin^2 \vartheta_L)^{\frac{1}{2}}} \quad (\gamma \leqslant 1)$$

From this formula we can learn a very useful lesson: that if some special circumstance operates to give a simple form for the scattering cross section, this simplicity is apt to be lost sight of in the laboratory coordinates. It is therefore general practice in presenting the data on nuclear scattering experiments to transform them to center-of-mass coordinates by means of (9.17b) and (9.18a), and the reader should never forget to notice which system is being used.

9.3 The Quantum Theory of Scattering— I

The theory of scattering processes is so important in modern physics that we are going to develop two different ways to approach it. They are, of course, at bottom mathematically equivalent, but they proceed from quite different formulations. The first way is to consider

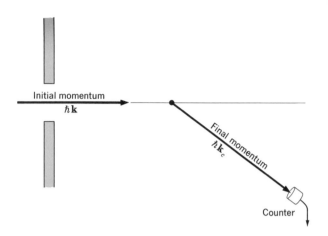

Fig. 9.7 Initial and final momentum states in scattering.

the scattering of a particle as a transition out of an initial state of given momentum into a final state of different momentum but the same energy, using the theory of time-dependent transitions, Sec. 8.7, to calculate the rate at which it occurs. The second approach is to regard the whole matter as a scattering of waves by an obstacle and set it up as a differential equation like any other diffraction problem. The first approach is somewhat more general; the second is somewhat more convenient; and each is of interest in itself as an example of how the theory works.

We start by considering the system shown in Fig. 9.7, in which a particle initially in a definite plane-wave state traveling toward the right undergoes a transition into one of the diverging bundle of states which brings it into the counter. We wish to calculate the probability of such a transition per unit time; applied to a beam with many particles, this will clearly yield a figure for the counting rate. The procedure is now exactly that of Sec. 8.7. We let $\hat{H}^{(0)}$ represent the kinetic energy of the free particles, incident and scattered, when they are outside the influence of the scattering potential $\hat{H}'$. This potential causes transitions to occur out of the initial state into a group of scattered states whose totality is given by φ_s. We now expand φ_s in terms of free-particle states $\varphi_n^{(0)}$ according to (8.88); this is physically reasonable because by the time the particles have left the scatterer and started out toward the detector they are free. Let the time-dependent free-particle wave function representing the initial state be $\varphi_a^{(0)}$, that of one of the final bundle of counted states be $\varphi_c^{(0)}$, and the wave function of the entire system, including interactions, be φ. The probability of finding the particle in the state φ_c after a time t will be given by

$$P_c = |a_c(t)|^2 \tag{9.20}$$

where $a_c(t)$ is given by (8.89). That equation is easy to integrate. Let the exact energy of the system be E and that of the state c be E_c (it is not yet time to set the two energies equal). Since $\hat{H}'$ is constant, we write (8.89) in terms of the corresponding time-independent functions as

$$i\hbar \dot{a}_c(t) = \exp{[i(E_c - E)t/\hbar]} \int \psi_c^{(0)*} \hat{H}' \psi$$

and integrate it from time zero to obtain

$$a_c(t) = -\frac{e^{i\varepsilon t/\hbar} - 1}{\varepsilon} M_c$$

where we have introduced the abbreviations

$$\varepsilon = E_c - E \qquad M_c = \int \psi_c^{(0)*} \hat{H}' \psi$$

The probability of finding the particle in state c is

$$P_c(t) = 2|M_c|^2 \frac{1 - \cos \varepsilon t/\hbar}{\varepsilon^2}$$

or

$$P_c(t) = \frac{2\pi t}{\hbar} |M_c|^2 \delta(\varepsilon) \tag{9.21}$$

by (8.107), where we have assumed that the system has been turned on long enough that the function of ε is extremely high and narrow as in Fig. 8.6 and can effectively be replaced by a delta function. The scattered particle thus has effectively $\varepsilon = 0$, or $E_c = E$, and the probability of finding it in any scattered beam increases linearly with t. These results are essentially exact.

We now have to calculate the counting rate in the detector. To do so, we must remember that the detector will accept particles in states with a variety of energies and moving in a variety of directions, and we must therefore sum over all these states to get the total probability of a count. We can represent this mathematically by

$$\mathbf{P}^{(c)} = \Sigma^{(c)} P_c$$

where the superscript (c) is to remind us that we have to specify what states are going to be counted.

It is convenient to replace the sum by an integral over the energies of the counted states, and this can be done by distributing them into energy intervals dE_c. Let $\rho^{(c)}(E_c)\, dE_c$ be the number of states to be counted in that energy range. Then the contribution to the sum from the states in this range is given by the value of P_c times the number of states in the range, and the sum over all ranges becomes

$$\mathbf{P}^{(c)} = \int P_c(E_c) \rho^{(c)}(E_c)\, dE_c \tag{9.22}$$

where we have written P_c as a function of E_c only. It will, of course, also be a function of the directions of the states c, but we are going to assume that they are contained in a narrow cone and so are essentially all in the same direction. Putting (9.21) into (9.22) gives an integral which is readily evaluated to give

$$\mathbf{P}^{(c)} = \frac{2\pi t}{\hbar} |M_c|^2 \rho^{(c)}(E)$$

Thus the probability of arrival in the counter in any unit time interval is

$$\dot{\mathbf{P}}^{(c)} = \frac{2\pi}{\hbar} |M_c|^2 \rho^{(c)}(E) \tag{9.23}$$

where now in evaluating M_c we take the energy E_c to be equal to E. This formula is the basic one for transitions into (or out of) a continuous range of states. It is the starting point for countless theoretical investigations, and it is known to Fermi's students as Golden Rule #2.

The density of states

To continue, we must now see how to evaluate the quantity $\rho^{(c)}(E)$, which is called the *density of states* in the neighborhood of the energy E. The value of ρ will differ from case to case according to what is being counted; in this case and many others of interest we wish to know the number of states per unit energy range for a single free particle. First, we must specify that the states to be counted are those which lie in a certain small cone of solid angle $d\Omega$ in the center-of-mass system, centered at the point where the interaction takes place. The angle $d\Omega$ is that subtended by the collector, and the calculation must take account of the fact that a particle traveling along any of the infinitely numerous sheaf of paths lying within the cone will be counted. Thus $\rho^{(c)}(E)$ is in fact infinite, and we shall have to resort to a stratagem in order to count the states at all. The stratagem is described in Sec. 3.4 (see especially Prob. 3.14), and we have already used it in Sec. 5.4 to enumerate the states of a one-dimensional system in a periodic potential. In one dimension, it consists in assuming that the system is closed upon itself in the form of a loop. Similarly, in two dimensions, we could wrap the system on a toroid; and a three-dimensional volume can analogously be closed if we imagine it as embedded in a four-dimensional space. But we need not worry about how this is done; for mathematically all that happens is that the wave function becomes periodic in each direction, with a periodicity which we shall call L. Denoting the general plane-wave solution of Schrödinger's equation for a free particle as $Ae^{i\mathbf{p}\cdot\mathbf{r}/\hbar}$, we readily see that the periodicity requires that

$$p_x = 2\pi n_x \hbar/L \qquad p_y = 2\pi n_y \hbar/L \qquad p_z = 2\pi n_z \hbar/L \tag{9.24}$$

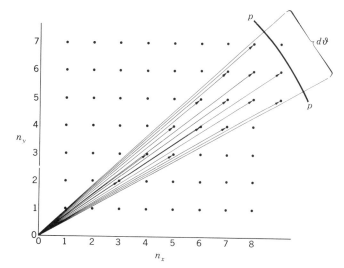

Fig. 9.8 Counting the number of states in a sheaf of directions whose width is $d\vartheta$.

where n_x, n_y, and n_z are integers (positive, negative, or zero). Each different combination of n_x, n_y, and n_z represents a different state of motion. Clearly, there are infinitely many of these, so we ask first how many standing-wave states there are corresponding to n's limited by the relation

$$(n_x{}^2 + n_y{}^2 + n_z{}^2)^{\frac{1}{2}} < n$$

We express this question graphically by representing the possible n's as a lattice of points on a three-dimensional set of axes analogous to the two-dimensional diagram of Fig. 9.8. Just as there is one lattice point per unit area in Fig. 9.8, so there is one per unit volume in three dimensions, and the number of states in the three-dimensional cone subtended by the counter is just equal to its volume:

$$N^{(c)}(n) = \tfrac{1}{3}n^3 \, d\Omega$$

or, by (9.24), in terms of the value of p corresponding to the limiting n,

$$N^{(c)}(p) = \frac{1}{3}\frac{Q}{(2\pi\hbar)^3} p^3 \, d\Omega \tag{9.25}$$

where $Q = L^3$ is the volume of the system. Returning to the definition of $\rho^{(c)}(E)$ as the number of states per unit energy range, we see that it is given by

$$\rho^{(c)}(E) = \frac{dN^{(c)}}{dE} = \frac{dN^{(c)}}{dp}\frac{dp}{dE}$$

For nonrelativistic free particles in the C.M. system, $E = p^2/2\mu$, so that $p \, dp/dE = \mu$, and

$$\rho^{(c)}(E) = \frac{Q\mu}{(2\pi\hbar)^3} p \, d\Omega \tag{9.26}$$

When the particle has a spin S, there are $2S + 1$ possible spin states for each momentum state, and $\rho^{(c)}$ must be multiplied by this factor.

Problem 9.9 Show, using relativistic mechanics, that when $M \gg m$ the general expression for $\rho^{(c)}(E)$ is

$$\rho^{(c)}(E) = \frac{QE}{(2\pi\hbar)^3 c^2} p \, d\Omega \qquad (9.27)$$

The scattering cross section

We are now ready to evaluate the differential scattering cross section, returning to the basic physical definition (9.2). We have been calculating in terms of a single particle inside a volume Q, assumed to be initially in a state of definite momentum. Such a state is represented by a plane wave of momentum $\hbar\mathbf{k}$ which uniformly fills the volume Q, so that the normalized wave function is

$$\psi^{(0)} = Q^{-\frac{1}{2}}e^{i\mathbf{k}\cdot\mathbf{r}} \qquad (9.28)$$

and the various possible final-state wave functions are all closely in the neighborhood of

$$\psi_c^{(0)} = Q^{-\frac{1}{2}}e^{i\mathbf{k}_c\cdot\mathbf{r}} \qquad (9.29)$$

where $\mathbf{k}_c$ points from the scattering center towards the counter. By the conservation of energy it is equal in magnitude to k. Further, the particle density in the incoming beam is Q^{-1}, so that I, the number of incoming particles per unit area per second, is Q^{-1} multiplied by their velocity $\hbar k/\mu$, that is,

$$I = \frac{\hbar k}{\mu Q}$$

The counting rate $dN(\vartheta)$ is what we have denoted by $\dot{\mathbf{P}}^{(c)}$. Thus, by (9.2) and (9.23),

$$d\sigma = \left(\frac{\mu Q}{2\pi\hbar^2}\right)^2 |M_c|^2 \, d\Omega$$

which we shall write as

$$\frac{d\sigma}{d\Omega} = |f(\vartheta)|^2 \qquad (9.30a)$$

with $f(\vartheta)$, the *scattering amplitude*, given by

$$f(\vartheta) = -\frac{\mu Q}{2\pi\hbar^2} M_c \qquad (9.30b)$$

(The negative sign is purely conventional.) Let us now introduce the formula for M_c and restrict attention to situations in which the interaction responsible for the scattering is a potential energy $V(\mathbf{r})$

and no spin phenomena occur. By (9.29), we have

$$f(\vartheta) = -\frac{\mu Q^{\frac{1}{2}}}{2\pi\hbar^2} \int e^{-i\mathbf{k}_c\cdot\mathbf{r}} V(\mathbf{r})\psi(\mathbf{r})\,dv \tag{9.31}$$

This formula is exact, and since it is derived merely from a re-writing of Schrödinger's equation, we seem to be mathematically no nearer to an evaluation of $d\sigma/d\Omega$ than when we started. This is, of course, because the ψ in the integral is the exact wave function for the entire system, which, if we know it, enables us at once to calculate anything we want. But the advantage of (9.31) is that it forms a valuable point of departure for approximations, which is almost the same as saying for real physics. We shall illustrate this assertion by considering the first approximate evaluation of (9.31) when the effect of the potential is relatively slight, corresponding to the first-order perturbation theory of Sec. 8.3.

The Born approximation

In the very earliest work on the quantum theory of scattering (1926), Max Born introduced an approximation which, although it is often quite rough and has many times been so applied as to give entirely misleading results, remains one of the most useful tricks in theoretical physics. It consists simply in supposing that if the wave function of the incident particles is not too greatly perturbed by the action of the potential, one can replace the $\psi(\mathbf{r})$ in (9.31) by the unperturbed expression $\psi^{(0)}$ of (9.28). Doing this, we find that

$$f(\vartheta) \approx -\frac{\mu}{2\pi\hbar^2} \int e^{i(\mathbf{k}-\mathbf{k}_c)\cdot\mathbf{r}} V(\mathbf{r})\,dv \tag{9.32}$$

The error of this approximation is greatest when the scattering is largest, but we shall postpone a quantitative estimate of the uncertainty until the next section.

If $V(\mathbf{r})$ is a spherically symmetrical function, as is often the case, the angular integrations in (9.32) can be carried out at once. We choose as polar axis the vector $\mathbf{k} - \mathbf{k}_c = \mathbf{K}$ (Fig. 9.9), so that

$$(\mathbf{k} - \mathbf{k}_c)\cdot\mathbf{r} = \mathbf{K}\cdot\mathbf{r} = Kr\cos\vartheta'$$

where K, the length of $\mathbf{K}$, is given by

$$K = 2k\sin\tfrac{1}{2}\vartheta \tag{9.33}$$

The integral is then

$$\int_0^\infty r^2\,dr \int_0^\pi \sin\vartheta'\,d\vartheta' \int_0^{2\pi} d\varphi\, e^{iKr\cos\vartheta'} V(r)$$

Fig. 9.9 Relation between **k**, **k**_c, and **K**.

Integration over φ and $\cos \vartheta'$ gives

$$4\pi \int_0^\infty \frac{\sin Kr}{Kr} V(r)r^2 \, dr \tag{9.34}$$

so that (9.32) can be written as

$$f(\vartheta) \approx -\frac{2\mu}{\hbar^2 K} \int_0^\infty \sin Kr V(r)r \, dr \tag{9.35}$$

This is the standard form of the approximation, which is known as the first Born approximation because in its replacement of the exact by the unperturbed wave function it corresponds to the first-order perturbation theory.

As an example, let us consider the potential

$$V(r) = \frac{A}{r} e^{-\alpha r}$$

which resembles a Coulomb potential for $r \ll \alpha^{-1}$, but for larger values falls off more rapidly. This is a rough model, for example, of the interaction of a charged particle with a neutral atom: the Coulomb field of the nucleus begins to be screened off by the orbital electrons at a distance α^{-1} of the order of 1 Bohr radius. The same type of potential is used also in approximate discussions of nuclear forces, but there A is too large and the scattering too great for the Born approximation to be valid. Evaluation of (9.35) gives

$$\left(\frac{d\sigma}{d\Omega}\right)_c = \left[\frac{2\mu A}{\hbar^2(\alpha^2 + 4k^2 \sin^2 \frac{1}{2}\vartheta)}\right]^2 \tag{9.36}$$

which is sketched in Fig. 9.10 for several values of the energy. The total scattering cross section is

$$\sigma = \left(\frac{2\mu A}{\hbar^2}\right)^2 \int_0^{2\pi} d\varphi \int_0^\pi \frac{\sin \vartheta \, d\vartheta}{(\alpha^2 + 4k^2 \sin^2 \frac{1}{2}\vartheta)^2}$$

$$= 2\pi \left(\frac{2\mu A}{\hbar^2}\right)^2 \int_0^\pi \frac{2 \sin \frac{1}{2}\vartheta \cos \frac{1}{2}\vartheta \, d\vartheta}{(\alpha^2 + 4k^2 \sin^2 \frac{1}{2}\vartheta)^2}$$

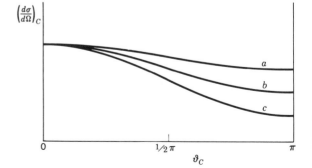

Fig. 9.10 Born approximation to cross section for scattering by a Yukawa potential (C.M. system). Curves a, b, and c are in order of increasing energy.

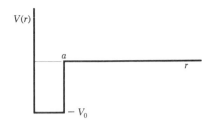

Fig. 9.11   Square-well potential to
illustrate Prob. 9.10.

Choosing $\sin^2 \tfrac{1}{2}\vartheta$ as a new variable of integration, we find without
difficulty

$$\sigma = \left(\frac{2\mu A}{\hbar^2}\right)^2 \frac{4\pi}{\alpha^2(\alpha^2 + 4k^2)} \tag{9.37}$$

These formulas will be most accurate for large values of k^2, corresponding to energetic electrons which are bent relatively little by the
potential. It is interesting to look at (9.36) in the limit as α goes to
zero (but note that the integral in (9.35) diverges if α is set equal to
zero to start with). If we write A as $zz'e'^2$ corresponding to a Coulomb potential, we get

$$\left(\frac{d\sigma}{d\Omega}\right)_c = \left(\frac{\mu zz'e'^2}{2\hbar^2 k^2 \sin^2 \tfrac{1}{2}\vartheta}\right)^2 \tag{9.38}$$

which with $\hbar^2 k^2/2\mu = E$ is exactly the classical expression (9.6) for
scattering by a Coulomb field. This is a remarkable coincidence. It
is another remarkable coincidence that the result thus calculated in
two approximations, classical physics and the Born approximation,
agrees with the result of an exact evaluation.[2] Neither of the two
approximations is ordinarily this good, and ordinarily they do not
agree, especially at low energies (long wavelengths), where diffraction effects invalidate the classical picture and the Born approximation is known to fail.

Problem 9.10   Evaluate the Born approximation to the scattering of particles by the square-well potential of Fig. 9.11. Show that[3]

$$\left(\frac{d\sigma}{d\Omega}\right)_c = \left(\frac{2\mu V_0 a^3}{\hbar^2}\right)^2 \left(\frac{\sin Ka - Ka \cos Ka}{K^3 a^3}\right)^2 \tag{9.39}$$

with K as in (9.33), and that the low-energy limit of this is

$$\left(\frac{d\sigma}{d\Omega}\right)_c = \left(\frac{2\mu V_0 a^3}{3\hbar^2}\right)^2 (1 - \tfrac{1}{5}K^2 a^2 + \cdots) \tag{9.40}$$

---

[2] See, for example, N. F. Mott and H. S. Massey, *Theory of Atomic Collisions*, 2d ed., Clarendon Press, Oxford, 1949. This is a most useful reference
work on many aspects of scattering theory.
[3] See L. I. Schiff, *Quantum Mechanics*, 2d ed., McGraw-Hill Book Company, Inc., New York, 1955, pp. 168–169.

Evaluate the total cross section in the limits of low and high energies; the answers, for future reference, are

$$\sigma = 4\pi \left(\frac{2\mu V_0 a^3}{3\hbar^2}\right)^2 (1 - \tfrac{1}{10}k^2a^2 + \cdots) \qquad \text{low energy} \qquad (9.41)$$

and

$$\sigma = \frac{\pi\mu V_0^2 a^4}{\hbar^2 E} \qquad\qquad\qquad \text{high energy} \qquad (9.42)$$

Let us compare the result (9.37) with (9.41) and (9.42) to see some common features of scattering formulas. First, we note that they depend only on A^2 and V_0^2, so that repulsive and attractive forces, in this approximation, produce equal scattering. Second, as is clear from (9.32), the low-energy limit depends only on the volume integral of the scattering potential; thus, for example, we have the combination $V_0 a^3$ in (9.41). Also, we see that at higher energies an inverse dependence on E is common to both potentials, and it is in fact quite usual. This result is more significant than the results at low energies because, as E increases, the scattering potential, provided that it is not too strong, will clearly make less and less difference, and we can expect the conditions of the Born approximation to be realized. Finally, since k and ϑ enter the general formula (9.35) only through the combination K, we can see that scattering becomes peaked more and more sharply forward (even in the center-of-mass system) at high energies.

9.4 The Quantum Theory of Scattering— II

In this section we shall approach the theory of scattering from quite a different point of view, that of the diffraction of waves by an obstacle. Figure 9.12 shows the general picture. What happens just

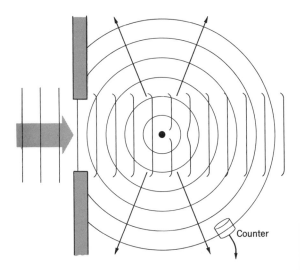

Fig. 9.12 Scattering of a plane wave by a localized disturbance.

behind the scatterer is not quite clear, since the intensity there is due partly to the scattered and partly to the unscattered wave and it is not obvious which is which. We shall therefore define precisely what we mean, by writing ψ, the total wave function of the entire process, as the sum of two terms,

$$\psi = \psi^{(0)} + \psi_s \tag{9.43}$$

where $\psi^{(0)}$ represents the incident wave as it would move through the system if there were no scattering at all and ψ_s is everything else. We suppose that $\psi^{(0)}$ satisfies the equation

$$(\hat{H}^{(0)} - E)\psi^{(0)} = 0 \qquad \hat{H}^{(0)} = -\frac{\hbar^2}{2m}\nabla^2 \tag{9.44}$$

where E is the energy of the particles of the system, whereas the exact ψ satisfies

$$\hat{H}\psi = E\psi \qquad \hat{H} = \hat{H}^{(0)} + V(\mathbf{r}) \tag{9.45}$$

where $V(\mathbf{r})$ is the scattering potential as used in the preceding section and E is the energy. From these we obtain the wave equation for ψ_s by operating with $(\hat{H}^{(0)} - E)$ on both sides of (9.43). We find

$$(\hat{H}^{(0)} - E)\psi = (\hat{H}^{(0)} - E)\psi^{(0)} + (\hat{H}^{(0)} - E)\psi_s$$

or, by (9.44) and (9.45),

$$(\hat{H}^{(0)} - E)\psi_s = -V\psi$$

It is convenient to write E in terms of the wave number of the incident particles,

$$E = \frac{\hbar^2 k^2}{2\mu} \tag{9.46}$$

We find

$$(\nabla^2 + k^2)\psi_s = \frac{2\mu}{\hbar^2}V\psi \tag{9.47}$$

In looking at this equation the reader should remember that the quantity V, and hence the product $V\psi$, is effectively equal to zero except in a microscopic region around the scatterer, which we shall take to be centered at the origin of coordinates. The whole character of the solution we shall obtain depends upon this fact.

Rather than build up the special machinery necessary to solve (9.47), we are going to stress its similarity to Poisson's equation in electrostatics and write down its solution in a form analogous to Poisson's integral. It will look more familiar if we replace the right-hand side of (9.47) by $-\rho$, so that we have

Poisson's equation	This equation
$\nabla^2 \varphi = -\rho$	$(\nabla^2 + k^2)\psi_s = -\rho$

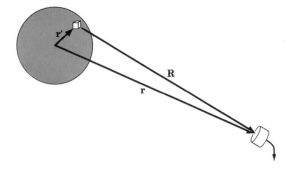

Fig. 9.13 Integration over the region
of the scatterer.

We look first at the elementary spherically symmetric solutions
of these equations when $\rho = 0$,

$$\varphi = \frac{q}{4\pi r} \qquad\qquad \psi_s = \frac{q}{4\pi}\frac{e^{ikr}}{r} + \frac{q'}{4\pi}\frac{e^{-ikr}}{r}$$

as is easily verified. The solution for ψ which we want results from
setting q' equal to zero; we shall see why in a moment. To solve
the general equations, we now let q, the charge in the electrostatic
case, be equal to $\rho(\mathbf{r}')\,dv'$ (see Fig. 9.13) and R be the distance from
dv' to the point of observation,

$$d\varphi(\mathbf{r}) = \frac{\rho\,dv'}{4\pi R} \qquad\qquad d\psi_s(\mathbf{r}) = \frac{\rho\,dv'\,e^{ikR}}{4\pi R}$$

and integrate over the distribution ρ,

$$\varphi(\mathbf{r}) = \frac{1}{4\pi}\int\frac{\rho\,dv'}{R} \qquad\qquad \psi_s(\mathbf{r}) = \frac{1}{4\pi}\int\frac{\rho e^{ikR}}{R}\,dv'$$

This is the solution we shall use. It is not proved by the above
argument (for example, the origin of the factor $1/4\pi$ is not obvious),
but it is easy to verify that the integrals we have written down do
in fact solve their respective equations (see Prob. 9.11).[4]

Problem 9.11 Verify that the above expression for ψ_s satisfies
the differential equation.[5]

Returning now to (9.47), we write the solution as

$$\psi_s = -\frac{1}{4\pi}\frac{2\mu}{\hbar^2}\int\frac{e^{ikR}}{R}V(\mathbf{r}')\psi(\mathbf{r}')\,dv' \qquad\qquad (9.48)$$

This expression can be simplified if we are interested only in the
value of ψ_s at the detector, that is, for $R \gg r'$ in Fig. 9.13. Let **u**

---

[4] The reader who wishes to understand this better may consult D. Bohm,
Quantum Theory, Prentice-Hall, Inc., Englewood Cliffs, N.J., 1951, sec. 21.25.

[5] A good discussion along traditional lines of the analogous question in electrostatics is given by H. Margenau and G. M. Murphy, *The Mathematics of
Physics and Chemistry*, D. Van Nostrand Company, Inc., Princeton, N.J., 1943,
1956, sec. 7.17.

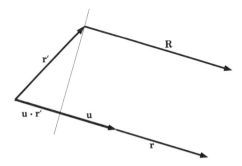

Fig. 9.14   Situation when $r \gg r'$; $\mathbf{u}$ is a
unit vector parallel to $\mathbf{r}$.

be a unit vector in the direction of $\mathbf{r}$ (Fig. 9.14). Then because $\mathbf{R}$
and $\mathbf{r}$ are so nearly parallel, the difference in their lengths is given
very accurately by

$$R \approx r - \mathbf{u} \cdot \mathbf{r'}$$

The quantity R occurs in (9.48) in two places. In the denominator,
there is no difficulty about replacing it by r, since the fractional error
in so doing is vanishingly small. In the numerator, however, we encounter the expression

$$e^{ikR} \approx e^{ikr}e^{-ik\mathbf{u}\cdot\mathbf{r'}}$$

and even though the second exponent may be much less than the
first, it may still be appreciably different from zero. We therefore
have the asymptotic relation

$$\psi_s \longrightarrow -\frac{1}{4\pi}\frac{2\mu}{\hbar^2}\frac{e^{ikr}}{r}\int e^{-ik\mathbf{u}\cdot\mathbf{r'}}V(\mathbf{r'})\psi(\mathbf{r'})\,dv' \tag{9.49}$$

We shall write this for convenience in the form

$$\psi_s \longrightarrow \frac{e^{ikr}}{r}f(\vartheta) \tag{9.50}$$

It depends on ϑ because it contains ψ, which depends on the direction of the incident beam, and $\mathbf{u}$, the unit vector pointing toward
the counter. Let us denote the combination $k\mathbf{u}$ by $\mathbf{k}_c$, a vector which
gives the magnitude and direction of the momentum of a particle
moving toward the counter. With this, we have

$$f(\vartheta) = -\frac{1}{4\pi}\frac{2\mu}{\hbar^2}\int e^{-i\mathbf{k}_c\cdot\mathbf{r'}}V(\mathbf{r'})\psi(\mathbf{r'})\,dv' \tag{9.51}$$

which is the same as (9.31) except for the unimportant normalizing
factor $Q^{\frac{1}{2}}$ which arises from the use of states in a closed box to derive
that expression. We see also the reason for the minus sign in (9.30b)
and for the name "scattering amplitude." It is simply the amplitude
of the scattered wave.

Now let us see what kind of thing is represented by a function of the form (9.50). Clearly, it is a wave corresponding to the momentum $\hbar k$, diverging from the origin. At the point (r,ϑ) the probability density is $|f(\vartheta)|^2/r^2$, obeying the inverse-square law. If the area presented by the counter is dA, then the probability per second of a particle's entering the counter is

$$dN(\vartheta) = v|f(\vartheta)|^2 \frac{dA}{r^2} = v|f(\vartheta)|^2 \, d\Omega \qquad (9.52)$$

by the definition of solid angle, where $v = \hbar k/\mu$ is the particle velocity. Suppose now that the incoming beam $\psi^{(0)}$ is given by

$$\psi^{(0)} = e^{i\mathbf{k}\cdot\mathbf{r}} \qquad (9.53)$$

It then contains one particle per unit volume, and the intensity of the incident beam is just v particles per unit area per second. The differential cross section is then given by (9.2) as

$$d\sigma = |f(\vartheta)|^2 \, d\Omega$$

or

$$\frac{d\sigma}{d\Omega} = |f(\vartheta)|^2 \qquad (9.54)$$

which is the same as (9.30a). The factor of Q, which distinguishes (9.31) from (9.51), arises in the following way. In the first method of approach, it was important in counting states to restrict attention to a single particle in the volume Q; hence, the normalization in (9.28). In the second method it was more convenient to take the incident beam to contain one particle per unit volume, as in (9.53). The resulting $\psi^{(0)}$'s, and hence the ψ's, vary by a factor of $Q^{1/2}$. In the future we shall banish factors of Q by normalizing according to (9.53), so that the asymptotic form of ψ is by (9.43)

$$\psi \rightarrow e^{i\mathbf{k}\cdot\mathbf{r}} + f(\vartheta) \frac{e^{ikr}}{r} \qquad (9.55)$$

where ϑ is the difference in direction between the initial wave vector $\mathbf{k}$ and the beam picked up by the detector.

Problem 9.12   Verify (9.52) by evaluating the current-density vector in this case.

We can now return to settle the question why the elementary solutions of the form e^{-ikr}/r were ignored in solving (9.47). The reason is the usual one in such cases: these solutions are inconsistent with the boundary conditions. In fact, a wave e^{-ikr}/r represents a radial wave converging toward the center, as though the center were to be ringed with a continuous source of electrons which directed them inward with their ψ functions coherently in phase. This is the time-reversed version of the normal scattering process. There is nothing in it which violates the laws of physics, but it appears quite impossible to arrange; and at any rate it has nothing to do with the process we are studying.

Validity of the Born approximation

Using the integral relation (9.46) we can establish a definite relation between the Born approximation and the perturbation expansion of the preceding chapter. Remembering (9.43), let us write (9.48) as

$$\psi_s = -\frac{1}{4\pi}\frac{2\mu}{\hbar^2}\int \frac{e^{ikR}}{R} V(\mathbf{r}')[\psi^{(0)}(\mathbf{r}') + \psi_s(\mathbf{r}')] \, dv' \tag{9.56}$$

The first term of this is just the first Born approximation $\psi_s^{(B)}$ to the whole function, so that

$$\psi_s = \psi_s^{(B)} - \frac{1}{4\pi}\frac{2\mu}{\hbar^2}\int \frac{e^{ikR}}{R} V(\mathbf{r}')\psi_s(\mathbf{r}') \, dv'$$

and this equation defines an approximation procedure, since one can substitute the entire expression for ψ_s into the integral on the right to get

$$\psi_s = \psi_s^{(B)} - \frac{1}{4\pi}\frac{2\mu}{\hbar^2}\int \frac{e^{ikR}}{R} V(\mathbf{r}')\psi_s^{(B)}(\mathbf{r}') \, dv'$$
$$+ \left(\frac{1}{4\pi}\frac{2\mu}{\hbar^2}\right)^2 \iint \frac{e^{ikR}}{R} V(\mathbf{r}')\frac{e^{ikR'}}{R'} V(\mathbf{r}'')\psi_s(\mathbf{r}'') \, dv' \, dv''$$

where $R' = |\mathbf{r}' - \mathbf{r}''|$, and one can in principle continue to substitute back, to get an infinite series. Since $\psi_s^{(B)}$ is proportional to V, the successive terms on the right of this equation will be of the order of V, V^2, V^3, etc. We must now ask: does the series converge, and are the integrations easy enough to perform that the series is of any practical use? Let us answer them in order.

There are really two questions of convergence: one can ask whether the series converges for all k and whether it converges for some particular k. With regard to the first, it can be proved that if $V(\mathbf{r})$ is

    a.   spherically symmetrical
    b.   no more singular at the origin than $1/r$ and finite elsewhere
    c.   of order e^{-ar} or smaller as r becomes infinite, with a any positive number
    d.   either attractive or repulsive, but weak enough that neither $V(\mathbf{r})$ nor $-|V(\mathbf{r})|$ produces a bound state

then the series will converge for all values of k. It may be that (a), (b), and (c) can be relaxed somewhat, but they are satisfied for most cases of practical interest. The crucial condition is (d), and it is necessary. As one might expect, the conditions for convergence become less stringent at higher energies. Criteria and examples have been given by Kohn.[6]

We come now to the computability of the successive terms of the series, and here the situation is very clear. The integrals, beyond the first one which gives $\psi_s^{(B)}$, are almost impossibly difficult to carry out, and most of those few cases where the second term has been evaluated could more profitably have been treated in another way. We ask, then, what if anything can be done in order to estimate the accuracy of the method. A reasonable answer is this: if the potential satisfies the condition for convergence, and if the second term can be shown to be smaller than the first, then it is probable that the higher terms will be smaller still, and so the first term alone will give a good estimate of the answer. It is not difficult to express this quantitatively. We are seeking a justification for omitting the $\psi_s(\mathbf{r}')$ on the right side of (9.56), so that only the first Born approximation remains. Since we are interested in the relative values of ψ_s and $\psi^{(0)}$ near the origin, let us evaluate them *at* the origin. By (9.53), $\psi^{(0)} = 1$ at the origin, and by (9.48), with $\psi \approx \psi^{(0)}$ inside the integral,

$$\psi_s(0) = -\frac{1}{4\pi}\frac{2\mu}{\hbar^2}\int \frac{e^{ikr'}}{r'}V(\mathbf{r}')e^{i\mathbf{k}\cdot\mathbf{r}'}\,dv'$$

$$= -\frac{2\mu}{\hbar^2 k}\int_0^\infty (e^{2ikr'}-1)V(\mathbf{r}')\,dr'$$

if $V(\mathbf{r})$ is spherically symmetrical. Thus our condition that the second term be negligible becomes[7]

$$|\psi_s(0)|^2 = \left|\frac{2\mu}{\hbar^2 k}\int_0^\infty (e^{2ikr'}-1)V(r')\,dr'\right|^2 \ll 1 \tag{9.57}$$

At high energies the exponential oscillates in sign within the range of the potential and tends to cancel out, so that the criterion approaches

$$\left|\frac{2\mu}{\hbar^2 k}\int_0^\infty V(r)\,dr\right|^2 \ll 1 \qquad \text{high energy} \tag{9.58a}$$

and at low energies

$$\left|\frac{4\mu}{\hbar^2}\int_0^\infty (1+ikr)V(r)r\,dr\right|^2 \ll 1 \qquad \text{low energy} \tag{9.58b}$$

Problem 9.13 Investigate the adequacy of the Born approximation to the scattering by a square well in Prob. 9.10. Consider especially the limiting forms (9.58a,b) and show by comparison with (9.41) and (9.42) that both may be expressed by requiring that $\sigma \ll \pi a^2$. Compare the criteria you have obtained with the criterion given by the theorem on the existence of a bound state, using the

[6] W. Kohn, Rev. Mod. Phys., **26**, 292, 472 (1954).
[7] This integral is evaluated for the potential $Ar^{-1}e^{-\alpha r}$ in Bohm, *op. cit.*

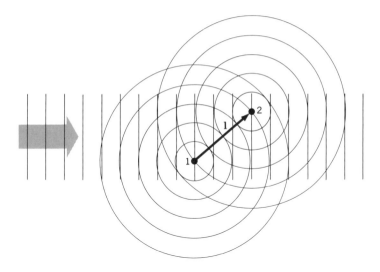

Fig. 9.15 Illustrating Prob. 9.14. A beam of particles is scattered by two centers.

discussion of square-well potentials in Sec. 7.4 to determine for what values of a and V_0 a bound state is possible.

Problem 9.14   A molecule of a homonuclear diatomic gas may roughly be regarded as composed of two identical spherically symmetric scattering centers separated by a (vectorial) distance $\mathbf{l}$ (Fig. 9.15). If the scattering amplitude for a certain kind of particle directed against the atom is known, what scattering cross section is measured for the molecules of the gas? Contrast the atomic and molecular cross sections, and neglect effects of multiple scattering, that is, of particles which bounce back and forth between the two centers.

Solution.   The problem divides itself into two parts: first the calculation of σ for a molecule in a particular spatial orientation and then the average over all orientations. The first thing to note is the difference in phase between the waves arriving at the two scattering centers: compared to the phase at the center of the molecule, that at 1 is $\frac{1}{2}\mathbf{k} \cdot \mathbf{l}$ early, while that at 2 is equally late. Thus the wave at the counter is

$$\psi_{sc} = e^{\frac{1}{2}i\mathbf{k}\cdot\mathbf{l}}\left[\frac{e^{ikR_1}}{R_1}f(\vartheta)\right] + e^{-\frac{1}{2}i\mathbf{k}\cdot\mathbf{l}}\left[\frac{e^{ikR_2}}{R_2}f(\vartheta)\right]$$

The denominators can be set equal to r without error (see Fig. 9.13), while in the exponents,

$$kR_1 = kr - \tfrac{1}{2}\mathbf{k}_c \cdot \mathbf{l} \qquad kR_2 = kr + \tfrac{1}{2}\mathbf{k}_c \cdot \mathbf{l}$$

Thus,

$$\psi_{sc} = \frac{e^{ikr}}{r} \left(e^{\frac{1}{2}i(\mathbf{k}\cdot\mathbf{1}-\mathbf{k}_c\cdot\mathbf{1})} + e^{-\frac{1}{2}i(\mathbf{k}\cdot\mathbf{1}-\mathbf{k}_c\cdot\mathbf{1})} \right) f(\vartheta)$$

so that

$$\frac{d\sigma}{d\Omega} = 4\cos^2 \left[\tfrac{1}{2}(\mathbf{k} - \mathbf{k}_c) \cdot \mathbf{1} \right] |f(\vartheta)|^2$$

The vector $\mathbf{k} - \mathbf{k}_c = \mathbf{K}$ is shown in Fig. 9.9, and its length is given by Eq. (9.33). The average over the directions of $\mathbf{1}$ and the rest of the discussion are left to the reader.

The optical theorem

We end this section with two proofs of a simple theorem on scattering which is often of use in practical calculations. First we note that with the normalization as in (9.53), the total scattering cross section can conveniently be expressed (why?) as

$$\sigma = \frac{\mu}{\hbar k} \frac{d}{dt} \int |\varphi_s|^2 \, dv \tag{9.59}$$

where φ, as before, represents a time-dependent wave function. It will be convenient to think of a wave packet of finite (though large) extension passing through the apparatus. The wave functions are then no longer strictly monochromatic, but they can be normalized. By (9.43), we have

$$|\varphi_s|^2 = |\varphi - \varphi^{(0)}|^2$$
$$= |\varphi^2| + |\varphi^{(0)}|^2 - \varphi^*\varphi^{(0)} - \varphi^{(0)*}\varphi$$
$$= |\varphi^2| + |\varphi^{(0)}|^2 - 2 \operatorname{Re} \varphi^{(0)*}\varphi$$

where Re denotes that one takes the real part of what follows. Putting this into (9.59), we note that

$$\frac{d}{dt} \int |\varphi|^2 \, dv = \frac{d}{dt} \int |\varphi^{(0)}|^2 \, dv = 0$$

since both these functions are assumed normalized. Further, using the wave equations for $\varphi^{(0)}$ and φ and the hermiticity of $\hat{H}^{(0)}$, we find that (9.59) is

$$\sigma = -\frac{2\mu}{\hbar^2 k} \operatorname{Im} \int \psi^{(0)*}(\mathbf{r}) V(\mathbf{r})\psi(\mathbf{r}) \, dv \tag{9.60}$$

where Im denotes that the imaginary part is to be taken. The integral is of exactly the same form as (9.51) with $\mathbf{k}_c$ replaced by $\mathbf{k}$, that is, with the scattering angle set equal to zero. Thus we have the *optical theorem*

$$\sigma = \frac{4\pi}{k} \operatorname{Im} f(0) \tag{9.61}$$

connecting the total scattering cross section with the imaginary part of the forward scattering amplitude. One can see that some connec-

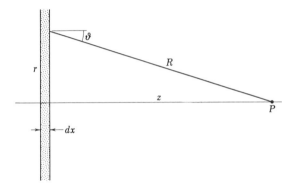

Fig. 9.16 Scattering by a
thin slab containing
scattering centers.

tion must exist between σ and $f(0)$ because of the fact that $\psi^{(0)}$ in
(9.43) takes no account of the depletion of the incident beam by the
scattering of particles out of it, so that $f(0)$ must contain a part
which cancels some of $\psi^{(0)}$ and makes the forward beam weaker than
it would be in the absence of the scatterer. What is perhaps unexpected is that only the imaginary part of $f(0)$ is involved. The reason
for this can be understood if we derive the same result by an explicit
scattering computation.

Consider the attenuation of a plane wave advancing along the
z axis by a thin slab containing N scattering centers per unit volume,
Fig. 9.16. Adding together the waves scattered by concentric rings
of scattering centers gives for the total amplitude at P

$$\psi_P = e^{ikz} + \int_0^\infty f(\vartheta)\, \frac{e^{ikR}}{R}\, N\, dx\, 2\pi r\, dr$$

where

$$\cos \vartheta = \frac{z}{R} \qquad r^2 = R^2 - z^2$$

Change the variable of integration to R (z being fixed).

$$\psi_P = e^{ikz} + 2\pi N\, dx \int_z^\infty f\left(\cos^{-1}\frac{z}{R}\right) \frac{e^{ikR}}{R}\, R\, dR$$

The integral becomes indeterminate at large values of R, so we
introduce a factor to make it converge,

$$\lim_{\alpha \to 0} \int_z^\infty f\left(\cos^{-1}\frac{z}{R}\right) e^{ikR - \alpha R}\, dR$$

Since z and R are of laboratory size, kR is enormously large; and
except for points very near the axis where it varies slowly with r,
the fluctuations of the exponential effectively nullify the integral.
This can be seen if it is integrated by parts to give

$$\lim_{\alpha \to 0} \left\{ \left[f\left(\cos^{-1}\frac{z}{R}\right) \frac{e^{ikR - \alpha R}}{ik - \alpha} \right]_z^\infty \right.$$

$$\left. - \frac{z}{ik - \alpha} \int_z^\infty \frac{f'[\cos^{-1}(z/R)]}{R(R^2 - z^2)^{1/2}}\, e^{ikR - \alpha R}\, dR \right\} = \frac{i}{k}\, e^{ikz} f(0)$$

plus terms which if the partial integration is repeated are found to be smaller than the term given by a factor of the order of kz and are therefore quite negligible. Therefore

$$\psi_P = e^{ikz}(1 + 2\pi i k^{-1} N \, dx \, f(0))$$

very accurately, and the intensity at P is

$$|\psi_P|^2 = [1 - 2\pi k^{-1} N \, dx \, \mathrm{Im}\, f(0)]^2 + [2\pi k^{-1} N \, dx \, \mathrm{Re}\, f(0)]^2$$
$$= 1 - 4\pi k^{-1} N \, dx \, \mathrm{Im}\, f(0)$$

plus terms of the order of $(dx)^2$. The second term clearly represents an interference between the incident wave and that scattered straight forward.

On the other hand, if σ is the total cross section, we know that the beam is attenuated in the distance dx by a factor of $N\sigma \, dx$, since this is the fraction of the total area which is obscured by scatterers. Thus

$$1 - N\sigma \, dx = 1 - 4\pi k^{-1} N \, dx \, \mathrm{Im}\, f(0)$$

from which follows (9.61). We see in this way why it is the imaginary part of $f(0)$ that determines the absorption from the beam and hence the total cross section.

We see, especially from the second proof, that the optical theorem is a way of expressing (among other things) the conservation of the number of particles, and it is here that a difficulty characteristic of the Born approximation appears; for the values of $f(\vartheta)$ obtained from the integral formula (9.35) are all real numbers. The Born approximation is therefore essentially nonconservative. It is, however, consistent, since if the first Born approximation to f is of the order of V, then σ is of the order of V^2 and so, by (9.61), is $\mathrm{Im}\, f(0)$.

Part of the interest attached to the optical theorem comes from the fact that although in the first proof we had to assume that ψ satisfies Schrödinger's equation with a certain $V(\mathbf{r})$, the second proof makes no use of the equation at all, but bases its argument entirely upon conservation. There is at present some feeling that, as applied to nuclear interactions, Schrödinger's equation may not be so firmly based as it was once thought to be, and there is a corresponding interest in attempts to circumvent it. We shall return to this question in Sec. 9.6.

There are other approximations than Born's. Some consist in the construction of a series which is guaranteed to converge, but of which the individual terms are fully as difficult as those of the Born expansion.[8] There are a number of variational methods[9] analo-

---

[8] R. Jost and A. Pais, Phys. Rev., **82**, 840 (1951).
[9] H. S. W. Massey, in *Encyclopedia of Physics*, Springer-Verlag OHG, Berlin, 1956, vol. 36.

gous to the method used in Sec. 8.6 for stationary-state calculations. Some of them satisfy the optical theorem exactly, but to discuss them would lead us beyond the limits of this book. We therefore turn, in the next section, to an examination of scattering formulas in the case in which the Born approximation is least satisfactory, that of very low energies.

9.5 Low-energy Scattering

The determining feature of scattering in the low-energy region is that (in the C.M. system) it is spherically symmetric. This can be seen from the fact that all the directional properties arise from the presence of the initial and final momentum vectors $\hbar\mathbf{k}$ and $\hbar\mathbf{k}_c$ in (9.51) [$\mathbf{k}$ is contained implicitly in $\psi(\mathbf{r}')$], so that as the length of these vectors approaches zero, no further directional properties remain. What this fact means dynamically is seen if we look at it in a semiclassical way (Fig. 9.17). The angular momentum of the particle shown approaching the scatterer is mva, or, in terms of k, $\hbar ka$. In quantum mechanics this quantity is quantized in multiples of $\hbar$, say $l\hbar$, where $l = 0, 1, 2, \ldots$. Roughly speaking, we can divide the plane of the scatterer into concentric circles of radius a, such that particles arriving inside the first circle are assigned zero angular momentum, particles arriving between the first circle and the second have $l = 1$, etc. The radius of the lth circle is given by

$$\hbar k a_1 = \hbar l \qquad a_1 = \frac{l}{k} \qquad l = 1, 2, \ldots \tag{9.62}$$

Now suppose that k is very small. The first circle extends far out, beyond the range r_0 of the scattering potential. Thus particles passing through the outer rings corresponding to $l > 0$ do not interact at all with the scatterer and do not appear in the scattered beam. The wave function ψ_s is then entirely composed of particles having zero angular momentum, and we have already seen in Chap. 7 that S-state wave functions are spherically symmetric. In this section we shall concern ourselves only with this case, which by (9.62) is char-

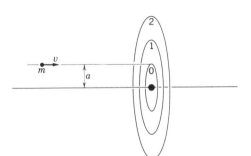

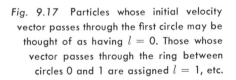

Fig. 9.17 Particles whose initial velocity vector passes through the first circle may be thought of as having $l = 0$. Those whose vector passes through the ring between circles 0 and 1 are assigned $l = 1$, etc.

acterized by

$$kr_0 \ll 1 \tag{9.63}$$

where r_0 is, as we have said, an effective range of the force field beyond which it may be neglected. The idea of an effective range is very useful in nuclear physics, where the characteristic nuclear potentials fall off rapidly with distance, but it cannot be used to characterize a field whose decrease is as gradual as a Coulomb field's. Our emphasis in this section will therefore be chiefly on short-range interactions such as occur in the scattering of slow neutrons by nuclei. States of higher angular momentum are described by wave functions which depend on ϑ by being proportional to the lth Legendre polynomial, as described in Chap. 14 on the states of the hydrogen atom. The treatment of these states, however, involves little that is new, and so we shall discuss only scattering in S states.

First, we must pick out the S states, in both the incident and scattered waves, from the other states that are present. Especially in the incident plane wave $\psi^{(0)}$, it is clear that we have to deal with a combination of all values of l. The selection is easily made by the use of the orthogonality theorem, by which eigenfunctions of angular momentum corresponding to different eigenvalues are orthogonal to each other. To select out the S states in $\psi^{(0)}$, we write it as

$$\psi^{(0)} = \sum_{l=0}^{\infty} \psi_l^{(0)}$$

then multiply by an eigenfunction of L_z and L^2 belonging to the eigenvalue zero and integrate over all space. Any function $p(r)$ depending on r only is such an eigenfunction; we have therefore

$$\int \psi^{(0)} p(r)\, dv = \int \psi_0^{(0)} p(r)\, dv$$

The integral on the left is

$$\int e^{i\mathbf{k}\cdot\mathbf{r}}\, p(r)\, dv = 4\pi \int_0^{\infty} \frac{\sin kr}{kr}\, p(r) r^2\, dr$$

[see the integration leading to (9.34)], whereas that on the right is

$$4\pi \int_0^{\infty} \psi_0^{(0)}(r) p(r) r^2\, dr$$

Since these are equal for any function $p(r)$, we must have

$$\psi_0^{(0)} = \frac{\sin kr}{kr} \tag{9.64}$$

The scattered wave is asymptotically of the form (9.50), but with f independent of ϑ; we shall write it as

$$\psi_0^{(s)} \rightarrow f_0 \frac{e^{ikr}}{r} \tag{9.65}$$

Problem 9.15   What is the Born approximation for f_0?

Problem 9.16   Up to about what energy, in the laboratory system, can the scattering of neutrons by protons be discussed in terms of S waves only?

In order to determine f_0, we shall work directly with Schrödinger's equation. We have already derived in Chap. 7 the form which it takes for spherically symmetric eigenfunctions; generalizing (7.43) from a Coulomb potential and omitting the unnecessary subscript 0, we have

$$\frac{d^2\psi}{dr^2} + \frac{2}{r}\frac{d\psi}{dr} + \left[k^2 - \frac{2\mu}{\hbar^2} V(r) \right] \psi = 0 \tag{9.66}$$

where we remember that by (7.41), $r\psi(r)$ approaches zero at the origin. It is convenient to introduce the variable

$$u(r) = r\psi(r) \tag{9.67}$$

in terms of which (9.66) becomes

$$\frac{d^2u}{dr^2} + \left[k^2 - \frac{2\mu}{\hbar^2} V(r) \right] u = 0 \tag{9.68}$$

with $u(0) = 0$. In the asymptotic region, where $V(r)$ vanishes, this becomes

$$\frac{d^2u}{dr^2} + k^2u = 0 \tag{9.69}$$

which has sines and cosines as solutions; we follow convention and write the general solution as

$$u = \frac{C}{k} \sin (kr + \delta) \qquad (r \gg r_0) \tag{9.70}$$

where C and δ are arbitrary constants which may in general be complex, though we shall see presently (Prob. 9.17) that in this case δ is real. Reverting to ψ, we now write (9.43) for spherical symmetry:

$$\frac{C}{kr} \sin (kr + \delta) = \frac{\sin kr}{kr} + f_0 \frac{e^{ikr}}{r} \qquad (r \gg r_0) \tag{9.71}$$

This is to be identically true for all sufficiently large r. We can best see what it implies by writing the sines as exponentials,

$$C(e^{i\delta}e^{ikr} - e^{-i\delta}e^{-ikr}) = e^{ikr} - e^{-ikr} + 2ikf_0 e^{ikr}$$

and this is true only if the coefficients of e^{ikr} and e^{-ikr} are respectively equal. This gives

$$Ce^{i\delta} = 1 + 2ikf_0, \qquad Ce^{-i\delta} = 1$$

and from these we see that

$$f_0 = \frac{Ce^{i\delta} - 1}{2ik} = \frac{e^{2i\delta} - 1}{2ik} = \frac{e^{i\delta} \sin \delta}{k}$$

(9.72)

The differential cross section (anticipating that δ is real) is

$$\frac{d\sigma}{d\Omega} = |f_0|^2 = \frac{\sin^2 \delta}{k^2}$$

and the total cross section is

$$\sigma = \frac{4\pi}{k^2} \sin^2 \delta$$

(9.73)

Problem 9.17 Show that σ satisfies the optical theorem if and only if δ is real.

Problem 9.18 Prove that a simple statement equivalent to the optical theorem for S waves is

$$\text{Im} \frac{1}{f_0} = -k$$

By (9.67) and (9.70), the total wave function outside the range of the scattering potential is

$$\psi_0(r) = \frac{e^{i\delta}}{kr} \sin (kr + \delta) \qquad (r \gg r_0)$$

(9.74)

Comparison with (9.64) shows that δ, which is called the *phase shift*, is a measure of the effect of the scattering potential on the asymptotic wave function; for when δ vanishes, (9.74) reduces to (9.64). Let us now stop to see graphically what it represents. The factor $\sin (kr + \delta)$ is quite simple if we remember that the de Broglie wavelength depends on the kinetic energy and that the kinetic energy changes inside the region of interaction. We thus have the situation shown in Fig. 9.18, where the wavelength is shorter or longer inside the region of interaction according as the interaction is attractive or repulsive. It should be noted that δ is positive when $V(r)$ is predominantly attractive and negative when it is repulsive. The scattering cross section, however, does not depend on the sign of δ.

The factor of $e^{i\delta}$ in (9.74) has an equally direct physical interpretation. Since δ is a constant, we can include it in the phase of the time-dependent wave function which we are calling φ,

$$e^{i\delta} e^{-iEt/\hbar} = e^{-iE(t-t_0)/\hbar} \qquad t_0 = \frac{\hbar \delta}{E}$$

If now $V(r)$ is repulsive, for example, then t_0 is negative, and the entire phase is somewhat more advanced than it would have been in the absence of interaction. This corresponds to the fact that if the incoming waves encounter a scattering region of finite size,

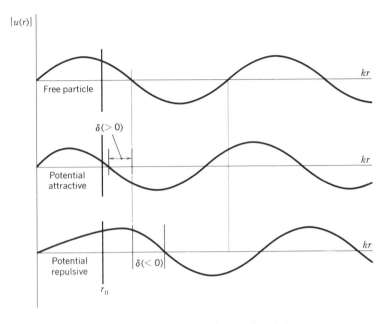

Fig. 9.18 Positive and negative phase shifts produced by attractive and repulsive scattering potentials.

they will start out on the scattered beam somewhat earlier than they would if they had to go all the way to the origin. On the other hand, if the potential is attractive, then the wave packet is somewhat delayed by multiple reflections in the neighborhood of the attracting center. This argument can be made explicit by seeing what happens to a wave packet when it is reflected. Since, however, it does not help us to compute anything, we shall not pursue it further.[10]

We shall now calculate the low-energy scattering cross section in two specific cases, the hard sphere and the square well, and then finish this section with some remarks on the general case.

Scattering from a hard sphere

Let r_0, the radius of the sphere, be such that $kr_0 \ll 1$. The scattering will then be spherically symmetrical. We can most easily calculate δ by noting that the solution (9.70) applies everywhere outside r_0 and that if the sphere is hard (that is, impenetrable), then the wave function must vanish inside the sphere and on its surface. It is therefore equal to

$$u_{\text{h.s.}} = \begin{cases} 0 & (r < r_0) \\ Ck^{-1} \sin\left[k(r - r_0)\right] & (r > r_0) \end{cases}$$

[10] H. S. W. Massey, *ibid.*, p. 247.

and the phase shift is therefore

$$\delta = -kr_0 \approx \sin \delta \qquad (9.75)$$

so that the total cross section is

$$\sigma = 4\pi r_0{}^2 \qquad (9.76)$$

It is therefore 4 times the classical value computed in Prob. 9.1. The discrepancy exists, of course, because the two situations are in no way similar, but it is quite characteristic of diffraction in general that the scattering effects extend beyond the edge of the geometrical shadow, and it is these that produce the extra cross section.

Scattering from a square potential well

This is a calculation which can be carried out both exactly and approximately and which is therefore very instructive in seeing how to do computations in the low-energy region. The entire question is of interest almost exclusively in studying the neutron-proton interaction, and since this is the subject of a separate discussion in Chap. 17, we shall develop only the bare outlines of the theory at this point.

The relevant equations are essentially those of Sec. 7.4, except that the energy is here positive, so that instead of (7.63) we write $E = \hbar^2 k^2 / 2\mu$. The solution inside the potential well is still of the form (7.68a):

$$u_{\text{in}} = A \sin Kr \qquad (0 \leqslant r \leqslant r_0) \qquad (9.77)$$

where

$$K^2 = \frac{2\mu}{\hbar^2} (E + V_0) \qquad (9.78)$$

whereas the exterior solution (9.70) will be written as

$$u_{\text{out}} = B \sin (kr + \delta) \qquad (r \geqslant r_0) \qquad (9.79)$$

The wave function and its derivative are to be continuous at r_0, and exactly as in the derivation of (7.70) we obtain

$$\left(\frac{u'_{\text{out}}}{u_{\text{out}}} \right)_{r_0} = k \cot (kr_0 + \delta) \qquad (9.80)$$

$$\left(\frac{u'_{\text{in}}}{u_{\text{in}}} \right)_{r_0} = K \cot Kr_0 \qquad (9.81)$$

and continuity of u'/u at r_0 gives

$$k \cot (kr_0 + \delta) = K \cot Kr_0 \qquad (9.82)$$

The zero-range approximation

To get a first rough orientation in neutron-proton scattering, we make two approximations. The first is to neglect the small quantity

kr_0 in (9.80), so that

$$\left(\frac{u'_{\text{out}}}{u_{\text{out}}}\right)_{r_0} \approx k \cot \delta \tag{9.83}$$

The second is to note that whereas the energies which we are discussing are just above zero, the energy of the ground state of the deuteron is just below zero, so one might expect that the inner wave function at low energies would be much like that of the ground state,

$$\left(\frac{u'_{\text{in}}}{u_{\text{in}}}\right)_{r_0}^{\text{scat}} = K \cot Kr_0 \approx \left(\frac{u'_{\text{in}}}{u_{\text{in}}}\right)_{r_0}^{\text{ground}} = -\kappa \tag{9.84}$$

by (7.68b). Thus, (9.82) implies, at least roughly, that

$$k \cot \delta \approx -\kappa \tag{9.85}$$

The total cross section now results from writing (9.73) as

$$\sigma = \frac{4\pi}{k^2 \csc^2 \delta} = \frac{4\pi}{k^2 + k^2 \cot^2 \delta} \tag{9.86}$$

or

$$\sigma = \frac{4\pi}{\kappa^2 + k^2} \tag{9.87}$$

a formula whose agreement with experiment in the neutron-proton case is marred by another feature of the interaction which is irrelevant to the present argument and will be discussed in Chap. 17.

The result which we have just derived is attractively simple, but it has the disadvantage that its accuracy is difficult to assess a priori. It represents essentially the situation which exists when the range r_0 is very small and the depth V_0 correspondingly great, and so it is usually called the *zero-range approximation*. In order to get some idea of its accuracy we must return to the exact relation (9.82) and treat it more carefully.

The effective-range approximation

By writing out $\cot(kr_0 + \delta)$ in (9.82) and solving, we can obtain an exact formula for $\cot \delta$,

$$\cot \delta = \frac{Kr_0 \cot Kr_0 \cot kr_0 + kr_0}{kr_0 \cot kr_0 - Kr_0 \cot Kr_0} \tag{9.88}$$

where the values of all the terms on the right are known, but this is an extremely difficult formula to make any intuitive sense out of, and it is particularly hard to see how it behaves at low energies, which are, of course, the energies at which it is most useful. We shall therefore again dispense with exactness and consider approximate forms of solution.

Problem 9.19   Derive Eq. (9.88).

Let us therefore start again with (9.82) and separate out powers of k. The left side is, by a Taylor expansion,

$$k \cot (kr_0 + \delta) = k \cot \delta - k^2 r_0 (1 + \cot^2 \delta) + \cdots \tag{9.89}$$

where the omitted terms are of order k^3 and higher.

Now let us expand the right-hand side. This gives a simple result only in a situation like that of the deuteron, in which the system has its ground state at an energy only slightly below zero and the bombarding particle has an energy only slightly above zero. Denoting the quantities relating to the ground state by the subscript g, we have from (7.70)

$$K_g \cot K_g r_0 = -\kappa \tag{9.90}$$

and we propose to express the right side of (9.82) in terms of this by writing

$$
\begin{aligned}
K \cot K r_0 &= K_g \cot K_g r_0 + (K - K_g) \frac{\partial}{\partial K_g} (K_g \cot K_g r_0) \\
&\qquad\qquad\qquad\qquad\qquad\qquad\qquad + \cdots \\
&= K_g \cot K_g r_0 \\
&\qquad + (K - K_g)(\cot K_g r_0 - K_g r_0 \csc^2 K_g r_0) + \cdots \\
&= -\kappa - (K - K_g)\left[\frac{\kappa}{K_g} + K_g r_0 \left(1 + \frac{\kappa^2}{K_g{}^2} \right) \right] \\
&\qquad\qquad\qquad\qquad\qquad\qquad\qquad + \cdots \\
&= -\kappa - (K - K_g) K_g r_0
\end{aligned}
$$

plus terms in κ/K_g which are small (why?). The quantity $K - K_g$ is equal to

$$
\begin{aligned}
K - K_g &= \left[\frac{2\mu}{\hbar^2} V_0 - \kappa^2 + (\kappa^2 + k^2) \right]^{\frac{1}{2}} - \left(\frac{2\mu}{\hbar^2} V_0 - \kappa^2 \right)^{\frac{1}{2}} \\
&= -(\kappa^2 + k^2) \frac{\partial}{\partial(\kappa^2)} \left(\frac{2\mu}{\hbar^2} V_0 - \kappa^2 \right)^{\frac{1}{2}} + \cdots \\
&= \frac{1}{2} (\kappa^2 + k^2) \left(\frac{2\mu}{\hbar^2} V_0 - \kappa^2 \right)^{-\frac{1}{2}} \\
&= \frac{\kappa^2 + k^2}{2K_g}
\end{aligned}
$$

so that finally

$$K \cot K r_0 \approx -\kappa - \tfrac{1}{2}(\kappa^2 + k^2) r_0 \tag{9.91}$$

which is a more accurate version of (9.84). Returning to the evaluation of (9.82), we note that replacing the $k^2 \cot^2 \delta$ in (9.89) by κ^2 according to (9.85) in a term already proportional to r_0 entails an error of the order of r_0^2, which is higher than those which we are considering, so that finally, equating (9.89) and (9.91), we have

$$k \cot \delta - (\kappa^2 + k^2)r_0 \approx -\kappa - \frac{1}{2}(\kappa^2 + k^2)r_0$$

or

$$k \cot \delta \approx -\kappa + \frac{1}{2}(\kappa^2 + k^2)r_0 \qquad (9.92)$$

as the next approximation beyond (9.85). The significant dependence of (9.92) on energy can be emphasized by writing it as

$$k \cot \delta = -\frac{1}{a} + \frac{1}{2}r_0k^2 \qquad (9.93)$$

where

$$\frac{1}{a} = \kappa - \frac{1}{2}r_0\kappa^2 \qquad (9.94)$$

These are the basic equations of the *effective-range approximation*, reducing to those of the zero-range approximation when r_0 is neglected. They have been much used in the interpretation of low-energy nuclear-scattering data. The quantity a, which gives the value of $k \cot \delta$ at zero energy, is known as the *scattering length;* we shall see the reason for this curious name in a moment. Putting (9.92) into (9.86) and retaining only the first power of r_0 gives

$$\sigma = \frac{4\pi}{k^2 + \kappa^2 - \kappa r_0(\kappa^2 + k^2)} = \frac{4\pi}{(1 - \kappa r_0)(\kappa^2 + k^2)} \qquad (9.95)$$

showing a constant multiplicative correction to our earlier approximate result (9.87) when the effective range is included.

Let us return to (9.93) and use it in (9.86) to write the scattering cross section

$$\sigma = \frac{4\pi a^2}{1 + (1 - r_0/a)k^2a^2}$$

neglecting higher terms in k^2. The scattering length can now be characterized by the fact that

$$\lim_{k \to 0} \sigma = 4\pi a^2 \qquad (9.96)$$

and the other parameter, r_0, can then be determined from measurements of how σ depends on the energy. As we have said, the situation in the neutron-proton interaction is complicated by other factors (see Chap. 17), but it is possible to determine the value of a as

$$a = 5.39 \text{ F} \qquad (9.97)$$

with uncertainty only in the last place. The value of r_0 comes from a number of experimental sources which are somewhat difficult to evaluate; it lies in the neighborhood of 1.7 F. We can therefore check to see to what extent the theory we have developed bears any relation to the actual interaction by calculating κ^{-1} from (9.94) and comparing it with the experimental value (7.64) determined directly from the known binding energy of the deuteron. We find

$$\kappa^{-1} = 4.34 \text{ F} \tag{9.98}$$

which is not only good agreement, but really too good, since the entire argument has been carried through for a square-well potential which must bear only a casual relation to the true state of affairs. This suggests that the relations (9.93) and (9.94) have perhaps some wider range of validity than is given them by the special argument by which they were derived, and we shall see in the next section that this is so.

The scattering length

Let us try to attach a physical significance to the scattering length a introduced in (9.93) and (9.94). To do this, we return to (9.70) and consider its zero-energy limit. Keeping only the largest terms, we have

$$u = \frac{C}{k} (\sin kr \cos \delta + \cos kr \sin \delta) \qquad (r \gg r_0)$$

$$\approx \frac{C}{k} (kr \cos \delta + \sin \delta) \tag{9.99}$$

This is a linear function of r. Remembering that the exact $u(r)$ must vanish at the origin, we can draw the three possible cases in Fig. 9.19. If now we ask for what value of r other than zero the wave function vanishes, we find from (9.99) that $r = -k^{-1} \tan \delta$ (in the limit as k approaches zero), and this is exactly the relation defining a in (9.93). Thus we have a geometrical interpretation for the scattering length and a way of visualizing the relation (9.96). In calculating the scattering by a hard sphere we set the wave function equal to zero at the edge of the sphere ($r = r_0$) and found in (9.76) $\sigma = 4\pi r_0^2$. In the present case, the wave function is zero at $r = a$ and a corresponding result is found. The only difference here is that a may be negative, and the same result will still hold. This picture of low-energy scattering was introduced by Fermi in 1934.

To see the meaning of the sign of a, we note in (9.68) that if $E = 0$, then in a region where $V(r)$ is attractive (negative) the wave function $u(r)$ must [if $u(r)$ is positive] have a negative second derivative and so be concave downward. The more negative $V(r)$ is, the greater the concavity. The question at issue is whether the concavity is sufficient to curve $u(r)$ over and start it downward by the time the force effectively ceases to act, at about r_0. It is in close relation to the question whether a bound state exists, for in this case it is necessary that $u(r)$ join smoothly on to a function of the form $e^{-\kappa r}$ for values of r greater than r_0, and this exponential function has necessarily a negative slope. Suppose that the potential is in

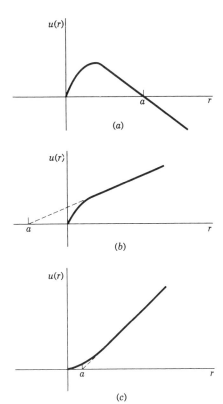

Fig. 9.19   (a) If the potential is strongly enough attractive to produce a bound state, the scattering length a is positive. (b) If it is more weakly attractive, a is negative. (c) If it is repulsive, a is positive. The parameter r_0 in (9.93) is related to the range of the force only in cases (a) and (b).

fact strong enough to produce a bound state, characterized by an $E < 0$. In the zero-energy state shown in Fig. 9.19, the downward concavity will be great enough to make a positive, as we have found it to be in (9.94). Conversely, if the potential is attractive but not strong enough to produce binding, a will be negative. For repulsive potentials it is again positive, and for potentials which either barely bind the system or barely fail to bind it, we see that a can take on very large values. It is the presence of a large negative a in the neutron-proton interaction which complicates the interpretation of the scattering data.

Problem 9.20   Prove that for a square-well potential, the phase shift is given by

$$\delta = \tan^{-1}\left(\frac{k}{K} \tan Kr_0\right) - kr_0$$

What happens to this formula when the potential is repulsive (negative V_0)? Explain qualitatively the dependence of δ on V_0 and k.

Problem 9.21   Suppose a square-well potential is strong enough to produce just n bound S states. For a given value of n, what is the limit of δ at zero energy? (The result is a general formula not re-stricted to any special potential shape.)

Problem 9.22   Calculate the first two terms of an expansion of σ as a function of the depth V_0 of a square well. Show that the first term is the same as the first Born approximation studied earlier. For what values of V_0 will the series converge? Is this related to earlier results in this chapter?

Problem 9.23   Prove that the general formula for the S-state scattering amplitude f_0 at low energies is

$$f_0 = -\frac{a}{1 + iak - \frac{1}{2}ar_0k^2}$$

and show that it satisfies the optical theorem.

Problem 9.24   Prove that for a square-well potential the scattering length is given by

$$a = r_0 - K_0^{-1}\tan K_0 r_0$$

where the well depth V_0 is $\hbar^2 K_0^2/2\mu$. What does this formula become if V_0 is negative? Sketch a as a function of V_0 for positive and negative values of V_0 and explain the qualitative features of the curve.

Problem 9.25   Whereas in low-energy scattering a simple attractive potential may be characterized by two parameters (for example range and depth, or r_0 and a), an attractive potential with a repulsive core needs three, for one must give the radius of the core. Derive a three-parameter expression for $k \cot \partial$ and show that it reduces to the correct limiting forms when the attractive or repulsive part of the well disappears. Show that it can be put into the form (9.93) but that it is not always wise to do so.

9.6   The Kramers-Heisenberg Approach

We have seen in (9.93) that the low-energy scattering of S waves by a square potential well can be characterized in terms of two quanti-ties, the scattering length a and the range r_0, each of which has a simple physical interpretation. Further, these two scattering pa-rameters are closely related by (9.94) to the parameter κ which gives the energy of the bound state, and we have seen that this rela-tion, though derived only for square wells, appears to apply accu-rately to the neutron-proton system. We are thus led to enquire in more general terms into the nature of the relationship between negative-energy and positive-energy states of the same system or, more precisely, between the kind of negative-energy states which one encounters in bound systems and the kind of positive-energy states which one encounters in scattering. The reader will recall that the essential fact about bound systems is the vanishing of the wave function at infinity. The general solution for $u(r) = r\psi(r)$ outside the range of interaction is of the form $Ae^{-\kappa r} + Be^{\kappa r}$, and we express the eigenvalue condition by requiring that

For bound states, the coefficient of $e^{\kappa r}$ is zero (9.100)

Now let us look at the asymptotic scattering wave function (9.74), splitting it into incoming and outgoing parts. We find

$$u_0 = r\psi_0$$
$$= k^{-1}e^{i\delta} \sin (kr + \delta)$$
$$= (2ik)^{-1}e^{2i\delta}(e^{ikr} - e^{-2i\delta}e^{-ikr})$$

It is customary to denote the quantity $e^{2i\delta}$ by the letter S. It is, of course, a function of k. Omitting constant factors which can be absorbed in normalization, we have

$$u_0 \approx e^{ikr} - \frac{e^{-ikr}}{S(k)}$$ (9.101)

Thus we can characterize $S(k)$ by the statement that

For scattering, the coefficient of the incoming wave is $1/S(k)$ (9.102)

We have several times had occasion to remark that mathematical expressions relating to bound states can be obtained from those relating to free states by letting k, defined for positive E by

$$k = \left(\frac{2\mu E}{\hbar^2}\right)^{1/2} \qquad (E > 0)$$ (9.103)

be replaced by the imaginary number which appears when E becomes negative. Here we must be explicit as to sign. For negative E, we write

$$k = i\kappa \qquad \kappa = \left(\frac{2\mu|E|}{\hbar^2}\right)^{1/2} \qquad (E < 0)$$ (9.104)

If this is done, then (9.101) becomes

$$u_0 \approx e^{-\kappa r} - \frac{e^{\kappa r}}{S(i\kappa)}$$ (9.105)

Comparing (9.105) with (9.100), we now see that they are the same provided that when κ corresponds to a bound state,

$$S(i\kappa) = \infty$$ (9.106)

To see what happens to (9.93) when $k = i\kappa$, we rewrite it in terms of $S(k)$,

$$k \cot \delta = k \frac{\frac{1}{2}(e^{i\delta} + e^{-i\delta})}{(1/2i)(e^{i\delta} - e^{-i\delta})} = ik \frac{S(k) + 1}{S(k) - 1}$$

so that

$$ik \frac{S(k) + 1}{S(k) - 1} = -\frac{1}{a} + \frac{1}{2}r_0 k^2$$ (9.107)

Let us assume that this scattering formula still has content when k is no longer a positive real number. Setting it equal to $i\kappa$, we find from (9.106) that

$$-\kappa = -\frac{1}{a} - \tfrac{1}{2}r_0\kappa^2$$

which is (9.94). Thus, (9.94) is in this sense a special case of (9.93), and we are no longer surprised to find that it holds for the neutron-proton system. Our surprise is perhaps transferred to the fact that one can so generalize positive-energy expressions by taking k to be imaginary. It need not be surprising for the square well, or for any other case in which we can solve the equations exactly, since the analytic processes work the same regardless of whether k is real or complex. But it is by no means so evident in more realistic situations, such as interactions which might not be expressible in terms of an energy and so could not be introduced as an interaction term in the hamiltonian function. The tendency nowadays is to think that the possibility of characterizing an interaction by a single set of formulas valid for either real or imaginary values of k may be part of a theory which is more general than quantum mechanics as we know it, and that this feature may possibly carry over into the physics of the future. The attempt to characterize physical systems in terms of operators and functions centering around the quantity S as an alternative to the usual description in terms of $\hat{H}$ was originated by Heisenberg in a series of papers published during the 1940s, and it was Kramers who pointed out the possibility of extending Heisenberg's considerations to complex values of k. Analytical methods of this kind now dominate the modern theory of elementary particles.

Problem 9.26   Starting from (9.88), show that for the square-well potential,

$$S(k) = e^{-2ikr_0}\frac{K \cot Kr_0 + ik}{K \cot Kr_0 - ik}$$

It will be convenient to start by proving that

$$S(k) = e^{2i\delta} = \frac{\cot \delta + i}{\cot \delta - i}$$

For what imaginary values of k does this become infinite? How is your result related to the properties of this potential studied earlier?

Problem 9.27   Prove that the S-wave scattering cross section is given in terms of $S(k)$ by

$$\sigma = \frac{\pi}{k^2}|S(k) - 1|^2$$

where k will, of course, be real and positive.

Problem 9.28 Show that the WKB approximation to S-wave scattering by an attractive potential is

$$\delta = \int_0^\infty \{[k^2 - V(r)]^{1/2} - k\} \, dr + \tfrac{1}{4}\pi$$

Evaluate this for an attractive Hulthén potential and examine its general features. It will be convenient to take $[k^2 - V(r)]^{1/2}$ as a new variable of integration.

Problem 9.29 In the next two problems it will be convenient to replace $u(r)$ by the function $v(r) = -2iku(r)$, which differs from $u(r)$ only by a factor of proportionality but which has the simple asymptotic form

$$v(k,r) \to e^{-ikr} - S(k)e^{ikr}$$

Let $k \to -k$, so that

$$v(-k,r) \to e^{ikr} - S(-k)e^{-ikr}$$

and show that $S(k)S(-k) = 1$. [Hint: compare the equations and the boundary conditions satisfied by $v(k,r)$ and $v(-k,r)$.]

Problem 9.30 Let k now become a complex variable, as in the last section, and consider the function $v^*(k^*,r)$. [This notation means that we replace k by k^* in $v(k,r)$ and then take the complex conjugate, so that the result is once more a function of k.] Then

$$v^*(k^*,r) \to e^{ikr} - S^*(k^*)e^{-ikr}$$

Prove that $S(k)S^*(k^*) = 1$.

Problem 9.31 Show that the last two results are equivalent to

$$\frac{1}{f_0(k)} - \frac{1}{f_0(-k)} = -2ik = \frac{1}{f_0(k)} - \frac{1}{f_0^*(k^*)}$$

For small values of k, approximate $f_0(k)$ by

$$f_0(k) = \frac{1}{c_0 + c_1 k + c_2 k^2 + c_3 k^3 + c_4 k^4}$$

and find what restrictions are placed on the coefficients $c_0 \cdots c_4$ by the relations just derived. Does the result agree with the effective-range approximation (Prob. 9.23)? Does it add anything? Write down the resulting formula for $k \cot \delta$ for comparison with (9.93).

Problem 9.32 Show that if the optical theorem is obeyed, the S-wave scattering cross section has the upper bound

$$\sigma_0 \leqslant \frac{4\pi}{k^2}$$

whatever the potential may be.

10

Electromagnetic Radiation

The contents of this chapter are of a rather provisional nature. We are going to discuss the absorption and emission of electromagnetic radiation by a method which neglects one of the most fundamental aspects of the problem, the fact that the electromagnetic field itself is subject to quantum-mechanical laws. For our purposes, however, the drawback is more conceptual than practical, and we shall be able to derive some accurate and useful formulas from a theory which admittedly has one foot in quantum and the other in classical theory. A more satisfactory treatment is available,[1] but it seems that the simpler form of the theory should probably be grasped first in order to appreciate the merits of the correct treatment.

10.1 Einstein's Relations

The easiest way to approach our subject is through Einstein's general relations between the emission and absorption of electromagnetic radiation. These relations first appeared in an extremely fruitful paper written in 1917 in the effort to understand the quantum nature of light.[2] The argument applies to black-body radiation, for which Planck's famous formula for the spectral distribution function had been available for many years: In an enclosure at thermal equilibrium at a temperature T, the energy density U of the radiation is distributed among the spectral frequencies ω according to

---

[1] See, for example, L. I. Schiff, *Quantum Mechanics*, 2d. ed., McGraw-Hill Book Company, Inc., New York, 1955, or R. B. Leighton, *Principles of Modern Physics*, McGraw-Hill Book Company, Inc., New York, 1959.

[2] A. Einstein, Physik. Z., **18,** 121 (1917).

the law

$$u(\omega) = \frac{\hbar\omega^3}{\pi^2 c^3} \frac{1}{e^{\hbar\omega/kT} - 1} \tag{10.1}$$

where $u(\omega) \, d\omega$ is the energy density of the radiation lying in the spectral range ω to $\omega + d\omega$ and k is Boltzmann's constant. The relation between $u(\omega)$ and U is

$$U = \int_0^\infty u(\omega) \, d\omega \tag{10.2}$$

The most remarkable feature of this law is its universality, for it can be shown from the second law of thermodynamics that $u(\omega)$ is independent of the material of which the enclosure is made or of any substances that might be present inside it. Einstein supposed that atoms are present in the enclosure which have a number of quantum states, and in particular a pair, m and n, separated by an energy $E_n - E_m = \hbar\omega$. We now consider the radiative transitions between these two levels in the light of three different processes that may occur.

1. *Spontaneous emission.* An atom in state n may decay spontaneously to state m. Let A_{nm} be the probability of this process per unit time.

2. *Absorption.* In the presence of radiation at the frequency ω, an atom in state m may jump to state n by absorbing a quantum. The rate of this process is proportional to the density of radiation present at the frequency ω, and we write its probability per unit time as $B_{mn}u(\omega)$.

3. *Induced emission.* The presence of radiation at the frequency ω may also provoke transitions downward from state n to state m with the emission of a quantum. This process, which we have already encountered in (8.111), is not so self-evident as the first two, but it may be understood as follows. Suppose that one pushes a child in a swing periodically with a period the same as that of the swing. If the push is in phase with the motion of the swing (or anywhere between 90° ahead and 90° behind it), the swing will gain energy. But if the phase of the push is in the 180° range out of phase with the swing, the swing will lose energy. This corresponds to induced emission, and we see that if the push is applied at random, the probabilities of gain and loss are equal. We write the probability per unit time of this process for an atom in state n as $B_{nm}u(\omega)$.

At thermal equilibrium, the rates of transitions up and down must be equal. If N_m and N_n are the numbers of atoms in the two states, we have therefore

$$N_m B_{mn} u(\omega) = N_n [A_{nm} + B_{nm} u(\omega)]$$

or

$$u(\omega) = \frac{A_{nm}}{(N_m/N_n)B_{mn} - B_{nm}}$$

At thermal equilibrium, Boltzmann's relation[3] tells us that

$$\frac{N_n}{N_m} = \frac{e^{-E_n/kT}}{e^{-E_m/kt}} = e^{-\hbar\omega/kT}$$

so that

$$u(\omega) = \frac{A_{nm}}{B_{mn}e^{\hbar\omega/kT} - B_{nm}}$$

This relation agrees with (10.1) only if $B_{mn} = B_{nm}$, as we have suggested above, and

$$A_{nm} = \frac{\hbar\omega^3}{\pi^2 c^3} B_{nm} \tag{10.3}$$

Einstein's argument, of course, gives no hint of the magnitudes of the A's and B's; they must be calculated from quantum mechanics, but we need now to calculate only one of the three coefficients. This is especially fortunate, because the B's are available from the elementary theory. We can find it by setting up a perturbation calculation in which the atom is driven from state m to state n by an electric field of frequency ω, and the apparatus of time-dependent perturbation theory will easily give the rate at which transitions occur. Then we can find A, but to calculate it directly, without using Einstein's relation, is something of a puzzle since there seems to be here no field to produce a perturbation. This is the inadequacy of the present half-classical approach. Actually, the electromagnetic field is always present; and even when there are no quanta, its fluctuations, analogous to the zero-point vibrations we have previously seen in atomic systems, produce the apparently spontaneous transitions we observe. In this sense, all transitions are induced.[4]

10.2 Absorption of Radiation

Let us consider the absorption of radiation from isotropic, unpolarized radiation whose spectral distribution function is $u(\omega)$, which may now be arbitrary. The only troublesome point in the calculation we shall perform is to understand the part played by radiation "at the frequency ω." The radiation is, of course, continuously distributed in frequency, and the atom absorbs energy from a band whose width, however small, is finite; otherwise, it would contain no energy. This is where one can use the delta functions introduced in Chap. 8, but it will be more instructive if we forget this artifice for a moment and carry out the calculation in a completely straightforward way. We shall avoid the difficult question of strict mono-

---

[3] A proof is given in Chap. 18.

[4] This is discussed in more detail in connection with Planck's law by D. Park and H. T. Epstein, Am. J. Phys., **17**, 301 (1949).

chromaticity, which crops up quite often in physics, by assuming that the radiation has been established only during the time interval from $t = 0$ to $t = T$, the present moment, so that even if the radiation were perfectly monochromatic in this interval, its spectral distribution as defined by a Fourier integral would still not be infinitely narrow. (We have performed a calculation mathematically equivalent to this in Sec. 2.4.) Actually, of course, the electric vector in even what purports to be a monochromatic beam of light is usually a very random affair, owing to the large number of incoherent radiative processes that compose it. Only in the beam from a continuous laser is anything like spectral purity attained.

Suppose that the electric vector of the radiation is $\mathbf{E}(t)$, random in direction. We have first to calculate $u(\omega)$. To do this, we write down the expression from Maxwell's theory[5] for the energy density of a field of radiation with electric and magnetic components $\mathbf{E}$ and $\mathbf{H}$,

$$U(t) = \tfrac{1}{2}[\varepsilon_0 E^2(t) + \mu_0 H^2(t)]$$

where the variable t has been included to remind us that these are varying quantities. The U and $u(\omega)$ which we have used earlier are not fluctuating quantities, they are the time averages of them:

$$U = \frac{1}{T} \int_0^T U(t)\, dt \tag{10.4}$$

where we may imagine that T eventually approaches infinity. It is shown in Maxwell's theory that on the average, the electric and magnetic components of a radiation field carry equal energy, so that we can write

$$U = \frac{\varepsilon_0}{T} \int_0^T E^2(t)\, dt \tag{10.5}$$

Now let us write $\mathbf{E}(t)$ as a Fourier integral,

$$\mathbf{E}(t) = \int_{-\infty}^{\infty} \mathbf{a}(\omega) e^{i\omega t}\, d\omega \tag{10.6}$$

where

$$\mathbf{a}(\omega) = (2\pi)^{-1} \int_{-\infty}^{\infty} \mathbf{E}(t) e^{-i\omega t}\, dt$$

or, since the signal has been in operation for only a finite interval,

$$\mathbf{a}(\omega) = (2\pi)^{-1} \int_0^T \mathbf{E}(t) e^{-i\omega t}\, dt$$

We note that because $\mathbf{E}(t)$ is a real number,

$$\mathbf{a}^*(\omega) = \mathbf{a}(-\omega) \tag{10.7}$$

[5] See Appendix 5.

With this we can evaluate (10.5), using the same technique as was used for similar integrals in Chap. 2.

$$U = \frac{\varepsilon_0}{T} \int_0^T \mathbf{E}(t)\, dt \cdot \int_{-\infty}^{\infty} \mathbf{a}(\omega) e^{i\omega t}\, d\omega$$

$$= \frac{\varepsilon_0}{T} \int_{-\infty}^{\infty} \mathbf{a}(\omega)\, d\omega \cdot \int_0^T \mathbf{E}(t) e^{i\omega t}\, dt$$

$$= 2\pi \frac{\varepsilon_0}{T} \int_{-\infty}^{\infty} \mathbf{a}(\omega) \cdot \mathbf{a}(-\omega)\, d\omega$$

$$= 4\pi \frac{\varepsilon_0}{T} \int_0^{\infty} |\mathbf{a}(\omega)|^2\, d\omega$$

where we have used first the fact that $\mathbf{a}(\omega) \cdot \mathbf{a}(-\omega)$ is an even function of ω and then (10.7). Comparing this with the integral formula (10.2), we see that

$$u(\omega) = \frac{4\pi\varepsilon_0}{T} |\mathbf{a}(\omega)|^2 \tag{10.8}$$

In reading this formula, it should be remembered that ω is used in what may be called the realistic sense—$u(\omega)$ and $\mathbf{a}(\omega)$ are Fourier amplitudes which take into account the fact that the field has been established for only a finite time.

Problem 10.1   Let $\mathbf{E}(t) = \mathbf{E}_0 \sin \omega_0 t$, starting at $t = 0$. Show, using (8.107), that as $T \to \infty$, $u(\omega)$ approaches the value

$$u(\omega) = \tfrac{1}{2}\varepsilon_0 E_0^2 [\delta(\omega - \omega_0) + \delta(\omega + \omega_0)]$$

and comment on the significance of this formula.

To calculate the rate of transitions from an initial state a to a final state b, we turn to (8.96) and (8.97). To find the perturbing energy $\hat{H}^{(1)}$, we assume that only the electric field of the radiation acts appreciably on an electron. (For the magnetic field to be important, the electron would have to be moving at a speed approaching that of light.) Also, we exclude light of very short wavelength. Around the visible region, the wavelength is at least of the order of hundreds of times the atomic diameter, so that the field is essentially uniform across the atom. In this case one can consider the field quasistatically and write for the interaction energy of the electron with the incident light

$$\hat{H}^{(1)}(r,t) = -e\mathbf{E}(t) \cdot \mathbf{r} \tag{10.9}$$

and the matrix element in (8.97) becomes

$$-e\mathbf{E}(t) \cdot \langle b|\mathbf{r}|a\rangle$$

so that

$$c_b(T) = \frac{ie}{\hbar} \langle b|\mathbf{r}|a\rangle \cdot \int_0^T \mathbf{E}(t) e^{i\omega t}\, dt$$

where $\hbar\omega = E_b - E_a$ and ω may be either positive or negative. (In Sec. 10.1, state n was always higher than state m. It is because the initial and final states are now arbitrary that we are using different letters to denote them here.) We find

$$c_b(T) = \frac{2\pi i e}{\hbar} \langle b|\mathbf{r}|a\rangle \cdot \mathbf{a}^*(\omega)$$

and so the probability of finding the state b is

$$P_b(T) = \left(\frac{2\pi e}{\hbar}\right)^2 |\langle b|\mathbf{r}|a\rangle \cdot \mathbf{a}^*(\omega)|^2 \qquad (10.10)$$

Assuming that the radiation is isotropic and randomly polarized, we can average this expression over the directions of $\mathbf{a}(\omega)$. If the squared term is written out, the cross terms vanish, and in the remainder we can write

$$|a_x(\omega)|^2 = |a_y(\omega)|^2 = |a_z(\omega)|^2 = \tfrac{1}{3}|\mathbf{a}(\omega)|^2 \qquad (10.11)$$

so that

$$P_b(T) = \frac{1}{3}\left(\frac{2\pi e}{\hbar}\right)^2 |\langle b|\mathbf{r}|a\rangle|^2 |\mathbf{a}(\omega)|^2$$

$$= \frac{\pi e^2 T}{3\varepsilon_0 \hbar^2} |\langle b|\mathbf{r}|a\rangle|^2 u(\omega) \qquad (10.12)$$

by (10.8), where

$$|\langle b|\mathbf{r}|a\rangle|^2 = |\langle b|x|a\rangle|^2 + |\langle b|y|a\rangle|^2 + |\langle b|z|a\rangle|^2$$

The rate of increase of $P_b(T)$ is linear, as it should be, and we can read off at once the formula for Einstein's B coefficient,

$$B_{ab} = \frac{\pi e^2}{3\varepsilon_0 \hbar^2} |\langle b|\mathbf{r}|a\rangle|^2 \qquad (10.13)$$

while by (10.3)

$$A_{ba} = \frac{e^2 \omega^3}{3\pi\varepsilon_0 \hbar c^3} |\langle b|\mathbf{r}|a\rangle|^2 \qquad (10.14)$$

Problem 10.2 Prove from (10.13) what Einstein's relation says must be true in general, that $B_{ab} = B_{ba}$.

The average rate at which an atom spontaneously radiates energy may be calculated by multiplying A_{ba}, the rate at which it radiates photons, by $\hbar\omega$, the energy of a photon. This gives

$$R_{ba} = \frac{e^2 \omega^4}{3\pi\varepsilon_0 c^3} |\langle b|\mathbf{r}|a\rangle|^2 \qquad \text{watts} \qquad (10.15)$$

It is rather striking that Planck's constant has canceled out of (10.15), and this suggests that one might examine the formula in the light of the correspondence principle (Sec. 1.3). Suppose, for example, that we have a charge which oscillates along the x axis with amplitude x_0, radiating energy. The power emitted into a small cone of directions of size $d\Omega$, making an angle ϑ with the axis of the oscillator, is given in classical physics by[6]

$$R = \frac{d\Omega e^2}{16\pi^2 \varepsilon_0 c^3} (\ddot{x})^2 \sin^2 \vartheta \tag{10.16}$$

Writing $x(t) = x_0 \cos \omega t$, we find that the time average rate of radiation of energy in all directions is

$$\bar{R} = \frac{e^2 \omega^4}{12\pi \varepsilon_0 c^3} x_0{}^2 \tag{10.17}$$

Comparison of (10.15) with (10.17) shows that the formulas correspond closely except for a factor of 4, which is characteristic of the classical-quantum correspondence and arises from the fact that whereas the time dependence of x is given classically by $x_0 \cos \omega t$, in quantum mechanics the same thing is written as $\frac{1}{2} x_0 (e^{i\omega t} + e^{-i\omega t})$, and as in the passage from (8.109) to (8.111), only half of this contributes to the emission process.[7]

Another result obtainable from this formalism is a figure for the lifetime of an excited state. In deriving A_{ba} it has been assumed that the system was certainly in the excited state b to start with. But after a short time the probability P_b of its being there will have decreased from unity, and the probability per unit time that a decay will occur is clearly proportional to P_b. We express this by writing

$$\dot{P}_b = -A_{ba} P_b \tag{10.18}$$

whence

$$P_b(t) = P_b(0) e^{-A_{ba} t} \tag{10.19}$$

Thus A_{ba} represents the *decay constant* of the state, and $\tau_{ba} = A_{ba}{}^{-1}$ is a measure of its lifetime. The order of magnitude of A_{ba} may be estimated if we make several approximations. We equate $\langle b|x|a \rangle$, etc. with a, the size of the atom, or better, that of the orbit from which a transition occurs. We equate the energy of the state E with $Z_e e'^2/a$, where Z_e is the effective nuclear charge acting at the orbit involved, and we say that the quantum energy $\hbar\omega$ will be roughly comparable with E. The answer is now easily expressed in terms of the dimensionless fine-structure constant $\alpha = e^2/4\pi\varepsilon_0\hbar c \approx \frac{1}{137}$. We find

$$A_{ba} \approx \alpha^3 Z_e{}^2 \omega$$

Problem 10.3 Estimate the lifetime of an excited state of hydrogen. Do the same for the X rays from the K shell of tungsten.

---

[6] See any text on electromagnetic theory.

[7] This correspondence is discussed by F. E. Low, Am. J. Phys., **29**, 298 (1961).

Problem 10.4 Evaluate the B coefficient for absorption in a different way, starting from (8.111). Show that the transition probability per second induced by radiation in the frequency range ω to $\omega + d\omega$ is

$$dP_b = \frac{\pi e^2}{3\varepsilon_0 \hbar} |\langle b|\mathbf{r}|a\rangle|^2 u(\omega)\, \delta(E_b - E_a - \hbar\omega)\, d\omega \tag{10.20}$$

and that (10.13) follows at once from this. What is the meaning of the delta function in this expression?

10.3 Selection Rules

We have now to evaluate the matrix elements which make up the quantity $|\langle b|\mathbf{r}|a\rangle|^2$. In doing so we shall encounter one of the most characteristic features of atomic theory, the selection rules which govern the transitions among the various eigenstates. Such rules, arising for the most part from considerations of symmetry, are found in many kinds of emission and absorption processes, notably electromagnetic radiation and absorption, beta decay, and the production and decay of elementary particles. Selection rules for electromagnetic transitions are a very obvious feature of atomic spectra, and they appeared as an empirical part of Bohr's theory which was not fully explained until the advent of quantum mechanics.

Harmonic oscillators

As a simple first example, let us consider the emission and absorption of radiation by a harmonic oscillator. (This is essentially also the theory of transitions among the vibrational states of a diatomic molecule.)

Classical considerations, interpreted via the correspondence principle, suggest what the answer is going to be. The oscillator, being essentially undamped, will not appreciably emit or absorb at any applied frequency other than its own. The selection rule, at least for a classical-sized oscillator, can be inferred from this fact; for if ω is the natural frequency, its energy levels are evenly spaced at intervals separated by $\hbar\omega$. The frequency of a quantum emitted or absorbed in a jump from one level to a level immediately adjacent is $\hbar\omega/\hbar = \omega$, and since the oscillator does not emit or absorb at any other frequencies, these must be the only transitions which take place. The selection rule inferred from the correspondence principle is thus

$$\Delta n = +1 \qquad \text{absorption} \tag{10.21a}$$

$$\Delta n = -1 \qquad \text{emission} \tag{10.21b}$$

To investigate the same question quantum-mechanically, let the oscillator be oriented along the x axis. Then since it is one-dimensional, $|\langle b|\mathbf{r}|a\rangle|^2$ reduces to $|\langle b|x|a\rangle|^2$. The integral is one which we have already encountered in Prob. 4.20,

$$\int_{-\infty}^{\infty} \psi_b^* x \psi_a \, dx = \left(\frac{\hbar}{2m\omega}\right)^{1/2} [a^{1/2}\delta_{b,a-1} + (a+1)^{1/2}\delta_{b,a+1}]$$

The selection rule is embodied in this formula, for the right-hand side is zero unless $b = a \pm 1$, and so the only allowed transitions are those in which the quantum number changes by one unit. All others are forbidden. The Einstein coefficients corresponding to the possible processes beginning at the bth state are

$$B_{b,b+1} = \frac{(b+1)\pi e^2}{6\varepsilon_0 \hbar m\omega} \qquad \text{absorption} \qquad (10.22a)$$

$$B_{b,b-1} = \frac{b\pi e^2}{6\varepsilon_0 \hbar m\omega} \qquad \text{emission} \qquad (10.22b)$$

$$A_{b,b-1} = \frac{b e^2 \omega^2}{6\pi\varepsilon_0 mc^3} \qquad (10.22c)$$

and the reader can at once verify that $B_{mn} = B_{nm}$.

The mathematical apparatus which we have constructed to deal with radiation theory will seem somewhat abstract to the reader encountering it for the first time, and this is because the theory as we have presented it has no clear connection with the classical picture. The same was already true in 1913 of Bohr's theory, for it is difficult to imagine how an electron orbiting at a certain angular frequency can, in making a transition, emit a photon of quite a different frequency. To see how this takes place, let us look at a one-dimensional system in the middle of a transition from state a, with a wave function $\psi_a(x)e^{-i\omega_a t}$, to state b, $\psi_b(x)e^{-i\omega_b t}$, where $\hbar\omega_a = E_a$ and $\hbar\omega_b = E_b$. The spatial wave functions may be assumed to be real (why?) and let us suppose that the system is centered so that in the two stationary states, $\langle x \rangle_a = \langle x \rangle_b = 0$. Halfway through the transition, when the system has an equal probability of being found in state a and state b, its wave function will be

$$\psi = 2^{-1/2}[\psi_a(x)e^{-i\omega_a t} + e^{i\gamma}\psi_b(x)e^{-i\omega_b t}]$$

where γ represents an arbitrary phase. At this moment, we calculate the expectation value of x and find

$$\langle x \rangle = \langle b|x|a \rangle \cos(\omega_{ab} t + \gamma)$$

where $\omega_{ab} = \omega_a - \omega_b$. The center of the wave packet is thus oscillating back and forth at the frequency required by Bohr's radiation condition and with an amplitude proportional to the matrix element. We can easily imagine that it is this motion that causes the radiation to be emitted. Dean[8] has calculated the wave function corresponding to an allowed transition of a particle in a square potential well, and Fig. 10.1, copied from his paper, shows its oscillation.

[8] C. Dean, Am. J. Phys., **27**, 161 (1959).

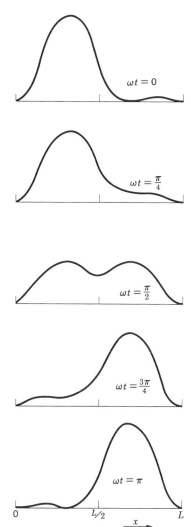

$\omega t = 0$

$\omega t = \frac{\pi}{4}$

$\omega t = \frac{\pi}{2}$

$\omega t = \frac{3\pi}{4}$

$\omega t = \pi$

Fig. 10.1   Plot of $|\psi|^2$ for the superposition of states corresponding to $n = 1$ and $n = 2$ of a particle in a square potential well. (After **C.** Dean. By permission.)

0 $L/2$ L

x

Hydrogen atoms

Let us consider the possible transitions between the ground state of a hydrogen atom and the various states with $n = 2$ whose wave functions are given in (7.56). It is found that all the matrix elements leading to the $2s$ state vanish,

$$\langle 2,0,0|x,y, \text{ or } z|1,0,0\rangle = 0$$

while of the remainder we have also

$$\langle 2,1,-1|z|1,0,0\rangle = \langle 2,1,1|z|1,0,0\rangle = 0$$

and

$$\langle 2,1,0|x \text{ or } y|1,0,0\rangle = 0$$

There remain only two nonzero integrals,

$$\langle 2,1,-1|x|1,0,0\rangle$$
$$= -i\langle 2,1,-1|y|1,0,0\rangle$$
$$= \langle 2,1,1|x|1,0,0\rangle$$
$$= i\langle 2,1,1|y|1,0,0\rangle$$
$$= (24\pi)^{-1}a_0^{-4}\int r^2 e^{-3r/2a_0}\,dv$$
$$= 2^7 3^{-5}a_0$$

and

$$\langle 2,1,0|z|1,0,0\rangle = 2^{\frac{1}{2}}(24\pi)^{-1}a_0^{-4}\int r^2 e^{-3r/2a_0}\,dv$$
$$= 2^{\frac{1}{2}}2^7 3^{-5}a_0$$

The corresponding matrix elements for transitions in the opposite direction, being the complex conjugates of these, are numerically the same.

Problem 10.5 Verify all these matrix elements.

Problem 10.6 The above matrix elements were calculated on the assumption that there is a single radiating particle, the electron. Actually the proton moves too. What corrections does this introduce?

Incident light, if its quantum energy is $\frac{3}{4}$ Ry, will produce transitions into the $2p$ states but not into the $2s$ state, and the emission processes go the other way. In particular, the $2s$ state will be relatively stable against a transition to the ground state, which must take place by some process other than that considered here. This is an example of the general selection rule $\Delta l = \pm 1$ for orbital angular momenta in a one-electron spectrum which in Bohr's theory had originally to be introduced as a postulate. (Later, correspondence arguments like that given above for the harmonic oscillator were used to explain the selection rules, but not, of course, to explain them fundamentally.)

10.4 More Exact Theory

We have already noted that the formalism given above is incomplete in that it seems to account for the absorption but not the spontaneous emission of radiation. We have now to confess that it is in fact conceptually wrong in a fundamental way. We can get an insight into the difficulty if we consider the general problem of determining the radiation from a charged particle. Classical physics gives formulas for the electromagnetic field components as functions of the particle's momentum and acceleration. But in quantum mechanics these quantities are both denoted by operators, so the field itself will become an operator, and we were wrong to introduce it as a simple function of x, y, z, and t. In fact, not even our treatment of absorption was consistent, since it accounts for the absorption of a certain amount of energy by the material system but not for its corresponding disappearance from the field. In classical theory this results from the fact that the material system, in absorbing its energy, moves in such a way as to emit radiation which is coherent with the incident wave but out of phase with it, so that part of the incident wave is canceled. Our calculation leaves this point obscure.

The theory is thus most inconsistent when it attempts to describe processes in which there is a transition in the number of quanta present, and in fact the whole idea of a field which contains a certain number of quanta is quite foreign to the classical Maxwellian theory. We were able to take account of it above in the rather heuristic arguments which lead to (10.13), but it is clear from even the most elementary considerations that the quantum hypothesis must be introduced everywhere at once. In the discussion of Heisenberg's gamma-ray microscope, for example, the uncertainty principle for the matter present can be derived only at the cost of assuming that the electromagnetic field comes in quanta—this is, in fact, one of the principal points of Heisenberg's argument. From this more general standpoint, ψ must be considered as an operator also, but the methods of this book are good enough for most situations which do not involve the creation and annihilation of electron-positron pairs.

The quantization of radiation fields is beyond the scope of this book, and it is more profitably discussed in the context of a relativistic theory. We shall therefore restrict ourselves to a few points where the semiclassical theory will set us in the right direction, leaving a more consistent treatment for the reader's later study.

To go further, we shall need to supplant the approximate interaction energy (10.9) by an exact expression. This can be done if we adopt the hamiltonian (7.89) for a particle in a magnetic field, where the operator $\hat{p}$ is replaced by $\hat{p} - e\mathbf{A}$. We shall put the whole radiation field into the vector potential, leaving $V(\mathbf{r})$ to describe the Coulomb forces or other static interactions. How this can be done is shown in Appendix 5. The vector potential is transverse, that is, perpendicular to the direction of propagation, and satisfies

$$\nabla \cdot \mathbf{A} = 0 \tag{10.23}$$

A plane wave can be written as

$$\mathbf{A}(\mathbf{r},t) = e a \cos{(\mathbf{k} \cdot \mathbf{r} - \omega t)} \qquad \mathbf{e} \cdot \mathbf{k} = 0 \tag{10.24}$$

where a is a constant scalar amplitude and $\mathbf{e}$ is a unit vector perpendicular to $\mathbf{k}$. The energy density of the plane wave is

$$\mathcal{E} = \frac{k^2 a^2}{\mu_0} \cos^2{(\mathbf{k} \cdot \mathbf{r} - \omega t)} \tag{10.25}$$

Finally, any radiation field can be expressed as a superposition of plane waves. It is convenient to write this in exponential form,

$$\mathbf{A}(\mathbf{r},t) = \int \mathbf{e}(\mathbf{k})a(\mathbf{k})e^{i(\mathbf{k}\cdot\mathbf{r}-\omega t)} \, d\mathbf{k} \tag{10.26}$$

where

$$\mathbf{k} \cdot \mathbf{e}(\mathbf{k}) = 0 \tag{10.27}$$

The hamiltonian operator describing a particle in a radiation field is

$$\hat{H} = \frac{1}{2m} [\hat{\mathbf{p}} - e\mathbf{A}(\mathbf{r},t)]^2 + V(\mathbf{r})$$

and multiplying this out gives

$$\hat{H} = \frac{1}{2m} (\hat{p}^2 - e\hat{\mathbf{p}} \cdot \mathbf{A} - e\mathbf{A} \cdot \hat{\mathbf{p}} + e^2 A^2) + V(\mathbf{r})$$

Now the difference between $\hat{\mathbf{p}} \cdot \mathbf{A}$ and $\mathbf{A} \cdot \hat{\mathbf{p}}$ acting on any ψ is given by

$$(\hat{\mathbf{p}} \cdot \mathbf{A} - \mathbf{A} \cdot \hat{\mathbf{p}})\psi = -i\hbar[\nabla \cdot (\mathbf{A}\psi) - \mathbf{A} \cdot \nabla\psi)]$$
$$= -i\hbar(\nabla \cdot \mathbf{A})\psi = 0$$

by (10.23). Therefore, an incidental feature of our choice of a representation for the radiation field is that we do not have to be careful about the order of the quantities $\hat{\mathbf{p}}$ and $\mathbf{A}$, and the hamiltonian may be written as

$$\hat{H} = \hat{H}^{(0)} - \frac{e}{m} \hat{\mathbf{p}} \cdot \mathbf{A}(\mathbf{r},t) + \frac{e^2}{2m} A^2(\mathbf{r},t) \tag{10.28}$$

where $\hat{H}^{(0)}$, including $V(\mathbf{r})$, is to be regarded as the unperturbed hamiltonian. Under normal circumstances, the third term on the right in (10.28) is much smaller than the second, and we shall neglect it.

We thus take for the interaction hamiltonian the operator

$$\hat{H}^{(1)} = - \frac{e}{m} \hat{\mathbf{p}} \cdot \mathbf{A} \tag{10.29}$$

so that the expressions for the transition probabilities involve matrix elements of the form

$$\langle b|\hat{H}^{(1)}|a\rangle = - \frac{e}{m} \int \psi_b^{(0)*}\hat{\mathbf{p}} \cdot \mathbf{A}\psi_a^{(0)} \, dv \tag{10.30}$$

Problem 10.7   What is the relation of (10.30) to the matrix element $\langle a|\hat{H}^{(1)}|b\rangle$ describing the inverse transition? Verify Einstein's relation $B_{ab} = B_{ba}$.

We must now verify that the matrix element formed from (10.9) is actually an approximation to (10.30). The following sketch can be filled in by the reader. The matrix element of (10.9) involves the quantity $\langle b|\mathbf{r}|a \rangle = \int \psi_b{}^{(0)*}\mathbf{r}\psi_a{}^{(0)} \, dv$, where $\mathbf{r}$ is x, y, or z. Assuming that $\psi_b{}^{(0)}$ and $\psi_a{}^{(0)}$ are unperturbed energy eigenfunctions of $\hat{H}^{(0)}$ belonging to the eigenvalues E_b and E_a, and remembering the hermiticity of $\hat{H}^{(0)}$, we have

$$\int \psi_b{}^{(0)*}[\hat{H}^{(0)},\mathbf{r}]\psi_a{}^{(0)} \, dv = (E_b - E_a)\int \psi_b{}^{(0)*}\mathbf{r}\psi_a{}^{(0)} \, dv$$

or

$$\langle b|\mathbf{r}|a \rangle = \frac{\langle b|[\hat{H}^{(0)},\mathbf{r}]|a \rangle}{E_b - E_a} = -\frac{i}{m\omega}\langle b|\hat{\mathbf{p}}|a \rangle \qquad (10.31)$$

where, as usual, $\hbar\omega = E_b - E_a$. This equation is the bridge between the two types of matrix element.

Problem 10.8 Prove that, if suitable approximations are made (what are they?), (10.9) is equivalent to (10.29).

Matrix elements for emission and absorption

There is a way of looking at formulas like (10.30) which opens a more advanced approach to quantum electrodynamics. Suppose we are calculating an absorption probability. We regard $\mathbf{A}$ as the wave function of a photon and $\mathbf{A}\psi_a$ as the wave function of a state containing one photon and one electron in state a. Then $\hat{\mathbf{p}}$ is the operator which causes the transition to the final state, consisting of an electron in state b and no photon. Thus (10.30) falls into the general pattern of the matrix element responsible for a transition:

$$\langle \text{final state}|\text{operator}|\text{initial state} \rangle$$

To find the matrix elements for the emission and absorption of radiation, we have only to follow up this hint. The photon wave function must be properly normalized to 1 photon in the volume Q. We shall henceforth take this volume equal to unity since, as we have seen, its magnitude does not matter. The photon density is obtained by dividing (10.25) by the energy per photon,

$$\overline{\mathfrak{N}} = \frac{\overline{\mathcal{E}}}{\hbar ck} = \frac{1}{2}\frac{ka^2}{\hbar c\mu_0}$$

where the bar and the ½ denote that a time average has been taken. Setting this equal to 1 gives for the normalized vector potential

$$\mathbf{A} = \left(\frac{2\hbar c\mu_0}{k}\right)^{1/2} \mathbf{e}\cos(\mathbf{k}\cdot\mathbf{r} - \omega t)$$

by (10.24). The matrix elements for absorption and emission can now be read from (10.30). That for absorption of a quantum whose propagation vector is $\mathbf{k}$ with simultaneous transition of the electron from state a to state b is

$$\langle b|\hat{H}^{(1)}|\mathbf{k},a \rangle = -\frac{e}{m}\left(\frac{2\hbar c\mu_0}{k}\right)^{1/2}\langle b|\tfrac{1}{2}\hat{\mathbf{p}}\cdot\mathbf{e}e^{i\mathbf{k}\cdot\mathbf{r}}|a \rangle$$

where the $\frac{1}{2}e^{i\mathbf{k}\cdot\mathbf{r}}$ comes from separating the cos $(\mathbf{k}\cdot\mathbf{r}-\omega t)$ into its exponential parts and keeping only that with the time dependence $e^{-i\omega t}$ which makes the energy of state b greater than that of state a. [See the argument leading to (8.111).]

We shall write the matrix element in terms of $e' = (4\pi\varepsilon_0)^{-\frac{1}{2}}e$ and the scalar quantity

$$p_e = \mathbf{e}\cdot\hat{\mathbf{p}} \qquad (\mathbf{e}\perp\mathbf{k})$$

Remembering that $\mu_0\varepsilon_0 = c^{-2}$, we find

$$\langle b|\hat{H}^{(1)}|\mathbf{k},a\rangle = -\frac{e'}{m}\left(\frac{2\pi\hbar}{ck}\right)^{\frac{1}{2}}\langle b|\hat{p}_e e^{i\mathbf{k}\cdot\mathbf{r}}|a\rangle \tag{10.32}$$

The matrix element for emission is the complex conjugate of this,

$$\langle \mathbf{k},a|\hat{H}^{(1)}|b\rangle = -\frac{e'}{m}\left(\frac{2\pi\hbar}{ck}\right)^{\frac{1}{2}}\langle a|\hat{p}_e e^{-i\mathbf{k}\cdot\mathbf{r}}|b\rangle \tag{10.33}$$

Einstein's emission coefficient

As an example of this expression, let us calculate the Einstein A coefficient directly. We take the initial state to be b. The transition is then into a continuum of final states, since although the state a is definite, the photon may come off in a variety of directions. The perturbation theory for such transitions has already been worked out in Sec. 8.8, and the final formula for the probability of the transition per unit time is

$$\dot{P}_a = \frac{2\pi}{\hbar}|\langle\mathbf{k},a|\hat{H}^{(1)}|b\rangle|^2\rho(E_f)$$

where $\rho(E_f)$ is the density of final states. We can think of the atom as stationary in space (it recoils only a little), and then $\rho(E_f)$ refers to the states of the outgoing photon. To be more precise, we note that if the photon is emitted in a certain direction, the atom's recoil is thereby exactly determined, so that a count of the photon states is a count of the final states of the whole system.[9] Suppose the states to be counted are those lying inside an element of solid angle $d\Omega$ in the direction $\mathbf{k}$. Then (9.25), with $E = cp$, gives the number of photon states with energy less than E as

$$N(E) = \frac{1}{3}\frac{Q}{(2\pi\hbar c)^3}E^3\,d\Omega$$

Therefore

$$\rho(E_f) = \frac{dN(E_f)}{dE_f} = \frac{Q}{(2\pi\hbar c)^3}E_f^2\,d\Omega \tag{10.34}$$

---

[9] Note that if as in beta decay the final state contains three particles, the problem of counting becomes somewhat more involved.

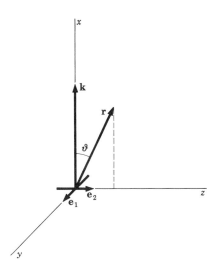

Fig. 10.2   Coordinates and polarization vectors
for evaluating (10.36).

so that with $E_f = \hbar\omega$ and Q, the normalization volume, equal to 1
as in (10.32),

$$\dot{P}_a = \frac{e'^2\omega\,d\Omega}{2\pi\hbar m^2 c^3}\,|\langle a|\hat{p}_e e^{-i\mathbf{k}\cdot\mathbf{r}}|b\rangle|^2 \tag{10.35}$$

To calculate ordinary optical emission probabilities, we can
replace $e^{-i\mathbf{k}\cdot\mathbf{r}}$ by 1. Then using (10.31) gives

$$\dot{P}_a = \frac{e'^2\omega^3\,d\Omega}{2\pi\hbar c^3}\,|\mathbf{e}\cdot\langle a|\mathbf{r}|b\rangle|^2 \tag{10.36}$$

The angular situation is shown in Fig. 10.2, where $\mathbf{e}_1$ and $\mathbf{e}_2$ are two
perpendicular directions of polarization. Emission is into both of
these, independently, so we shall wish to take a sum. The sum is
of the form

$$\sum_{\text{pol}} |\mathbf{e}\cdot\mathbf{M}|^2 = |\mathbf{e}_1\cdot\mathbf{M}|^2 + |\mathbf{e}_2\cdot\mathbf{M}|^2$$

$$= |M_y|^2 + |M_z|^2$$

with $\mathbf{M}$ denoting the matrix element. Since the direction of $\mathbf{k}$ is arbi-
trary, we can write this as $|M_x|^2 + |M_y|^2 + |M_z|^2 - |M_x|^2$, or

$$\sum_{\text{pol}} |\mathbf{e}\cdot\mathbf{M}|^2 = |\mathbf{M}|^2 - \frac{|\mathbf{k}\cdot\mathbf{M}|^2}{k^2} \tag{10.37}$$

With $|\mathbf{k}\cdot\mathbf{M}|^2 = k^2|M|^2\cos^2\vartheta$, we find

$$\sum_{\text{pol}} |\langle a|\mathbf{e}\cdot\mathbf{r}|b\rangle|^2 = |\langle a|\mathbf{r}|b\rangle|^2 \sin^2\vartheta$$

and

$$\dot{P}_a = \frac{e'^2\omega^3\sin^2\vartheta\,d\Omega}{2\pi\hbar c^3}\,|\langle a|\mathbf{r}|b\rangle|^2 \tag{10.38}$$

Integrating this over all directions of $d\Omega$ gives

$$A_{ba} = \frac{4e'^2\omega^3}{3\hbar c^3} |\langle a|\mathbf{r}|b\rangle|^2 \tag{10.39}$$

as in (10.14). The angular distribution in (10.38) corresponds with the classical formula (10.16) for radiation from a simple harmonic oscillator.

Forbidden transitions

With the more exact matrix elements, (10.32) and (10.33), we can investigate the probability of transitions which violate the selection rules. Suppose, for example, that we have a harmonic oscillator oriented along the z axis. Expanding (10.33) gives

$$\langle \mathbf{k},a|\hat{H}^{(1)}|b\rangle = -\frac{e'}{m}\left(\frac{2\pi\hbar}{ck}\right)^{1/2} \langle a|\hat{p}_e(1 - i\mathbf{k}\cdot\mathbf{r})|b\rangle \tag{10.40}$$

plus contributions of higher order. The first term gives the transitions we have already computed. The second involves the matrix element

$$i\langle a|(\hat{\mathbf{p}}\cdot\mathbf{e})(\mathbf{k}\cdot\mathbf{r})|b\rangle = ie_z k_z\langle a|\hat{p}_z z|b\rangle$$

To evaluate this, we note that by (4.110) and Prob. 4.19,

$$z\psi_n = \left(\frac{\hbar}{2m\omega}\right)^{1/2} [(n + 1)^{1/2}\psi_{n+1} + n^{1/2}\psi_{n-1}]$$

and similarly,

$$\hat{p}_z\psi_n = i\left(\frac{\hbar m\omega}{2}\right)^{1/2} [(n + 1)^{1/2}\psi_{n+1} - n^{1/2}\psi_{n-1}]$$

Applying the operators in succession, we have

$$\hat{p}_z z\psi_b = \tfrac{1}{2}i\hbar\{[(b + 1)(b + 2)]^{1/2}\psi_{b+2} - \psi_b - [b(b - 1)]^{1/2}\psi_{b-2}\}$$

so that

$$\langle a|\hat{p}_z z|b\rangle = \tfrac{1}{2}i\hbar\{[(b + 1)(b + 2)]^{1/2}\delta_{a,b+2} - \delta_{ab} - [b(b - 1)]^{1/2}\delta_{a,b-2}\} \tag{10.41}$$

Spontaneous transitions can therefore occur by this process from a state b to the state $b - 2$, and the transition probability is

$$\dot{P}_{b-2} = \frac{b(b - 1)\hbar e'^2 k\, d\Omega}{8\pi m^2 c^2} (e_z k_z)^2 \qquad (b \to b - 2)$$

This can be summed over the polarization states of the emitted radiation by using Fig. 10.2, where the direction of $\mathbf{r}$ is now called the z axis. Since $e_{1z} = 0$ while $e_{2z} = \sin\vartheta$, the sum has only one term, in which

$$e_{2z}k_z = k\sin\vartheta\cos\vartheta$$

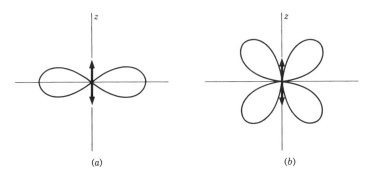

Fig. 10.3   Lobe patterns for (a) allowed and
(b) first-forbidden radiation from a dipole oriented
along the z axis.

Thus,

$$\sum_{\text{pol}} \dot{P}_{b-2} = \frac{b(b-1)\hbar e'^2 k^3}{8\pi m^2 c^2} \sin^2 \vartheta \cos^2 \vartheta \, d\Omega \qquad (b \to b-2)$$

Finally, the integral over angles is

$$\int \sin^2 \vartheta \cos^2 \vartheta \, d\Omega = \frac{8\pi}{15}$$

and the quantum frequency ck is twice the oscillator's natural frequency ω, so that

$$A_{b,b-2} = \frac{8b(b-1)\hbar e'^2 \omega^3}{15m^2 c^5} \tag{10.42}$$

The directional patterns of allowed and forbidden radiation are compared in Fig. 10.3. Even this *first-forbidden* radiation satisfies the
strict selection rule inherent in the matrix element (10.41); transitions involving higher degrees of "forbiddenness" are analyzed by
extending the series in (10.40) beyond the second term. The patterns in Fig. 10.3 are characteristic of what are called dipole and
quadrupole radiation in classical physics, and a similar decomposi-
tion is made in quantum theory.[10]

   In Fig. 10.1 we have shown how the wave function in the course
of an allowed transition resembles an oscillating dipole. Figure 10.4
shows the motion of the wave function of a particle in a square well
during a transition $n \to n-2$. This type of oscillation is known as
quadrupole, and in classical physics, as well as in quantum, one finds
that it gives rise to the angular pattern of Fig. 10.3b.

----

[10] W. Heitler, *The Quantum Theory of Radiation*, Clarendon Press, Oxford,
1936, 1944, 1954.

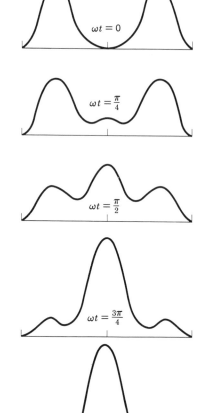

$\omega t = 0$

$\omega t = \frac{\pi}{4}$

$\omega t = \frac{\pi}{2}$

$\omega t = \frac{3\pi}{4}$

$\omega t = \pi$

Fig. 10.4 Plot of $|\psi|^2$ for the superposition of states $n = 1$ and $n = 3$ of a particle in a square-well potential, corresponding to a first-forbidden transition. [From C. Dean, Am. J. Phys., **27**, 161 (1959). Reproduced by permission.]

To see that quadrupole transitions occur much less often than dipole, we note that the ratio of $A_{b,b-2}$ to the allowed $A_{b,b-1}$ is

$$\frac{A_{b,b-2}}{A_{b,b-1}} = \frac{4}{5} (b - 1) \frac{\hbar\omega}{mc^2} \tag{10.43}$$

If the oscillator is an electron, then $mc^2 = 0.511$ MeV, and under ordinary circumstances, unless b is enormously large, the forbidden radiation will be inconspicuous.

Problem 10.9 Formula (10.40) suggests that the ratio of the matrix elements for forbidden and allowed transitions is of the order of $k\langle z\rangle_b$, so that the ratio of the A's should be of the order of $(k\langle z\rangle_b)^2$. Is this so?

We see that the so-called forbidden transitions are not really forbidden, but are merely improbable relative to those which are allowed, and that they arise when one begins to take into account the change in phase of the potential $A(r,t)$ from one side of the emitting system to the other. If an atom is in an excited state from which an allowed transition will take it to a lower state, it will normally choose this route; whereas if there is only a forbidden one, the resulting "metastable" state is relatively long-lived and will normally be de-excited by a collision rather than by radiation. But sometimes, as in the aurora borealis, the collisions may be so infrequent that radiation predominates, and then if there are no allowed transitions through which the de-excitation can take place, the forbidden lines appear in full strength.

Problem 10.10 Prove that transitions between two states with $l = 0$ are *absolutely* forbidden.

Selection rules

Now we shall look at the same questions from a more general point of view and establish not only the selection rules for allowed radiation but also the polarization of the radiation emitted in various directions by an atom whose orientation is known (say, because it has been prepared by magnetic fields). According to (10.36), the probability of an allowed transition from a state a, which we shall suppose characterized by angular-momentum quantum numbers l and m, to a state b, with l' and m', is proportional to the square of the quantity

$$M = \langle b|\mathbf{e} \cdot \mathbf{r}|a \rangle$$

where $\mathbf{e}$ is a unit vector in the direction of polarization of the emitted light, which is, of course, some direction perpendicular to the direction in which the light is emitted. There are two selection rules, one on $m' - m$ and the other on $l' - l$, and we shall consider them in turn. We prove the first by (8.26) and the second by a simple generalization of it.

We start with light emitted parallel to the y axis. It may have either of two directions of plane polarization, $\mathbf{e}_z$ and $\mathbf{e}_x$, as shown in Fig. 10.5. Suppose the polarization is to be vertical. The value of M is

$$M = \langle l'm'|\mathbf{e}_z \cdot \mathbf{r}|lm \rangle = \langle l'm'|z|lm \rangle$$

where we have written only the angular quantum numbers characterizing states a and b. To evaluate this, we consider the operator identity

$$[\hat{L}_z, z] = 0$$

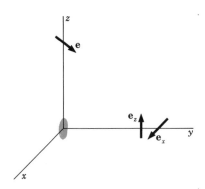

Fig. 10.5   Polarization vectors for radiation
in different directions.

and evaluate

$$\langle l'm'|[\hat{L}_z,z]|lm\rangle = \langle l'm'|\hat{L}_z z - z\hat{L}_z|lm\rangle$$
$$= (m' - m)M = 0$$

by the hermiticity of $\hat{L}_z$. Thus $M = 0$ and there is no transition, unless

$$m' = m \qquad (\mathbf{k}\|y, \mathbf{e}\|z) \tag{10.44}$$

where k represents the direction of propagation.

For the polarization transverse to this, given by $\mathbf{e}_x$, we need

$$M = \langle l'm'|x|lm\rangle$$

It will be convenient to represent x as

$$x = \tfrac{1}{2}(x_+ + x_-) \qquad x_\pm = x \pm iy$$

because $x_\pm$ satisfy the commutation rule

$$[\hat{L}_z,x_\pm] = \pm x_\pm$$

We now evaluate

$$\langle l'm'|[L_z,x_+] - x_+|lm\rangle = (m' - m - 1)\langle l'm'|x_+|lm\rangle$$
$$= 0 \tag{10.45}$$

and similarly,

$$(m' - m + 1)\langle l'm'|x_-|lm\rangle = 0 \tag{10.46}$$

Thus $M = 0$ unless one of these matrix elements is different from zero, that is, unless

$$m' = m \pm 1 \qquad (\mathbf{k}\|y, \mathbf{e}\|x) \tag{10.47}$$

If we observe the radiating system from along the z axis through an analyzer, it is clear from symmetry that all orientations of the analyzer will give the same intensity. One might at first conclude that the light is unpolarized, but in fact the components polarized parallel to x and y are coherent in phase and combine to form circu-

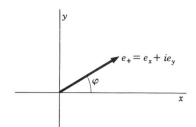

Fig. 10.6 Complex representation of the polarization
vector as seen from a point on the positive z axis.

larly polarized light, as we can easily show. Consider the entire
matrix element

$$M = \langle l'm'|e_x x + e_y y|lm\rangle$$

and write it as

$$M = \tfrac{1}{2}\langle l'm'|e_+ x_- + e_- x_+|lm\rangle$$

Suppose now that $m' = m - 1$. By (10.45) and (10.46),

$$M = \tfrac{1}{2}e_+\langle l'm'|x_-|lm\rangle$$

To interpet this physically, we remember from Sec. 8.8 that the
Fourier component of a periodic disturbance associated with the
emission of a quantum of energy $\hbar\omega$ is proportional to $e^{-i\omega t}$. Let us
write the matrix element $\langle l'm'|x_-|lm\rangle$ in polar form as $\alpha e^{i\beta}$ and also
represent the quantity $e_+ = e_x + ie_y$ as a unit vector $e^{i\varphi}$ in a complex xy plane which one sees on looking at the radiator along the z
axis (Fig. 10.6). If E and E', with $E' = E - \hbar\omega$, are the initial and
final energies of the transition, the time dependence associated with
M is of the form $e^{iE't/\hbar}e^{-iEt/\hbar} = e^{-i\omega t}$ where ω is the frequency of the
emitted light. Including this time dependence, we have

$$Me^{-i\omega t} = \tfrac{1}{2}\alpha e^{i(\varphi-\omega t+\beta)}$$

Since we are considering the relative phases of the linear components of polarization, we must look at the amplitude M and not the
probability $|M|^2$. This amplitude is constant if φ satisfies

$$\varphi = \varphi_0 + \omega t$$

so that if one looks toward the radiator, the plane of constant amplitude rotates toward the left. By convention, the light is said to be
left-circularly polarized. By comparison with (10.46), we have the
selection rule

$$m' = m - 1 \qquad (\mathbf{k}\|z, \text{ left circular polarization}) \tag{10.48}$$

and similarly

$$m' = m + 1 \qquad (\mathbf{k}\|z, \text{ right circular polarization}) \tag{10.49}$$

Selection rule for l

Finally, let us look at the selection rule in l. By analogy with our procedure above, we should form the matrix elements of the commutators of $\hat{L}^2$ with x, y, and z. But $[\hat{L}^2,x]$ involves y and z; we must therefore go to the more complicated form $[\hat{L}^2,[\hat{L}^2,x]]$. Evaluating this requires some work, but the result is very simple,

$$[\hat{L}^2,[\hat{L}^2,x]] = 2(\hat{L}^2x + x\hat{L}^2)$$

and similarly for y and z, where we have used the fact that

$$\mathbf{r} \cdot \hat{\mathbf{L}} = 0$$

identically. Proceeding as before, we have

$$\langle l'm'|[\hat{L}^2,[\hat{L}^2,x]]|lm\rangle = 2\langle l'm'|\hat{L}^2x + x\hat{L}^2|lm\rangle$$

$$[l'(l'+1) - l(l+1)]^2\langle l'm'|x|lm\rangle$$
$$= 2[l'(l'+1) + l(l+1)]\langle l'm'|x|lm\rangle$$

The first numerical coefficient is $(l'+l+1)^2(l'-l)^2$, and the second can be written as $(l'+l+1)^2 + (l'-l)^2 - 1$. Thus,

$$[(l'+l+1)^2 - 1][(l'-l)^2 - 1]\langle l'm'|x|lm\rangle = 0$$

We know (Prob. 10.10) that there is no radiation when $l' = l = 0$. Ignoring this case, therefore, we see that the first factor on the left is never zero. The matrix element of x therefore vanishes unless $l' - l = \pm 1$, and the same is true for y and z. We conclude that

$$l' = l \pm 1 \tag{10.50}$$

for all allowed transitions.

The physical significance of these results is easy to see, for it is nothing but the conservation of angular momentum. We see from (10.48) and (10.49) that photons of left or right circularly polarized light carry away an angular momentum of $\hbar$ or $-\hbar$, respectively, in the positive z direction.

The light in the y direction is, like that just discussed, made up of two components polarized perpendicularly to each other. The e_z component, however, arises from transitions in which $\Delta m = 0$, whereas the e_x component involves $\Delta m = \pm 1$. Since these three different kinds of transition take place independently of each other, the light seen in this direction is a simple mixture of the two polarization states.

The selection rule in l can be interpreted as an example of the addition of angular momenta. Suppose that the atom in its final state has an angular momentum l' and that the photon has unit angular momentum. Then the combined system might be expected to have

$$l = l' - 1, \; l', \; \text{or} \; l' + 1$$

and this should be the same as the initial l of the atom. But the second of these three values is lacking: there are only two independent states for the radiated photon, corresponding to the fact that there are only two states of polarization (longitudinal polarization is lacking). It is found by a relativistic argument[11] that this restriction to only two independent states is characteristic of particles of zero mass, no matter what their spin.

The entire preceding discussion has been in terms of the angular-momentum quantum numbers. An orbiting electron has in addition a radial quantum number n, and we have said nothing of the selection rules which it may impose. It is found that all values of Δn are allowed for a hydrogen atom, though the harmonic oscillator is restricted to $\Delta n = \pm 1$, and in general the selection rules on the nonangular variables, as well as the probabilities of the different transitions, must be determined separately in each case.

10.5 Photoelectric Effect

Having calculated the probability that a photon will give rise to a transition from one atomic state to another a little above it, we may now ask what happens if the quantum is more energetic and is able to produce ionization. In the first case the quantum had to have exactly the right energy or else no transition occurred. In the second, which is the photoelectric ionization of an atom, the energies of the final states lie in a continuum and so any photon energy is possible. The situation is mathematically similar to the emission of radiation as discussed in the preceding section, where also there was a continuum of final states, but there are enough differences in detail to make it worth analyzing separately.

For mathematical simplicity we shall consider the electron to be initially in a hydrogen-like ground state; the formulas to be obtained will describe essentially the ejection of an electron from a K shell and will thus give the combined intensities of the X rays which arise from the reoccupation of this shell. The situation is shown in Fig. 10.7, where we assume that the incident radiation is monochromatic of frequency $\omega = ck$ and polarized in the plane of the paper.

To calculate the transition rate, we again use the general formula (9.23) to give the probability of transitions into a state in which the electron's momentum is $\hbar\mathbf{K}$,

$$\dot{\mathbf{P}}_k = \frac{2\pi}{\hbar} |\langle \mathbf{K}|\hat{H}^{(1)}|\mathbf{k},g\rangle|^2 \rho(E) \tag{10.51}$$

where the matrix element refers to transitions from the electronic ground state g to a state with momentum $\hbar\mathbf{K}$ and $\rho(E)$ is the density

[11] E. P. Wigner, Rev. Mod. Phys., **29**. 255 (1957).

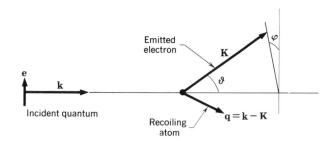

Fig. 10.7 Illustrating the photoelectric effect.

of the electron's final states, already calculated in (9.26),

$$\rho(E) = \frac{mK \, d\Omega}{(2\pi)^3 \hbar^2} \tag{10.52}$$

where the differences arise from using the electron's physical mass m, instead of the reduced mass, from setting Q equal to 1, and from using K to denote the momentum divided by $\hbar$.

To evaluate the matrix element, we need the wave functions of the initial and final states. They are

$$\psi_g = \left(\frac{\alpha^3}{\pi}\right)^{1/2} e^{-\alpha r} \qquad \left(\alpha = \frac{Z}{a_0}\right) \tag{10.53}$$

as in (7.56), and (normalized to 1 electron per cubic meter)

$$\psi = e^{i\mathbf{K}\cdot\mathbf{r}} \tag{10.54}$$

if we neglect distortions produced by the nucleus and by other electrons. The use of (10.32) now gives

$$(\mathbf{K}|\hat{H}^{(1)}|\mathbf{k},g) = -\frac{e'}{m}\left(\frac{2\hbar\alpha^3}{ck}\right)^{1/2} \int e^{-i\mathbf{K}\cdot\mathbf{r}}(\hat{\mathbf{p}}\cdot\mathbf{e})e^{i\mathbf{k}\cdot\mathbf{r}}e^{-\alpha r} \, dv$$

To evaluate the integral we use first the hermiticity of $\hat{\mathbf{p}}$ to get

$$(\mathbf{K}|\hat{H}^{(1)}|\mathbf{k},g) = -\frac{e'\hbar(\mathbf{K}\cdot\mathbf{e})}{m}\left(\frac{2\hbar\alpha^3}{ck}\right)^{1/2} \int e^{i\mathbf{q}\cdot\mathbf{r}}e^{-\alpha r} \, dv$$

where $\hbar q$ (Fig. 10.7) denotes the momentum of the recoiling atom. The remaining integral is of a type which is often encountered. We evaluate it in polar coordinates, taking $\mathbf{q}$ as the polar axis. Then if $\cos \vartheta = \mu$,

$$\int e^{i\mathbf{q}\cdot\mathbf{r}}e^{-\alpha r} \, dv = \int_0^{2\pi} d\varphi \int_0^\infty r^2 \, dr \, e^{-\alpha r} \int_{-1}^1 e^{iqr\mu} \, d\mu$$

$$= \frac{8\pi\alpha}{(q^2 + \alpha^2)^2}$$

The final answer is best expressed as a cross section, defined through (9.2). Since the incident beam contains 1 photon per unit volume, the intensity I is equal to c; and combining the preceding formulas we find

$$\frac{d\sigma}{d\Omega} = 32 \frac{e'^2}{\hbar c} \left(\frac{K}{\alpha}\right)^3 \frac{\sin^2 \vartheta \cos^2 \varphi}{k^2} \frac{\hbar k}{mc} \left(\frac{q^2}{q^2 + \alpha^2}\right)^4 \tag{10.55}$$

where ϑ and φ are as in Fig. 10.7. The formula is written in this way to emphasize that it has the dimensions of an area (k^{-2}), but it is somewhat unenlightening as it stands, and we can simplify it by making some approximations.

In writing down (10.54) we have already made the approximation that the electron is undisturbed by atomic forces in its departure. Clearly, this will be the case if $\hbar^2 K^2 / 2m \gg I$, where

$$I = \frac{\hbar^2 \alpha^2}{2m} \tag{10.56}$$

is the atom's ionization potential. Conservation of energy for the system gives

$$\hbar c k = \frac{\hbar^2 K^2}{2m} + I \tag{10.57}$$

whence

$$\hbar c k \gg I \tag{10.58}$$

and $\hbar c k \approx \hbar^2 K^2 / 2m$, which can be written as

$$K^2 \approx \frac{2mck}{\hbar} = \left(\frac{2mc^2}{\hbar c k}\right) k^2 \tag{10.59}$$

To keep within the limits of a nonrelativistic theory, we must have the quantum energy $\hbar c k \ll mc^2$, so that from (10.58) and (10.59) we can derive the double inequality

$$\frac{I}{\hbar c} \ll k \ll K \tag{10.60}$$

with which we can simplify the expression for the cross section. First we look at the last factor in (10.55), where by Fig. 10.7,

$$q^2 = k^2 + K^2 - 2kK \cos \vartheta$$

so that, neglecting small terms,

$$q^2 + \alpha^2 \approx K^2 - 2kK \cos \vartheta \approx \frac{2mck}{\hbar} \left(1 - \frac{\hbar K}{mc} \cos \vartheta\right)$$

by (10.59). The ratio $\hbar K / mc$ is v/c for the electron, which we abbreviate as usual by β, so that

$$q^2 + \alpha^2 \approx \frac{2mck}{\hbar} (1 - \beta \cos \vartheta)$$

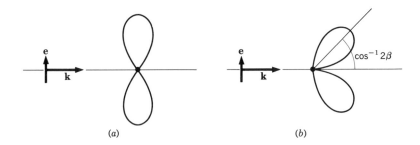

Fig. 10.8 Angular distribution of photoelectrons at (a) low and
(b) high quantum energies. The electrons are ejected into two
lobes whose maxima lie in the same plane as the
polarization vector e.

Further, by (10.56) and (10.59)

$$\left(\frac{K}{\alpha}\right)^3 = \left(\frac{K^2}{\alpha^2}\right)^{3/2} \approx \left(\frac{\hbar c k}{I}\right)^{3/2}$$

The rest of the reduction is arithmetic, and we find

$$\frac{d\sigma}{d\Omega} = \frac{64}{137 Z^2} \left(\frac{I}{\hbar c k}\right)^{7/2} \frac{\sin^2 \vartheta \, \cos^2 \varphi}{(1 - \beta \cos \vartheta)^4} \, a_0{}^2 \tag{10.61}$$

where a_0 is the radius of the first Bohr orbit and we have substituted
for the fine-structure constant $e'^2/\hbar c$ its approximate value $1/137$.
Integration over all directions gives

$$\sigma = \frac{256}{3 \times 137} \frac{\pi a_0{}^2}{Z^2} \left(\frac{I}{\hbar c k}\right)^{7/2} \tag{10.62}$$

with neglect of a relativistic term in v^2/c^2 (the calculation is left for
the reader). For all elements but hydrogen the K shell has two electrons, and to get the total K-shell absorption, the above value of σ
must be doubled and Z replaced by its effective value, Z_{eff}. If we
assume that each K electron spends half its time shielding the
nucleus from the other, then $Z_{\text{eff}} = Z - \frac{1}{2}$. It will be shown in
Chap. 15 that a better value is $Z - \frac{5}{16}$. Thus,

$$\sigma_K = \frac{512}{3 \times 137} \frac{\pi a_0{}^2}{(Z - \frac{5}{16})^2} \left(\frac{I}{\hbar c k}\right)^{7/2} \tag{10.63}$$

The angular distribution of the photoelectrons is into two lobes,
as shown in Fig. 10.8. This is to be expected, since the electric field,
which acts upon the electrons to throw them out, lies in the vertical
plane.[12]

[12] For comparisons of (10.63) with experiment, together with the errors
introduced by the Born approximation and by neglect of relativity, see Heitler,
op. cit., fig. 8.

Problem 10.11   Calculate the attenuation of a beam of 100-keV X rays in lead and in aluminium by ejection of photoelectrons from the K shell. The answer should be the distance in which, if no other processes were operating, the radiation would be reduced to e^{-1} of its initial intensity.

Problem 10.12   Estimate the total cross section for ejection of electrons from the L shell. Describe the initial states by hydrogen-like wave functions formed with $Z_{\text{eff}} = Z - 5$. (This is arrived at by assuming that the two K electrons lie between the L electrons and the nucleus, reducing Z to $Z - 2$, and that the six L electrons half-shield each other.) Compare the L and K cross sections.

Problem 10.13   Calculate the cross sections for the processes inverse to those considered above: a proton captures an electron directly into the K or L shell with emission of a photon.

11

Systems Containing
Identical Particles

We have already seen in Chap. 7 how to write down wave functions
and wave equations for systems consisting of several particles. What
happens is that the wave function contains an x, y, and z corresponding to each individual particle. Thus the wave function of even so
simple a system as the hydrogen atom is a function of six spatial
variables and t, and is clearly not at all the same kind of thing as any
of the waves studied in classical physics. In this chapter we shall
study the new features which arise when the particles are identical.
The situation is quite different from the two-particle system discussed earlier; for now there is only one field, say, the photon field
or the electron field, and the existence of several different quanta of
this field, photons or electrons, is best described by saying that the
entire field is in one of its higher states of quantum excitation. The
study of the quantum theory of fields begins at about the level at
which this book leaves off, and the reader will be introduced to it in
any of the more advanced texts. In this chapter we shall construct
the wave function of a system of identical particles as a generalization of the case in which the particles are not identical. The new features which appear are all in the nature of symmetry requirements,
and they will be developed in the next three sections.

11.1 Symmetry and Antisymmetry

The considerations to follow are well enough exemplified if there are
only two identical particles, so we shall begin by considering that
case. Let $\hat{H}(\mathbf{r}_1,\mathbf{r}_2)$ be the hamiltonian function which defines it, with
the six variables $\mathbf{r}_1$ and $\mathbf{r}_2$ referring to the two particles. A typical

hamiltonian of this kind would be written as

$$\hat{H}(\mathbf{r}_1,\mathbf{r}_2) = \frac{1}{2m}(\hat{p}_1{}^2 + \hat{p}_2{}^2) + V(\mathbf{r}_1) + V(\mathbf{r}_2) + W(|\mathbf{r}_1 - \mathbf{r}_2|) \tag{11.1}$$

where

$$\hat{p}_1{}^2 = -\hbar^2\left(\frac{\partial^2}{\partial x_1{}^2} + \frac{\partial^2}{\partial y_1{}^2} + \frac{\partial^2}{\partial z_1{}^2}\right)$$

and similarly for $\hat{p}_2{}^2$. V is the potential in some external field of force, assumed to be the same function for each particle since the two are identical, and W is an interaction between the two particles, depending only on the distance which separates them. $\hat{H}$ could also contain spin-dependent interactions, but we shall not treat them here.

The symmetry of $\hat{H}$ reflects the fact that the two particles are identical: if $\hat{P}$ is an operator which interchanges the labels on the particles, then

$$\hat{P}\hat{H}(\mathbf{r}_1,\mathbf{r}_2) = \hat{H}(\mathbf{r}_2,\mathbf{r}_1) = \hat{H}(\mathbf{r}_1,\mathbf{r}_2) \tag{11.2}$$

or, as we have expressed it in Chap. 5,

$$[\hat{P},\hat{H}] = 0 \tag{11.3}$$

As long as this relation is satisfied, no dynamical process described by $\hat{H}$ can possibly single out or distinguish one particle from the other.

With this remark about $\hat{H}$, let us now look at the wave function of the system. We know from Chap. 5 that wave functions which are simultaneous eigenfunctions of $\hat{P}$ and $\hat{H}$ can be found. If we write

$$\hat{P}\psi(\mathbf{r}_1,\mathbf{r}_2) = \psi(\mathbf{r}_2,\mathbf{r}_1) = p\psi(\mathbf{r}_1,\mathbf{r}_2)$$

then p can take on only the two values ± 1 and the eigenfunctions corresponding to them will be denoted symmetrical and antisymmetrical:

$$\psi_{\text{sym}}(\mathbf{r}_2,\mathbf{r}_1) = \psi_{\text{sym}}(\mathbf{r}_1,\mathbf{r}_2) \qquad \psi_{\text{anti}}(\mathbf{r}_2,\mathbf{r}_1) = -\psi_{\text{anti}}(\mathbf{r}_1,\mathbf{r}_2)$$

These eigenvalues ± 1 are independent of time: a system which is once started in a symmetrical or antisymmetrical state remains in such a state forever.

Problem 11.1   Prove the last statement.

The general energy eigenfunction can be written as an arbitrary linear combination of symmetrical and antisymmetrical ψ's,

$$\psi = a\psi_{\text{sym}} + b\psi_{\text{anti}} \tag{11.4}$$

and it is, of course, not an eigenfunction of $\hat{P}$ unless a or b is zero, since

$$\hat{P}\psi = a\psi_{\text{sym}} - b\psi_{\text{anti}} \tag{11.5}$$

Indistinguishable particles

In order to pick out from among the two-particle states given by (11.4) those which correspond to actual two-particle systems in nature, we shall now introduce a new postulate of indistinguishability that rests solely on experience and cannot be derived from any of our earlier assumptions. In the foregoing expressions it is necessary to label the coordinates corresponding to the two particles by the suffixes 1 and 2 in order to write down the mathematics. In this sense, the two particles have been treated as distinct. The postulate of indistinguishability asserts that in real physical states, the probability of finding one particle in the element of volume dv_1 and the other in dv_2 is independent of which way they are labeled,

$$|\psi(\mathbf{r}_2,\mathbf{r}_1)|^2 \, dv_1 \, dv_2 = |\psi(\mathbf{r}_1,\mathbf{r}_2)|^2 \, dv_1 \, dv_2 \tag{11.6}$$

and this clearly requires, by comparison of (11.4) and (11.5), that ψ must be either exactly symmetrical or exactly antisymmetrical.

To make it clear what is involved here, let us consider the wave function of the two-electron system shown in Fig. 11.1, in which the electrons belong to two distinct hydrogen atoms and are not dynamically related at all. In the absence of the postulate of indistinguishability, one would be tempted to write the two-electron wave function as a product,

$$\psi(1,2) = \psi_s(1)\psi_p(2) \tag{11.7}$$

where 1 and 2 refer to the two electrons. This is justified by the following argument. The probability of finding the first electron in the volume element dv_1 is $|\psi_s(1)|^2 \, dv_1$, and similarly for the second. On the other hand, $|\psi(1,2)|^2 \, dv_1 \, dv_2$ represents the probability of finding the first electron in dv_1 and simultaneously the second in dv_2. The fact that, according to (11.7), this turns out to be

$$|\psi(1,2)|^2 \, dv_1 \, dv_2 = |\psi_s(1)|^2 \, dv_1 \, |\psi_p(2)|^2 \, dv_2 \tag{11.8}$$

is merely a reflection of the dynamical independence of the two systems—the probability that two independent events occur simultaneously is the product of the individual probabilities. The expectation

Fig. 11.1 A system of two noninteracting electrons belonging to two separated hydrogen atoms. The first electron is in an s state and is described by the normalized wave function $\psi_s(1)$ centered at the left-hand nucleus. The second electron is in a p state described by $\psi_p(2)$.

ψ_s ψ_p

value of some two-particle dynamical quantity $\hat{F}(1,2)$ (such as the energy or the angular momentum) would accordingly be

$$\langle \hat{F}(1,2) \rangle = \int \psi_s^*(1)\psi_p^*(2)\hat{F}(1,2)\psi_s(1)\psi_p(2) \, dv_1 \, dv_2 \tag{11.9}$$

if the particles could be distinguished

This manner of forming the wave function of two independent systems as a product is quite general in physics, and we have used it in Chap. 7 to describe an electron and a proton, but if the two particles are identical, we must instead use a wave function which satisfies the principle of indistinguishability. Such a wave function is

$$\psi^{(+)}(1,2) = N^{(+)}[\psi_s(1)\psi_p(2) + \psi_s(2)\psi_p(1)] \tag{11.10a}$$

or

$$\psi^{(-)}(1,2) = N^{(-)}[\psi_s(1)\psi_p(2) - \psi_s(2)\psi_p(1)] \tag{11.10b}$$

where the normalizing factors are to be determined by the probability interpretation of the wave function, which we must now examine carefully. It cannot be said that $|\psi^{(\pm)}(1,2)|^2 \, dv_1 \, dv_2$, for example, has the same interpretation as (11.8), that is, that the electron labeled 1 is in the s state on the left-hand atom and that labeled 2 is in the p state on the right-hand atom. This is because if we were to look for electron 1 on the right-hand atom and electron 2 on the left, we would not find them there and (11.8) is accordingly (practically) zero, whereas $|\psi^{(\pm)}(1,2)|^2 \, dv_1 \, dv_2$ is not zero because it contains the term $\psi_s(2)\psi_p(1)$. Thus the interpretation of $|\psi^{(\pm)}(1,2)|^2 \, dv_1 \, dv_2$ is not (7.26) but rather

$|\psi^{(\pm)}(1,2)|^2 \, dv_1 \, dv_2$ is the probability that one of the electrons lies in the volume element dv_1 at (x_1,y_1,z_1) and the other lies in dv_2 at (x_2,y_2,z_2). $\tag{11.11}$

In this definition we have abandoned the pretense that the electrons can be labeled, even in principle, so as to distinguish them. We see now the important fact that the subscripts 1 and 2 label not particles in any sense, but only coordinates in a six-dimensional configuration space. With this in mind, we can determine the normalization in (11.10a,b). We square $\psi^{(\pm)}(1,2)$ to get

$$|\psi^{(\pm)}(1,2)|^2 = |N^{(\pm)}|^2[|\psi_s(1)|^2|\psi_p(2)|^2 + |\psi_s(2)|^2|\psi_p(1)|^2 \\ \pm \psi_s^*(1)\psi_s(2)\psi_p^*(2)\psi_p(1) \pm \psi_s^*(2)\psi_s(1)\psi_p^*(1)\psi_p(2)] \tag{11.12}$$

If we know that one electron is in the s state on one atom and the other in the p state on the other and that there is no appreciable overlap, then the product $\psi_s^*(1)\psi_s(2)$, for example, will be essentially zero, and

$$|\psi^{(\pm)}(1,2)|^2 \approx |N^{(\pm)}|^2[|\psi_s(1)|^2|\psi_p(2)|^2 + |\psi_s(2)|^2|\psi_p(1)|^2]$$

Since the sum of the probabilities in (11.11) must be equal to unity, we have in this case

$$\int |\psi^{(\pm)}(1,2)|^2 \, dv_1 \, dv_2 \approx |N^{(\pm)}|^2 [\int |\psi_s(1)|^2 \, dv_1 \int |\psi_p(2)|^2 \, dv_2$$
$$+ \int |\psi_s(2)|^2 \, dv_2 \int |\psi_p(1)|^2 \, dv_1]$$
$$= 2|N^{(\pm)}|^2 = 1$$

so that in this approximation, except for a phase factor, $N^{(\pm)} = 2^{-\frac{1}{2}}$. Now because of the lack of overlap just mentioned, these two terms will not simultaneously be appreciably different from zero for any values of (x_1, y_1, z_1) and (x_2, y_2, z_2). Suppose that the first term dominates. Then

$$|\psi^{(\pm)}(1,2)|^2 \, dv_1 \, dv_2 \approx \tfrac{1}{2}|\psi_s(1)|^2 \, dv_1 \, |\psi_p(2)|^2 \, dv_2$$

This is the same as (11.8), except for the factor of $\frac{1}{2}$ which reflects the other possible labeling of the coordinates, and this shows that for practical purposes, when the electrons are widely separated, the two-electron wave function factors so as to indicate dynamical independence in the same way as (11.8).

In the more important case in which the wave functions overlap appreciably, the value of $N^{(\pm)}$ must be determined by direct integration of (11.12). (Note that $\psi_s(1)$ and $\psi_p(1)$ are here not orthogonal, because they are centered at different points and thus belong effectively to different hamiltonians.) The wave functions (11.10a,b) have the required symmetry properties, but they may hardly seem reasonable according to our earlier argument because they are not expressed in the form of products; so that the dynamical independence of the two systems, evident in Fig. 11.1 and clearly expressed in (11.8), has disappeared. One would expect this to lead to momentous and essentially nonclassical results, and we shall see that it does, but at the same time it seems hardly possible that our earlier idea of statistical independence can be completely wrong. Let us calculate the expectation value of some quantity $\hat{F}(1,2)$ in the new states, remembering that if the particles are truly indistinguishable, then $\hat{F}$ itself cannot distinguish between them and so it must satisfy

$$\hat{P}\hat{F}(1,2) = \hat{F}(2,1) = \hat{F}(1,2) \tag{11.13}$$

We find

$$\langle \hat{F}(1,2) \rangle^{(\pm)} = 2|N^{(\pm)}|^2 \{ \int \psi_s^*(1)\psi_p^*(2)\hat{F}(1,2)\psi_s(1)\psi_p(2) \, dv_1 \, dv_2$$
$$\pm \int \psi_s^*(1)\psi_p^*(2)\hat{F}(1,2)\psi_s(2)\psi_p(1) \, dv_1 \, dv_2 \} \tag{11.14}$$

Problem 11.2 Suppose that $\hat{F}$ is independent of time, and that the states s and p have different energies. Find the time dependence of $\langle \hat{F}(1,2) \rangle^{(\pm)}$. (The two-electron situation is different in time dependence from the one-electron situation of p. 121.)

Are $\psi^{(+)}$ and $\psi^{(-)}$ orthogonal to each other? Is there any general reason why they should be?

Problem 11.3 Derive Eq. (11.14).

The first term in (11.14) is, except for the normalizing factor, the same as (11.9). The second is called the *exchange* term, and it represents something quite new. It contradicts (11.9), but not for widely separated electrons, since the integral involves the product $\psi_s^*(1)\psi_s(2)$, for example, and we have just seen that this is vanishingly small. We have seen that in this case $N^{(\pm)}$ can be set equal to $2^{-\frac{1}{2}}$. Thus the intuitive relation (11.9) remains essentially correct. The difference appears only when the two systems are brought close enough together that there is a significant amount of overlap—that is, there is a significant probability that the identities of two electrons may become confused. This could happen also in the classical view, but here one would say that if one were clever enough, one could always keep track of which electron is which. In quantum theory, this possibility really does not exist, because the wave functions are not sufficiently localized in space to enable one to keep them distinct. The impossibility of distinguishing between two electrons whose wave functions overlap is forced upon us by the uncertainty principle.

A two-particle wave function

The actual form of a many-particle wave function is usually somewhat difficult to visualize because of the number of dimensions involved. We shall therefore give a two-dimensional example in which the characteristic effects of symmetry and antisymmetry can clearly be seen. Consider two identical uncharged particles constrained to move in a closed loop of circumference L. We shall assume that they do not affect each other dynamically at all, so that a typical eigenstate for particle 1 is

$$\psi_m(1) = L^{-\frac{1}{2}}e^{ik_m x_1}$$

where

$$k_m = \frac{2\pi m}{L} \qquad m = 0, \pm 1, \pm 2, \ldots$$

and similarly for particle 2. The symmetrical wave function corresponding to two particles with different momenta $\hbar k_m$ and $\hbar k_n$ is

$$\psi^{(+)}(1,2) = 2^{-\frac{1}{2}}L^{-1}\left(e^{i(k_m x_1 + k_n x_2)} + e^{i(k_m x_2 + k_n x_1)}\right)$$

and with a little algebra this can be written as

$$\psi^{(+)}(1,2) = 2^{\frac{1}{2}}L^{-1}\cos\left[\tfrac{1}{2}(k_m - k_n)(x_1 - x_2)\right]e^{iKX} \tag{11.15a}$$

where $\hbar K$ is the total momentum,

$$K = k_1 + k_2$$

and X is the coordinate of a point which we shall call the center of mass,

$$X = \tfrac{1}{2}(x_1 + x_2)$$

The probability of finding one particle in dx_1 and the other simultaneously in dx_2 is

$$|\psi^{(+)}(1,2)|^2 \, dx_1 \, dx_2 = 2L^{-2} \cos^2 \left[\tfrac{1}{2}(k_m - k_n)(x_1 - x_2)\right] dx_1 \, dx_2 \qquad (11.15b)$$

and this is quite remarkable, for it states that the positions of the two particles are statistically correlated, even though there is no dynamical interaction between them. Thus, for example, if the separation $x_1 - x_2$ is such that $\tfrac{1}{2}(k_m - k_n)(x_1 - x_2) = \pi/2$, there is no probability at all that the two particles will ever be found simultaneously in dx_1 and dx_2. On the other hand, if either $k_m = k_n$ or $x_1 = x_2$, there is a maximum in the probability. This fact is sometimes described as a tendency to clump together in position and momentum, in the sense that if $x_1 = x_2$, then the probability is a maximum for any value of k_m and k_n, and vice versa. The essential feature, however, is a periodicity in a distribution which one would intuitively expect to be perfectly uniform.

A system in an antisymmetric state has similarly

$$\psi^{(-)}(1,2) = 2^{1/2}iL^{-1} \sin \left[\tfrac{1}{2}(k_m - k_n)(x_1 - x_2)\right]e^{iKX} \qquad (11.16a)$$

and

$$|\psi^{(-)}(1,2)|^2 = 2L^{-2} \sin^2 \left[\tfrac{1}{2}(k_m - k_n)(x_1 - x_2)\right] \qquad (11.16b)$$

This state exhibits what is called a *statistical repulsion:* there is no likelihood of finding the two particles either at the same point in space or possessing the same momentum.

Both types of statistical distribution are in fact met with in nature, and we shall see that the impossibility of having m equal to n in the antisymmetrical state is closely related to the Pauli exclusion principle which asserts that two electrons in the same physical system will never have all their quantum numbers equal.

Finally, given the physical content of a properly symmetrized and normalized two-particle wave function, it is natural to ask how to calculate from it the probability $P(\mathbf{r}) \, dv$ of finding *one* particle near a given point $\mathbf{r}$. This is found from (11.11) by integrating one of the coordinates over all space and setting the other equal to $\mathbf{r}$,

$$P(\mathbf{r}) \, dv = dv \!\int |\psi(\mathbf{r},\mathbf{r}')|^2 \, dv' \qquad (11.17a)$$

Clearly,

$$\int P(\mathbf{r})\, dv = 1 \tag{11.17b}$$

To summarize in a more general notation, the wave functions for two noninteracting particles in two orthogonal states m and n are either antisymmetric or symmetric,

$$\psi_{mn}^{(-)}(1,2) = 2^{-\frac{1}{2}}[\psi_m(1)\psi_n(2) - \psi_m(2)\psi_n(1)] \qquad (m \neq n) \tag{11.18a}$$

$$\psi_{mn}^{(+)}(1,2) = 2^{-\frac{1}{2}}[\psi_m(1)\psi_n(2) + \psi_m(2)\psi_n(1)] \qquad (m \neq n) \tag{11.18b}$$

If the states m and n happen to be the same, then only a symmetric combination is possible:

$$\psi_{mm}^{(+)} = \psi_m(1)\psi_m(2) \tag{11.18c}$$

If the particles interact, it is no longer possible to represent $\psi(1,2)$ in terms of simple products, but the same two types of symmetry behavior are found.

The normalization in (11.18a,b) has been written down on the hypothesis that ψ_m is orthogonal to ψ_n. If m and n refer to two different eigenfunctions of the same hamiltonian or angular-momentum operator, they are orthogonal, or can be made so; but for the system in Fig. 11.1, for example, this is not so, and the normalization must be carried out by the usual integration. In this case it will depend on the separation of the two atoms; an example will be encountered later in the normalization of (16.4).

Problem 11.4   Derive Eqs. (11.15a) and (11.16a). Discuss the situation, not mentioned above, when $k_m = k_n$.

Problem 11.5   Evaluate $P(\mathbf{r})$ for the system shown in Fig. 11.1. Do any new considerations arise when both the atoms are in the same quantum state?

Problem 11.6   Evaluate $P(x)$ for the symmetrical and antisymmetrical wave functions around a loop discussed above. Is the result physically reasonable?

Problem 11.7   Find Ehrenfest's theorems (Sec. 3.3) for a two-particle system when the particles are identical and when they are not. Use the hamiltonian (11.1). Comment on significant features.

Spin functions

The considerations of this section are closely analogous to those of Sec. 6.4 on the two-spin system. The differences are in the interpretation, which is more difficult because of the spatial distributions described by the ψ's. It was found that corresponding to the vectorial addition $\mathbf{S} = \mathbf{S}_1 + \mathbf{S}_2$ one can define a set of two-particle spin functions χ_{sm} such that

$$\hat{S}^2\chi_{sm_s} = s(s+1)\chi_{sm_s}, \qquad \hat{S}_z\chi_{sm_s} = m_s\chi_{sm_s}$$

In terms of the one-spin functions $\chi_\pm(1)$ and $\chi_\pm(2)$, the χ_{sm_s} are given by

$$\chi_{00} = 2^{-\frac{1}{2}}[\chi_+(1)\chi_-(2) - \chi_+(2)\chi_-(1)] \qquad (11.19)$$

$$\chi_{11} = \chi_+(1)\chi_+(2)$$

$$\chi_{10} = 2^{-\frac{1}{2}}[\chi_+(1)\chi_-(2) + \chi_+(2)\chi_-(1)] \qquad (11.20)$$

$$\chi_{1-1} = \chi_-(1)\chi_-(2)$$

These are exactly analogous to the combinations (11.18a,b,c), and like them are valid only when the two systems are uncoupled. Since there is usually no real point in considering two dynamically independent systems as a single one, it might seem that these wave functions and spin functions are of little use. In answer, two points must be made. First, as far as spins are concerned, the dynamical interaction between two spins is normally very small—that in an atom, for example, contributes to the fine structure and can often be neglected. Second, the main utility of functions like (11.18a,b,c) lies in their role as unperturbed functions $\psi^{(0)}$ with which to begin a perturbation calculation.

Problem 11.8   Two identical particles are bound in one dimension by the same harmonic force. Further, they interact by a force which is proportional to the distance between them (but not strong enough to disrupt the system, if it is repulsive). The potential energy is thus

$$V(x_1,x_2) = \tfrac{1}{2}K(x_1{}^2 + x_2{}^2) + \tfrac{1}{2}\alpha(x_1 - x_2)^2$$

Find the exact eigenfunctions and eigenvalues of this system. Write down the first four eigenfunctions and classify them according to their symmetry. [In solving this, the trick is to introduce new variables $\xi = 2^{-\frac{1}{2}}(x_1 + x_2)$ and $\eta = 2^{-\frac{1}{2}}(x_1 - x_2)$.]

11.2   The Helium Spectrum

In the preceding section we have seen how to construct the space and spin parts of two-electron wave functions. We shall now look carefully at an actual two-electron system—the helium atom is a natural choice—to see whether these wave functions in fact describe anything that exists in nature. Deferring a quantitative analysis to Chap. 15, let us look for a moment at the empirical term diagram of helium shown in Fig. 11.2 and see what states are there.

There are two sets of levels, with radiative transitions occurring among the levels of each set subject to the usual selection rule

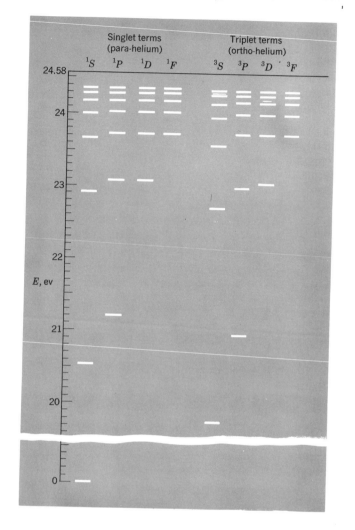

Fig. 11.2 Term diagram
of helium.

$\Delta L = \pm 1$, but the transitions between levels belonging to different sets are forbidden. The two kinds of helium so distinguished are called para-helium and ortho-helium. The levels of para-helium are all singlets, whereas those of ortho-helium are found under high resolution to be triplets except for the S levels, which are singlets. The general theoretical interpretation of this spectrum is quite familiar. The energy levels of the normal spectrum represent the possible states of a helium atom in which one electron remains in its ground state and the other executes transitions (why?). Since the ground state is an s state, the atom's entire orbital angular momentum is contributed by the excited electron. The triplet structure of ortho-helium is due to the three possible orientations of a unit angular momentum, the spins of the two electrons being parallel. They are described by the symmetrical spin functions χ_{11}, χ_{10}, and χ_{1-1} in (11.20), and the splitting is due to small magnetic effects involving the electrons' magnetic moments.[1] These effects vanish when $S = 0$, and the para states, belonging to antiparallel spins with the antisymmetrical spin function χ_{00}, are all singlets. The spin effects vanish also when $L = 0$ (why?), so that the S states of ortho-helium are not split either, but it is convenient to designate them as triplet levels anyhow, since they form a part of the triplet series of levels. The relative scarcity of radiative transitions between ortho- and para-helium arises from the fact that, as can easily be shown by direct calculation, a change in **L** is very much more probable than a change in **S**.

Let us now look at some of the states individually. For this purpose we shall make qualitative estimates by simple perturbation theory, deferring a more careful evaluation to Chap. 15. As the un-perturbed system we shall use a "double hydrogen atom" of two electrons moving independently in hydrogen-like orbits. The main perturbation is then the Coulomb interaction between the electrons. This amounts to breaking up the hamiltonian of (11.1) into two terms. The unperturbed energy is

$$\hat{H}^{(0)} = \frac{1}{2m}\,(\hat{p}_1{}^2 + \hat{p}_2{}^2) - 2e'^2\left(\frac{1}{r_1} + \frac{1}{r_2}\right) \tag{11.21}$$

and the electrons' Coulomb interaction energy

$$\hat{H}^{(1)} = \frac{e'^2}{|r_1 - r_2|} \tag{11.22}$$

is the perturbation. The unperturbed energy is the energy of the electron which remains in the ground state (-4 Ry) plus that of the other electron, $-4n^{-2}$ Ry, where n is its principal quantum number. The perturbation energy is

$$E^{(1)} = \int \psi^{(0)*}(1,2)\,\frac{e'^2}{|r_1 - r_2|}\,\psi^{(0)}(1,2)\,dv_1\,dv_2 \tag{11.23}$$

where the unperturbed wave function is of the form (11.18a,b,c).

There is a simple notation suggested by this approximation procedure which is used to describe how atomic states are built up. Say, for example, that one electron in the eigenfunction of the un-perturbed hamiltonian is in the ground state $1s$ and the other is in a $2p$ state. This structure is then denoted as a $1s2p$ state. The whole atom is then in a P state, since $L = 1$. But there are several such states. The spins may be parallel (triplet series) or antiparallel

[1] They are of two kinds: a spin-orbit coupling proportional to **L · S** and a spin-spin interaction analogous to the classically computed interaction of two small permanent magnets. An estimate of these splittings is not hard to obtain, but the situation is complicated by the fact that the two effects are generally of the same order of magnitude. See H. A. Bethe and E. E. Salpeter in *Encyclopedia of Physics*, Springer-Verlag OHG, Berlin, 1957 vol. 35, p. 271.

(singlets), and if parallel, the resultant S may assume three differ-ent orientations with respect to L. We accordingly decorate the P giving the orbital state with a superscript to the left giving the multiplicity and a subscript to the right giving the total angular momentum. The singlet state built up in this way has the complete formula $1s2p\,^1P_1$; in the three triplet states the last symbol would be $^3P_0$, $^3P_1$, or $^3P_2$. The ground state is in this notation $(1s)^2\,^1S_0$. We shall now look at the structure of the ground state and the first excited state of helium.

Ground state, $(1s)^2\,^1S_0$

This is a para-helium state. The orbital part of the unperturbed state is of the form $(11.18c)$; the wave function is accordingly written as

$$^1U_{1S}(1,2) = \psi_{1s}(1)\psi_{1s}(2)\chi_{00} \tag{11.24}$$

where χ_{00} is the singlet spin function, U represents the combination of space and spin variables, and the superscript denotes the singlet state. The perturbation energy is

$$E^{(1)} = \int \psi_{1s}^{2}(1)\, \frac{e'^{2}}{|r_1 - r_2|}\, \psi_{1s}^{2}(2)\chi_{00}^{*}\chi_{00}$$

integrated over both space and spin variables, in which the spin part at once integrates to unity and the remaining integral, see (15.10), is $\tfrac{5}{2}$ Ry. Thus the first-order perturbation estimate for the ground-state energy, defined as minus the work required to remove one electron from the atom, is

$$E_g = -(4 - \tfrac{5}{2})\,\text{Ry} = -20.3\,\text{eV}$$

as compared with the experimental value of -24.6 eV. Remarkably, the three corresponding states for ortho-helium are not found on the energy-level diagram at all, and this fact does not follow from any of the postulates we have used so far.

First excited singlet state, $1s2s\,^1S_0$

The wave functions for this state will be of the form

$$^1U_{2S}(1,2) = 2^{-\frac12}[\psi_{1s}(1)\psi_{2s}(2) \pm \psi_{1s}(2)\psi_{2s}(1)]\chi_{00} \tag{11.25}$$

The unperturbed energy $E^{(0)}$ of the radiating electron is -1 Ry; the perturbation energy is an expression of the form (11.14), which since all ψ's are real becomes

$$E^{(1)} = K \pm A \tag{11.26}$$

$$K = \int \psi_{1s}^{2}(1)\, \frac{e'^{2}}{|r_1 - r_2|}\, \psi_{2s}^{2}(2)\, dv_1\, dv_2 \tag{11.27a}$$

$$A = \int \psi_{1s}(1)\psi_{2s}(1)\, \frac{e'^{2}}{|r_1 - r_2|}\, \psi_{1s}(2)\psi_{2s}(2)\, dv_1\, dv_2 \tag{11.27b}$$

The first of these integrals gives the ordinary Coulomb interaction between two charged clouds; the second, arising from the overlapping wave functions, is an exchange term which is clearly a positive number (why?). Thus one would expect to find two different $2S$ levels for para-helium. Similarly, there should be two for ortho-helium, and except for small effects of magnetic interaction the singlet and triplet levels should be at the same energy. This is not what is observed. There is one level for para-helium and one for ortho-helium, and they are separated by 0.8 eV. They are, in fact, the para-helium level $E^{(0)} + K + A$ and the ortho-helium level $E^{(0)} + K - A$. The approximate wave functions of the observed states are

$$^1U_{2S}(1,2) = 2^{-\frac{1}{2}}[\psi_{1s}(1)\psi_{2s}(2) + \psi_{1s}(2)\psi_{2s}(1)]\chi_{00} \tag{11.28a}$$

and

$$^3U_{2S}(1,2) = 2^{-\frac{1}{2}}[\psi_{1s}(1)\psi_{2s}(2) - \psi_{1s}(2)\psi_{2s}(1)]\chi_{1m} \tag{11.28b}$$

where $m = -1, 0, +1$. Exactly similar considerations hold for the $2P$ and higher levels.

Looking over the results just found, we see that half the levels which one might have expected to find are not there and that this suppression of states produces a marked difference between the singlet and triplet spectra. This difference, it must be understood, is due not to any difference in the dynamical interactions of parallel and antiparallel spins, but to the opposite symmetries of the *spatial* part of the wave functions. Which states are allowed and which are omitted? Examination of (11.25) and (11.28a,b), plus the higher states, together with an immense quantity of spectroscopic data on other atoms, shows that the allowed states are those and only those which are antisymmetric in the space and spin variables taken together,

$$U(1,2) = -U(2,1) \tag{11.29}$$

Let $\hat{P}_r$ be the operator which interchanges space coordinates and similarly, $\hat{P}_s$ be that which interchanges spin coordinates. A two-electron system is symmetrical under the operator $\hat{P}_r\hat{P}_s$, whose eigenvalues are ± 1. The states which occur in nature belong to the eigenvalue -1. This restriction is the quantum-mechanical form of the Pauli exclusion principle; it was first given by Heisenberg and Dirac in 1926. It was originally a purely empirical discovery, and it completes the postulate of indistinguishability with which we began this chapter.

11.3 Antisymmetrical Wave Functions

To denote the space-and-spin function of a single particle, we write $U_{a,m_s} = \psi_a(r)\chi_{m_s}$ or, more briefly, U_α, where α specifies the values of

a and m_s. The most general wave function formed from single-particle wave functions which changes sign under the combined operation $\hat{P}_r\hat{P}_s$ is of the form

$$U_{\alpha\beta}(1,2) = 2^{-\frac{1}{2}}[U_\alpha(1)U_\beta(2) - U_\alpha(2)U_\beta(1)] \tag{11.30}$$

This satisfies $\hat{P}_r\hat{P}_s U_{\alpha\beta} = -U_{\alpha\beta}$, but it is not in general an eigenfunction of either $\hat{P}_r$ or $\hat{P}_s$. We assume that states α, β, etc. are orthogonal (see Prob. 11.14). $U_{\alpha\beta}$ can be written in the form of a determinant

$$U_{\alpha\beta}(1,2) = 2^{-\frac{1}{2}} \begin{vmatrix} U_\alpha(1) & U_\beta(1) \\ U_\alpha(2) & U_\beta(2) \end{vmatrix}$$

and in general, for n electrons,

$$U(1 \cdots n) = (n!)^{-\frac{1}{2}} \begin{vmatrix} U_{\alpha_1}(1) & U_{\alpha_2}(1) & \cdots & U_{\alpha_n}(1) \\ U_{\alpha_1}(2) & U_{\alpha_2}(2) & \cdots & U_{\alpha_n}(2) \\ \cdots\cdots\cdots\cdots\cdots\cdots\cdots \\ U_{\alpha_1}(n) & U_{\alpha_2}(n) & \cdots & U_{\alpha_n}(n) \end{vmatrix} \tag{11.31}$$

Wave functions of this form are called Slater determinants.[2]

We recall the fundamental symmetry properties of a determinant: that the interchange of any two rows or of any two columns changes the sign of the determinant; and consequently, if two rows or two columns are the same, the determinant vanishes. Now let us look at (11.31). It has the following properties:

1. *Antisymmetry* with respect to the interchange of any two rows. Since the rows differ only by the label attached to them, this means that the whole wave function is antisymmetrical with respect to the interchange of any two labels,

$$U(1,2, \ldots ,i, \ldots ,j, \ldots ,n)$$
$$= -U(1,2, \ldots ,j, \ldots ,i, \ldots ,n) \tag{11.32}$$

This is the direct generalization of (11.29).

2. *The exclusion principle.* As stated by Pauli in 1924, this principle asserts that no two electrons in an atom can have exactly the same quantum numbers in any unperturbed state. If two of the α's in (11.31) are equal, then two columns of the determinantal wave function are equal and the wave function vanishes. There can therefore be no such state. It should be emphasized that Pauli's statement of the principle refers to an unperturbed state which is imagined to consist of electrons moving independently in the field of the nucleus, and to which the electrons' Coulomb interaction is applied as a perturbation. It also refers specifically to the quantum numbers of the individual electrons; therefore, a two-electron wave function must be of the form (11.30), for example, rather than a product like

---

[2] J. C. Slater, Phys. Rev., **34**, 1293 (1929).

(11.28a or b), in which the spin function is associated with both electrons at the same time.

3. *Statistical repulsion.* If any two electrons with the same spin are also at the same point in space, the wave function vanishes. This and the exclusion principle are closely analogous, arising respectively from the equality of two rows and two columns of U. A special example of this has already been commented upon in (11.16a,b), where the quantum numbers k_m and k_n appear exactly symmetrically with the spatial coordinates x_1 and x_2 and the equality of either pair causes the wave function to vanish.

As an example of the use of a Slater wave function, let us calculate the expectation value of a two-particle operator, for example, the interelectron energy, in a three-particle system. The Coulomb energy is of the form

$$V(1,2) + V(2,3) + V(3,1)$$

and its expectation value is

$$\langle V \rangle = \tfrac{1}{6} \int \begin{vmatrix} U_\alpha^*(1) & U_\beta^*(1) & U_\gamma^*(1) \\ U_\alpha^*(2) & U_\beta^*(2) & U_\gamma^*(2) \\ U_\alpha^*(3) & U_\beta^*(3) & U_\gamma^*(3) \end{vmatrix}$$
$$[V(1,2) + V(2,3) + V(3,1)] \cdot \begin{vmatrix} U_\alpha(1) & U_\beta(1) & U_\gamma(1) \\ U_\alpha(2) & U_\beta(2) & U_\gamma(2) \\ U_\alpha(3) & U_\beta(3) & U_\gamma(3) \end{vmatrix}$$

where the integration is over both space and spin variables. First we note that by changing the names of the variables of integration this can be shortened to

$$\langle V \rangle = \tfrac{1}{2} \int |\det|^* V(1,2) |\det|$$

Next we carry out the integral over (x_3, y_3, z_3). To do this, we expand each determinant by minors of its bottom row:

$$\begin{vmatrix} U_\alpha(1) & U_\beta(1) & U_\gamma(1) \\ U_\alpha(2) & U_\beta(2) & U_\gamma(2) \\ U_\alpha(3) & U_\beta(3) & U_\gamma(3) \end{vmatrix} = U_\alpha(3) \begin{vmatrix} U_\beta(1) & U_\gamma(1) \\ U_\beta(2) & U_\gamma(2) \end{vmatrix}$$
$$- U_\beta(3) \begin{vmatrix} U_\alpha(1) & U_\gamma(1) \\ U_\alpha(2) & U_\gamma(2) \end{vmatrix} + U_\gamma(3) \begin{vmatrix} U_\alpha(1) & U_\beta(1) \\ U_\alpha(2) & U_\beta(2) \end{vmatrix}$$

On integration the cross terms drop out and we are left with

$$\langle V \rangle = \tfrac{1}{2} \int [|U_\beta(1) U_\gamma(2) - U_\beta(2) U_\gamma(1)|^2 \\ + |U_\alpha(1) U_\gamma(2) - U_\alpha(2) U_\gamma(1)|^2 \\ + |U_\alpha(1) U_\beta(2) - U_\alpha(2) U_\beta(1)|^2] V(1,2) \quad (11.33)$$

integrated over spatial coordinates 1 and 2 and over all three spin coordinates. This is as far as we can go without making some assumption about the spin variables. Suppose that the spins of states α and β are up and the spin of γ is down. Then on carrying out the spin integration in (11.33) only the last cross term remains,

$$\langle V \rangle = \int[|U_b(1)|^2|U_c(2)|^2 + |U_a(1)|^2|U_c(2)|^2 + |U_a(1)|^2|U_b(2)|^2$$
$$- U_a^*(1)U_b(1)U_b^*(2)U_a(2)]V(1,2)\,dv_1\,dv_2 \qquad (11.34)$$

where a, b, and c represent the orbital states corresponding to α, β, and γ. It is clear that as far as electrons with dissimilar spins are concerned, exchange terms do not arise, and this of course reflects the fact that one could continue to distinguish them even if the spatial wave functions overlapped. One would use this formula, for example, in calculating the states of the lithium atom.

Problem 11.9   What is the expectation of a one-particle operator independent of spin (say, the kinetic energy) in the n-particle state given by (11.31)?

Problem 11.10   It is customary to begin a calculation of atomic structure by writing down the appropriate Slater determinants. Show that the wave function for the states $1s2s$ of helium with $S_z = 0$ is doubly degenerate, in that two different Slater determinants correspond to the same state. Treating this as a problem in degenerate perturbation theory, find the stabilized eigenfunctions by the method of Prob. 8.7 and write down the perturbed energy in terms of integrals like (11.27a,b). To what states do the two stabilized eigenfunctions correspond?

Problem 11.11   Since $\hat{P}_r$ commutes with $\hat{H}$ in (11.1), this hamiltonian should have eigenfunctions symmetrical and antisymmetrical under $\hat{P}_r$. Show how to make linear combinations of degenerate 2×2 Slater determinants which have this property. Are these new wave functions eigenfunctions of $\hat{P}_s$? Show how to write all four unperturbed $1s2s$ wave functions of helium as Slater determinants or linear combinations thereof.

Problem 11.12   Write out the determinantal wave function for the ground state $1s^2 2s\,^2S_{1/2}$ of lithium and express the energy of this state in terms of the appropriate definite integrals.

Problem 11.13   Do the same for the ground state of beryllium.

Problem 11.14   We have assumed in the preceding discussion that the various states α, β, etc. are orthogonal. Suppose that α_1 and α_2 are not orthogonal, and prove from the general properties of determinants that

$$U' = N \begin{vmatrix} U'_{\alpha_1}(1) & U_{\alpha_2}(1) & \cdots \\ U'_{\alpha_1}(2) & U_{\alpha_2}(2) & \cdots \\ \cdots & \cdots & \cdots \end{vmatrix}$$

where $U'_{\alpha_1} = U_{\alpha_1} - U_{\alpha_2}\int U^*_{\alpha_2}U_{\alpha_1}$, is exactly equal to the determinant in (10.37) but that U'_{α_1} is now orthogonal to U_{α_2}. Normalize U' assuming that all other pairs of U's are orthogonal.

Problem 11.15   Construct a set of spin eigenfunctions for a three-spin system using (6.56) and (6.57) to add a third spin to a two-spin system.[3] How is the resulting formula symmetrical under the interchange of labels?

Problem 11.16   In our initial discussion of the two-electron system, we introduced the operators $\hat{P}_r$ and $\hat{P}_s$ which interchanged spatial and spin coordinates separately, and we found the eigenfunctions of each in order to arrive most easily at the stabilized eigenfunctions of the entire system. For a three-electron system there are six $\hat{P}_r$'s and six $\hat{P}_s$'s. What are they? Why cannot the same approach be used in this case? Why does the operator $\hat{P}_r\hat{P}_s$ play the decisive role here? Your remarks may be illustrated by reference to the results of Prob. 11.15. [Hint: Do the various $\hat{P}_r$'s (and $\hat{P}_s$'s) commute with each other?]

Spin and statistics

We have presented the exclusion principle as an empirical fact, and this is what it was in 1924, but later work has shown that it is inherent in the structure of a very general class of field theories which, as far as is known, seems to describe all the fields met with in nature. It was proved by Pauli[4] in 1940 and later by Pauli and other authors in increasing generality, that as a consequence of relativistic invariance and a few other simple properties, any field of particles whose spin is $\frac{1}{2}$, $\frac{3}{2}$, $\frac{5}{2}$, etc., must obey the exclusion principle. Particles of this kind are said to obey Fermi-Dirac statistics (see Chap. 19), and they are called *fermions* for short.

There is also another possibility, that instead of changing sign under the permutation of any two labels as in (11.32), the wave function may remain unchanged,

$$U(1,2, \ldots ,i, \ldots ,j, \ldots ,n)$$
$$= U(1,2, \ldots ,j, \ldots ,i, \ldots ,n) \tag{11.35}$$

The general effect of such symmetry has already been exhibited in (11.15a,b), and it is, roughly speaking, the opposite of that of the exclusion principle; for particles tend preferentially to cluster into the same place and the same quantum state. Such a possibility cannot be explained on the basis of any classical model of a swarm of particles, but it was put forward by the Indian physicist S. N. Bose

---

[3] See L. I. Schiff, *Quantum Mechanics*, 2d ed., McGraw-Hill Book Company, Inc., New York, 1955, p. 235.

[4] W. Pauli, Phys. Rev., **58**, 716 (1940).

and followed further by Einstein[5] in 1924 on the pragmatic grounds that it led to a simple derivation of Planck's law of black-body radiation. We shall see in Chap. 19 how (11.35) leads to Bose's assumptions; what is important here is the fact that there is an elementary particle, the photon, which satisfies (11.35) and not (11.32). Photons are well known to have a spin of 1, for example, because atomic systems change their angular momentum by one unit when a quantum is emitted. Thus they need not satisfy the exclusion principle, and in fact Pauli showed in his original paper that particles with integer spin will be described by symmetrical wave functions. In addition to photons, π mesons and K mesons, and some of the very unstable newer particles, come into this category because they have spin 0, 1, or 2. Particles of this kind are described by what is called Bose-Einstein statistics (see Chap. 19), and they are termed *bosons*.

Finally, we come to the question of the symmetry of composite particles. Suppose we have two identical isolated systems, each consisting of n fermions. The wave function U describing them is a function of $2n$ labeled sets of coordinates. Interchanging the labels of the two composite systems can be done by interchanging those of pairs of corresponding fermions, one pair at a time. Since each such elementary interchange changes the sign of U, the interchange of the two systems changes it n times; and we see that if n is odd, the systems are fermions, whereas if it is even, they are bosons. Clearly, the inclusion of some bosons among the elementary particles composing the two systems does not alter the conclusion.[6]

These considerations often have quite a pronounced effect upon physical phenomena. Two isotopes of the same substance, for example, chemically identical but differing by an odd number of neutrons, obey opposite statistics. This fact has a marked influence on certain molecular spectra (see Sec. 11.5), but perhaps its most striking effect is in the behavior of helium at low temperatures, where He^4 exhibits the strange phenomena of superfluidity in the neighborhood of 2°K, whereas He^3 does not. This is strong evidence that they are essentially quantum phenomena.

Problem 11.17   Does the connection between spin and statistics described above also hold for composite particles?

11.4   Scattering of Identical Particles

We have seen how the identity of particles affects the energy levels of a bound system. In this section we shall look briefly at the corre-

---

[5] S. N. Bose, Z. Physik, **26**, 178 (1924); A. Einstein, Sitzber. Deut. Akad. Wiss. Berlin, Kl. Gesellschaftswiss., 261 (1924).

[6] This elementary argument suffices for most cases of practical interest, but further discussion is needed if the two systems interact strongly enough to perturb each other's internal structure. See P. Ehrenfest and J. R. Oppenheimer, Phys. Rev., **37**, 333 (1931).

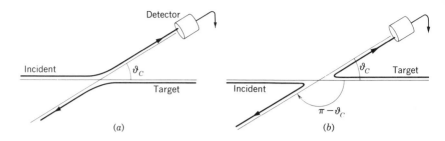

Fig. 11.3 Indistinguishable possibilities in the scattering of
identical particles (C.M. system).

sponding effects in an unbound system, where the symmetry properties of wave functions influence the size and angular dependence of
the scattering cross section.

Let us imagine an experiment in which helium atoms scatter
each other. Viewing the process classically in the C.M. system, we
can picture it as in Fig. 11.3a, in which the detector at an angle ϑ_c
to the incident beam registers the scattered particles. The rate of
counting the incident particles at this angle is proportional to $\sigma_c(\vartheta_c)$.
But Fig. 11.3b shows another possibility. It may be the target particles which are registered in the detector; since they are identical
with the incident particles, there is no way to discriminate them. In
this case the scattering angle of the incident particles is $\pi - \vartheta_c$, and
we must express the total counting rate (subscript T) in terms of the
combined cross sections of the two contributory processes,

$$\left(\frac{d\sigma_T(\vartheta)}{d\Omega}\right)_c = \left(\frac{d\sigma(\vartheta)}{d\Omega}\right)_c + \left(\frac{d\sigma(\pi - \vartheta)}{d\Omega}\right)_c \qquad (11.36)$$

the first and most obvious effect of which is that the counting rate
will always be symmetrical between front and back.

Now let us express the same situation in quantum mechanics.
Figure 11.4 shows how we must look at scattering in the C.M. system. The unscattered beams move along the z axis, and we consider
only the scattering within a small volume Q. Suppose that the beams
contain, on the average, one incident particle and one target particle
per unit volume. Then as in (11.15a), the unscattered wave function,
moving along the z axis, is given by

$$\psi^{(0)} = e^{i(k_1 z_1 + k_2 z_2)} + e^{i(k_1 z_2 + k_2 z_1)}$$
$$= 2 \cos [\tfrac{1}{2}(k_1 - k_2)(z_1 - z_2)]e^{iKz}$$

where k_1 and k_2 are the two momenta. The normalization of this
wave function should be noted. By integrating $|\psi^{(0)}|^2$ over a unit
volume, we find that $\psi^{(0)}$ corresponds to two particles per unit volume: one incident particle and one target particle. In the C.M. sys-

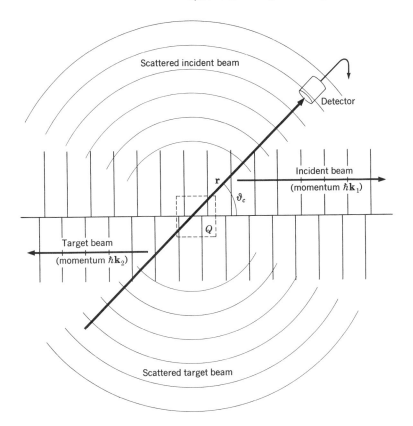

Fig. 11.4 Wave picture of scattering in the C.M. system. The
incident beam and its scattered wave are shown in the upper
half of the figure. In the lower half are the target and its
scattered wave. The detector moves with the target particles
before collision. Only the incident and asymptotic scattered
waves are shown; in the zone of interaction the scattered
waves are complicated in form. A relative displacement
vector $\mathbf{r} = \mathbf{r} - \mathbf{r}_2$ is shown.

tem things become simpler, for in terms of the classical particle
velocity v we have from (9.9)

$$\hbar k_1 = -\hbar k_2 = \mu v$$

whence $K = 0$ and

$$\hbar(k_1 - k_2) = 2\mu v = 2\hbar k$$

where $\hbar k = \mu v$ may be called the reduced momentum of the system.
The k so defined is, in the C.M. system, the exact analogue of the
k's which appear in Secs. 9.3 and 9.4. Introducing the relative co-

ordinate $z = z_1 - z_2$ as in the standard transformation (7.32), we have

$$\psi^{(0)} = 2 \cos kz = e^{ikz} + e^{-ikz} \tag{11.37}$$

The remainder of the argument has already been set up in Prob. 9.7 and goes as in (9.50) and the following equations. We have chosen $D_i = D_t = 1$, so that

$$d\sigma_c = \frac{dN(\vartheta_c)}{Qv}$$

To find $dN(\vartheta_c)$, we note first that substitution of $-z$ for z in (9.55) amounts simply to interchanging left and right. Thus the scattering amplitude for e^{-ikz} is $f(\pi - \vartheta)$, and as in (9.55), the asymptotic form of ψ is

$$\psi \rightarrow e^{ikz} + e^{-ikz} + [f(\vartheta) + f(\pi - \vartheta)] \frac{e^{ikr}}{r} \tag{11.38}$$

We must now find the total scattered intensity originating from the volume Q. To do so, we rewrite $\psi_{sc}(1,2)$ in terms of C.M. variables, getting a new function which we shall denote by $\psi_{sc}(\mathbf{r})$ because, as is evident from (11.38), it is independent of $\mathbf{R}$, the coordinates of the center of mass. The intensity of the scattered wave is proportional to $|\psi_{sc}(\mathbf{r})|^2$, and it is evident from the results of Prob. 7.12 that the total probability of finding a scattered wave of this form is given by integrating $|\psi(\mathbf{r})|^2$ over $\mathbf{R}$, which just multiplies it by Q. Thus,

$$dN(\vartheta_c) = Qv|f(\vartheta_c) + f(\pi - \vartheta_c)|^2 \, d\Omega$$

as in (9.52), so that

$$\left(\frac{d\sigma}{d\Omega}\right)_c = |f(\vartheta_c) + f(\pi - \vartheta_c)|^2 \tag{11.39}$$

On squaring this, we find

$$\left(\frac{d\sigma}{d\Omega}\right)_c = |f(\vartheta_c)|^2 + |f(\pi - \vartheta_c)|^2 + 2 \operatorname{Re} f^*(\vartheta_c)f(\pi - \vartheta_c) \tag{11.40}$$

which differs from the classical result (11.36) by the cross term, representing interference between the two types of scattered wave. The result (11.39) which we have derived is intuitively plain, and it is quite generally taken to be obvious. We have derived it in detail in order to make clear the meaning (and especially the normalization) of the two-particle wave function and to show how to calculate in the C.M. system.

We shall not evaluate the helium-helium scattering further here, since even at energies below 1 eV the angular dependence is complicated. It may be noted, however, that at zero energy, where the scattering finally becomes isotropic, the scattering cross section is twice that which would be given by the classical formula (11.36). (Why?)

Proton-proton scattering

This example is more interesting because the fundamental calculations are simpler and because the protons have spin, so that symmetric and antisymmetric spatial states appear. As in (11.28), we consider the spatial and spin wave functions together, even though spin plays no dynamical part in the scattering process. The ordinary situation is that in which the spin directions of incident and target protons are randomly oriented, so that we have to average over the different possible spin states of the two-particle system. Because the subtle point in many calculations is the carrying out of such an average, we shall perform it here in three different ways.

First, we average over the spins of the two protons considered individually. Since each can take on two orientations, there are four possible states, in two of which the spins are parallel and in the other two antiparallel. If the spins are antiparallel, none of the doctrine of indistinguishable particles as developed above applies [cf. (11.34)]; for by the use of a suitable Stern-Gerlach arrangement it would be possible to distinguish which proton is being detected. Thus the classical viewpoint suffices, and the cross section in this case is given by (11.36),

$$\left(\frac{d\sigma(\vartheta)}{d\Omega}\right)_c = |f(\vartheta_c)|^2 + |f(\pi - \vartheta_c)|^2 \qquad (\uparrow\downarrow \text{ or } \downarrow\uparrow)$$

But if the spins are parallel, then the protons are truly indistinguishable. The spin function being symmetrical, the spatial function must be antisymmetrical, and

$$\left(\frac{d\sigma(\vartheta)}{d\Omega}\right)_c = |f(\vartheta_c) - f(\pi - \vartheta_c)|^2 \qquad (\uparrow\uparrow \text{ or } \downarrow\downarrow)$$

Averaging over these four spin arrangements gives

$$\left(\frac{d\sigma_T(\vartheta)}{d\Omega}\right)_c = |f(\vartheta_c)|^2 + |f(\pi - \vartheta_c)|^2 - \operatorname{Re} f^*(\vartheta_c)f(\pi - \vartheta_c) \qquad (11.41)$$

which differs from (11.40) in the interference term.

Second, suppose we consider the spin states of the two spins taken together. As in (11.28), there are three states with spatially antisymmetrical wave function and one with symmetrical, and the average cross section formed with them is

$$\left(\frac{d\sigma_T(\vartheta)}{d\Omega}\right)_c = \tfrac{3}{4}|f(\vartheta_c) - f(\pi - \vartheta_c)|^2 + \tfrac{1}{4}|f(\vartheta_c) + f(\pi - \vartheta_c)|^2$$

and this is again equal to (11.41). The averaging procedure which we have used here is, however, somewhat less transparent than that in the earlier method, and it should be carefully noted, for nothing in our earlier development of quantum mechanics has told us how to carry it out. We encounter here for the first time the fundamental problem of statistical mechanics, "How does one carry out an average over a number of possibilities distributed at random?" The answer to this question is not obvious; in fact, it is far from obvious what the question means or how it can be translated into mathematics, and such considerations lie far outside the scope of this book. The rule which emerges, applicable to situations like the one before us, is, however, quite simple: If a number of degenerate quantum states are possible, then each is equally probable. In the two averages we have just performed the states were differently defined, but this rule was followed in each.[7]

As a third method of approach, closely related to the second, we shall construct an operator which distinguishes between the possible spin situations. The simplest way to introduce this operator is to write it down:

$$\hat{f}(\vartheta_c) = f(\vartheta_c) - \tfrac{1}{2}(1 + 4\hat{\mathbf{S}}_1 \cdot \hat{\mathbf{S}}_2)f(\pi - \vartheta_c) \tag{11.42}$$

The merit of mixing a spin operator with spatial amplitudes in this way is that there are only two possible types of spin eigenstate: the symmetrical and the antisymmetrical. For symmetrical spin states (see Sec. 6.4), the spin operator may be replaced by $\tfrac{1}{4}$ and f may therefore be replaced by the antisymmetrical combination $f(\vartheta_c) - f(\pi - \vartheta_c)$, satisfying the Pauli principle. For antisymmetrical spin states, $\hat{\mathbf{S}}_1 \cdot \hat{\mathbf{S}}_2$ becomes $-\tfrac{3}{4}$ and $\hat{f}$ becomes $f(\vartheta_c) + f(\pi - \vartheta_c)$. All possible cases are represented by linear combinations of symmetrical and antisymmetrical states, and the differential cross section may be represented by

$$\left(\frac{d\sigma(\vartheta)}{d\Omega}\right)_c = \langle |\hat{f}(\vartheta_c)|^2\rangle$$

where the brackets denote the appropriate average over spins. This can be written as

$$\begin{aligned}
\left(\frac{d\sigma(\vartheta)}{d\Omega}\right)_c =\ & |f(\vartheta_c) - \tfrac{1}{2}f(\pi - \vartheta_c)|^2 \\
& - 4\,\mathrm{Re}\,[f^*(\vartheta_c) - \tfrac{1}{2}f^*(\pi - \vartheta_c)]f(\pi - \vartheta_c)\langle\hat{\mathbf{S}}_1 \cdot \hat{\mathbf{S}}_2\rangle \\
& + 4|f(\pi - \vartheta_c)|^2\langle(\hat{\mathbf{S}}_1 \cdot \hat{\mathbf{S}}_2)^2\rangle
\end{aligned} \tag{11.43}$$

Remembering the eigenvalues of $\hat{\mathbf{S}}_1 \cdot \hat{\mathbf{S}}_2$, we have

$$\langle\hat{\mathbf{S}}_1 \cdot \hat{\mathbf{S}}_2\rangle = \tfrac{1}{4}(\tfrac{1}{4} + \tfrac{1}{4} + \tfrac{1}{4} - \tfrac{3}{4}) = 0$$

$$\langle(\hat{\mathbf{S}}_1 \cdot \hat{\mathbf{S}}_2)^2\rangle = \tfrac{1}{4}(\tfrac{1}{16} + \tfrac{1}{16} + \tfrac{1}{16} + \tfrac{9}{16}) = \tfrac{3}{16}$$

---

[7] A derivation of the second method of averaging from the first, using the plausible hypothesis that the phases of the wave functions in a statistical aggregate are distributed at random, is given in Sec. 17.2. The clearest and most painstaking discussion of the foundations of quantum statistics is still that of R. C. Tolman, *Statistical Mechanics*, Oxford University Press, London, 1938.

and putting these into (11.43) again gives us (11.41). This is only a roundabout method of carrying out the average according to the second method; but because it is quite automatic, it is often easier in a more complex calculation.

To calculate the angular distribution, we need the analytic expression for $f(\vartheta_c)$. We have already evaluated it in the Born approximation for the Coulomb interaction in Chap. 9. As in (9.38), we have

$$f_B(\vartheta_c) = -\frac{Me'^2}{\hbar^2 k^2 \sin^2 \frac{1}{2}\vartheta_c}$$

where M is the proton mass. Putting this into (11.41), we find

$$\left(\frac{d\sigma(\vartheta)}{d\Omega}\right)_c \approx \left(\frac{Me'^2}{\hbar^2 k^2}\right)^2 \left(\frac{1}{\sin^4 \frac{1}{2}\vartheta_c} + \frac{1}{\cos^4 \frac{1}{2}\vartheta_c} - \frac{1}{\sin^2 \frac{1}{2}\vartheta_c \cos^2 \frac{1}{2}\vartheta_c}\right) \quad (11.44)$$

But for Coulomb scattering it is possible to integrate the wave equation exactly, and one finds[8]

$$f(\vartheta_c) = -\frac{Me'^2}{\hbar^2 k^2 \sin^2 \frac{1}{2}\vartheta_c} \frac{\Gamma(1 + in)}{\Gamma(1 - in)} e^{-2in \ln \sin \frac{1}{2}\vartheta_c}$$

where

$$n = \frac{e'^2}{\hbar v}$$

and v is the protons' relative velocity. The exact scattering cross section is therefore

$$\left(\frac{d\sigma(\vartheta)}{d\Omega}\right)_c = \left(\frac{Me'^2}{\hbar^2 k^2}\right)^2 \left[\frac{1}{\sin^4 \frac{1}{2}\vartheta_c} + \frac{1}{\cos^4 \frac{1}{2}\vartheta_c} - \frac{\cos\left(2n \ln \tan \frac{1}{2}\vartheta_c\right)}{\sin^2 \frac{1}{2}\vartheta_c \cos^2 \frac{1}{2}\vartheta_c}\right] \quad (11.45)$$

which is close to (11.44) at high energies (where the Born approximation is best) except for angles ϑ_c close to 0 and π.

This formula was first published by Mott[9] in 1930, and the process which it describes is commonly known as Mott scattering. Of particular interest are the deviations from this law which occur at energies above a few Mev, where the specifically nuclear interactions between the protons come into play.[10] The interference effect in Mott's formula is quite marked at all energies and is shown in Fig. 11.5, taken from his paper.

[8] See N. F. Mott and H. S. W. Massey, *Theory of Atomic Collisions*, Clarendon Press, Oxford, 1933, 1949.

[9] N. F. Mott, Proc. Roy Soc. London, Ser. A, **126**, 259 (1930).

[10] See H. A. Bethe and P. Morrison, *Elementary Nuclear Theory*, 2d ed., John Wiley & Sons, Inc., New York, 1956, chap. 13.

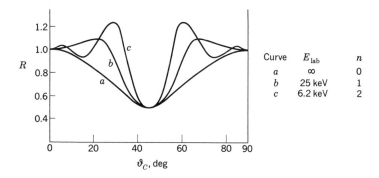

Fig. 11.5 Plot of R, the ratio of the Mott cross section for p-p scattering to that calculated without the interference term. (By permission of the Royal Society of London.)

Problem 11.18 Electrons are scattered by hydrogen atoms. Considering the protons to be at rest, two types of scattering amplitude must be distinguished,

$$f(\vartheta) = -\frac{1}{4\pi}\frac{2m}{\hbar^2} \int \psi_c^{(0)*}(1,2)\,V(1,2)\psi(1,2)\,dv_1\,dv_2$$

and

$$g(\vartheta) = -\frac{1}{4\pi}\frac{2m}{\hbar^2} \int \psi_c^{(0)*}(2,1)\,V(1,2)\psi(1,2)\,dv_1\,dv_2$$

[see (9.51)], where $\psi_c^{(0)}$ is the *unsymmetrized* wave function which describes one electron at the atom and the other being scattered, and ψ is the corresponding exact wave function. (They are the wave functions which would be used if the electrons were almost, but not quite, identical.) The amplitude $g(\vartheta)$ refers to the possibility that the incident electron is captured and the one previously bound is emitted into the counter. Prove that the optical theorem now reads

$$\sigma = \frac{4\pi}{k} \operatorname{Im}\left[f(0) - \tfrac{1}{2}g(0)\right] \tag{11.46}$$

11.5 Symmetry and Molecular Spectra

The connection between the spin of a particle and the symmetry of its wave function leads to measurable effects in molecular spectra which enable one to determine the spin of a nucleus by means of spectroscopy. The basic idea of this method, suggested in 1927 by Heisenberg and Hund, is very simple, and it can be illustrated by the theory of a rigid diatomic molecule whose nuclei are exactly alike.

The wave function of a homonuclear diatomic molecule is either symmetrical or antisymmetrical under exchange of the two nuclei according as the nuclei are bosons or fermions. It is written as the product of a space part and a spin part, $U(1,2) = \psi(1,2)\chi(1,2)$ and, neglecting spin-orbit effects, we can say that ψ and χ each has a certain symmetry so that the symmetry of U is their product.

The hamiltonian for a rigid rotator is derived from the classical formula

$$\hat{H} = \frac{\hbar^2 \hat{L}^2}{2J}$$

where J is the moment of inertia, and its eigenvalues are

$$E_k = \frac{\hbar^2 k(k+1)}{2J} \qquad (k = 0,1,2, \ldots) \qquad (11.47)$$

The eigenfunctions are spherical harmonics (see Appendix 4), and all we need to know is that their spatial symmetry is even or odd according as k (the analogue of our earlier l) is even or odd. [This property can be verified in the hydrogen wave functions of (7.56).]

The spin eigenfunctions are formed from the spins χ_m and $\chi_{m'}$ of the two nuclei: odd eigenfunctions are of the form

$$\chi_{mm'}^{(-)}(1,2) = 2^{-\frac{1}{2}}[\chi_m(1)\chi_{m'}(2) - \chi_m(2)\chi_{m'}(1)] \qquad (m \neq m') \qquad (11.48$$

and even ones are

$$\chi_{mm'}^{(+)}(1,2) = 2^{-\frac{1}{2}}[\chi_m(1)\chi_{m'}(2) + \chi_m(2)\chi_{m'}(1) \qquad (m \neq m') \qquad (11.49)$$

or

$$\chi_{mm'}^{(+)}(1,2) = \chi_m(1)\chi_m(2) \qquad (m = m') \qquad (11.50)$$

Radiation of a photon decreases k, and one might at first suppose that it would obey the selection rule of (10.3) and decrease by one unit. But such a transition would change the parity of $\psi(1,2)$ and hence of U, which it cannot, unless there is a compensating change in the parity of the spin state $\chi(1,2)$. But nuclei have very small magnetic moments and their spins are very weakly coupled to the radiation field; hence such a change is very unlikely and the usual selection rule is $k \rightarrow k - 2$. The emitted quanta have energies

$$E_k - E_{k-2} = \frac{3(k-1)\hbar^2}{J} \qquad (11.51)$$

and the spectral lines fall into two separate series according as k is even or odd.

The intensity of the spectral line corresponding to a given k depends on the initial population of that state, and this depends on the spins of the nuclei. For each k there are $2k + 1$ orbital states, and in addition, if the nuclear spin is I, each nucleus has $2I + 1$ states χ_m $(m = -I, \ldots, +I)$ available to it. The number of odd spin states of two nuclei is the number of states of the form (11.48): the number of unlike pairs chosen from $2I + 1$ objects is

$\frac{1}{2}(2I + 1)(2I + 1 - 1)$, so that

$$N_{\text{odd}} = I(2I + 1) \tag{11.52}$$

For even states, there is an equal number of the form (11.49) plus $(2I + 1)$ of the form (11.50), giving

$$N_{\text{even}} = (I + 1)(2I + 1) \tag{11.53}$$

Let us calculate the ratio of the intensities of two adjacent lines of the rotational spectrum. One will have an odd spin function and the other an even one; their values of k will differ by 1. The intensities will be proportional to the number of atoms in the two initial states, that is, to their multiplicities, since, as in the preceding section, each state is equally probable. Let us say that the odd spin state corresponds to the greater value of k. The intensity ratio will be

$$\begin{aligned} R &= \frac{N_{\text{odd}}}{N_{\text{even}}} \frac{2k + 1}{2(k - 1) + 1} \\ &= \frac{I}{I + 1} \frac{k + \frac{1}{2}}{k - \frac{1}{2}} \end{aligned} \tag{11.54}$$

The point of the argument is that values of k which are much larger than 1 are present, so that over most of a band the second factor is effectively unity. The relation

$$R \approx \frac{I}{I + 1} \tag{11.55}$$

thus holds regardless of which spin state corresponds to the greater value of k, and a careful measurement of the intensity ratio between adjacent pairs of lines at once gives the value of I. Further, the same ratio will be found in absorption spectra, depending also on the populations of the initial states, and for practical reasons this is the measurement usually made. The only precaution to be taken is that the absorbing gas must be hot enough that the Boltzmann factor does not operate significantly in favor of lower initial states.

The most striking examples of (11.54) are found in diatomic molecules containing spinless nuclei such as $(C^{12})_2$ or $(O^{16})_2$, where

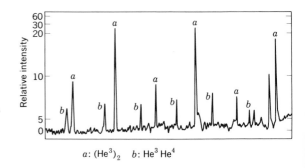

Fig. 11.6 Near infrared spectrum of He$_2$ gas greatly enriched in He^3. Lines due to (He^3)$_2$ and to He^{3}He^4 are distinguished. The latter show no alternation of intensities. [Reproduced by permission from A. E. Douglas and G. Hertzberg, Phys. Rev., **76**, 1529 (1949).]

Relative intensity

a: (He^3)$_2$ b: He^3 He^4

half the lines are missing altogether. Figure 11.6 shows the alternation of intensities in an infrared band.

Problem 11.19   What is the nuclear spin of He^3?

Problem 11.20   Show that for identical particles of arbitrary spin s, the optical theorem analogous to (11.46) is

$$\sigma = \frac{4\pi}{k} \operatorname{Im}\left[f(0) \pm \frac{g(0)}{2s + 1} \right]$$

where the plus sign is for bosons and the minus sign for fermions.

part II
Applications

The subject of waves is of less immediate importance for any practical application than some other parts of hydraulics; but besides that it is intimately connected with the phenomena of the tides, it affords an elegant employment for speculative investigation. . . .

Dr. Thomas Young

The Theory of Alpha Decay

12.1 The Escape of an Alpha Particle

The most characteristic feature of all radioactive decay processes is the exponential law they follow: N, the number of atoms which have not decayed, decreases with time according to

$$N = N_0 e^{-\lambda t} \qquad (12.1)$$

In order to see what this law states with regard to any one atom, we differentiate it to find

$$\frac{dN}{dt} = -\lambda N \qquad (12.2)$$

so that the rate of decay each second is proportional to the number present. It follows that λ represents the probability that any given nucleus will decay in any given unit interval of time. This constant probability, independent of the age of the nucleus, is very hard to understand on the basis of the traditional concepts of physics, and it is only with the advent of quantum mechanics that explanations have been found.

In this chapter we shall study the emission of α particles from a nucleus. The situation here is different from that in β or γ decay, for example; for those particles do not exist in the nucleus, but are formed at the moment of emission. The material comprising the α particle, however, is a part of the nucleus, and we are going to assume that, because of the extraordinary stability of this configuration (once formed, it takes 20.5 MeV to remove a neutron from an

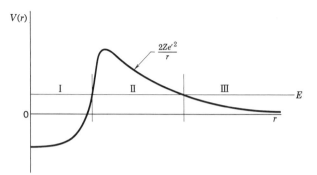

Fig. 12.1 Qualitative behavior of the potential acting on an α particle inside and outside the nucleus

α particle in isolation from other nuclear matter), the neutrons and protons inside a nucleus spend an appreciable fraction of their time all made up as α particles and ready to be emitted. How they escape from the forces binding the nucleus together was explained simultaneously and independently by Gamow[1] and by Condon and Gurney[2] as an example of the quantum-mechanical penetration of a potential barrier. That such a barrier exists can be seen if one looks at it from either side: an alpha particle incident from outside will be repelled by the Coulomb field of the nucleus, and on the other hand it is clear that a nucleus would disperse altogether under the influence of the Coulomb repulsion of its charges if it were not enclosed by the barrier of some stronger force. The situation is therefore as shown in Fig. 12.1, where only the outer extremity of the barrier can be drawn with certainty, since it is due to a Coulomb force (Z is the atomic number of the *daughter* nucleus). Because it is difficult to be more detailed, we shall assume only that a single α particle is always present in the nucleus, and we shall calculate its probability of escape.

We are going to evaluate the wave function in the WKB approximation, but this at once raises a difficulty, since the method as we have developed it starts from the time-independent Schrödinger equation for a stationary state, whereas here we are assuming that a bound α particle will ultimately leak away and the wave function is therefore not a periodic function of the time. We can, however, treat the problem approximately by making use of the fact that if the barrier is nearly impenetrable, the wave function inside will be nearly that of the corresponding stationary state. The situation is essentially three-dimensional, but by considering only spherically symmetrical wave functions, corresponding to the emission of α particles with angular momentum equal to zero (see Chap. 5), we can reduce the computation to one dimension. Let us assume that ψ is a function of $r = (x^2 + y^2 + z^2)^{1/2}$ only, and let us introduce for con-

[1] G. Gamow, Z. Physik, **51**, 204 (1928).
[2] E. U. Condon and R. W. Gurney, Nature, **122**, 439 (1928); Phys. Rev., **33**, 127 (1929).

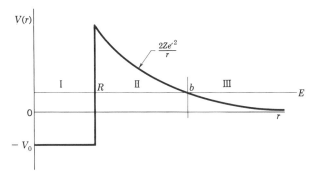

Fig. 12.2   Simplified version
of Fig. 12.1.

venience a new variable $u(r)$ defined by $\psi(r) = u(r)/r$. On evaluating
the laplacian of this expression we find that

$$\nabla^2 \psi = \frac{1}{r} \frac{d^2 u}{dr^2}$$

so that Schrödinger's equation becomes

$$\frac{d^2 u}{dr^2} + \frac{2m}{\hbar^2} [E - V(r)]u = 0$$

(We shall not carry out the differentiation here, since the result is
derived in detail in Chap. 7.) If ψ is to be finite at the origin, we
must require that

$$u(0) = 0 \qquad\qquad (12.3)$$

In order to avoid the worst computation difficulties, we shall
assume a somewhat simplified model due to Bethe, in which the
alpha particle is assumed to move in a constant potential, which is
the smoothed-out effect of all its nuclear interactions, until it reaches
the edge of the nucleus, where an abrupt rise takes place. In the three
regions of Fig. 12.2, we have

$$u_{\text{I}} = A \sin Kr \qquad\qquad (0 < r < R) \qquad (12.4)$$

$$u_{\text{II}} = C\kappa^{-\frac12} \exp\left(-\int_R^r \kappa\, dr\right) + D\kappa^{-\frac12} \exp\left(\int_R^r \kappa\, dr\right)$$
$$(R < r < b) \qquad (12.5)$$

$$u_{\text{III}} = A'k^{-\frac12} \exp\left(i\int_b^r k\, dx\right) \qquad (b < r) \qquad (12.6)$$

Here

$$K = \left[\frac{2m}{\hbar^2}(E + V_0)\right]^{\frac12}$$

$$\kappa = \left[\frac{2m}{\hbar^2}\left(\frac{2Ze'^2}{r} - E\right)\right]^{\frac12}$$

$$k = \left[\frac{2m}{\hbar^2}\left(E - \frac{2Ze'^2}{r}\right)\right]^{\frac12}$$

and the boundary condition (12.1) has been used for u_I. The wave functions in regions II and III will be estimated by the WKB approximation, which is here valid for the slowly varying Coulomb potential. The second turning point b is given by

$$b = \frac{2Ze'^2}{E} \tag{12.7}$$

To join the wave functions at the nuclear radius, we have from the continuity of u

$$A \sin KR = (C + D)[\kappa(R)]^{-\frac{1}{2}} \tag{12.8}$$

and from that of u',

$$AK \cos KR = (-C + D)[\kappa(R)]^{\frac{1}{2}} \tag{12.9}$$

where in evaluating the derivative on the right we have included the rapid dependence of u on r through the exponential and neglected its relatively slow dependence through the amplitude. To match wave functions at $r = b$, we write

$$u_{II} = Ce^{-\sigma}\kappa^{-\frac{1}{2}} \exp\left(-\int_b^r \kappa \, dr\right) + De^{\sigma}\kappa^{-\frac{1}{2}} \exp\left(\int_b^r \kappa \, dr\right) \tag{12.10}$$

where

$$\sigma = \int_R^b \kappa(r) \, dr \tag{12.11}$$

and comparison with (4.76) and (12.6) shows that

$$C = \vartheta^* e^{\sigma} A' \qquad D = \tfrac{1}{2}\vartheta e^{-\sigma} A' \qquad (\vartheta = e^{i\pi/4}) \tag{12.12}$$

We shall see later that σ is at least of the order of 10, so that D is much smaller than C, as one would expect from (12.5). The α particle escapes only after a very long time, and its wave function is therefore essentially that of a particle in a stationary state, which would have D equal to zero (Fig. 12.3).

Fig. 12.3 Wave function for the simplified version. The amplitude of the outer wave is greatly exaggerated.

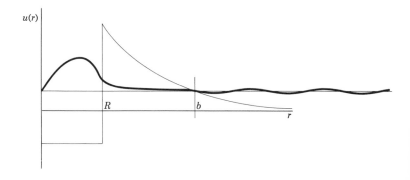

The probability per second of decay is denoted by λ and is equal to

$$\lambda = \frac{4\pi\hbar|A'|^2}{m} \tag{12.13}$$

Problem 12.1   Prove Eq. (12.13).

By (12.12), we have

$$\lambda = 4\pi \frac{\hbar}{m} e^{-2\sigma}|C|^2 \tag{12.14}$$

and from (12.9), neglecting D,

$$\lambda = 4\pi \frac{\hbar K^2}{m\kappa(R)} |A|^2 e^{-2\sigma} \cos^2 KR \tag{12.15}$$

This formula can be simplified if we assume that the α particle within the nucleus is in the lowest quantum state. (This is reasonable because α particles do not obey the exclusion principle.) The nuclear barrier then reduces the wave function almost to zero at the edge of the nucleus, and we have

$$KR \approx \pi \qquad 4\pi|A|^2 \approx \frac{2}{R} \tag{12.16}$$

Problem 12.2   Justify (12.16).

Thus finally, in this approximation,

$$\lambda = \frac{2\pi^2\hbar}{mR^3\kappa(R)} e^{-2\sigma}$$

In order to gain some physical insight into this formula, let us rewrite it (using $KR \approx \pi$) as

$$\lambda = 2 \frac{\hbar K}{mR} \frac{K}{\kappa(R)} e^{-2\sigma}$$

The quantity $\hbar K/m$ is the velocity of the α particle within the nucleus, v_{in}, and $K/\kappa(R)$ is in the general neighborhood of unity. Thus, very roughly,

$$\lambda \approx \frac{v_{in}}{R} e^{-2\sigma} \tag{12.17}$$

which can be given a simple interpretation: the α particle oscillates around in the nucleus, hitting the nuclear barrier about v_{in}/R times per second. At each impact, there is a probability $e^{-2\sigma}$ of penetrating the barrier, so that the probability of penetration per second is approximately that given by λ.

Problem 12.3   Show that $e^{-2\sigma}$ plays the part assigned it in the foregoing argument.

12.2 Evaluation of the Formula

As we have developed it here, the theory is admittedly very rough, for we have neglected, among others, two factors which should be important:

1. The fact that the α particle itself has a structure, of size comparable to that of the nucleus, and presumably has no permanent existence inside the nucleus at all.

2. The fact that angular momenta greater than zero are surely often present. We thus cannot expect the theory to be accurate in detail, and we shall be justified in evaluating it somewhat roughly.

We know that α particles leave the nucleus with velocities in the neighborhood of 10^9 cm/sec and that $R \approx 10^{-12}$ cm. Assuming that v_{in} is also about 10^9 cm/sec (and this is justified in nuclear theory) we have from (12.17)

$$\lambda \approx 10^{21} e^{-2\sigma} \qquad \sec^{-1} \tag{12.18}$$

The integral σ in (12.11), since it appears in the answer exponentially, must be done with care.

$$\sigma = \left(\frac{2m}{\hbar^2}\right)^{1/2} \int_R^b \left(\frac{2Ze'^2}{r} - E\right)^{1/2} dr$$

$$= \left(\frac{2mE}{\hbar^2}\right)^{1/2} \int_R^b \left(\frac{b}{r} - 1\right)^{1/2} dr$$

by (12.7). This is easily evaluated by the substitution $r = b\cos^2 u$ to give

$$\sigma = \left(\frac{2mE}{\hbar^2}\right)^{1/2} b \left\{ \cos^{-1}\left(\frac{R}{b}\right)^{1/2} - \left[\frac{R}{b}\left(1 - \frac{R}{b}\right)\right]^{1/2} \right\} \tag{12.19}$$

Problem 12.4 Evaluate the integral for σ.

It is easy to see from (12.7) that b is ordinarily several times R, so that we can approximate (12.19), using

$$\cos^{-1} x^{1/2} \approx \frac{\pi}{2} - x^{1/2} \qquad [x(1 - x)]^{1/2} \approx x^{1/2} \tag{12.20}$$

as

$$\sigma = \left(\frac{2mE}{\hbar^2}\right)^{1/2} b \left[\frac{\pi}{2} - 2\left(\frac{R}{b}\right)^{1/2}\right]$$

$$= \frac{(2m)^{1/2} e^2}{4\varepsilon_0 \hbar} ZE^{-1/2} - Z^{1/2} R^{1/2} \left(\frac{4me^2}{\pi\varepsilon_0 \hbar^2}\right)^{1/2}$$

The only variables in this expression are R, Z, and E. Measuring E in MeV and R in the characteristic nuclear unit of 10^{-13} cm (often called the fermi) we find

$$\sigma = 1.97 ZE^{-1/2} - 1.49 Z^{1/2} R^{1/2} \tag{12.21}$$

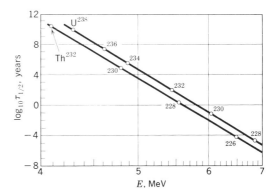

Fig. 12.4 Geiger-Nuttall plot of $\log_{10}$ $\tau_{1/2}$ against $E^{-1/2}$ (plotted toward the left, with the scale given in terms of E) for isotopes of U and Th.

For comparison with experiment it is usual to consider the logarithm (to base 10) of the half-life in years:

$$\log_{10} \tau_{1/2} = \log_{10} \frac{\ln 2}{3.15 \times 10^7 \lambda}$$

$$= -29 + 0.8686\sigma$$

$$= -29 - 1.29Z^{1/2}R^{1/2} + 1.71ZE^{-1/2} \qquad (12.22)$$

The energies of α decay range from 4 to 9 MeV, and it is the last term of (12.22), with Z in the neighborhood of 100, that accounts for the enormous range of α lifetimes (10^{-7} sec to 10^9 years). We see also the reason for the empirical law of Geiger and Nuttall, that a plot of $\log_{10}\tau_{1/2}$ against decay energy is smooth and fairly straight. Clearly, it would be better to plot $\log_{10} \tau_{1/2}$ against $E^{-1/2}$ for a given value of Z, and this is done in Fig. 12.4 for the isotopes of thorium and uranium.[3] Empirically, the data on thorium ($Z = 90$) are fitted by a formula of the form

$$\log_{10} \tau_{1/2} = 144.19E^{-1/2} - 60.7635$$

According to (12.22), the coefficient of $E^{-1/2}$ is expected to be 154, and this gives us some idea of the accuracy of the method used. From the other term we find that $R = 6.8 \times 10^{-13}$ cm. This is comparable with, but somewhat smaller than, the value obtained from nuclear scattering experiments. [It should be remembered, too, that the constant in (12.22) was roughly estimated.]

Problem 12.5 Show that the WKB approximation is valid where it has been used in this calculation.

Problem 12.6 Extend the calculation by including the next terms of the expansions in (12.20). How does this affect the estimate for R?

[3] The graph is adapted from I. Perlman and J. O. Rasmussen, Alpha Radioactivity, in *Encyclopedia of Physics*, Springer-Verlag OHG, Berlin, Vol. 42, by permission of Springer-Verlag and the authors.

Problem 12.7 Assuming that nuclei of the same mass number have equal radii, find the formula which compares $\log_{10} \tau_{1/2}$ for a pair of such nuclei as a function of their different Z's and E's. Ra^{226} emits a 4.78-MeV alpha with a half-life of 1622 years. What is the half-life of the 6.33-MeV alpha from Th^{226}? (The experimental value is 30.9 min.)

Problem 12.8 An alpha-active nucleus usually emits alphas of several different energies. Show that, other things being equal, the ratio of the intensities at two different energies E_1 and E_2 is given by $\exp\left[-3.84\ Z(E_1^{-1/2} - E_2^{-1/2})\right]$, and compare this formula with experimental values found in the literature.

Although the approximations which we have made preclude any claim to exactness, it is clear that they afford an insight into the phenomenon which is better than qualitative. Historically this theory was the first successful application of quantum mechanics to a nuclear problem.

12.3 Remarks

The discussion which we have given fails somewhat in rigor because it ignores the fact that an α particle inside a nucleus is obviously not in a stationary state and that its initial state must therefore properly be represented by a linear combination of wave functions belonging to different values of E. The important range of values of E is small, being given by the uncertainty relation $\tau_{1/2}\ \Delta E \approx \hbar$, which is why our theory was successful, but one should also be able to do the calculation in a rigorous way. It has been carried out by Fermi,[4] and it leads (except for an unimportant factor of 2) to the results we have obtained above.

When the theory of radioactive decay is pursued further, unexpected results begin to emerge. The famous exponential law of radioactive decay turns out to be only an approximation. By the end of a few hundred times $\tau_{1/2}$ the decay has become much slower than formerly, and it finally ends up in an inverse power of t, the decay being given under rather general circumstances as

$$N(t) = N_0 \left\{ e^{-\lambda t} + \frac{1}{2\pi}\left[\frac{\lambda}{(E_0/\hbar)^2 + \frac{1}{4}\lambda^2}\right]^2 t^{-2} \right\}$$

plus a rapidly fluctuating term arising out of interference between the two modes of decay. Instead of (12.2) we therefore find at very long times

$$\frac{dN}{dt} = -2\frac{N}{t}$$

4 E. Fermi, *Nuclear Physics*, University of Chicago Press, Chicago, 1950.

so that the probability of decay per second has become $2/t$. A rough way of understanding this is to note that since the initial wave function is not a stationary state, it is a mixture of such states, and the components with higher energy tend to decay first. The general analysis requires a knowledge of complex variables;[5] the special case of a barrier in the form of a δ function is more academic, but it can be worked out in detail.[6]

REFERENCES

H. A. Bethe, Rev. Mod. Phys., **9,** 69 (1937).

E. Fermi, *Nuclear Physics*, University of Chicago Press, Chicago, 1950.

I. Perlman and J. O. Rasmussen, Alpha Radioactivity, in *Encyclopedia of Physics*, Springer-Verlag OHG, Berlin, 1957, vol. 42. This work contains experimental data and a selected and annotated list of references to earlier theoretical discussions.

[5] L. A. Khalfin, Soviet Phys. JETP **6,** 1053 (1958).

[6] R. G. Winter, Phys. Rev., **123,** 1503 (1961).

Electrons in a Periodic Lattice

13.1 The Periodic Potential

Many of the characteristic electrical properties of metals and semi-conductors can be traced to the fact that in them the energies of the conduction electrons are not free to take any value, but are restricted to lie in certain ranges, the so-called *conduction bands*. In this chapter we shall study this phenomenon through the analysis of a system which is particularly simple but which nonetheless exhibits all the principal features, the one-dimensional motion of electrons in a potential V which is periodic in a distance l:

$$V(x + l) = V(x) \tag{13.1}$$

Since this is not true at the two ends of the lattice, we imagine that it has been bent into the shape of a ring of circumference Nl, with x still measured along the circumference. N is thus the number of cells in the complete loop, and we shall be interested in the case in which it is very large (say, 10^{23}). Clearly, the entire hamiltonian function $\hat{H}$ is invariant under displacement through l, so that introducing the nonhermitian operator $\hat{D}$ as in (5.9), we have

$$[\hat{D}, \hat{H}] = 0 \tag{13.2}$$

The eigenfunctions of $\hat{H}$ are thus simultaneously eigenfunctions of $\hat{D}$, and these have already been determined in Sec. 5.4, where it was shown that they are all of the form (5.18),

$$\psi(x) = e^{ikx} u_k(x) \tag{13.3}$$

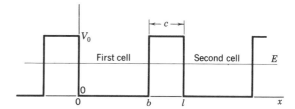

Fig. 13.1   Assumed form of a
square potential lattice.

(which we shall assume to be normalized) with

$$k = \frac{2\pi n}{Nl} \qquad (n = \ldots, -2, -1, 0, 1, 2, \ldots) \tag{13.4}$$

and

$$u_k(x + l) = u_k(x) \tag{13.5}$$

so that

$$\psi(x + l) = e^{ikl}\psi(x) \tag{13.6}$$

where e^{ikl} is the complex eigenvalue of the nonhermitian operator $\hat{D}$. We shall call k the *propagation constant* of the state. The great advantage which has been gained is that once we know the value of $\psi(x)$ in the first cell of the lattice, (13.6) enables us to write it down for all the other cells. We can therefore confine our attention to the first cell in solving the equations.

Although all the essential features of metallic conduction are already inherent in the general picture just presented,[1] it will be easiest if we carry out an explicit calculation for a particular form of lattice, that illustrated in Fig. 13.1, in which the wells are rectangular and the solutions may be written down at once.[2] With

$$E = \frac{\hbar^2 k_1{}^2}{2m} \qquad V_0 - E = \frac{\hbar^2 \kappa_2{}^2}{2m} \tag{13.7}$$

we can write for the first cell

$$\psi(x) = A e^{ik_1 x} + B e^{-ik_1 x} \qquad (0 \leqslant x \leqslant b) \tag{13.8}$$

$$\psi(x) = C e^{-\kappa_2 x} + D e^{\kappa_2 x} \qquad (b \leqslant x \leqslant 1) \tag{13.9}$$

and for the left side of the second cell

$$\psi(x) = [A e^{ik_1(x-l)} + B e^{-ik_1(x-l)}]e^{ikl} \qquad (l \leqslant x \leqslant l + b) \tag{13.10}$$

by (13.6). In order to form a solution of Schrödinger's equation, these pieces must join smoothly at $x = b$ and $x = l$. The continuity of ψ and $\partial\psi/\partial x$ at these points yields four simultaneous equations in A, B, C, and D; and in order for these to be soluble, the determi-

---

[1] H. A. Kramers, Physica, **2**, 483 (1935).

[2] R. de L. Kronig and W. G. Penney, Proc. Roy. Soc. London, Ser. A, **130**, 499 (1930).

nant of the coefficients of A, B, C, and D must vanish. This entails some algebra, which we omit here, but the result is quite simple:

$$\cos k_1 b \cosh \kappa_2 c - \frac{k_1{}^2 - \kappa_2{}^2}{2k_1\kappa_2} \sin k_1 b \sinh \kappa_2 c$$

$$= \cos kl \qquad (E < V_0)$$

$$= \cos 2\pi \frac{n}{N} \qquad (13.11)$$

by (13.4). This is an implicit equation for the energy E exactly analogous to the explicit equation (4.43), for example. But aside from the fact that E is now a little harder to find, there is an important difference in that the right side of (13.11) is a periodic function of n (or k), going through a complete cycle in N steps. N being large, these steps lie so close together that we shall frequently speak of k as though it had a continuous range of variation.

When the energy E lies above V_0, the quantity κ_2 in (13.7) becomes imaginary, say, $\pm ik_2$; and since nothing has been assumed about the reality of κ_2 in deriving (13.11), we can at once write down the equation

$$\cos k_1 b \cos k_2 c - \frac{k_1{}^2 + k_2{}^2}{2k_1 k_2} \sin k_1 b \sin k_2 c = \cos kl \qquad (E > V_0) \qquad (13.12)$$

The remarkable feature of these equations is that for certain ranges of values of E, they cannot be satisfied. Let $k_1 b$ in (13.11) be $m\pi$, for example, where m is any integer. The equation becomes

$$(-1)^m \cosh \kappa_2 c = \cos kl \qquad (13.13)$$

which is impossible for nonzero real values of the parameters. It is easy to see why this value of k_1 is not possible, for with it every wave, in traversing a potential well and partially reflecting back across it, oscillates through an integral number of complete cycles, and so the reflected waves from all the cells are in phase and interfere constructively. The reflection is so strong that the wave cannot get through.

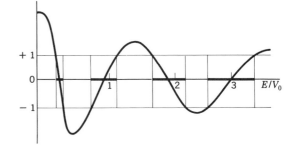

Fig. 13.2 Plot of the left sides of (13.11) and (13.12) as functions of E. The heavy lines show the allowed values of E.

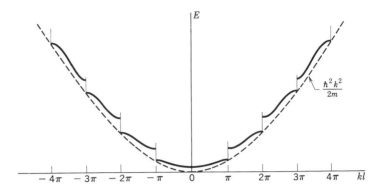

$$\frac{\hbar^2 k^2}{2m}$$

Fig. 13.3 E as a function of k for the square potential lattice. The dotted line is the relation for a free particle.

Problem 13.1   Derive (13.11).

Problem 13.2   Show that if E is greater than V_0 and such that $k_1 b + k_2 c = m\pi$, the wave equation cannot be satisfied. How is this fact to be interpreted physically?

Problem 13.3   Prove that if one allows the spacing c between wells to become infinite without changing b or V_0, the energy bands for $E < V_0$ become narrower and finally reduce to isolated energy levels identical with those directly calculated for an isolated potential well.

The situation can be better understood if we plot the left sides of (13.11) and (13.12) as functions of E. The functions join smoothly together at $E = V_0$, and we find a curve like that of Fig. 13.2. Solutions can exist only when the functions take values between -1 and $+1$, and the ranges of E for which this occurs have been indicated by dark shading. These ranges are known as the *conduction bands* of the lattice; they are separated by the *forbidden bands*.[3]

It is useful to think of E as a function of k, which goes from 0 to π/l across the first conduction band and from π/l to $2\pi/l$ across the second, etc., so that E takes discontinuous jumps at π/l, $2\pi/l$, etc. This leads to the graph of Fig. 13.3, where the gaps in the permitted values of E are again apparent and where the dotted line is the graph of the relation

$$E = \frac{\hbar^2 k^2}{2m} \tag{13.14}$$

[3] The limiting case of this model in which the potential barriers become infinitely high and narrow leads to explicit formulas for a number of the relationships studied here (see the reference of footnote 2). A detailed study of the energy bands as a function of well depth has been made by G. Allen, Phys. Rev., **91**, 531 (1953).

It is clear that the parameter k plays a part which is somewhat like that of the propagation constant of a free plane wave. And yet there are striking differences, which we must now investigate.

13.2 Effective Mass

The best way of trying to find out what k represents is to adopt a somewhat changed point of view and ask what is the dynamical behavior of electrons in a state characterized by given values of k and E. We shall imagine that a wave packet has been established in the crystal, moving at the group velocity v_g, and that it encounters a region in which there is a small local electric field of strength F. Its rate of energy increase will obviously be

$$\frac{dE}{dt} = eFv_g \tag{13.15}$$

and we wish to find its acceleration.

First, we must find v_g. To see how fast electrons of a given energy move through the lattice, we must calculate the group velocity corresponding to the Bloch wave functions. As in deriving (1.27), we imagine the superposition of two waves of slightly different k and ω,

$$\psi = u_k(x)e^{i(kx-\omega t)} + u_{k+\Delta k}(x)e^{i[(k+\Delta k)x-(\omega+\Delta\omega)t]}$$

If Δk is very small, the two functions u, which are amplitude modulations whose periodicity in x is fixed, may be regarded as equal. This gives

$$\psi = 2u_k(x)e^{i[(k+\frac{1}{2}\Delta k)x-(\omega+\frac{1}{2}\Delta\omega)t]}\cos\left(\frac{\Delta k}{2}x - \frac{\Delta\omega}{2}t\right)$$

$$|\psi|^2 = 4|u_k(x)|^2\cos^2\left(\frac{\Delta k}{2}x - \frac{\Delta\omega}{2}t\right)$$

whose modulation pattern progresses at the rate

$$v_g = \frac{\partial\omega}{\partial k} = \hbar^{-1}\frac{\partial E}{\partial k} \tag{13.16}$$

as $\Delta k \to 0$.[4] This looks exactly like the analogous relations for a free electron (Figs. 13.3 and 13.4). With F causing a slight change

[4] More general proofs of (13.16) abound in the literature of solid-state physics, but many of them run into difficulties. The reader will have no trouble, for example, in proving that $\langle i\hbar^{-1}[\hat{H},x]\rangle_\psi = 0$ when ψ is any eigenfunction of $\hat{H}$; this disposes of a number of attempts and, at the same time, shows the necessity of considering a superposition of eigenstates, as we have done above.

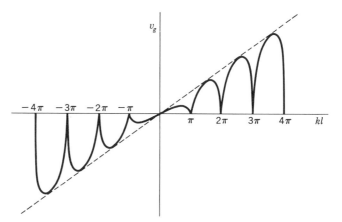

Fig. 13.4 The group velocity v_g as a function of k for the square potential lattice. The dotted line shows the relation for a free particle.

in E, we can write dE/dt in (13.15) in the form

$$\frac{dE}{dt} = \frac{\partial E}{\partial k}\frac{dk}{dt}$$

so that

$$eFv_g = \hbar v_g \frac{dk}{dt}$$

whence

$$\hbar \frac{dk}{dt} = eF \tag{13.17}$$

which corresponds surprisingly well to Newton's second law, considering that $\hbar k$ is not the momentum of an electron nor is eF the total force acting on it. From this,

$$\frac{dv_g}{dt} = \frac{\partial v_g}{\partial k}\frac{dk}{dt}$$

$$= \frac{1}{\hbar^2}\frac{\partial^2 E}{\partial k^2} eF \tag{13.18}$$

Thus, from a classical standpoint, $(1/\hbar^2)\,\partial^2 E/\partial k^2$ plays the role of a reciprocal mass, and for a free electron that is exactly what it is; but it is clear from Fig. 13.3 that the $\partial^2 E/\partial k^2$ is by no means independent of k. Nevertheless, we shall write (13.18) in the form

$$m^*\frac{dv_g}{dt} = eF \tag{13.19}$$

where

$$\frac{\hbar^2}{m^*} = \frac{\partial^2 E}{\partial k^2} \tag{13.20}$$

calling m^* the *effective mass* of the electron in the lattice. Thus an electron in the lattice behaves rather like a free electron, except

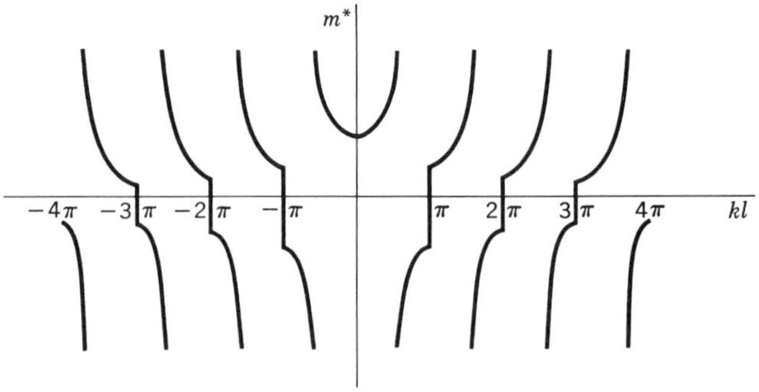

Fig. 13.5 Effective mass
as a function of k for a
particle in a square
potential lattice.

that its mass is a function of its k value and may even be negative
for energies toward the top of a band (Fig. 13.5). It is exactly this
paradoxical property which will enable us to develop a consistent
picture of electronic conduction in the next section.

Problem 13.4 Prove that the group velocity of electrons whose
energy puts them at the bottom or the top of a conduction band is
zero.

Problem 13.5 Doing the partial integrations carefully, show
that for a particle confined to a loop of circumference L

$$\frac{d\langle x \rangle}{dt} = \frac{Ls}{e} + \frac{i}{\hbar} \langle [\hat{H}, x] \rangle$$

where s is the usual expression for the current density in one dimension. How does this simplify when ψ is an eigenfunction of $\hat{H}$? Apply
the simplified formula to the motion of a free particle ($V = 0$) and
show that the result is reasonable.

We shall now express the relation between effective mass and
group velocity for electrons near the edge of an energy band in a way
which will be useful later. We note first that at the band edge, which
we shall denote by a subscript zero, the dependence of E on k is
essentially quadratic (since E is a roughly linear function of $\cos kl$).
Thus we can write E as

$$E(k) \approx E_0 + \left(\frac{\partial E}{\partial k}\right)_{k_0} (k - k_0) + \frac{1}{2}\left(\frac{\partial^2 E}{\partial k^2}\right)_{k_0} (k - k_0)^2$$

The second term on the right vanishes (Prob. 13.4), so that

$$E(k) \approx E_0 + \frac{\hbar^2}{2m^*}(k - k_0)^2 \tag{13.21}$$

and further differentiation of this gives

$$m^* v_g \approx \hbar(k - k_0) \tag{13.22}$$

Thus the effective mass is positive or negative according as k lies just above or just below a band edge, and it becomes infinite at a point of inflection lying between.

13.3   Electronic Conductivity in Solids

In order to speak of real materials, we must now see to what extent the foregoing analysis of the behavior of a single electron in a lattice may be used when many electrons are present.

In the first place, it is clear that not all electrons take part in the conduction process, since some are tightly bound to their atoms. The conduction electrons will be, roughly speaking, the valence electrons, and the periodic potential in which each one moves will be that due to (1) the nuclei of the atoms, (2) the closely bound electrons, and (3) the other conduction electrons. This being the case, the one-electron model will correspond fairly closely to reality provided that the effect of all these interactions can be approximated by a periodic potential. This turns out to be possible provided that one can ignore the thermal vibrations of the lattice (which are responsible for most of the electrical resistance) and that the conduction electrons move essentially at random and do not, for example, take part in some collective oscillation which would make contribution (3) time-dependent. In fact such oscillations can exist in a metal, but their first level of excitation is somewhat above the range of energies normally involved in the conduction process.[5]

The crucial factor in determining the distribution in energy of the conduction electrons is the Pauli exclusion principle, which asserts that no electronic state can be occupied by more than one electron.[6] Let us first consider the situation at the absolute zero of temperature, when the system as a whole has its least possible energy. The various energy levels will be filled up, starting from the bottom, until there are as many occupied states as there are electrons. The energy of the highest occupied state is called the *Fermi level*. States of higher energy will be unoccupied. To count the states, we use the fact that k takes on discrete values, going in the nth band from $(n-1)\pi/l$ to $n\pi/l$ in $\frac{1}{2}N$ steps. But Fig. 13.3 shows that for each value of E there are two states, for which k has opposite signs, so that there are a total of N different translational states to be occupied in one band. Finally, each electron has two possible spin states, making a total of $2N$ electronic states per band. It is clear that each full band corresponds to zero total current, since for each electron with positive k there is one with negative k, and

[5] See D. Pines, Electron Interaction in Metals, *Solid State Phys.*, Academic Press Inc., New York, 1955, vol. 1.

[6] The reader will already have encountered the exclusion principle in the elementary theory of atomic spectra.   Its formulation in quantum mechanics is given in Chap. 11.

that even an unfilled band at absolute zero will not spontaneously carry any current, if we neglect the minute amount which would be transferred by one or two individual unpaired electrons. It is this fact that makes superconductivity so hard to understand.[7]

The physical picture of electrical conduction is as follows. If a field is applied, it can do work on an electron, raising it to a higher energy state if one is available. An electron whose energy is near the Fermi level will have vacant states close above it; such electrons will then be in a mobile state and a current will flow.

Problem 13.6 Distinguish in the foregoing argument between what happens to an electron whose original value of k is parallel to the applied field and what happens to one whose original value of k is antiparallel.

Ordinary conductors, however, exhibit resistance, which amounts to an irreversible exchange of energy between electrons and lattice and which does not arise from the calculation we have performed. The origin of resistance turns out to be in the fact that the lattice is in random thermal motion, so that as an electron passes through, it encounters cells of uneven length. The effect of this is to scatter it out of its original state of motion—it forgets how it was going unless urged on by an electric field.[8]

The process of conduction will take place as described above unless there is no vacant state immediately above the filled states— that is, unless the number of electrons available is just enough to fill a band. According to the one-dimensional picture, calcium should therefore be an insulator, since each of the N atoms in the ring will contribute its two valence electrons to the conduction band. For actual three-dimensional lattices, however, the arrangement of bands is rather complicated and depends on the crystal structure. But owing to the spin doubling, the number of electrons per atom in a filled band is always even, and so only elements of even valence can be insulators. Sulfur, with the lowest conductivity of any element, has four electrons in its outer (3d) shell, and carbon is also four-valent. An insulating crystal like NaCl may be considered as composed of NaCl units, each with effectively a full shell of eight electrons.

Conduction by holes

We shall now consider the phenomenon of conductivity in a conduction band which is nearly full. Since a full band carries no cur-

---

[7] Superconductivity can be explained only if one considers the coupled motions of the electrons and the lattice in which they move. See Bardeen, Cooper, and Schrieffer, Phys. Rev., **108**, 1175 (1957); L. Cooper, Am. J. Phys., **28**, 91 (1960); D. M. Ginsberg, Am. J. Phys., **30**, 433 (1962).

[8] An excellent discussion of this subject is given by V. Weisskopf, Am. J. Phys., **11**, 1 (1943).

rent, and corresponds physically to an insulator, it is convenient to focus attention on the few unoccupied states, the *holes*, rather than on the many occupied ones. We shall visualize a hole in a state corresponding to the propagation constant k as though an extra state corresponding to $-k$ had been added to the assembly so as to cancel the effect of one of the electrons in it. Let us see what properties this extra state must have. If an electric field is turned on so that the k's increase with time according to (13.17), then $-k$, which we shall call k_h, must increase in the same way,

$$\hbar \frac{dk_h}{dt} = -eF \qquad (13.23)$$

Thus, a hole behaves dynamically like a state of a particle with a charge of $-e$. On the other hand, the acceleration of the hole is given by (13.18) independently of the sign of its k value:

$$\frac{dv_g}{dt} = \frac{1}{\hbar^2} \frac{\partial^2 E}{\partial k^2} eF = -\frac{1}{\hbar^2} \frac{\partial^2 E}{\partial k^2} (-eF)$$

Thus, the effective mass of a hole is $-(1/\hbar^2)\, \partial^2 E/\partial k^2$, and we have

$$k_h = -k \qquad e_h = -e \qquad m_h^* = -m^* \qquad (13.24)$$

The reason why this point of view is so useful is now apparent, since, as we have seen, m^* is negative at the top of a band. The hole concept enables us to think of a band which is almost full as having current carriers which have positive charge and positive mass, analogous to the electrons with negative charge and positive mass for one which is almost empty. The fact that the effective carriers in a nearly full band have a positive charge can be verified experimentally by a study of the Hall effect, and values of m^* can be obtained from measurements of the cyclotron resonance frequency.[9] Since the one-dimensional theory does not cover the experimental situation here, we shall not discuss it.

The theory of conductivity which we have developed can be briefly summarized as follows.

If the number of valence electrons present is enough to fill a band partly, then a small applied field can cause transitions among the energy states so that states with k in one direction outnumber the others and a copious current flows. If the band is just filled, conduction can occur only if the field is so strong or the temperature so high that electrons are excited into the next band. If the gap between bands is wide, the material is an insulator. If it is narrow, or if the band normally contains a few carriers (that is, is nearly empty or nearly full), the material is called a semiconductor. (The latter situation is usually brought about by the presence of impurities which inject a few electrons or holes.) The resistivity of a metal at room temperature is of the order of 10^{-5} to 10^{-6} ohm-cm; that of an insulator is 10^{14} ohm-cm or above. Semiconductors occupy the middle of this enormous range, say, 10^{-2} to 10^9 ohm-cm, and are quite distinct in many ways from metals or insulators.

Many of the electric properties of matter can be qualitatively understood in terms of the one-dimensional picture presented above. Any detailed discussion, however, requires the concept of Brillouin zones, which goes beyond the limits of this text. The references below will introduce the reader to the world of three dimensions.

REFERENCES

W. Hume-Rothery, *Electrons, Atoms, Metals and Alloys*, Philosophical Library, Inc., New York, 1955. A very readable introduction, starting from elementary principles.

C. Kittel, *Introduction to Solid State Physics*, 2d ed., John Wiley & Sons, Inc., New York, 1956.

R. E. Peierls, *Quantum Theory of Solids*, Clarendon Press, Oxford, 1955.

G. H. Wannier, *Elements of Solid State Theory*, Cambridge University Press, London 1959.

R. A. Smith, *Wave Mechanics of Crystalline Solids*, Chapman and Hall, Ltd., London, 1961.

S. Flugge (ed.), *Encyclopedia of Physics*, Springer-Verlag OHG, Berlin, 1958, vol. 19. The articles by Slater (The Electronic Structure of Solids), Gerritsen (Metallic Conductivity, Experimental Part), and Jones (Theory of Electrical and Thermal Conductivity in Metals) are very useful at a somewhat more advanced level than the foregoing texts, and they contain extensive literature references.

H. A. Kramers, Das Eigenwertproblem im eindimensionalem periodischen Kraftfelde, Physica, **2,** 483 (1935) or *Collected Papers*, p. 669. This paper shows very simply how the existence of allowed and forbidden energy bands follows from the periodicity of a potential.

J. Callaway, *Energy Band Theory*, Academic Press Inc., New York, 1964.

14

The Hydrogen Atom

In Chap. 7 we have discussed the lowest states of the hydrogen atom in some detail. There is much to be gained, however, from pursuing the subject further, partly because it then becomes a practical exercise in applying some of the methods worked out in the first part of this book and partly because it provides a chance to study in detail the representation of angular-momentum states through their angular dependence. We shall therefore first study the exact wave functions of the unperturbed atom and then various perturbations—first those arising from inside the atom owing to effects of relativity and spin and then those due to external influences. We have already studied the effect of moderate electric and magnetic fields. Here we shall look at strong magnetic fields and then finally at the transition from weak-field to strong-field behavior.

14.1 The Wave Equation

The system to be discussed consists of an electron of mass m bound to a nucleus of mass M and charge Ze. Z will be equal to 1, 2, 3 for H, He+, Li++, etc. (The treatment of systems containing two electrons is discussed in Chap. 15.) The reduced mass of the system is

$$\mu = \frac{mM}{m + M}$$

by (7.34), and the wave equation for the motion with respect to the center of mass is

$$\left(-\frac{\hbar^2}{2\mu} \nabla^2 - \frac{Ze'^2}{r} \right) \psi = E\psi \tag{14.1}$$

It is shown in Appendix 4 that the angular dependence of the ψ defined by this equation can be discussed quite independently of its radial dependence, for it is entirely independent of the form of the centripetal potential provided only that the latter is spherically symmetrical. This corresponds to the fact that such a potential conserves angular momentum and that the angular-momentum properties of a wave function reside entirely in its angular dependence. Writing

$$\psi(r,\vartheta,\varphi) = f(r) Y_l{}^m(\vartheta,\varphi) \tag{14.2}$$

we find from Appendix 4 that the radial wave function $f(r)$ satisfies the equation

$$\left\{ -\frac{\hbar^2}{2\mu} \left[\frac{d^2}{dr^2} + \frac{2}{r}\frac{d}{dr} - \frac{l(l+1)}{r^2} \right] - \frac{Ze'^2}{r} - E \right\} f(r) = 0 \tag{14.3}$$

It is convenient to simplify this by introducing the new variable $u_l(r) = rf(r)$, where we have written a suffix l because there are different solutions corresponding to different values of the total angular-momentum quantum number l. [On the other hand, (14.3) does not contain the azimuthal quantum number m_l (why?), and so we do not need a suffix m_l.] The equation for u_l is

$$u_l'' - \frac{l(l+1)}{r^2} u_l + \frac{2\mu}{\hbar^2}\left(\frac{Ze'^2}{r} + E\right) u_l = 0 \tag{14.4}$$

and in order to satisfy (7.41) and have $|\psi|^2$ integrable we shall require that u_l vanish both at $r = 0$ and $r = \infty$. With spherical harmonics normalized as in Appendix 4, it follows that the normalization integrals for f_l and u_l are

$$\int_0^\infty r^2[f_l(r)]^2\,dr = 1 \qquad \int_0^\infty [u_l(r)]^2\,dr = 1 \tag{14.5}$$

(The notation shows that we are considering f_l and u_l to be real. Does this represent any loss in generality?)

If $l = 0$, the general form of (14.4) is, except for the boundary condition at $r = 0$, the same as one would expect for a one-dimensional system with a potential energy of $-Ze'^2/r$. With $l > 0$, it is as though the potential were

$$V_{\text{eff}} = -\frac{Ze'^2}{r} + l(l+1)\frac{\hbar^2}{2\mu r^2}$$

The form of this function is shown in Fig. 14.1, and clearly the effect of the second term is to keep the electron away from the origin. In terms of classical concepts, the force due to the second term is $l(l+1)\hbar^2/\mu r^3$. To see what this means, we write for $l(l+1)\hbar^2$ the square of the classical angular momentum of a particle moving in a circle of radius r with velocity v, μvr. The force is then $\mu v^2/r$, which we recognize as the centrifugal force. From the one-dimen-

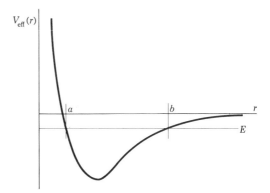

Fig. 14.1 Effective potential of an electron in a hydrogen atom. The allowed region is between $r = a$ and $r = b$.

sional standpoint it is as though (for $l > 0$) the electron were acted upon by this force tending to pull it outward from the origin, and a bound state can be formed only because for large enough r the centripetal force deriving from Ze'^2/r overcomes it. A particle bound with the (negative) energy E must in classical physics oscillate between the two turning points a and b in Fig. 14.1. In quantum physics the wave function will resemble that of a harmonic oscillator, having a certain number of nodes in the allowed region and tending toward zero on each side. These general features can be observed in the wave functions already calculated in Chap. 7, and they are characteristic of all atomic wave functions.[1]

14.2 Solution of the Equation

For solving the radial equation either of the two methods used for the harmonic oscillator in Chap. 4 may be employed. The purely analytical approach is probably the more general, especially where approximate calculations are to be done, and we shall follow it here. First, let us see how the solutions behave for small values of r. When $l > 0$, this is very easy. The centrifugal term in (14.4) outbalances all the others, and we have

$$u_l'' \approx \frac{l(l + 1)}{r^2} u_l \qquad (r \approx 0) \tag{14.6}$$

whose two independent solutions may be found by setting u proportional to r^γ. The equation is satisfied with $\gamma = -l$ or $l + 1$, but the solution with $\gamma = -l$ does not satisfy the boundary condition at the origin and must be rejected. We have left

$$u_l \approx A r^{l+1} \qquad (r \approx 0) \tag{14.7}$$

---

[1] The WKB energy levels are given by (7.81) with $V(r)$ replaced by V_{eff}, but a simplification applicable to any calculation of this sort is given by E. C. Titchmarsh, Proc. Roy. Soc., **A245**, 147 (1958).

When $l = 0$, the situation is not quite so obvious. It is exemplified by the ground state already calculated in Chap. 7, where ψ was of the form $e^{-\alpha r}$, and u is thus $re^{-\alpha r}$. The other independent solution[2] is of the form

$$re^{-\alpha r} \int_a^r r^{-2} e^{2\alpha r} \, dr \tag{14.8}$$

with arbitrary lower limit. This cannot be evaluated in terms of elementary functions, but clearly it does not approach zero at the origin and it diverges at infinity; it is therefore useless for our purposes. It can easily be verified that the companion solutions to all the other solutions we shall obtain diverge similarly.

In solving the radial equation, it will save many unnecessary letters if we adopt a suitable system of units and measure all distances in terms of the first Bohr radius a_0 and all energies in Rydbergs. We therefore introduce new variables ρ and ε by

$$r = \frac{\hbar^2}{\mu e'^2} \rho \qquad E = \frac{\mu e'^4}{2\hbar^2} \varepsilon$$

and find that (14.4) reduces to

$$\frac{d^2 u_l}{d\rho^2} + \left[\frac{2Z}{\rho} - \frac{l(l+1)}{\rho^2} + \varepsilon \right] u_l = 0 \tag{14.9}$$

which the reader should verify for himself.

Having looked at the behavior of u_l near the origin, we next look at it at the other extreme. When ρ is very large, all that remains of (14.4) is

$$\frac{d^2 u_l}{d\rho^2} + \varepsilon u_l \approx 0 \tag{14.10}$$

---

[2] Since the construction of the "other solution" is not widely known, we give a simple version of it here. Suppose that u and v are two different solutions of (14.4), which we shall abbreviate as

(a) $u'' + p(r)u = 0,$ (b) $v'' + p(r)v = 0$

Write v as uw and put it into (b),

$$u''w + 2u'w' + uw'' + p(r)uw = 0$$

By (a), this is $uw'' + 2u'w' = 0$. Multiplied by the integrating factor u, it is

$$(u^2 w')' = 0$$

which can easily be solved for w,

$$w = C \int \frac{dr}{u^2}$$

so that the "other solution" is

$$v = Cu \int \frac{dr}{u^2}$$

If $\varepsilon > 0$, the solutions are periodic in r and correspond to free particles not bound by the Coulomb potential. If $\varepsilon < 0$, we write it as $\varepsilon = -\beta$, where β represents the (positive) binding energy, the amount of work necessary to dissociate the atom into an electron and a nucleus at rest and infinitely far apart. The solutions of (14.10) are then of the form

$$u_l \approx \exp\left(\pm\beta^{\frac{1}{2}}\rho\right)$$

The decreasing one is suitable for our purposes.

Following the same procedure as with the harmonic oscillator, we now separate off the exponential behavior by writing

$$u_l(\rho) = [\exp\left(-\beta^{\frac{1}{2}}\rho\right)]v_l(\rho) \tag{14.11}$$

and concentrating our attention on v_l. We find that v_l must satisfy

$$v_l'' - 2\beta^{\frac{1}{2}}v_l' + \left(\frac{2Z}{\rho} - \frac{l(l+1)}{\rho^2}\right)v_l = 0 \tag{14.12}$$

and the normalizability of u_l requires that v_l diverge more slowly than $\exp\left(\beta^{\frac{1}{2}}\rho\right)$ at infinity.

The series solution

The usual device for solving an equation such as (14.12) is to assume that its solution can be expressed in terms of a power series in ρ. The series need not start with ρ^0, however, and we must suppose that it starts with ρ^γ. We then write the power series as

$$v_l = \rho^\gamma \sum_0^\infty c_m\rho^m \tag{14.13}$$

and emphasize that it starts at ρ^γ by requiring that $c_0 \neq 0$. (Any of the other c's may of course be equal to zero.) Substituting this series into (14.12) gives

$$\sum_0^\infty c_m[(m+\gamma)(m+\gamma-1)\rho^{m+\gamma-2} - 2(m+\gamma)\beta^{\frac{1}{2}}\rho^{m+\gamma-1}$$
$$+ 2Z\rho^{m+\gamma-1} - l(l+1)\rho^{m+\gamma-2}] = 0$$

or

$$\sum_0^\infty c_m\{[(m+\gamma)(m+\gamma-1) - l(l+1)]\rho^{m+\gamma-2}$$
$$- 2[(m+\gamma)\beta^{\frac{1}{2}} - Z]\rho^{m+\gamma-1}\} = 0 \tag{14.14}$$

The fundamental fact we are going to use in solving the equation is that if a power series in ρ is equal to zero for all values of ρ, then every term of the sum must vanish individually. The difficulty is that we have here two separate power series. To make them the same, we transform the sum in $\rho^{m+\gamma-2}$. First we take out the first term and write it separately,

$$c_0[\gamma(\gamma - 1) - l(l + 1)]\rho^{\gamma-2} + \sum_{m=1}^{\infty} c_m[(m + \gamma)(m + \gamma - 1)$$
$$- l(l + 1)]\rho^{m+\gamma-2}$$

Next, in the remaining sum, we relabel the terms by a new index m' equal to $m - 1$: $m = m' + 1$ and

$$c_0[\gamma(\gamma - 1) - l(l + 1)]\rho^{\gamma-2} + \sum_{m'=0}^{\infty} c_{m'+1}[(m' + \gamma + 1)(m' + \gamma)$$
$$- l(l + 1)]\rho^{m'+\gamma-1}$$

We can now put this back with the rest of (14.14), dropping the now unnecessary prime,

$$c_0[\gamma(\gamma - 1) - l(l + 1)]\rho^{\gamma-2} + \sum_{m=0}^{\infty} \{c_{m+1}[(m + \gamma)(m + \gamma + 1)$$
$$- l(l + 1)] - 2c_m[(m + \gamma)\beta^{\frac12} - Z]\}\rho^{m+\gamma-1} = 0$$

For the coefficient of each power of ρ to vanish separately, we must have

$$c_0[\gamma(\gamma - 1) - l(l + 1)] = 0 \tag{14.15}$$

and

$$c_{m+1} = 2 \frac{(m + \gamma)\beta^{\frac12} - Z}{(m + \gamma)(m + \gamma + 1) - l(l + 1)} c_m \tag{14.16}$$

It is now clear why the first term has been singled out for special treatment. We have required that c_0 should not vanish; therefore, the expression in brackets must vanish. This gives an equation for γ, known as the *indicial equation*, whose solutions are

$$\gamma = -l, l + 1$$

as we have already found in another way for $l > 0$ by looking at (14.6). Since $\gamma = -l$ is not admissible[3] even for $l = 0$, we have only one case to consider. Putting $\gamma = l + 1$ in (14.16) gives

$$c_{m+1} = 2 \frac{(m + l + 1)\beta^{\frac12} - Z}{(m + 1)(m + 2l + 2)} c_m$$

The power series defined by this relation (called a *recurrence relation*) is well known to mathematicians as the associated Laguerre function.

[3] We reject it because of (7.41), with $\gamma = \alpha + 1$, but a simpler argument can be given: the solution with $\alpha = -1$ does not satisfy Schrödinger's equation at the origin. To see this, consider the laplacian of r^{-1}. From electrostatics, we known that r^{-1} is the potential of a point charge, and $\nabla^2 r^{-1}$ is therefore proportional to the density of a point charge. A moment's thought shows that this density is a delta function. Since no other delta function appears in the equation to cancel it, the equation cannot be satisfied at the origin. (Essentially the same argument has already been applied to one-dimensional systems in Sec. 4.1.)

Let us look at the asymptotic form of the power series. As $m \to \infty$, we have

$$c_{m+1} \approx \frac{2\beta^{1/2}}{m} c_m \tag{14.17}$$

and it is clear intuitively that for very large values of ρ the value of a series is determined by the asymptotic behavior of the coefficients.[4] The behavior described by (14.17) is exactly the same as that of the coefficients of the series for $\exp{(2\beta^{1/2}\rho)}$, and therefore $v_l(\rho)$ will behave for large ρ like this exponential. By (14.11), the radial wave function $u_l(\rho)$ will therefore diverge as $\exp{(\beta^{1/2}\rho)}$, and cannot represent a physical state. The only escape from this conclusion is if the series terminates at some value of m; for if $c_{m+1} = 0$, then all the higher terms will likewise vanish and $u_l(\rho)$ will have the form of a polynomial multiplied by $\exp{(-\beta^{1/2}\rho)}$, which is convergent at infinity. The series terminates at some particular value of m if the value of β is such that $(m + l + 1)\beta^{1/2} = Z$ for this value of m. Prevailing usage writes $m + l + 1$ as n, so that $\beta = Z^2/n^2$ and, reverting to ordinary units,

$$E = -\frac{Z^2}{n^2} \quad \text{Ry} \tag{14.18}$$

where because both m and l may be equal to zero, $n = 1, 2, 3, \ldots,$ ∞. This is the Balmer formula as first derived by Bohr in 1913. We see that for a given value of n, l may have any value from 0 up to $n - 1$, and displaying the different values of l and n gives rise to the familiar term diagram for the hydrogen-like atoms shown in Fig. 14.2. Further, each of these terms is $(2l + 1)$-fold degenerate with respect to the quantum number m_l. The total degeneracy of the nth level is thus

$$\sum_{l=0}^{n-1} (2l + 1) = n^2 \tag{14.19}$$

as can easily be proved. It must be emphasized that this degeneracy is only approximate and that it is peculiar to hydrogen. The l degeneracy arises from the Coulomb potential assumed in (14.3), whereas the m_l degeneracy exists because (14.3) does not involve m_l at all, that is, because the original hamiltonian has spherical symmetry and all orientations of the system are equivalent. Neither of these degeneracies is exact. We shall see in the next section that the relativity effect of change of mass destroys the l degeneracy, whereas the existence of electron spin, which must point one way or the other, destroys the symmetry of the center-of-mass motion described by (14.3). (The entire system of spin and orbital motion is still, of course, indifferent as to direction.)

[4] See E. T. Whittaker and G. N. Watson, *Modern Analysis*, 4th ed., Cambridge University Press, London, 1927, chap. 2.

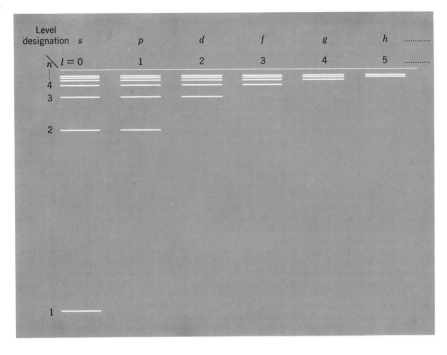

Fig. 14.2   Term diagram for hydrogen as given by
Schrödinger's equation.

Problem 14.1   Derive (14.19), by mathematical induction or some other method.

Problem 14.2   Evaluate all the radial wave functions belonging to $n = 1$, 2, and 3. Express them in ordinary units and normalize them according to (14.5).

Problem 14.3   Introducing the angular dependences, write the complete normalized wave functions belonging to $n = 1$ and 2. Compare them with the results in Chap. 7.

Problem 14.4   The optical spectrum of sodium is due almost entirely to transitions of the valence electron among the states available to it. Intuitively one would suppose that in its higher states of excitation it is acted upon essentially by the nucleus with $Z = 11$ screened by the 10 inner electrons, that is, by a Coulomb field corresponding to unit charge. Examine a term diagram for sodium for evidence in support of this view. In what way is it evident that the lower states cannot be regarded in this way?

Problem 14.5   What happens when an attempt is made to construct the power-series expansion of the (improper) v_l corresponding to $\gamma = 0$ (that is, $\gamma = -l$ with $l = 0$)? Explain your result by reference to (14.8).

14.3   The Fine Structure of Hydrogen

The hydrogen spectrum begins to become more complicated than
that given by Bohr's formula when we consider effects due to relativity and spin. By relativity we mean here just the small effects
traceable to the increase in mass of a moving body. The spin is also
a relativistic effect, though this fact is by no means obvious if one
thinks of an electron as a little ball spinning around its axis. It is an
immediate consequence of Dirac's relativistic wave equation, and
since it is best approached from that direction, we shall not seek to
give any quasi-classical explanation of it here. Two spins are
involved: the spin of the electron and that of the nucleus. The
former, along with the mass effect, contributes to the fine structure
of the energy levels; the latter is responsible for the hyperfine structure. These are of very different magnitudes because the magnetic
moment of an electron or a proton is given, according to Dirac's
theory, by

$$M = \frac{e\hbar}{m} \tag{14.20}$$

where m is the particle mass. Owing to the complex structure of the
particle which we know as a proton, this formula is only roughly
valid for protons, but it gives the order of magnitude of all nuclear
moments, and it explains why they are some 10^3 times smaller than
the electron moment, which is given with great (though not perfect)
accuracy by (14.20). We shall not discuss the hyperfine structure
here, for the calculation is very much like that of the much larger
splitting due to electron spin which is discussed below.[5]

In 1915 Arnold Sommerfeld modified Bohr's theory to include
relativistic effects (but not of course spin, which had never been
heard of) and derived an extremely accurate formula for the energy
levels of hydrogen. For a fixed nucleus, Sommerfeld's energy levels
are

$$E_{nk} = mc^2 \left\{ 1 + \left[\frac{\alpha}{n - k + (k^2 - \alpha^2)^{\frac{1}{2}}} \right]^2 \right\}^{-\frac{1}{2}} \tag{14.21}$$

where α is the fine-structure constant $e'^2/\hbar c \approx \frac{1}{137}$, $n = 1, 2, 3,$
. . . , and $k = 1, 2, 3, \ldots n$. The energy given by the formula
includes the electron's rest energy mc^2 (m is the electron's rest mass),
but in calculating energy differences this large constant part drops
out. Since α is very small, the $-k$ in the denominator is almost
canceled by the radical following it, and E_{nk} is therefore mainly a
function of n; the n different values of k possible for each n split the
nth level into n different components. This fine structure of the

---

[5] For a discussion of hyperfine structure, see Bethe and Salpeter, listed
under References at the end of this chapter.

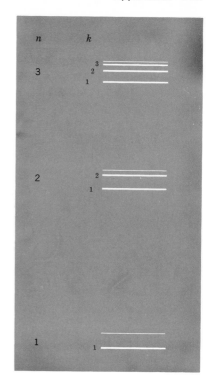

Fig. 14.3 Sommerfeld's description of the fine structure of hydrogen, drawn with the scale of the fine structure greatly exaggerated. The light lines represent the undisplaced levels given by the simple Schrödinger theory.

levels, illustrated in Fig. 14.3, can best be seen from an expansion of (14.21) in powers of the small number α. If E_n is the value of the energy as given by Bohr's formula, we find

$$E_{nk} = mc^2 + E_n - \frac{\alpha^2 Z^2}{4n^2} |E_n| \left(\frac{4n}{k} - 3\right) + \cdots \tag{14.22}$$

where the neglected terms are of the order of α^4 and smaller. Because $\alpha = e'^2/\hbar c$ these are essentially the first three terms in an expansion of E in powers of $1/c^2$. This is the expansion which is usually used to distinguish relativistic from nonrelativistic effects and which will form the basis of the perturbation calculations to follow. Sommerfeld's formula agrees closely with experiments. Our task is to reproduce it by a quantum-mechanical argument and, in particular, to give an interpretation of the quantum number k in terms of the properties of the atom.

The mass correction

When a particle of rest mass m moves with velocity v, the mass increases to the value $m(1 - v^2/c^2)^{-\frac{1}{2}}$ and the total energy is given in terms of this mass multiplied by c^2,

$$E = mc^2 \left(1 - \frac{v^2}{c^2}\right)^{-\frac{1}{2}} + eV \tag{14.23}$$

where V is the potential as usual. To express this in terms of the momentum,

$$p = mv \left(1 - \frac{v^2}{c^2}\right)^{-\frac{1}{2}} \tag{14.24}$$

instead of the velocity, we square (14.23) to get

$$(E - eV)^2 = m^2c^2 \frac{c^2}{1 - v^2/c^2} = m^2c^2 \frac{v^2 + c^2 - v^2}{1 - v^2/c^2}$$

or

$$(E - eV)^2 = c^2p^2 + (mc^2)^2 \tag{14.25}$$

Since the rest energy mc^2 is about 0.5 MeV, it is by far the largest part and we can expand by the binomial theorem to get

$$E = mc^2 \left[1 + \left(\frac{p}{mc}\right)^2\right]^{\frac{1}{2}} + eV \tag{14.26}$$

$$E = mc^2 + \frac{p^2}{2m} - \frac{p^4}{8m^3c^2} + eV \tag{14.27}$$

plus terms of order smaller than $1/c^2$. The first two terms here correspond effectively to the first two of (14.22), while the third gives the relativistic correction we wish to find. In first order, it is

$$E_r{}^{(1)} = - \frac{1}{8m^3c^2} \langle \hat{p}^4 \rangle_{nl}$$

evaluated in the unperturbed state whose quantum numbers are n and l (we omit m_l, which depends only on the orientation). Since the unperturbed ψ_{nl} satisfies

$$\hat{p}^2 \psi_{nl} = 2m(E - V)\psi_{nl}$$

we can write

$$\langle \hat{p}^4 \rangle = \int \hat{p}^2 \psi^* \cdot \hat{p}^2 \psi = \int 2m(E - V)\psi^* \cdot 2m(E - V)\psi$$

whence

$$E_r{}^{(1)} = - \frac{1}{2mc^2} (E_n{}^2 - 2E_n\langle V \rangle_{nl} + \langle V^2 \rangle_{nl}) \tag{14.28}$$

Here and in the sequel we shall need three expectation values[6] of

---

[6] Expectation values of this kind are calculated by making use of the general properties of the radial functions. Since relatively few problems in quantum mechanics can be solved to the point where such properties can be known, these methods and formulas are of somewhat limited use. The interested reader is referred to H. Margenau and G. M. Murphy, *The Mathematics of Physics and Chemistry*, 2d ed., D. Van Nostrand Company, Inc., Princeton, N.J., 1956, p. 388, and Bethe and Salpeter, listed under References at the end of this chapter, p. 103.

inverse powers of r,

$$\left\langle\frac{1}{r}\right\rangle_{nl} = \frac{Z}{n^2 a_0} \tag{14.29a}$$

$$\left\langle\frac{1}{r^2}\right\rangle_{nl} = \frac{Z^2}{(l + \frac{1}{2})n^3 a_0^2} \tag{14.29b}$$

$$\left\langle\frac{1}{r^3}\right\rangle_{nl} = \frac{Z^3}{l(l + \frac{1}{2})(l + 1)n^3 a_0^3} \qquad (l > 0) \tag{14.29c}$$

We find

$$E_r^{(1)} = -\frac{\alpha^2 Z^2}{4n^2}|E_n|\left(\frac{4n}{l + \frac{1}{2}} - 3\right) \tag{14.30}$$

which is like the relativistic term in (14.22) except that instead of the integer k we have here $l + \frac{1}{2}$.

Problem 14.6 The unperturbed energy states corresponding to a given value of n are mostly degenerate. Why was it unnecessary to use the theory of the perturbation of degenerate states to find ΔE_r?

Problem 14.7 Another approach to the relativistic energy is to solve exactly the wave equation implicit in (14.25). Show that this equation leads to a radial wave equation of exactly the same form as (14.4) except that some of the letters have different meanings. The earlier procedure can therefore be followed to solve this equation and find an exact expression for E_{nk}. Show finally that the result (14.30) follows from this expression.

The spin-orbit correction

Suppose from the classical point of view that one were to sit on the electron as it circles the nucleus. The nucleus would then appear to circle the electron. The electron, thus in the center of a current loop, experiences a magnetic field **B** which would act upon its spin to produce an energy $-\mathbf{B} \cdot \mathbf{M}$, where **M** is the magnetic moment. If $\mathbf{v}_n$ is the velocity of the nucleus relative to the electron and $\mathbf{r}_{en}$ the radius vector from electron to nucleus, then according to the law of Biot and Savart, the magnetic field at the electron is

$$\mathbf{B} = \frac{\mu_0 Z e \mathbf{r}_{en} \times \mathbf{v}_n}{4\pi r_{en}^3}$$

where μ_0 is the permeability of free space. The radius vector **r** from nucleus to electron is $-\mathbf{r}_{en}$, and the electron's velocity **v** relative to the nucleus is $-\mathbf{v}_n$. Since $\mathbf{r} \times m\mathbf{v}$ is the electron's angular momentum **P**, we have

$$\mathbf{B} = \frac{\mu_0 Z e \mathbf{P}}{4\pi m r^3} \tag{14.31}$$

Further, the electron's magnetic moment is proportional to its spin angular momentum,

$$\mathbf{M} = -\frac{2e\hbar}{m}\mathbf{S}$$

where the negative sign corresponds to the negative charge. Finally, we use the Maxwellian relation between μ_0, ε_0, and the speed of light (see Appendix 5),

$$\mu_0\varepsilon_0 = \frac{1}{c^2}$$

to find

$$-\mathbf{B}\cdot\mathbf{M} = \frac{Ze^2\hbar^2}{4\pi\varepsilon_0 m^2 c^2 r^3}\mathbf{L}\cdot\mathbf{S} \tag{14.32}$$

where $\mathbf{P} = \hbar\mathbf{L}$.

Problem 14.8   Derive (14.32) by the use of the relativity transformation which gives the magnetic field perceived by an observer (the electron) in motion with respect to a coordinate system in which an electric field is established.[7]

To use this classical quantity for our purposes, we must now make two changes. The first is to replace $\mathbf{L}$ and $\mathbf{S}$ by their operator equivalents. The second is to divide by 2. This factor arises from a curious relativistic effect called the Thomas precession, which we have not taken into account in changing from the point of view of the electron to that of the nucleus. Let ω_L be the electron's precessional frequency, $-eB/m$, in the magnetic field due to the nucleus. This is, of course, measured with respect to the electron's inertial system. But this inertial system is not the same as that of the nucleus; it precesses backward at a rate which can be shown to be equal to $\frac{1}{2}\omega_L$. Therefore, with respect to the nucleus (and the laboratory), the electron seems to precess at a rate $\omega_L - \frac{1}{2}\omega_L = \frac{1}{2}\omega_L$. To take this effect into account, we make the effective magnetic field in (14.32) only half as large, so that the interaction hamiltonian becomes[8]

$$\hat{H}_{\text{s-o}} = \frac{Z}{2}\left(\frac{e'\hbar}{mc}\right)^2\frac{\hat{\mathbf{L}}\cdot\hat{\mathbf{S}}}{r^3} \tag{14.33}$$

---

[7] See, for example, R. P. Winch, *Electricity and Magnetism*, 2d ed., Prentice-Hall, Inc., Englewood Cliffs, N.J., 1962, chap. 19.

[8] Since the final justification for these considerations lies not in any classical argument, but in a rigorous derivation from Dirac's relativistic theory of the electron, we shall not go into the details here. An excellent discussion from the standpoint of classical relativity is given by R. B. Leighton, *Principles of Modern Physics*, McGraw-Hill Book Company, Inc., New York, 1959. The derivation from Dirac's theory is given by Bethe and Salpeter.

The phenomenon described by this operator is called *spin-orbit coupling*, since it depends on the relation between spin and orbital angular momenta, and it is at the bottom of those features of atomic spectra which are described by the vector model of the atom with $l - s$ coupling.

Problem 14.9 Using (14.31) and the Bohr picture of the atom, what is the magnitude of B for the ground state $l = 1$, $n = 1$? (This is not, of course, the ground state in quantum mechanics.) How does this field strength compare with those which can be produced in the laboratory?

To find the shift in energy levels due to the torques described by (14.33), we note first that the system of constants of motion used in the calculation neglecting spin is somewhat changed. In the first place, $\hat{\mathbf{L}}$ no longer represents a constant of the motion, since the spin-orbit coupling exerts a torque on it which causes it to precess, but $\hat{L}^2$ is still constant as before. The place of $\hat{\mathbf{L}}$ is taken by $\hat{\mathbf{J}} = \hat{\mathbf{L}} + \hat{\mathbf{S}}$, which is constant in magnitude and direction, with the component vectors precessing about it as shown in Fig. 7.16.

Problem 14.10 Writing the total hamiltonian as $\alpha + \beta \hat{\mathbf{L}} \cdot \hat{\mathbf{S}}$, where α and β have spherical symmetry, verify that $\hat{L}^2$, $\hat{S}^2$, $\hat{\mathbf{L}} \cdot \hat{\mathbf{S}}$, $\hat{J}^2$, and $\hat{\mathbf{J}}$ are constant, but $\hat{\mathbf{L}}$ and $\hat{\mathbf{S}}$ are not.

Problem 14.11 Prove that $\hat{L}^2$, $\hat{S}^2$, $\hat{\mathbf{L}} \cdot \hat{\mathbf{S}}$, $\hat{J}^2$, and $\hat{J}_z$ commute among each other.

In view of the results of these problems, we can characterize the stationary states in terms of the quantum numbers j, m_j, and l. As we have already seen, $\hat{S}^2 = \frac{1}{2} \times \frac{3}{2}$ and is not a variable, whereas the identity

$$\hat{J}^2 = \hat{L}^2 + \hat{S}^2 + 2\hat{\mathbf{L}} \cdot \hat{\mathbf{S}}$$

enables us to write the eigenvalue of $\hat{\mathbf{L}} \cdot \hat{\mathbf{S}}$ as

$$\tfrac{1}{2}[j(j + 1) - l(l + 1) - \tfrac{3}{4}] = \begin{cases} l & (j = l + \tfrac{1}{2}) \\ -(l + 1) & (j = l - \tfrac{1}{2}) \end{cases}$$

We can now write down the energy perturbation caused by the spin-orbit coupling as

$$E_{\text{s-o}}^{(1)} = \frac{Z}{2} \left(\frac{e'\hbar}{mc}\right)^2 \left\langle \frac{1}{r^3} \right\rangle_{nl} \langle \hat{\mathbf{L}} \cdot \hat{\mathbf{S}} \rangle_{jl} \tag{14.34}$$

or by (14.29c)

$$E_{\text{s-o}}^{(1)} = \begin{cases} \dfrac{\alpha^2 Z^2}{2n} \dfrac{l}{l(l + \tfrac{1}{2})(l + 1)} |E_n| & (j = l + \tfrac{1}{2}) \\[3mm] -\dfrac{\alpha^2 Z^2}{2n} \dfrac{l + 1}{l(l + \tfrac{1}{2})(l + 1)} |E_n| & (j = l - \tfrac{1}{2}) \end{cases}$$

The factors in l have not been canceled in order to call attention to a difficulty which has arisen. The expectation value (14.29c) becomes infinite (why?) when $l = 0$. On the other hand, $\langle \hat{\mathbf{L}} \cdot \hat{\mathbf{S}} \rangle$ vanishes for $l = 0$. (Note that because j and l are not negative, $j = l + \frac{1}{2}$ is the only possibility here.) The energy correction therefore involves the fraction $0/0$, and is indeterminate.

To find the shift when $l = 0$, we must again refer to the exact relativistic theory. The details are somewhat complicated and will be found in the article by Bethe and Salpeter; the conclusion is that the correct answer is obtained by canceling the l's, so that

$$
E^{(1)}_{\text{s-o}} =
\begin{cases}
\dfrac{\alpha^2 Z^2}{2n} \dfrac{|E_n|}{(l + \frac{1}{2})(l + 1)} \\
\qquad\qquad (j = l + \frac{1}{2}, \; l = 0,1,2, \ldots n-1) \\[2mm]
-\dfrac{\alpha^2 Z^2}{2n} \dfrac{|E_n|}{l(l + \frac{1}{2})} \\
\qquad\qquad (j = l - \frac{1}{2}, \; l = 1,2, \ldots n-1)
\end{cases}
$$

The fine structure

Adding the spin-orbit perturbation to that due to the mass increase, we find

$$
E^{(1)} = E_r^{(1)} + E^{(1)}_{\text{s-o}} = -\frac{\alpha^2 Z^2}{4n^2} |E_n|
$$

$$
\times
\begin{cases}
\dfrac{4n}{l + 1} - 3 & (j = l + \frac{1}{2}) \\[2mm]
\dfrac{4n}{l} - 3 & (j = l - \frac{1}{2})
\end{cases}
\tag{14.35}
$$

or in terms of j,

$$
E^{(1)} = -\frac{\alpha^2 Z^2}{4n^2} |E_n| \left(\frac{4n}{j + \frac{1}{2}} - 3 \right)
\tag{14.36}
$$

where $j = \frac{1}{2}, \frac{3}{2}, \ldots, n - \frac{1}{2}$ for both orientations of the spin. The effect is only the replacement of $l + \frac{1}{2}$ in (14.30) by $j + \frac{1}{2}$, but it is what was needed in order to bring the result into coincidence with Sommerfeld's formula; for $j + \frac{1}{2}$ is Sommerfeld's integer k. The term diagram can be drawn as in Fig. 14.4. Each term with $l > 0$ is split into two, that with the higher j having the higher energy, and the splitting is readily found to be

$$
\delta = \frac{\alpha^2 Z^4}{n^3 l(l + 1)} \qquad \text{Ry}
\tag{14.37}
$$

Since $E_r^{(1)}$ depends only on l, this splitting is due entirely to the spin-orbit coupling. The doublets of the principal series are a prominent feature of one-electron spectra like the spectrum of sodium.

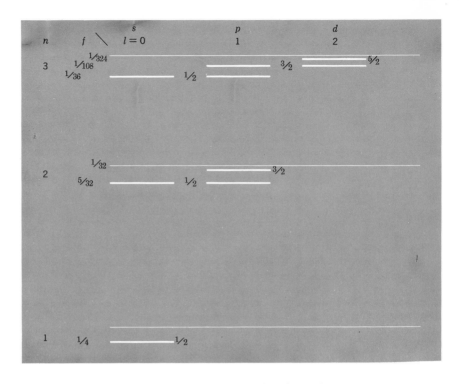

Fig. 14.4 Energy levels of hydrogen and hydrogen-like ions corrected for spin-orbit interaction and relativistic mass effect. The drawing is purely schematic, because the shifts are very small if drawn to scale. Numbers next to the lines give the values of j. The numbers f give the deviations from the unperturbed levels (light lines) in units of $\alpha^2 Z^4$ Ry.

Problem 14.12 Compare the doublet splittings of the principal series of sodium graphically with those predicted by (14.37) for increasing values of l and n. (Be sure to use the correct values of n.) What can be concluded from the comparison?

14.4 The Zeeman Effect

In this section we shall calculate in some detail what happens if a hydrogen atom is immersed in a magnetic field. The results will provide insight into the Zeeman effect of any atom. If the atom has a single radiating electron, the results may be applied directly; otherwise, the calculation must be carried out along these lines but in the framework of the l-s and j-j coupling schemes.

The essential complicating feature here is the electron spin, and especially the spin-orbit coupling treated in the preceding section. We have seen that this coupling arises because the electron spin normally experiences quite a strong magnetic field. A weak field externally applied will perturb this situation only slightly, and the energy levels will be split up and somewhat displaced. On the other hand, the applied field, if it is very strong, will dominate the hamiltonian function and the spin-orbit coupling and the mass correction will be relatively small perturbations. Finally, we shall have to consider the transitional range in which the two influences are of comparable magnitude.

Weak field

The hamiltonian of the unperturbed system is

$$\hat{H}^{(0)} = \hat{H}_0 + \hat{H}_r + \hat{H}_{s\text{-}o}$$

where $\hat{H}_0$ is the kinetic and Coulomb energy, while the perturbation due to a magnetic field $\mathbf{B}$ is (neglecting reduced-mass effects)

$$\hat{H}_B = \frac{e\hbar}{2m}\,\mathbf{B}\cdot(\hat{\mathbf{L}} + 2\hat{\mathbf{S}})$$

If $\mathbf{B}$ is taken to be parallel to the z axis, then

$$\hat{H}_B = \frac{e\hbar B}{2m}\,(\hat{L}_z + 2\hat{S}_z)$$

$\hat{H}^{(0)}$ commutes with the angular operators $\hat{L}^2$, $\hat{J}^2$, and $\hat{J}_z$, while $\hat{H}_B$ commutes with $\hat{L}^2$ and $\hat{J}_z$. We can take the eigenfunctions of $\hat{H}^{(0)}$ to be eigenfunctions also of $\hat{L}^2$, $\hat{J}^2$, and $\hat{J}_z$; these are given in (6.58) and (6.59), and their properties are summarized in Table 6.1. Since the energy $E^{(0)}$ corresponding to $\hat{H}^{(0)}$ depends only on j [cf. (14.36)], each unperturbed level is doubly degenerate, the superposed levels corresponding to $l = j - \frac{1}{2}$ and $j + \frac{1}{2}$. In addition, there is a $(2j + 1)$-fold degeneracy corresponding to the possible orientations of the vector $\mathbf{J}$. According to the general principles of perturbation theory, Sec. 8.4, the resulting $2(2j + 1)$-fold degeneracy may be ignored in calculating the perturbed energy if operators which commute with $\hat{H}_B$ and which have different eigenvalues for every sublevel can be found. This is accomplished exactly by $\hat{L}^2$ and $\hat{J}_z$, and so the perturbation of every state is given simply by the expectation value of $\hat{H}_B$ for that state. This has already been calculated in Prob. 6.26 and listed in Table 6.1; adapting the results, we have

$$\langle\hat{H}_B\rangle = \frac{e\hbar B}{2m}\frac{l+1}{l+\frac{1}{2}}\,m_j \qquad (-j \geqslant m_j \geqslant j, \ \ j = l + \tfrac{1}{2})$$

and   (14.38)

$$\langle\hat{H}_B\rangle = \frac{e\hbar B}{2m}\frac{l}{l+\frac{1}{2}}\,m_j \qquad (-j \geqslant m_j \geqslant j, \ \ j = l - \tfrac{1}{2})$$

The degenerate levels corresponding to different values of l are separated by the perturbation, and in addition the spatial degeneracy is removed so that each original level splits into $2(2j + 1)$ com-

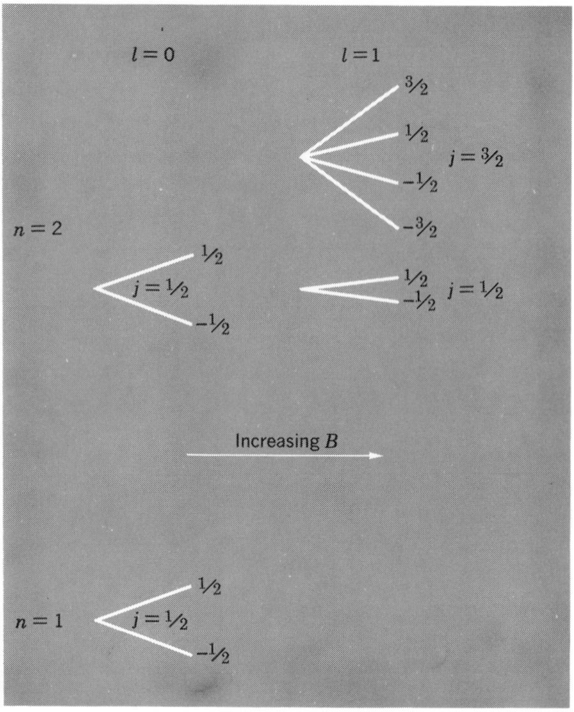

Fig. 14.5 Splitting of the states $n = 1$ and $n = 2$ of hydrogen in a weak magnetic field, depicted as increasing toward the right to a value of about 1000 Oe (0.1 Wb/m²). On the scale at which the fine structure is represented, the level $n = 1$ would be about 1 km below the levels for $n = 2$. Numbers attached to lines are values of m_j.

ponents. This is illustrated for the lowest levels of hydrogen in Fig. 14.5.

Paschen-Back effect

If the field is very strong, it decouples the l and s vectors and they precess independently in the field. The striking change in the spectrum when this occurs is known as the Paschen-Back effect. Here the unperturbed hamiltonian (omitting the term quadratic in B) is $\hat{H}^{(0)} + \hat{H}_B$, where $\hat{H}^{(0)}$ is the kinetic and Coulomb energy. This hamiltonian commutes with $\hat{L}^2$, $\hat{S}^2$, $\hat{L}_z$, and $\hat{S}_z$, and its eigenfunctions are of the form.

$$\psi_{n,l,m_l,m_s}^{(0)} = \psi_{n,l,m_l}\chi_{m_s}$$

where the ψ_{n,l,m_l} are the spinless eigenfunctions calculated in Sec. 14.1. The unperturbed energy is

$$E^{(0)} = -\frac{Z^2}{n^2}\text{Ry} + \frac{e\hbar B}{2m}(m_l + 2m_s) \tag{14.39}$$

and is still degenerate with respect to l. Fortunately, $\hat{L}^2$ and $\hat{J}_z$ commute with the perturbation

$$\hat{H}^{(1)} = \hat{H}_r + \hat{H}_{s\text{-}o}$$

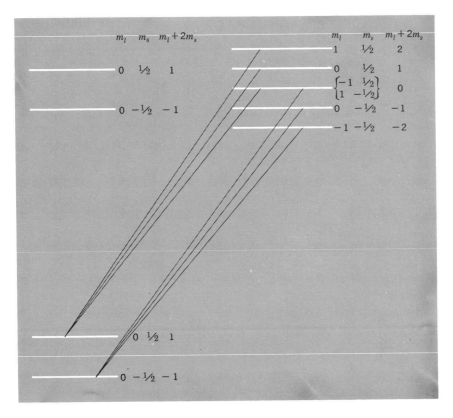

Fig. 14.6   Splitting of states with $n = 1$ and $n = 2$ in a huge field. Same exaggerated scale as in the preceding figure.

and serve to define the stabilized eigenfunctions, so that by (14.30) and (14.34) the perturbation in the energy is

$$\langle \hat{H}^{(1)} \rangle = -\frac{\alpha^2 Z^2}{4n^2} |E_n| \left(\frac{4n}{l + \frac{1}{2}} - 3 \right)$$
$$+ \frac{Z}{2} \left(\frac{e'\hbar}{mc} \right)^2 \left\langle \frac{1}{r^3} \right\rangle_{nl} \langle \hat{\mathbf{L}} \cdot \hat{\mathbf{S}} \rangle_{l,m_l,m_s}, \qquad (14.40)$$

Since, as can easily be shown, $\langle \hat{L}_x \rangle = \langle \hat{L}_y \rangle = 0$, the last factor reduces to

$$\langle \hat{L}_z \hat{S}_z \rangle_{l,m_l,m_s} = m_l m_s$$

so that with (14.29c)

$$\langle \hat{H}^{(1)} \rangle = -\frac{\alpha^2 Z^2}{4n^2} |E_n| \left[\frac{4n}{l + \frac{1}{2}} - 3 - \frac{2n m_l m_s}{l(l + \frac{1}{2})(l + 1)} \right] \qquad (14.41)$$

and again, when $l = m_l = 0$, the zeros may be canceled. Figure 14.6 shows the splitting of levels given by (14.39).

Problem 14.13   Prove that $\langle \hat{L}_x \rangle = \langle \hat{L}_y \rangle = 0$.

Problem 14.14 Compare the relativistic, spin-orbit, and external-field energies for the various $2p$ levels of hydrogen when

$$B = 40,000 \text{ Oe} = 4 \text{ Wb/m}^2$$

Calculate the spectral lines to be observed from the $2p - 1s$ transitions and their fine structure.

Problem 14.15 Discuss the neglect of the interaction quadratic in B in the foregoing calculation. Make a numerical comparison with the results of the preceding problem.

Problem 14.16 Ignoring the relativistic part of (14.41), which contributes to the displacement of the terms from their unperturbed values but not to their splitting, show that (14.41) can be applied to evaluate the perturbed energy (14.40) in the one-electron spectrum of alkali atoms, where the exact wave function is not known, in terms of the splitting with zero field δ, of (14.37).

Intermediate fields

In this case the magnetic, spin-orbit, and relativistic corrections must all be considered on the same footing. Again it is convenient to use $\psi_{j=l\pm\frac{1}{2},m_j}$ for the unperturbed eigenfunctions, but here a new circumstance arises in that $\psi_{j=l+\frac{1}{2},m_j}$ and $\psi_{j=l-\frac{1}{2},m_j}$ are degenerate, and we have no immediate way of choosing the right combination. We must therefore resort to the machinery of Sec. 8.4 for finding perturbed energies when the stabilized eigenfunctions are not known. We shall write the four matrix elements in an obvious notation, as W_{++}, W_{+-}, W_{-+}, and W_{--}, where, for example,

$$W_{++} = \int \psi^*_{j=l+\frac{1}{2},m_j}(\hat{H}_r + \hat{H}_{s-o} + \hat{H}_B)\psi_{j=l+\frac{1}{2},m_j}$$

Most of the work is already done above; we find, using (14.38),

$$W_{++} = \Delta E^{(+)} + \frac{e\hbar B}{2m}\frac{l+1}{l+\frac{1}{2}}m_j$$

where $\Delta E^{(+)}$ is the spin-orbit plus relativity correction given in (14.35) for $j = l + \frac{1}{2}$. Similarly,

$$W_{--} = \Delta E^{(-)} + \frac{e\hbar B}{2m}\frac{l}{l+\frac{1}{2}}m_j$$

whereas for W_{+-} and W_{-+} we need only calculate with $\hat{H}_B$,

$$W_{+-} = \int \psi^*_{j=l+\frac{1}{2},m_j}\hat{H}_B\psi_{j=l-\frac{1}{2},m_j}$$

(This is the advantage in choosing the wave functions $\psi_{j=l+\frac{1}{2},m_j}$ and $\psi_{j=l-\frac{1}{2},m_j}$ to start with.) We find

$$W_{+-} = W_{-+} = \frac{e\hbar B}{2m}\frac{[(l+\frac{1}{2})^2 - m_j^2]^{\frac{1}{2}}}{2l+1}$$

and putting these into (8.24) gives after some simplification

$$E^{(1)} = \overline{\Delta E} + \beta m_j \pm \frac{1}{2}\left(\delta^2 + 4\delta\beta \frac{m_j}{2l+1} + \beta^2\right)^{1/2} \tag{14.42}$$

where $\overline{\Delta E}$ is the average of the two values in (14.35), that is, the center of the doublet, δ is their difference, the doublet separation, and $\beta = e\hbar B/2m$. In order to relate this formula to the limiting cases found above, we consider first $\delta \gg \beta$ and then $\delta \ll \beta$, taking the first two terms of the expansion of the square root and treating the two choices of sign separately. We find for the two signs in (14.42)

Weak field ($\beta \ll \delta$)	Strong field ($\beta \gg \delta$)
$\overline{\Delta E} + \frac{1}{2}\delta + \dfrac{e\hbar B}{2m}\dfrac{l+1}{l+\frac{1}{2}}\,m_j$	$\overline{\Delta E} + \delta\dfrac{m_j}{2l+1} + \dfrac{e\hbar B}{2m}(m_j + \frac{1}{2})$
$\overline{\Delta E} - \frac{1}{2}\delta + \dfrac{e\hbar B}{2m}\dfrac{l}{1+\frac{1}{2}}\,m_j$	$\overline{\Delta E} - \delta\dfrac{m_j}{2l+1} + \dfrac{e\hbar B}{2m}(m_j - \frac{1}{2})$

The results for weak field are the same as (14.38), and the two signs are seen to correspond to $j = l + \frac{1}{2}$ and $l - \frac{1}{2}$, respectively. For the strong field we write the field-dependent part of (14.39) as $(e\hbar B/2m)(m_j + m_s)$, and we see that the two signs correspond to $m_s = +\frac{1}{2}$ and $-\frac{1}{2}$. For intermediate fields these simple assignments of quantum numbers fail. This is because (see Table 6.1) the only dynamical variables which commute with the whole perturbing hamiltonian $\hat{H}_r + \hat{H}_{s-o} + \hat{H}_B$ are L^2 and J_z. Therefore, only these quantities can take on the fixed values denoted by a quantum number, and the only quantum numbers available are l and m_j.

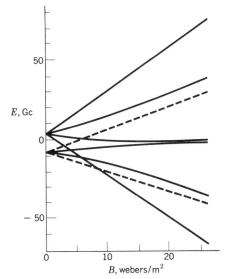

Fig. 14.7 Splitting of the $n = 2$ levels of hydrogen in a magnetic field. The dashed lines represent the states with $l = 0$; the rest are $l = 1$. One gigacycle (Gc) $= 10^3$ Mc. One weber per square meter (Wb/m^2) $= 10^4$ Oe. The states can be identified by comparison with the preceding two figures.

Figure 14.7 shows the transition from weak to strong field for the hydrogen levels (^2s and ^2p) with $n = 2$.

Problem 14.17 When $m_j = \pm (l + \frac{1}{2})$, the unperturbed state from which we start is not degenerate (see Sec. 6.5). Carry through the above calculations for these levels. (They are the straight lines corresponding to $m = \pm \frac{3}{2}$ in Fig. 14.7.)

REFERENCES

H. A. Bethe and E. E. Salpeter, *Encyclopedia of Physics*, Springer-Verlag OHG, Berlin, 1957, vol. 35. This is by far the most detailed treatment of the subject. It derives from Bethe's article in the old *Handbuch der Physik*, to which reference may be made if the new one is not available.

G. W. Series, *The Spectrum of Atomic Hydrogen*, Clarendon Press, Oxford, 1957. The excellent textbooks of Schiff, Bohm, Landau and Lifschitz, and many others may also be consulted.

15

The Helium Atom

In this chapter we shall study the lowest states of helium and the two-electron ions which resemble it. The general structure of the helium spectrum has been explained in Chap. 11, and the lowest states are shown in more detail in Fig. 15.1. We shall first calculate the energy of the (singlet) ground state of ortho-helium in three successive ways, of increasing accuracy. Then Sec. 15.2 will discuss the first excited state of ortho-helium and the (triplet) ground state of para-helium. Section 15.3 will deal with the corrections necessary when the motion of the nucleus is allowed for. The purpose of this chapter is not so much to initiate the reader into the mysteries which surround the general calculation of atomic states—unfortunately, this is a very complicated matter—as it is to give him practice in simple computational procedures which are of use in a variety of situations.

15.1 The Ground State

The two-electron systems to be considered here begin with the negative hydrogen ion, H^-, in which a hydrogen atom absorbs an extra electron and holds it in a very loosely bound state, followed by He, Li^+, Be^{2+}, and B^{3+}. The spectra of all of them have been measured with great accuracy except for H^-, which is ionized by an energy of $1/18$ eV and which has no excited bound states at all. This ion is difficult to study in the laboratory, but it appears to be of great importance in considerations of stellar structure, where its ionization by photons emerging from the interior of a star, followed by re-formation with the re-emission of a photon, is probably the

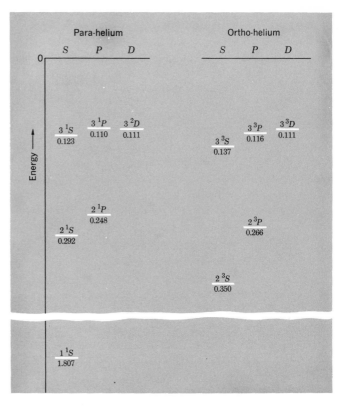

Fig. 15.1 The lowest states of para- and ortho-helium. Energies are given in rydbergs (1 Ry = 13.60 eV).

principal cause of the extreme opacity of stellar atmospheres. The problem to be solved here is to determine the eigenfunctions and eigenvalues of the equation

$$\left[-\frac{\hbar^2}{2m} \left(\nabla_1{}^2 + \nabla_2{}^2 \right) - Ze'^2 \left(\frac{1}{r_1} + \frac{1}{r_2} \right) + \frac{e'^2}{|r_1 - r_2|} \right] \psi(r_1, r_2)$$
$$= E\psi(r_1, r_2) \qquad (15.1)$$

Like the corresponding three-body problem in classical physics, it cannot be solved exactly, but we shall find that it is not hard to find the energy correct to a few percent.

Perturbation theory

The simplest way to approach the calculation of the ground-state energy is by a first-order perturbation. The unperturbed system is taken to be a double hydrogen atom, in which the electrons interact with the nucleus of charge Z but not with each other. One would expect this approximation to be best for large values of Z, where the interaction between the electrons may legitimately be considered small compared with their interaction with the nucleus. The normalized ground-state wave function of a single electron can be taken from (7.56),

$$\psi(r) = \left(\frac{\alpha^3}{\pi}\right)^{1/2} e^{-\alpha r} \tag{15.2}$$

where

$$\alpha = Z \frac{me'^2}{\hbar^2} \tag{15.3}$$

which is like (7.45) except that since we are neglecting the nuclear motion, we do not use the reduced mass, and since the factor e'^2 in (7.43) has here been replaced by Ze'^2, we can make the corresponding replacement in formulas such as (7.45) which are derived from (7.43). The (symmetrical) unperturbed ground state is

$$\psi^{(0)}(r_1, r_2) = \frac{\alpha^3}{\pi} e^{-\alpha r_1} e^{-\alpha r_2} \tag{15.4}$$

and the corresponding energy is

$$E^{(0)} = -2Z^2 \quad \text{Ry} \tag{15.5}$$

To find the perturbed energy, we must take the expectation value of the electrons' interaction in the unperturbed state,

$$E^{(0)} = \iint \frac{e'^2}{|\mathbf{r}_1 - \mathbf{r}_2|} |\psi^{(1)}(\mathbf{r}_1, \mathbf{r}_2)|^2 \, dv_1 \, dv_2 \tag{15.6}$$

or, reinstating for a moment the charge e in mks units,

$$E^{(1)} = \frac{\alpha^3}{\pi} e \int e^{-2\alpha r_1} V(r_1) \, dv_1 \tag{15.7}$$

where

$$V(r_1) = \frac{\alpha^3}{\pi} \frac{e}{4\pi\varepsilon_0} \int e^{-2\alpha r_2} \frac{dv_2}{|\mathbf{r}_1 - \mathbf{r}_2|} \tag{15.8}$$

We have broken the sixfold integration into two parts, and we can proceed without difficulty when we notice the physical significance of the mathematical expressions; for $V(r_1)$ is just the electrostatic potential, evaluated at a distance r_1 from the origin, of a spherically symmetric charge distribution whose density is $(e\alpha^3/\pi)e^{-2\alpha r_2}$. The calculation of $V(r_1)$ is very simple if we do it right, which is by dividing the charge distribution into concentric shells (Fig. 15.2) and remembering that the Coulomb potential of a shell evaluated at a point P is the same as though the shell were concentrated at its center if P is outside the shell, is constant if P is inside, and is continuous on the shell. If the shell is of radius r_2 and thickness dr_2,

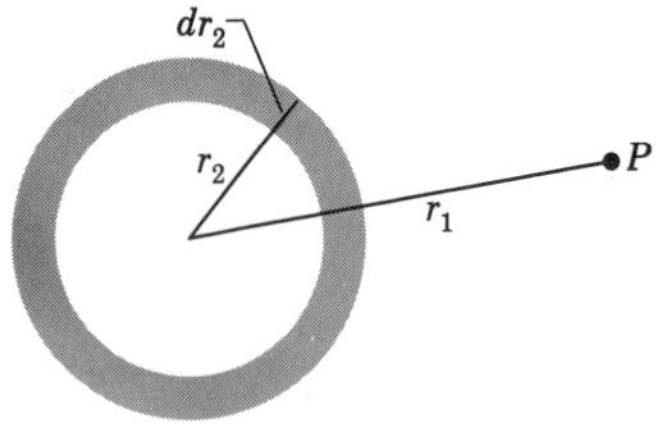

Fig. 15.2 For evaluating (15.8).

the potential at r_1 is therefore

$$dV(r_1) = \begin{cases} \dfrac{4\pi r_2{}^2(e\alpha^3/\pi)e^{-2\alpha r_2}\,dr_2}{4\pi\varepsilon_0 r_1} & (r_2 \leqslant r_1) \\[3mm] \dfrac{4\pi r_2{}^2(e\alpha^3/\pi)e^{-2\alpha r_2}\,dr_2}{4\pi\varepsilon_0 r_2} & (r_2 \geqslant r_1) \end{cases}$$

so that the total potential is

$$V(r_1) = \frac{e\alpha^3}{\pi\varepsilon_0}\left[\frac{1}{r_1}\int_0^{r_1} r_2{}^2 e^{-2\alpha r_2}\,dr_2 + \int_{r_1}^{\infty} r_2 e^{-2\alpha r_2}\,dr_2\right]$$

which, as the reader will readily verify, is equal to

$$V(r_1) = \frac{e}{4\pi\varepsilon_0 r_1}[1 - (1 + \alpha r_1)e^{-2\alpha r_1}] \qquad (15.9)$$

Problem 15.1 What is the potential energy of a particle of charge e at a distance r from the center of a hydrogen atom? Verify that your answer has the limiting behavior that one would expect at large and at small values of r.

Having found the potential due to one charge distribution, we now evaluate (15.7) to find the potential energy of a second distribution with respect to it. The integral is

$$E^{(1)} = \frac{e^2}{4\pi\varepsilon_0}\,\frac{\alpha^3}{\pi}\,4\pi\int_0^{\infty} r_1[1 - (1 + \alpha r_1)e^{-2\alpha r_1}]\,e^{-2\alpha r_1}\,dr_1$$

or

$$E^{(1)} = \frac{5}{8}\frac{e^2\alpha}{4\pi\varepsilon_0} \qquad (15.10)$$

(The reader will note that this is of the order of magnitude that would be expected.) We now put in (15.3), expressing the result in rydbergs, and combine it with (15.5) to obtain an estimate for the binding energy

$$E_{\text{pert}} = E^{(0)} + E^{(1)} = (-2Z^2 + \tfrac{5}{4}Z) \qquad \text{Ry} \qquad (15.11)$$

Problem 15.2 Why does the interaction energy of the two electrons turn out to contain a factor of Z?

For helium, (15.11) gives

$$E_{\text{pert}} = -11\tfrac{1}{2}\,\text{Ry} = -74.83\,\text{eV} \qquad (15.12)$$

This is the binding energy of both electrons. Spectroscopically, one finds ordinarily only the energy necessary to ionize one of the electrons, and the other remains in its ground state. Therefore, in order to compare (15.12) with an experimental value, we must imagine that the atom has been ionized once, requiring an energy which we shall call I_I. What remains is a helium ion, whose ionization energy we shall call I_II. Experimentally, it is found that[1]

$$I_\mathrm{I} = 24.58 \text{ eV} \qquad I_\mathrm{II} = 54.40 \text{ eV}$$

so that the experimental value of E is minus the sum of these, or -78.98 eV. The error of (15.12) is 5.3 percent.

For purposes of comparison with experiment, it will be more convenient to derive a theoretical value for I_I. Since it requires Z^2 Ry to remove the second electron, we have

$$\begin{aligned} I_{\mathrm{I,pert}} &= (2Z^2 - \tfrac{5}{4}Z - Z^2) \qquad \text{Ry} \\ &= (Z^2 - \tfrac{5}{4}Z) \qquad \text{Ry} \end{aligned} \tag{15.13}$$

Table 15.1 compares theoretical with measured values and shows, remarkably, a constant discrepancy. As anticipated, the accuracy improves percentagewise with increasing Z.

Table 15.1 First ionization energy and other parameters for two-electron atoms and ions

	Z	Experi- ment, Ry	Pertur- bation, Ry	Error, Ry	Varia- tion, Ry	Error, Ry	ζ	Radial corre- lation, Ry	Error, Ry	ν	ζ
H⁻	1	0.055[a]	−0.25[b]	−0.31	−0.05	−0.11	0.69	0.027	−0.028	0.57	0.66
He	2	1.81	1.50	−0.31	1.70	−0.11	1.69	1.75	−0.06	0.30	1.69
Li⁺	3	5.56	5.25	−0.31	5.45	−0.11	2.69	5.50	−0.06	0.23	2.69
Be⁺⁺	4	11.31	11.00	−0.31	11.20	−0.11	3.69	11.25	−0.06	0.19	3.69
B³⁺	5	19.06	18.75	−0.31	18.95	−0.11	4.69	19.00	−0.06	0.17	4.69

[a] This is in accordance with several recent theoretical calculations [S. Geltman, Astrophys. J. 136, 935 (1962)]. The experimental value is estimated as 0.057 ± 0.002 Ry [J. D. Weisner and B. H. Armstrong, Proc. Phys. Soc. (London) 83, 31 (1964)].

[b] The negative value means that the second electron is not bound. The energy E_pert is -0.75 Ry, whereas the hydrogen energy is -1 Ry. By losing its electron, therefore, the H⁻ ion would pass into a more stable state.

The perturbation theory has thus given us an estimate of the first ionization energy but no more than a zeroth approximation for the wave function. We shall now see how to improve the energy

[1] Charlotte E. Moore, Atomic Energy Levels, Natl. Bur. Standards Circ. 467, vol. I.

value and also find a wave function which takes into account, even if very roughly, the interaction between the electrons.

Variational calculation

This next step of approximation is motivated by the fact that each electron must partially screen the nucleus from the other, and we are led to try to find the value of the effective nuclear charge, which we shall call ζe, which each electron sees in the presence of the other. We shall do this by taking α as unknown rather than fixed by (15.3) and by defining ζ through the new relation

$$\alpha = \zeta \frac{me'^2}{\hbar^2} \tag{15.14}$$

The value of ζ will be evaluated variationally; that is, we shall evaluate the total energy as a function of ζ and then choose the value of ζ which minimizes it. Returning to (15.4) and (15.10), in which α is now unspecified, we evaluate the expectation value of the total energy in this state and find

$$E = \frac{\hbar^2 \alpha^2}{m} - (2Z - \tfrac{5}{8})e'^2 \alpha \tag{15.15}$$

and using (15.14) simplifies this to

$$E = 2[\zeta^2 - 2(Z - \tfrac{5}{16})\zeta] \qquad \text{Ry} \tag{15.16}$$

This does indeed go through a minimum when

$$\zeta = Z - \tfrac{5}{16} \tag{15.17}$$

and with this value,

$$E_{\text{var}} = -2(Z - \tfrac{5}{16})^2 \qquad \text{Ry} \tag{15.18}$$

Problem 15.3 Derive (15.15).

Problem 15.4 Find the (exact) eigenfunction and eigenvalue of the ground state of hydrogen and the one-electron ions of nuclear charge Z by the variational procedure, starting with a trial wave function of the form (15.2).

If (15.18) is multiplied out, it is

$$E_{\text{var}} = (-2Z^2 + \tfrac{5}{4}Z - \tfrac{25}{128}) \qquad \text{Ry} \tag{15.19}$$

which is the same as (15.11) except for the constant term. The total energy of helium in the ground state is lowered from (15.12) to

$$E_{\text{var}} = -\frac{3^6}{2^7} \text{Ry} = -5.695 \text{ Ry} = -77.48 \text{ eV}$$

an error of only 1.9 percent, and the relative error for larger values of Z is correspondingly less. As in (15.13), the first ionization potential is

$$I_{\text{I,var}} = (Z^2 - \tfrac{5}{4}Z + \tfrac{25}{128}) \qquad \text{Ry} \tag{15.20}$$

We have already seen in Table 15.1 that compared with experiment the perturbation result had an error of 0.31 Ry, independent of Z, and the variational procedure has given a constant correction of 0.195 Ry. The new values are also listed in Table 15.1. As the reader may have surmised, (15.20) gives the first three terms of a series in descending powers of Z. This representation of the energy was first given by Hylleraas in 1930. The first two terms of (15.20) are exact, and a number of further coefficients have now been estimated by variational methods.

Correlation effects

The variational calculation just performed represents about the best that can be done without taking into account the fact that the electrons influence each other's motion from moment to moment, so that their positions are in fact correlated and the two-particle wave function therefore cannot possibly be a product like (15.4). Roughly speaking, the Coulomb repulsion produces two types of correlation, angular and radial. The former refers to the fact that the electrons are more likely to be found on opposite sides than on the same side of the nucleus; the latter means that if one electron moves in nearer the nucleus, it tends to force the other one farther out. Wave functions exhibiting angular correlation are apt to be extremely complicated in form and difficult to visualize, but radial correlations can be introduced in a relatively simple way which involves only a small amount of numerical computation.[2] We assume only that the two electrons shield each other differently, the effective nuclear charge seen by the electrons further out and further in being written as $(1 - \nu)\zeta e$ and $(1 + \nu)\zeta e$, respectively. The wave function if the two electrons were distinguishable would be

$$\psi(r_1,r_2) = Ne^{-(1+\nu)\alpha r_1}e^{-(1-\nu)\alpha r_2}$$

with α given by (15.14), but since they are identical and their spins in this state are antiparallel, we must use the symmetrized form

$$\psi(r_1,r_2) = N[e^{-(1+\nu)\alpha r_1-(1-\nu)\alpha r_2} + e^{-(1-\nu)\alpha r_1-(1+\nu)\alpha r_2}] \tag{15.21}$$

This must first be normalized and then used to compute the expectation value of the energy. We omit the details here (they are sketched in the reference just given, and the interested reader will be able to reconstruct the calculation). Introducing the abbreviation

---

[2] See H. Shull and P. Löwdin, J. Chem. Phys., **25**, 1035 (1956), for results and other references.

$p = 1 - \nu^2$, it is found that the minimum value of E occurs when

$$\zeta = \frac{16Z - 4p - p^2 + 16Zp^3 - 5p^3}{8(2 - p + p^4)}$$

and that it is equal to

$$E = -\frac{(16Z - 4p - p^2 + 16Zp^3 - 5p^3)^2}{128(1 + p^3)(2 - p + p^4)} \quad \text{Ry}$$

This expression must now (for each value of Z) be minimized with respect to the parameter p. This is straightforward, and the results are given in Table 15.1. The average nuclear charge ζ is almost exactly that found in the simple variational procedure, but the splitting is quite substantial; in helium, for example, the effective nuclear charges seen by the two electrons are 1.18 and 2.20. The fact that the latter is greater than 2 suggests that while the nucleus is pulling the inner electron inward, the outer one is pushing it in the same direction.

The total ground-state energy of helium is found to be

$$E_{\text{cor}} = -5.751 \text{ Ry} = -78.24 \text{ eV}$$

with an error of just under 1 percent.

Having exhibited the ground-state calculation in these successive refinements of detail, we shall go on in the next section to evaluate some of the excited states without aiming at an accuracy of better than a few percent.

Comments

The reader may wonder how it has happened that quantum mechanics, which superficially looks so much more difficult than Newtonian mechanics, is able to obtain good solutions for problems which the older theory cannot touch. The answer to this question is twofold. Part of it is that the reputed mathematical difficulty of quantum mechanics lies largely in its unfamiliarity—the methods and viewpoints which we regard as "easy" are to a great extent conditioned by Newtonian physics. The other part of the answer, closely related to the first, is that the program of the quantum theory is really the more modest; for the indeterminacy principle is built into it from the beginning, and we do not have to imagine the detailed specification of positions and motions which are the goal of the classical theory. This fact is clearly evident in expressions like (15.7) and (15.8), for example, in which each electron, for computational purposes, is treated as a spherically symmetrical cloud of charge; and it should be recalled that this was not an idealization put into the theory arbitrarily in order to simplify it, but, rather, that it has emerged as an automatic consequence of the perturbation formalism. Of course, calculations involving many particles are still very hard, but they are gradually becoming less so with the development of new machine computational methods.

Problem 15.5 If a negative muon of mass about 206 electron masses passes close to the nucleus of an atom of helium gas, there is a possibility that the muon will replace one of the electrons in the atom to form (temporarily, until the muon decays) a new kind of three-particle system. What energy is released when this capture process occurs?

Problem 15.6 Calculate the diamagnetic susceptibility of helium gas at atmospheric pressure and 0°C, using the wave function (15.21). Compare with the experimental value of -1.05×10^{-9}. The solution should start with the generalization of (8.37) to the case in which more than one electron is present.

15.2   The Lowest Excited States

The states we shall deal with are those in which one electron has received energy and the other remains in the ground state. In this section we shall be concerned chiefly with the $2p$ states, in which the designation refers to the excited electron. As we have seen in Chap. 11, the general form of the energy of such a state is given by a formula like

$$E = E^{(0)} + K \pm A \qquad \begin{matrix} + : \text{singlet states} \\ - : \text{triplet states} \end{matrix}$$

in which $E^{(0)}$ is the unperturbed energy, K is the mutual Coulomb energy of the two electron clouds as calculated in the preceding section, and A is the exchange energy. Figure 15.1 shows the levels, and we can see from it that for the $2p$ states,

$$E^{(0)} + K = -0.257 \text{ Ry} \qquad A = 0.009 \text{ Ry} \qquad (15.22)$$

The first of these is what the energy would be if the two electrons were distinguishable; the second reflects the fact that they are not. Let us consider first the case of distinguishable electrons. Here we would have one in the $1s$ state and the other in a $2p$ state, circling around outside it. The inner electron would shield the outer one, and to a first approximation the outer one sees a nuclear charge of e and the inner one sees $2e$. The outer electron has therefore the same wave function and energy as the $2p$ state of hydrogen; they are

$$\psi = Nze^{-\frac{1}{4}\alpha r} \qquad (15.23)$$

plus two other states having the same energy, and

$$E = -\frac{1}{4} \text{ Ry} \qquad (15.24)$$

and we see from (15.22) that this simple argument gives the first part of the energy with an error of less than 3 per cent. Now we can estimate A, using a $1s$ wave function with a nuclear charge of 2 for the inner electron and a $2p$ wave function with $Z = 1$ for the outer one. To the extent that these wave functions actually are a reasonable approximation to the truth, this should give a good value for A, but it should be emphasized that this is a way of doing the calculation which is more intuitive than systematic and that it would be difficult to obtain this procedure as part of a step-by-step analysis of perturbations.

The normalized eigenfunctions are conveniently written as

$$\psi_1 = \frac{2^{3/2}\beta^{3/2}}{\pi^{1/2}} e^{-2\beta r} \qquad \psi_2 = \frac{\beta^{5/2}}{2^{5/2}\pi^{1/2}} z e^{-1/2\beta r}$$

where

$$\beta = \frac{me'^2}{\hbar^2}$$

and in terms of them the exchange integral

$$A = \iint \psi_1(r_1)\psi_2(r_1) \frac{e'^2}{|\mathbf{r} - \mathbf{r'}|} \psi_1(r_2)\psi_2(r_2) \, dv_1 \, dv_2 \tag{15.25}$$

can be written out as

$$A = \frac{e'^2\beta^8}{(2\pi)^2} \int e^{-5/2\beta r_1} z_1 \, dv_1 \int e^{-5/2\beta r_2} \frac{z_2 \, dv_2}{|\mathbf{r}_1 - \mathbf{r}_2|} \tag{15.26}$$

The second of these integrals is a function of $\mathbf{r}_1$. Let us integrate it in polar coordinates r_2, ϑ_2, and φ_2, taking advantage of the liberty we have in the choice of polar axis to choose the axis parallel to $\mathbf{r}_1$, which we consider fixed until the time comes to evaluate the first integral. The coordinates are shown in Fig. 15.3, in which the z direction, which we consider to be fixed in space, appears inclined relative to the polar axis $\mathbf{r}_1$. The quantity z_2 is $r_2 \cos \chi$, but we shall need to express this in terms of ϑ_2 and φ_2 in order to integrate it. To do so, we borrow from spherical trigonometry the well-known law of cosines, which gives the angular distance between two points on the

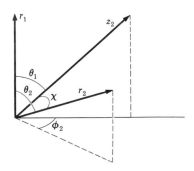

Fig. 15.3   Coordinates for evaluating (15.26).

earth's surface whose latitudes and longitudes are given and which in our notation is[3]

$$\cos \chi = \cos \vartheta_1 \cos \vartheta_2 + \sin \vartheta_1 \sin \vartheta_2 \cos \varphi_2$$

Further, we have

$$|\mathbf{r}_1 - \mathbf{r}_2| = (r_1{}^2 - 2\mathbf{r}_1 \cdot \mathbf{r}_2 + r_2{}^2)^{1/2} = (r_1{}^2 - 2r_1r_2 \cos \vartheta_2 + r_2{}^2)^{1/2}$$

Thus the second integral is

$$\int e^{-\frac{1}{2}\beta r_2} r_2{}^3 (\cos \vartheta_1 \cos \vartheta_2 + \sin \vartheta_1 \sin \vartheta_2 \cos \varphi_2)$$

$$\frac{\sin \vartheta_2 \, dr_2 \, d\vartheta_2 \, d\varphi_2}{(r_1{}^2 - 2r_1r_2 \cos \vartheta_2 + r_2{}^2)^{1/2}}$$

First we integrate over φ_2 to get

$$2\pi \cos \vartheta_1 \int_0^\infty e^{-\frac{1}{2}\beta r_2} r_2{}^3 \, dr_2 \int_0^\pi \frac{\cos \vartheta_2 \sin \vartheta_2 \, d\vartheta_2}{(r_1{}^2 - 2r_1r_2 \cos \vartheta_2 + r_2{}^2)^{1/2}} \qquad (15.27)$$

Next we do the ϑ_2 integral. It can be done easily if we take $\cos \vartheta_2$ as the variable of integration, and it is equal to $\frac{2}{3} r_</r_>{}^2$, where $r_<$ and $r_>$ designate the smaller and the larger of the pair r_1 and r_2. Thus we get for the second integral

$$\frac{4\pi}{3} \cos \vartheta_1 \int_0^\infty e^{-\frac{1}{2}\beta r_2} r_2{}^3 \frac{r_<}{r_>{}^2} \, dr_2$$

and this, exactly as in the calculation of (15.9), can be broken up into two parts to give

$$\frac{4\pi}{3} \cos \vartheta_1 \left(\frac{2}{5\beta}\right)^5 \frac{3}{r_1{}^2} \{8 - [\tfrac{1}{8}(5\beta r_1)^3 + (5\beta r_1)^2 + 4(5\beta r_1) + 8]e^{-\frac{1}{2}\beta}\} \qquad (15.28)$$

Problem 15.7   Evaluate the integral (15.27). The ϑ_2 integral (with $\cos \vartheta_2 = x$) is readily available in tables, but in using them it should be remembered that the square root of an algebraic expression is always to be taken positive, for example,

$$(r_1{}^2 + r_2{}^2 - 2r_1r_2)^{1/2} = |r_1 - r_2| = r_> - r_<$$

To continue with the evaluation of (14.26), we again adopt polar coordinates, taking z_1 as the polar axis. Now z_1 is measured in the same direction as z_2, so that the polar angle in these coordinates is just the ϑ_1 of Fig. 15.3. Thus, (15.26) becomes

$$A = \frac{e'^2\beta^3}{(4\pi)} \left(\frac{2}{5}\right)^5 \int e^{-\frac{1}{2}\beta r_1} r_1 \{\ldots\} \cos^2 \vartheta_1 \sin \vartheta_1 \, dr_1 \, d\vartheta_1 \, d\varphi_1$$

---

[3] See any school text in which spherical trigonometry is mentioned, or derive it by evaluating the dot product of two unit vectors whose components are written in polar coordinates.

in which the remaining integrations are easily carried out to give

$$A = \frac{2^8 \times 7}{3 \times 5^7} \text{Ry} = 0.00765 \text{ Ry} \qquad (15.29)$$

and this is to be compared with the experimental value of 0.0093 Ry derived from accurate spectroscopic data. The accuracy, while scarcely startling, is sufficient to show that we have explained, by virtue of the Pauli principle, how it is that the relative spin orientation of the electrons can have a dynamic effect far greater than would be expected from a purely magnetic interaction.

Problem 15.8   Carry out the integration leading to (15.29).

Problem 15.9   In the same approximation as that just used for the $2P$ levels, calculate the $2S$ levels of ortho- and para-helium. Pay particular attention to the normalization of the two-particle wave function. Why are the results substantially poorer than those obtained above?

Problem 15.10   Plan and carry out a better approximate calculation of the $2S$ levels. Experimentally, the levels are centered at 0.32117 ± 0.00014 Ry, whereas A is 0.02926 Ry, with negligible uncertainty. (Level differences can be measured more accurately than the levels themselves.)

Problem 15.11   Taking (15.7) as a model, show that any exchange integral (15.25) can be written in the form

$$A = -\int V^* \nabla^2 V \, dv$$

where V is a suitably defined potential function, and consequently that such integrals are always nonnegative. What generalization concerning the helium spectrum does this lead to?

15.3   Nuclear Motion in Helium

In Chap. 7 we have seen how the motion of the nucleus of a hydrogen atom may be taken into account through the introduction of coordinates which separate out the center of mass. In helium, as befits the three-body problem, the calculation is somewhat more difficult, but we shall sketch it here and estimate the size of the effects to which it gives rise.

Figure 15.4 shows the notations for the coordinates to be used. The center of mass is located at $\mathbf{R}$, and the vector $\mathbf{R}_0$ gives the position of the nucleus relative to O, whereas $\mathbf{r}_1$ and $\mathbf{r}_2$ locate the electrons relative to the nucleus and are therefore the same coordinates as we have used above. The atom is completely specified by the coordi-

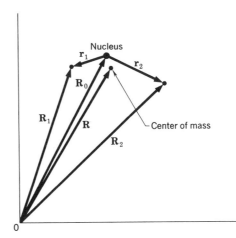

Fig. 15.4 Introduction of
center-of-mass coordinates.

nates $\mathbf{R}$, $\mathbf{r}_1$, and $\mathbf{r}_2$. If M is the nuclear mass and m the mass of an electron, then

$$(M + 2m)\mathbf{R} = M\mathbf{R}_0 + m(\mathbf{R}_1 + \mathbf{R}_2) \tag{15.30}$$

and

$$\mathbf{r}_1 = \mathbf{R}_1 - \mathbf{R}_0 \qquad \mathbf{r}_2 = \mathbf{R}_2 - \mathbf{R}_0 \tag{15.31}$$

It will be convenient to introduce notations such as $\partial/\partial\mathbf{R}_0$ to represent the gradient operator whose components are $(\partial/\partial X_0,\ \partial/\partial Y_0,\ \partial/\partial Z_0)$ and $\partial^2/\partial\mathbf{R}_0^2$ for the corresponding laplacian. In terms of these, the hamiltonian operator of the entire system is

$$\hat{H} = -\tfrac{1}{2}\hbar^2\left[\frac{1}{M}\frac{\partial^2}{\partial\mathbf{R}_0^2} + \frac{1}{m}\left(\frac{\partial^2}{\partial\mathbf{R}_1^2} + \frac{\partial^2}{\partial\mathbf{R}_2^2}\right)\right]$$
$$- e'^2\left(\frac{2}{r_1} + \frac{2}{r_2} - \frac{1}{|\mathbf{r}_1 - \mathbf{r}_2|}\right) \tag{15.32}$$

To transform this to the new coordinates, we write

$$\frac{\partial}{\partial X_0} = \frac{\partial\mathbf{R}}{\partial X_0}\cdot\frac{\partial}{\partial\mathbf{R}} + \frac{\partial\mathbf{r}_1}{\partial X_0}\cdot\frac{\partial}{\partial\mathbf{r}_1} + \frac{\partial\mathbf{r}_2}{\partial X_0}\cdot\frac{\partial}{\partial\mathbf{r}_2}$$

$$= \frac{M}{M + 2m}\frac{\partial}{\partial X} - \frac{\partial}{\partial x_1} - \frac{\partial}{\partial x_2}$$

and similarly

$$\frac{\partial}{\partial X_1} = \frac{m}{M + 2m}\frac{\partial}{\partial X} + \frac{\partial}{\partial x_1} \qquad \frac{\partial}{\partial X_2} = \frac{m}{M + 2m}\frac{\partial}{\partial X} + \frac{\partial}{\partial x_2}$$

Squaring these operators and substituting them into $\hat{H}$ gives

$$\hat{H} = -\left[\frac{\hbar^2}{2(M + 2m)}\frac{\partial^2}{\partial\mathbf{R}^2} + \frac{\hbar^2}{2\mu}\left(\frac{\partial^2}{\partial\mathbf{r}_1^2} + \frac{\partial^2}{\partial\mathbf{r}_2^2}\right) + \frac{\hbar^2}{M}\frac{\partial^2}{\partial\mathbf{r}_1\cdot\partial\mathbf{r}_2}\right]$$
$$+ e'^2\left(\frac{2}{r_1} + \frac{2}{r_2} - \frac{1}{|\mathbf{r}_1 - \mathbf{r}_2|}\right) \tag{15.33}$$

where μ is the reduced mass of an electron relative to the nucleus, given by

$$\frac{1}{\mu} = \frac{1}{M} + \frac{1}{m}$$

The first term in the expression for $\hat{H}$ represents the kinetic energy of the atom as a whole, and it can be omitted from further consideration. The remaining terms describe an atom whose center of mass is at rest with respect to the arbitrary origin O, and we now choose O to be at the center of mass.

The term

$$\hat{H}^{(1)} = -\frac{\hbar^2}{M}\frac{\partial^2}{\partial\mathbf{r}_1 \cdot \partial\mathbf{r}_2} = \frac{\hat{\mathbf{p}}_1 \cdot \hat{\mathbf{p}}_2}{M}$$

is small because $M \gg \mu$, and the remainder of $\hat{H}$ is (with the replacement of m by μ) the hamiltonian with which we began this chapter. Thus we must replace m in (15.1) by μ, and we must in addition estimate the effect of $\hat{H}^{(1)}$ by a first-order perturbation. It perturbs a simple product wave function such as (15.4) not at all, for if

$$\psi^{(0)}(\mathbf{r}_1,\mathbf{r}_2) = \varphi(\mathbf{r}_1)\varphi(\mathbf{r}_2)$$

then

$$\langle\hat{H}^{(1)}\rangle^{(0)} = \frac{1}{M}\langle\hat{\mathbf{p}}_1 \cdot \hat{\mathbf{p}}_2\rangle^{(0)}$$

$$= \frac{1}{M}\int \varphi^*(\mathbf{r}_1)\hat{\mathbf{p}}_1\varphi(\mathbf{r}_1)\, dv_1 \cdot \int \varphi^*(\mathbf{r}_2)\hat{\mathbf{p}}_2\varphi(\mathbf{r}_2)\, dv_2$$

$$= 0$$

because each integral represents the expectation value of a component of the momentum of an electron in a bound state, and since the bound state pattern is stationary, this must be zero. Thus the effects of $\hat{H}^{(1)}$ are apparent only in a wave function which exhibits correlation effects. If

$$\psi^{(0)}(\mathbf{r}_1,\mathbf{r}_2) = 2^{-1/2}[\varphi_m(\mathbf{r}_1)\varphi_n(\mathbf{r}_2) \pm \varphi_n(\mathbf{r}_1)\varphi_m(\mathbf{r}_2)]$$

then only the cross terms remain, and

$$\langle\hat{H}^{(1)}\rangle^{(0)} = \pm\frac{1}{M}\int \varphi_m^*(\mathbf{r}_1)\hat{\mathbf{p}}_1\varphi_n(\mathbf{r}_1)\, dv_1 \cdot \int \varphi_n^*(\mathbf{r}_2)\hat{\mathbf{p}}_2\varphi_m(\mathbf{r}_2)\, dv_2 \tag{15.34}$$

Even with the spherically symmetrical form (5.21) this is still zero; it exists only for a two-electron wave function which exhibits angular correlation effects or one in which m and n belong to different values of the angular momentum. Thus $\hat{H}^{(1)}$ describes the way in which the two electrons, acting together in a correlated manner, cause the nucleus to move around. All other effects are taken into account with the introduction of the reduced mass μ.

Problem 15.12 Derive (15.33) from (15.32).

Problem 15.13 Show analytically that $\langle \hat{\mathbf{p}} \rangle$ for an electron in a bound state is zero.

Problem 15.14 Evaluate the energy correction arising from (15.34) and the reduced mass for the excited states of helium treated in the last section.

REFERENCES

The best general discussion of the subjects treated above is that of

H. A. Bethe and E. E. Salpeter, *Encyclopedia of Physics*, Springer-Verlag OHG, Berlin, 1957, vol. 35.

in which the reader can find a mass of computational material relating to two-electron systems. A somewhat different approach is followed by

W. V. Houston, *Principles of Quantum Mechanics*, McGraw-Hill Book Company, Inc., New York, 1951, chap. X.

An old but excellent elementary presentation of atomic and molecular problems can be found in

L. Pauling and E. B. Wilson, Jr., *Introduction to Quantum Mechanics*, McGraw-Hill Book Company, Inc., New York 1935.

The classic discussion of the more complex atomic systems is

E. U. Condon and G. H. Shortley, *Theory of Atomic Spectra*, Cambridge University Press, London, 1935.

A more up-to-date short treatment is

D. R. Hartree, *The Calculation of Atomic Structures*, John Wiley & Sons Inc., New York, 1957.

J. C. Slater, *Quantum Theory of Atomic Structure*, McGraw-Hill Book Company, Inc., New York, vols. I and II, 1960.

is an encyclopedic modernization of Condon and Shortley with much new material.

An early paper which carries out rather rough evaluations of two- and three-electron states by variational means is

C. Eckart, Phys. Rev., **36,** 878 (1930).

A basically different and more accurate approach to the two-electron problem, in which the interelectron potential no longer appears as a perturbation, is given by

P. Pluvinage, Ann. Phys. (Paris), (12) **5,** 145 (1950).

16

Chemical Forces in H_2^+

We have mentioned earlier that quantum theory provides the explanation of the attractive and repulsive interatomic and inter-molecular forces which determine the structure of matter and, in particular, of chemical compounds. In Sec. 4.7 a crude calculation showed that an electron which is able to jump from one potential well to a neighboring one produces an energy which, depending on the electron's state, either increases or decreases as the two wells are brought closer together and which can therefore be considered as causing a repulsive or attractive force. If one attempts to follow up this calculation by a consideration of some actual molecular systems, one soon encounters computational difficulties so extreme that the pedagogical value of the result is lost sight of in a mass of figures and approximations. We shall therefore confine our attention in this chapter to a simple system which exhibits physically significant aspects of chemical interaction, the hydrogen molecule-ion H_2^+, and calculate its approximate binding energy in its lowest electronic state. From this one can infer the chemical force. Finally, we shall discuss the applicability of the classical notion of interatomic force in a situation which is properly discussed in quantum-mechanical terms.

16.1 The Hydrogen Molecule-Ion

This simplest of all chemical compounds consists of two protons and a single electron. From a classical point of view its stability is incomprehensible, but in fact an energy of 2.64 eV is required in order to dissociate it into a proton plus a hydrogen atom in the ground state.

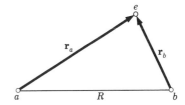

Fig. 16.1 Coordinates to describe $H_2{}^+$. The two protons are a and b; e is the electron.

We shall think of the protons as two classical centers of force, stationary in space with a separation R, with the electron orbiting around them. This picture (Fig. 16.1) ignores the fact that the two protons are themselves in motion and must be treated by quantum mechanics; we shall return to this question later.

The Schrödinger equation for the electron is

$$-\frac{\hbar^2}{2m}\nabla^2\psi - \left(\frac{e'^2}{r_a} + \frac{e'^2}{r_b}\right)\psi = E\psi \tag{16.1}$$

It will be convenient to change units so that distance is measured in terms of the first Bohr orbit a_0 and E in rydbergs. Putting these into (16.1) and using the same letters to denote the old quantities in the new units, we have

$$\nabla^2\psi + 2\left(\frac{1}{r_a} + \frac{1}{r_b}\right)\psi + E\psi = 0 \tag{16.2}$$

This will simplify the arithmetic and make the results easier to visualize.

In order to get an answer with a minimum of calculation, we shall approach the problem by guessing a rough solution and using it to evaluate the expectation value of the energy. We know from Sec. 8.6 that the true value of the energy lies below this expectation value, so that if we are able to find a stable state for the ion by our procedure, then an exact calculation can give only a still more stable state.

To find the trial wave function, we imagine that the ion is formed by bringing together a proton and a hydrogen atom, and we assume that at moderate values of R the exact wave function will somewhat resemble this. We therefore consider a trial function of the form

$$\psi = \psi_a \tag{16.3}$$

where ψ_a is a hydrogen ground-state wave function centered at one of the nuclei, say, a. But this cannot even approximate an eigenfunction of the hamiltonian in (16.2) because the hamiltonian is symmetric under a reflection in the central plane of the molecule, or, more simply, under interchange of the indices a and b. If $\hat{R}$ is the operator which performs this interchange, then the exact wave function will be an eigenfunction of $\hat{R}$ and our trial function should be chosen with this in mind. Clearly, the appropriate generalization of (16.3) is of the form

$$\psi_{\pm} = N_{\pm}(\psi_a \pm \psi_b) \tag{16.4}$$

where ψ_a is centered at proton a and ψ_b at proton b. This is, of course, quite a different thing from (16.3); as we shall see, it contains all the qualitative features needed for a solution. This type of approximation, starting from a *linear* combination of *atomic orbitals*, is called by the letters LCAO.

Problem 16.1 Instead of using the symmetry principle to establish the trial function (16.4), use the variational principle, starting with a (normalized) wave function of the form $N(\psi_a + c\psi_b)$. Show that the values $c = \pm 1$ make the energy a minimum.

Let us first find the normalization constants $N_{\pm}$. We have

$$\begin{aligned}
|N_{\pm}|^{-2} &= \int |\psi_{\pm}|^2 \, dv \\
&= \int (\psi_a{}^2 + \psi_b{}^2 \pm 2\psi_a\psi_b) \, dv
\end{aligned} \tag{16.5}$$

where ψ_a and ψ_b, in our units, are of the form

$$\psi_a = \pi^{-\frac{1}{2}} e^{-r_a} \qquad \psi_b = \pi^{-\frac{1}{2}} e^{-r_b} \tag{16.6}$$

The first two integrals in (16.5) are each equal to 1. The last one is

$$2\pi^{-1} \int e^{-(r_a + r_b)} \, dv \tag{16.7}$$

and is less simple, being of the kind known as a *two-center integral*, since it involves the distances between the point of integration (x,y,z) and two different fixed points, a and b. This one can most easily be evaluated by a change of coordinate system from the usual cartesian or polar coordinates to a new system in which r_a and r_b appear explicitly. Let us locate the point of integration in terms of these distances and the usual azimuthal angle φ measured around the axis of the molecule. We choose as the new coordinates[1]

$$\frac{r_a + r_b}{R} = \xi \qquad \frac{r_a - r_b}{R} = \eta \qquad \text{and} \qquad \varphi \tag{16.8}$$

One sees readily by looking at Fig. 16.1 that the ranges of ξ, η, and φ are

$$1 \leqslant \xi < \infty \qquad -1 \leqslant \eta \leqslant +1 \qquad 0 \leqslant \varphi \leqslant 2\pi \tag{16.9}$$

---

[1] These are called prolate spheroidal coordinates. Surfaces of constant ξ are a family of prolate spheroids having points a and b as foci, whereas surfaces of constant η are two-sheeted hyperboloids which have the same foci and everywhere cut the spheroids at right angles. (These facts help to visualize the coordinates, but they are not essential to what we are going to do.) See H. Margenau and G. M. Murphy, *The Mathematics of Physics and Chemistry*, D. Van Nostrand Company, Inc., Princeton, N.J., 1943, 1956.

The element of volume may be evaluated either by reference to the coordinate geometry of the new system or by the straightforward evaluation of the Jacobian

$$J = \begin{vmatrix} \dfrac{\partial \xi}{\partial x} & \dfrac{\partial \xi}{\partial y} & \dfrac{\partial \xi}{\partial z} \\[2mm] \dfrac{\partial \eta}{\partial x} & \dfrac{\partial \eta}{\partial y} & \dfrac{\partial \eta}{\partial z} \\[2mm] \dfrac{\partial \varphi}{\partial x} & \dfrac{\partial \varphi}{\partial y} & \dfrac{\partial \varphi}{\partial z} \end{vmatrix}$$

in terms of which we have[2]

$$dv = dx\,dy\,dz = \frac{d\xi\,d\eta\,d\varphi}{J}$$

We choose the z axis as the axis of symmetry, so that

$$r_a = [x^2 + y^2 + (z + \tfrac{1}{2}R)^2]^{\frac{1}{2}} \qquad r_b = [x^2 + y^2 + (z - \tfrac{1}{2}R)^2]^{\frac{1}{2}}$$

$$\varphi = \tan^{-1}\frac{y}{x}$$

The differentiations are straightforward, and we find

$$dv = \tfrac{1}{8}(\xi^2 - \eta^2)R^3\,d\xi\,d\eta\,d\varphi \tag{16.10}$$

Returning now to the integral (16.7), we write it as

$$\frac{R^3}{4\pi}\int_0^{2\pi} d\varphi \int_{-1}^{1} d\eta \int_1^{\infty} (\xi^2 - \eta^2)e^{-\xi R}\,d\xi = 2\Delta$$

where

$$\Delta = (1 + R + \tfrac{1}{3}R^2)e^{-R}$$

and putting this into (16.5), we can write the normalization integral as

$$|N_{\pm}|^{-2} = 2(1 \pm \Delta) \tag{16.11}$$

The quantity Δ is called the *overlap* integral. If $R = 0$, so that points a and b coincide, it is clearly equal to 1, whereas if R is very large, we see that wherever ψ_a is large ψ_b is small, and vice versa, so that their product is everywhere small and the integral goes exponentially to zero.

Problem 16.2   Evaluate the Jacobian of the above transformation so as to verify (16.10).

---

[2] See any textbook on advanced calculus in which change of variables in multiple integrals is discussed.

We can now find the expectation value of the energy in the states given by (16.4),

$$W_\pm = |N_\pm|^2 \int (\psi_a \pm \psi_b) \left(-\nabla^2 - \frac{2}{r_a} - \frac{2}{r_b} \right) (\psi_a \pm \psi_b) \, dv \qquad (16.12)$$

This is at once simplified when we remember that ψ_a is a hydrogen eigenfunction corresponding to an energy of -1 Ry and satisfies

$$\nabla^2 \psi_a + \frac{2}{r_a} \psi_a = \psi_a$$

and similarly for ψ_b. Thus $W_\pm$ becomes

$$W_\pm = -|N_\pm|^2 \int (\psi_a \pm \psi_b) \left[\left(1 + \frac{2}{r_b} \right) \psi_a \pm \left(1 + \frac{2}{r_a} \right) \psi_b \right] dv$$

and multiplying this out gives

$$W_\pm = -|N_\pm|^2 \int \left[(\psi_a \pm \psi_b)^2 + \frac{2}{r_b} \psi_a{}^2 + \frac{2}{r_a} \psi_b{}^2 \right.$$
$$\left. \pm \left(\frac{2}{r_b} \psi_a \psi_b + \frac{2}{r_a} \psi_a \psi_b \right) \right]$$

$$= -1 + |N_\pm|^2 (2K \pm 2A) \qquad (16.13)$$

or

$$W_\pm = -1 + \frac{K \pm A}{1 \pm \Delta} \qquad (16.14)$$

where

$$K = -2 \int \frac{1}{r_a} \psi_b{}^2 \, dv \qquad (16.15)$$

and

$$A = -2 \int \frac{1}{r_a} \psi_a \psi_b \, dv \qquad (16.16)$$

are two integrals which we shall call the *Coulomb integral* and the *exchange integral*, respectively. In simplifying (16.13) we have made use of the symmetry of all the expressions with respect to the interchange of a and b. The occurrence of integrals like K and A is noted in Chap. 11. K has a simple physical interpretation. If $\psi_b{}^2$ is regarded as the density of an electron cloud centered at b, then K is the electrostatic potential energy of the proton a in the field produced by this cloud. The exchange integral, however, has no such simple interpretation. It also represents a Coulomb interaction, but of a typically quantum-mechanical kind which, arising from the principle of superposition, has no counterpart in classical physics. We notice, however, that it operates at a shorter range than K, for it depends on the overlap of the two Coulomb wave functions. On evaluation of K and A we find

$$K = -\frac{2}{R} + 2\left(\frac{1}{R} + 1\right)e^{-2R} \tag{16.17}$$

and

$$A = -2(1 + R)e^{-R} \tag{16.18}$$

Problem 16.3 Evaluate the integrals for K and A.

The total energy of the two-proton system including the electron is given by $W_\pm$ plus the mutual potential energy of the protons,

$$E_\pm = W_\pm + \frac{2}{R}$$

or

$$E_\pm = -1 + \frac{2}{R}\frac{\pm(1 - \tfrac{2}{3}R^2)e^{-R} + (1 + R)e^{-2R}}{1 \pm (1 + R + \tfrac{1}{3}R^2)e^{-R}} \tag{16.19}$$

The exact form of these functions is given in Fig. 16.2, and it is seen that E_+, corresponding to the symmetrical approximate eigenfunction in (16.14), decreases with decreasing R to a minimum at $R \approx 2.50$. Thus the system is stable in this state at this separation, and the total binding energy is 1.13 Ry. Suppose now that the ion is gradually dissociated by increasing R. It will finally come apart into a proton and a hydrogen atom of energy -1 Ry. Thus the binding energy of the ion itself is 0.13 Ry or 1.8 eV. If one were doing it more exactly, one would have to put in the fact that the ion in its

Fig. 16.2 Energy of H_2^+ as a function of the separation of the nuclei for symmetrical $(+)$ and antisymmetrical $(-)$ states.

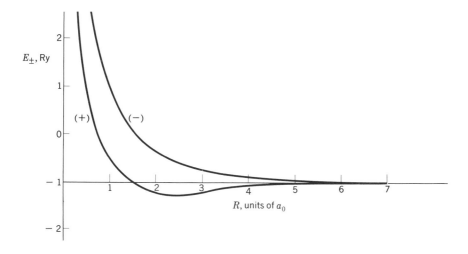

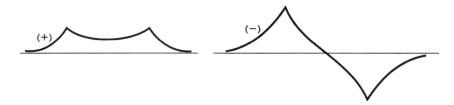

Fig. 16.3 Electron wave function of H_2^+ evaluated along the line of centers for symmetrical and antisymmetrical states.

ground state is vibrating about this equilibrium position at a frequency ω_0 and with a zero-point energy of $\frac{1}{2}\hbar\omega_0$. This amounts to about 0.1 eV, so that the theoretical binding energy is about 1.7 eV. The experimental value is, of course, considerably greater than this, being about 2.65 eV, and our rough calculation would have to be supplemented by a more detailed use of the variational principle in order to obtain a better value.

Problem 16.4 Carry through the calculations necessary to obtain a rough estimate of the zero-point vibrational energy.

To understand how the binding force arises, we note that the potential part of the energy integral (16.12),

$$V_\pm = -2|N_\pm|^2 \int (\psi_a \pm \psi_b)^2 \left(\frac{1}{r_a} + \frac{1}{r_b}\right) dv \tag{16.20}$$

is understandable as the classical Coulomb self-interaction energy of a decidedly nonclassical charge distribution, but if we look carefully at the distribution, we can understand the energy. Figure 16.3 shows the wave functions $|N_\pm|(\psi_a \pm \psi_b)$ evaluated along the line of centers of the molecule, and Fig. 16.4 shows the charge densities calculated by squaring these quantities. It is clear that if we think of the protons as being attracted by the electron and repelled by each other, the symmetrical state will be the more tightly bound because the electron spends a greater fraction of its time between the protons, where it attracts both of them. Chemical bonds formed in this way by the Coulomb attraction of shared electrons congregated in the region between the two ions are called *homopolar* or *covalent*. Since the entire effect arises from the symmetry properties

Fig. 16.4 Electron probability density evaluated from the wave functions in Fig. 16.3.

of the wave function, it clearly cannot be explained on classical grounds.

The other main type of chemical bond occurs when two dissimilar neutral atoms are brought together and their outer electrons, in distributing themselves between the two, tend to favor one or the other. The favored atom becomes somewhat negatively charged, one might loosely call it an ion, and the other one is left with a positive charge. The two atoms thus attract each other with a bonding force which is called *heteropolar* or *ionic*. A familiar example of this is the NaCl molecule, in which the Cl tends to borrow an electron from the Na. However, it is clear from our description that the mechanism of the covalent bond continues to operate in these cases also. In fact, it is a mistake to see a profound distinction between the two types of bonding, for they represent extremes seldom realized, and most chemical bonds contain something of each.

Problem 16.5 Instead of the hydrogen wave functions (16.6), introduce wave functions corresponding to an effective proton charge Z. Calculate the energy as a function of Z and R and so choose Z as to minimize it. (The value of Z thus obtained varies with R.) For what value of R is the energy a minimum, and what is the associated value of Z? What is the energy?

16.2 The Mechanics of a Molecule

The calculation which we have just finished contains a feature which is questionable. It is that we have regarded the two centers of force as fixed when solving the wave equation for the electron. Actually, of course, the protons themselves are governed by a wave equation, and from a classical point of view they are vibrating and rotating in space. The electron is thus subject to rapidly varying constraints, but the argument of Sec. 7.5, with obvious simple modifications, shows that the vibratory and rotatory motions are slower then the motions of the electrons by successive powers of $(m/M)^{1/2}$, so that the nuclear motion is essentially adiabatic, and we can consider the value of R in the preceding section as an instantaneous value.

To see how this works, let us study for a moment the complete quantum theory of the H_2^+ ion. It will be convenient to use the coordinates shown in Fig. 16.5, in which M represents the proton's mass and m that of the electron. The hamiltonian for the entire system is

$$\hat{H} = -\frac{m}{M}(\nabla_1{}^2 + \nabla_2{}^2) + \frac{2}{R} - \nabla^2 - \frac{2}{r_a} - \frac{2}{r_b} \tag{16.21}$$

where the factor of m/M comes from the units employed and the subscript on $\nabla_1{}^2$ refers to differentiation with respect to x_1, y_1, z_1, and similarly for $\nabla_2{}^2$. We write the entire wave function as $\Psi(\mathbf{r}_1, \mathbf{r}_2, \mathbf{r})$ and

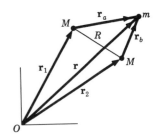

Fig. 16.5   Coordinates to describe the entire H_2^+ ion.

make, as before, a guess as to the correct form of it. The guess is governed by the supposed adiabatic behavior of the electron orbit; we assume that the electron's motion and that of the molecule as a whole take place statistically independently of each other, so that the wave function factors into an electronic part ψ and a nuclear part φ,

$$\Psi(\mathbf{r}_1,\mathbf{r}_2,\mathbf{r}) = \psi(\mathbf{r},\mathbf{r}_1,\mathbf{r}_2)\varphi(\mathbf{r}_1,\mathbf{r}_2) \tag{16.22}$$

where ψ depends on $\mathbf{r}_1$ and $\mathbf{r}_2$ as well as $\mathbf{r}$ because the electron is attracted toward the momentary position of the nuclei. (The argument from statistical independence to a factored wave function is as in Sec. 11.1.) We assume that ψ satisfies (16.2), remembering that E is a function of R and hence of $\mathbf{r}_1$ and $\mathbf{r}_2$. The form of φ will be chosen in a moment, but we shall restrict this elementary treatment to ψ's which are real. The trial energy is given by the expectation value of $\hat{H}$,

$$W = \int \psi(\mathbf{r},\mathbf{r}_1,\mathbf{r}_2)\varphi^*(\mathbf{r}_1,\mathbf{r}_2)\left[-\frac{m}{M}(\nabla_1{}^2 + \nabla_2{}^2) + \frac{2}{R} - \nabla^2 \right.$$
$$\left. - \frac{2}{r_a} - \frac{2}{r_b} \right]\psi(\mathbf{r},\mathbf{r}_1,\mathbf{r}_2)\varphi(\mathbf{r}_1,\mathbf{r}_2)\,dv\,dv_1\,dv_2$$

which, because of (16.2), simplifies at once to

$$W = \int \psi(\mathbf{r},\mathbf{r}_1,\mathbf{r}_2)\varphi^*(\mathbf{r}_1,\mathbf{r}_2)\left[-\frac{m}{M}(\nabla_1{}^2 + \nabla_2{}^2) + \frac{2}{R} + E(R) \right]$$
$$\psi(\mathbf{r},\mathbf{r}_1,\mathbf{r}_2)\varphi(\mathbf{r}_1,\mathbf{r}_2)\,dv\,dv_1\,dv_2$$

Evaluating the laplacians gives

$$W = \int \psi\varphi^*\left\{ -\frac{m}{M}\left[\psi(\nabla_1{}^2 + \nabla_2{}^2)\varphi + \varphi(\nabla_1{}^2 + \nabla_2{}^2)\psi \right. \right.$$
$$\left. + 2\nabla_1\psi\cdot\nabla_1\varphi + 2\nabla_2\psi\cdot\nabla_2\varphi \right] + \left[\frac{2}{R} + E(R) \right]\psi\varphi \right\}\,dv\,dv_1\,dv_2 \tag{16.23}$$

We now choose φ to satisfy the equation

$$\left[-\frac{m}{M}(\nabla_1{}^2 + \nabla_2{}^2) + \frac{2}{R} + E(R) \right]\varphi = J\varphi$$

where J represents the energy due to the nuclear motion and the electronic energy $E(R)$ has been taken as part of the nuclear potential energy. It is the potential function which describes the covalent bond between the protons. We find

$$W = \int \psi\varphi^* \left\{ J\psi\varphi - \frac{m}{M} [\varphi(\nabla_1{}^2 + \nabla_2{}^2)\psi + 2\nabla_1\psi \cdot \nabla_1\varphi \right.$$
$$\left. + 2\nabla_2\psi \cdot \nabla_2\varphi] \right\} dv \, dv_1 \, dv_2$$

Let us now suppose that the electronic wave function is normalized in the sense that

$$\int [\psi(r, r_1, r_2)]^2 \, dv = 1$$

for all values of r_1 and r_2. The expression for W now involves integrals like

$$\int \psi \nabla_1 \psi \, dv = \tfrac{1}{2} \nabla_1 \int \psi^2 \, dv = 0$$

and its last two terms accordingly drop out. Further, φ will satisfy

$$\int |\varphi(r_1, r_2)|^2 \, dv_1 \, dv_2 = 1$$

so that W is

$$W = J - \frac{m}{M} \int |\varphi|^2 \, \psi(\nabla_1{}^2 + \nabla_2{}^2)\psi \, dv \, dv_1 \, dv_2 \qquad (16.24)$$

This expression is very similar to the variational formula (8.67), where the second term corrects the first; and if it can be shown to be small, the presumption is that the trial function (16.22) was a good one and that W is close to J. This is in fact the case, for J has the order of magnitude of the electronic energies which go into it via $E(R)$, whereas the integral has the same general size and is multiplied by the very small number m/M (see Prob. 16.6). Our analytical procedure thus justifies the picture which has been used in this chapter and shows how the motions of electrons and nuclei can be considered as separate problems with little error.

Problem 16.6 Evaluate the **r** integral in (16.24) by using the approximation (16.4) for ψ, and show by estimating the sizes of the remaining integrals that the second term is indeed much smaller than the first.

16.3 Forces in Molecules

In Sec. 16.1, and especially in connection with Fig. 16.4, we have spoken of the force between the two protons of H$_2$$^+$ as being produced by their mutual repulsion together with the attraction of each toward the electronic cloud which surrounds them. The purpose of this section is to examine this notion of force a little more closely and, in particular, to see how it happens that the electron, which according to the classical picture is an orbiting point charge, comes to be regarded as a cloud. Let us look at the energy of the electron, considered as a function of the parameter R, and vary it, let us say, by varying the position of proton b. Let $\Phi(r,R)$ be the exact, normalized electronic wave function corresponding to this value of R. Then the exact energy, including the proton-proton repulsion, is given by

$$E = \int \Phi^* \hat{H} \Phi \, dv \qquad \hat{H}\Phi = E\Phi \qquad\qquad (16.25)$$

with

$$\hat{H} = -\nabla^2 + \frac{2}{R} - \frac{2}{r_a} - \frac{2}{r_b} \qquad\qquad (16.26)$$

Suppose we now ask how E changes with R; for it is $\partial E/\partial R$ which leads to the classical notion of a force. We have

$$\frac{\partial E}{\partial R} = \int \frac{\partial \Phi^*}{\partial R} \hat{H}\Phi \, dv + \int \Phi^* \frac{\partial \hat{H}}{\partial R} \Phi \, dv + \int \Phi \hat{H} \frac{\partial \Phi}{\partial R} \, dv$$

$$= E \frac{\partial}{\partial R} \int \Phi^*\Phi \, dv + \int \Phi^* \frac{\partial \hat{H}}{\partial R} \Phi \, dv$$

where we have used (16.25) and the hermiticity of $\hat{H}$, and so

$$\frac{\partial E}{\partial R} = \left\langle \frac{\partial \hat{H}}{\partial R} \right\rangle \qquad\qquad (16.27)$$

since Φ is normalized. This equation has a very simple interpretation. Since the kinetic-energy operator is independent of R, we have

$$-\frac{\partial E}{\partial R} = \frac{2}{R^2} + 2 \int \frac{\partial}{\partial R} \left(\frac{1}{r_a} + \frac{1}{r_b} \right) |\Phi|^2 \, dv$$

whose first term is obvious, while the second represents the sum of the forces of attraction between the nuclei a and b and a cloud of negative charge of density $|\Phi|^2$. If we imagine that R is increased by moving proton b and let $\mathbf{R}$ be a vector from a to b, we have

$$\frac{\partial}{\partial R} \left(\frac{1}{r_a} + \frac{1}{r_b} \right) = \frac{\partial}{\partial R} \frac{1}{r_b} = \frac{\mathbf{R}}{R} \cdot \nabla \frac{1}{r_b} = -\frac{\mathbf{R} \cdot \mathbf{r}_b}{R r_b^3}$$

and the force can now be evaluated directly (though the integral is a little difficult) without going through the evaluation of E.

What we have proved in (16.27) is a special case of a theorem due to Hellmann[3] which gives an immediate generalization of this: the force on any nucleus in a general molecular system is the sum of the forces due to the other nuclei and those due to all the electrons, considered as clouds of charge. This theorem is sometimes

[3] H. Hellmann, *Einführung in die Quantenchemie*, F. Deuticke, Leipzig, 1937, and, independently, R. P. Feynman, Phys. Rev., **56**, 340 (1939). See also a slightly more general discussion by E. H. Kerner, Phys. Rev. Letters, **2**, 152, (1959).

useful in a computation in which the value of E does not have to be known. Generally, however, one has to find E anyhow in the course of determining the right wave function to use.

REFERENCES

The literature on the theory of molecular structure is enormous; we mention here only a few places where the reader may make a start for himself.

N. F. Mott and I. N. Sneddon, *Wave Mechanics and Its Applications*, Clarendon Press, Oxford, 1948.

J. C. Slater, *Introduction to Chemical Physics*, McGraw-Hill Book Company, Inc., New York, 1939; *Quantum Theory of Matter*, McGraw-Hill Book Company, Inc., New York, 1951.

K. S. Pitzer, *Quantum Chemistry*, Prentice-Hall, Inc., Englewood Cliffs, N.J., 1953.

A discussion of chemical bonding in solids is given by

G. H. Wannier, *Elements of Solid State Theory*, Cambridge University Press, London, 1959.

In the review volume

Advances in Chemical Physics, **2** (1959)

P.-O. Löwdin reviews different approaches to the correlation problem in atoms and simple molecules, and H. Yoshizumi contributes an extensive bibliography.

Qualitative insight into the nature of the chemical bond is given by

V. F. Weisskopf, in Brittin, Downs, and Downs (eds.) *Lectures in Theoretical Physics*, vol. 3, Interscience Publishers, New York, 1961, p. 80.

17

The Neutron-Proton Interaction

Because of its fundamental physical importance, the interaction of neutrons and protons has been extensively studied, both theoretically and experimentally. The basic theory leads into the depths of meson field theory, and we shall make no attempt to follow it. The complications which arise from the mesonic origin of the interaction set in the MeV range; below this, the phenomena do not depend markedly on the nature of the interaction, and a description of the kind known as phenomenological, which characterizes the interaction in terms of a small number of empirically determined parameters, will suffice to relate the various phenomena to each other. We shall therefore be concerned in this chapter only with phenomena in the low-energy range, say, below 10 MeV.

Basically, the phenomena to be discussed fall into two classes, those relating to bound states and those relating to free states. Others, notably the various processes by which a deuteron is disintegrated into a neutron and a proton, of course involve both. Of equal importance from a fundamental point of view are interactions between two protons or between two neutrons. These are less suitable for discussion here, however, because there is no stable bound state of a pair of protons or neutrons. Besides this, the Coulomb interaction between free protons complicates the analysis by making it impossible to restrict attention to s states at any range (this is because of its long-range character), while owing to the lack of a neutron target, there are no direct low-energy data on neutron-neutron scattering, though, of course, much is known about the interaction from indirect measurements. We shall first summarize below the essential facts about the deuteron derived in Sec. 7.4 and then go on to discuss the scattering phenomena from which most of our knowledge derives.

17.1   The Bound State

The deuteron has a single bound state whose binding energy is

$$-E = 2.226 \pm 0.002 \text{ MeV} \tag{17.1}$$

and as we shall see later, this is a triplet state, in which the spins of neutron and proton are parallel. We conclude at once that the interaction is spin-dependent, since there would otherwise be a bound state with antiparallel spins. We shall be interested in evaluating the strength of this dependence.

The ground state has predominantly the spectral designation $^3S_1$; that is, the orbital angular momentum is zero and the spins of neutron and proton are parallel. We say "predominantly" because an effect of the spin dependence of the interaction is to mix in with this a small fraction of the state $^3D_1$, whose effects we shall hereafter ignore. The spatial part of the deuteron wave function is therefore essentially spherically symmetrical. Writing $u(r) = r\psi(r)$, we have for the ground state

$$(7.62) \qquad u'' + \frac{M}{\hbar^2}[E - V(r)]u = 0 \tag{17.2}$$

where $u(0) = 0$ and the interaction $V(r)$ is of short range. M is the nucleon mass (assuming that $M_n = M_p$) and the equation is valid in the C.M. system. If $V(r)$ is effectively zero beyond a certain range r_0, then

$$u \approx e^{-\kappa r} \qquad (r > r_0) \tag{17.3}$$

where

$$(7.63) \qquad \kappa^2 = -\frac{ME}{\hbar^2} \tag{17.4}$$

and by (17.1)

$$\kappa^{-1} = 4.316 \text{ F} \tag{17.5}$$

where $1 \text{ F} = 10^{-13}$ cm.

Since the binding energy is only a single number, it cannot uniquely determine the binding potential, which has a range, a strength, and a shape. If the potential is taken as a square well of range r_0 and depth V_0, the wave function is found to be of the form

$$u(r) = \begin{cases} \left(\frac{\kappa}{2\pi}\right)^{\frac{1}{2}} (1 + \kappa r_0)^{-\frac{1}{2}} \sin Kr & (r < r_0) \\[2mm] \left(\frac{\kappa}{2\pi}\right)^{\frac{1}{2}} e^{\kappa r_0} \left(1 + \frac{\kappa^2}{K^2}\right)^{-\frac{1}{2}} (1 + \kappa r_0)^{-\frac{1}{2}} e^{-\kappa r} & (r > r_0) \end{cases} \tag{17.6}$$

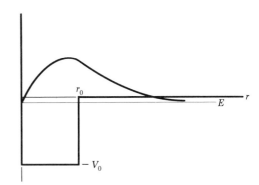

Fig. 17.1   Square-well potential and wave
function for the deuteron.

where

$$K^2 = \frac{M}{\hbar^2}(E + V_0) \tag{17.7}$$

Kr_0 is the phase of the wave function at the edge of the potential
well, and it is about 105°, so that the wave function is still quite
close to the maximum value which it attains at 90°. It is shown in
Fig. 17.1. The relation between range and well-depth for this
potential is approximately

(7.74) $$V_0 = \frac{\hbar^2}{M}\left[\left(\frac{\pi}{2r_0}\right)^2 + \frac{2\kappa}{r_0}\right] \tag{17.8}$$

as long as the binding energy is much less than the well depth.

This approximate relation between V_0 and r_0 is all that can be
learned about the spin-independent part of the potential from the
behavior of the deuteron. To learn more, we must consider the situations in which the energy can be given arbitrary values, and this is
what is done in the experiments on scattering.

17.2   Neutron-Proton Scattering

Let the energy of the incident beam, $E = \hbar^2 k^2/M$ in the C.M.
system, be low enough that only S wave scattering occurs. (This
will be true up to about $E_{\text{lab}} = 10$ MeV.) We now summarize the
relevant parts of Chap. 9. The wave function exterior to the potential is of the form

(9.79) $$u(r) = B \sin (kr + \delta) \qquad (r \geqslant r_0) \tag{17.9}$$

where δ, the phase shift, is a measure of the strength of the scattering
potential. As $r \to r_0$, we have

(9.80) $$\left(\frac{u'}{u}\right)_{r_0} = k \cot (kr_0 + \delta) \approx k \cot \delta \tag{17.10}$$

in the zero-range approximation. The scattering cross section is

$$(9.86) \qquad \sigma = \frac{4\pi}{k^2} \sin^2 \delta = \frac{4\pi}{k^2 \cot^2 \delta + k^2} \qquad\qquad (17.11)$$

or

$$\sigma \approx \frac{4\pi}{(u'/u)_{r_0}^2 + k^2} \qquad\qquad (17.12)$$

in this approximation. If the energy in the scattering experiment is only slightly above zero, whereas the bound-state energy is only slightly below, we can assume that the wave function in the inner region is roughly the same in both cases. The latter joins smoothly on to (17.3), so that $(u'/u)_{r_0} \approx -\kappa$ and

$$(9.87) \qquad \sigma \approx \frac{4\pi}{\kappa^2 + k^2} \qquad\qquad (17.13)$$

The effect of taking the range into account is, to a first approximation, just to multiply this by a numerical factor,

$$(9.95) \qquad \sigma \approx \frac{4\pi}{(1 - \kappa r_0)(\kappa^2 + k^2)} \qquad\qquad (17.14)$$

The general formula for $k \cot \delta$ at low energies for any short-range force may be written

$$(9.93) \qquad k \cot \delta = -a^{-1} + \tfrac{1}{2} r_0 k^2 \qquad\qquad (17.15)$$

where a is the scattering length, related to κ by

$$(9.94) \qquad a^{-1} = \kappa - \tfrac{1}{2} r_0 \kappa^2 \qquad\qquad (17.16)$$

A knowledge of κ and an estimate for r_0 thus enable one to calculate the scattering cross section at low energies ($k \approx 0$). The predicted value comes out to be[1] 3.9 b. The experimental curve for the scattering of neutrons on protons in a solid target is given in Fig. 17.2 for a large range of energies. There is no agreement. The cross section is nearly constant from 1 eV to 10^4 eV, but at much too high a value, and it rises still higher at very low energies.

The trouble, of course, is that we have treated the system as though neutrons and protons interact in a way which is independent of their relative spin orientations, whereas we already know from studying the bound state that this is not so. There are two orientations, singlet (antiparallel) and triplet (parallel), and the binding energy tells us only about the latter. If unpolarized neutrons are incident upon an unpolarized target, there are four spin states available, three triplet and one singlet, given in the table following (6.43). That each of these is equally probable can be seen by a simple argument,[2] as follows.

[1] 1 barn (b) = 10^{-24} cm^2 = 100 F^2.
[2] D. Bohm, *Quantum Mechanics*, Prentice Hall, Inc., Englewood Cliffs, N.J., 1951, p. 400.

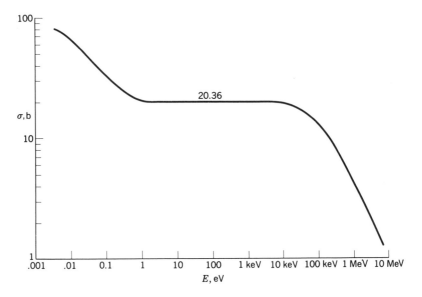

Fig. 17.2 Cross section for the scattering of neutrons on bound protons for laboratory energies from 0.005 eV to 10 MeV.

A beam containing neutrons oriented at random is in a statistical mixture of states of the kind described in Sec. 3.7. We can write a typical spin state as

$$\chi_n = 2^{-1/2}[e^{i\varphi_1}\chi_+(n) + e^{i\varphi_2}\chi_-(n)]$$

where n stands for neutron and the φ's are random phases. The proton target will have

$$\chi_p = 2^{-1/2}[e^{i\varphi_3}\chi_+(p) + e^{i\varphi_4}\chi_-(p)]$$

and the combined spin function is $\chi_n\chi_p$. Let $\hat{\Sigma}$ be some operator involving the neutron and proton spins. Then as in deriving (3.55),

$$\langle\hat{\Sigma}\rangle = \tfrac{1}{2}[\langle\hat{\Sigma}\rangle_{++} + \langle\hat{\Sigma}\rangle_{+-} + \langle\hat{\Sigma}\rangle_{-+} + \langle\hat{\Sigma}\rangle_{--}]$$

where

$$\langle\hat{\Sigma}\rangle_{+-} = \int\chi_+^*(n)\chi_-^*(p)\hat{\Sigma}\chi_+(n)\chi_-(p)$$

etc., the cross terms having all averaged out. This idea of a mixture of properties corresponds to classical physics. We can also write $\chi_n\chi_p$ in the notation of Sec. 6.4 as

$$\chi_n\chi_p = \tfrac{1}{2}[e^{i(\varphi_1+\varphi_3)}\chi_1^{(s)} + e^{i(\varphi_2+\varphi_4)}\chi_{-1}^{(s)}$$
$$+ 2^{-1/2}(e^{i(\varphi_1+\varphi_4)} + e^{i(\varphi_2+\varphi_3)})\chi_0^{(s)}$$
$$+ 2^{-1/2}(e^{i(\varphi_1+\varphi_4)} - e^{i(\varphi_2+\varphi_3)})\chi_0^{(a)}]$$

and again, averaged over the phases,

$$\langle\hat{\Sigma}\rangle = \langle\hat{\Sigma}\rangle_1^{(s)} + \langle\hat{\Sigma}\rangle_0^{(s)} + \langle\hat{\Sigma}\rangle_{-1}^{(s)} + \langle\hat{\Sigma}\rangle_0^{(a)} \qquad (17.17)$$

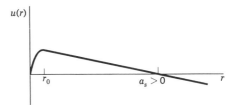

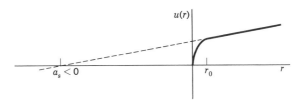

Fig. 17.3 Zero-energy wave functions corresponding to the two possible signs of a_s.

This is again a mixture with equal weighting between the three triplet states and the singlet state. Thus if the cross sections in the singlet and triplet spin states are denoted by σ_s and σ_t, we have for the average

$$\sigma = \tfrac{1}{4}\sigma_s + \tfrac{3}{4}\sigma_t \tag{17.18}$$

and this is consistent with the plateau value of 20.36 b if

$$\sigma_s \approx 68 \text{ b}$$

(We shall consider the rise at very low energies in a moment.)

By the general relation (9.96)

$$\sigma = 4\pi a^2 \qquad (k = 0) \tag{17.19}$$

we see that the singlet scattering length is quite large in absolute value,

$$|a_s| \approx 23 \text{ F} \tag{17.20}$$

but we cannot immediately determine its sign. In graphical terms, we cannot say whether the potential is just strong enough to produce binding (Fig. 17.3a) or just too weak (Fig. 17.3b). The point can be settled by a study of coherent scattering (Sec. 17.3), but for the moment let us suppose what is in fact the case, that the triplet state is the only bound state. It follows that a_s is negative, and by a careful fit with experimental values one finds for the two scattering lengths and effective ranges[3]

	Singlet	Triplet	
a	-23.74 ± 0.09 F	5.39 ± 0.03 F	(17.21)
r_0	2.67 ± 0.02	1.70 ± 0.03	

[3] MacGregor, Moravcsik, and Stapp, *Ann. Rev. Nucl. Sci.*, **10**, 291 (1960).

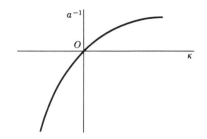

Fig. 17.4 Schematic plot of the dependence of a^{-1}
on κ for an attractive potential.

Let us see what the negative scattering length means in terms of the theory of bound states as we have discussed it earlier. The singlet scattering satisfies (17.12), but $(u'/u)_{r_0}$ is now positive. This means that it is impossible to join the interior wave function to an exterior one of the form $e^{-\kappa_s r}$ unless κ_s is negative. Such a wave function is, of course, unnormalizable and makes no sense physically, but it provides the mathematical bridge between the two cases. In scattering calculations, the wave function in the external region is sinusoidal and not exponential, and we used (17.13) (with $\kappa > 0$) only to get an estimate of $(u'/u)_{r_0}$. We now do the same with $\kappa_s < 0$. How this occurs can be seen in (17.8), where if we let V_0 become smaller for a given r_0, κ will decrease and pass through zero. The entire calculation goes through as before. Equation (17.16) is unchanged, and the phase shifts are given by (17.15) with

$$a^{-1} = -(|\kappa_s| + \tfrac{1}{2}r_0\kappa_s^2)$$ (17.22)

The relation between a^{-1} and κ_s is shown schematically in Fig. 17.4, and it is seen that the sign of a follows that of κ. States with negative κ are known as *virtual states*.

Problem 17.1 Calculate κ_s (the spurious root results from the approximation used), and compare the depths V_0 of the equivalent square potential wells corresponding to the singlet and triplet states.

Problem 17.2 Show that both virtual and bound states can be characterized as states for which the function $S(k)$ becomes infinite. How do the values of k defining these states differ in the two cases?

Scattering of thermal neutrons

Ordinarily, the target protons in an $n\text{-}p$ scattering experiment are chemically bonded to other atoms. These may be other protons, as in the scattering of neutrons by hydrogen gas to be discussed in the next section, or they may occur in the form of hydrocarbons containing many hydrogen and carbon atoms. If the neutrons are energetic enough that the struck protons recoil with a few volts of energy, then the chemical bonding makes no difference. But at very low energies the proton is not free to recoil, and a more detailed analysis is required. At vanishing energy the scattering amplitude (9.51) becomes

$$\lim_{E \to 0} f = -\frac{1}{4\pi} \frac{2\mu}{\hbar^2} \int V(r)\psi(r) \, dv \qquad (17.23)$$

where ψ is the exact wave function. The result of a rather long argument[4] is that the value of the integral is essentially unchanged by the chemical bonding, and the main effect is on the effective mass μ. If the proton is bound to a molecule of atomic mass A, then

$$\mu = \frac{A}{1 + A} M \qquad (17.24)$$

whereas for a free proton, $\mu = \frac{1}{2}M$. The ratio of bound and free scattering amplitudes is therefore $f_b/f_f = 2A/(1 + A)$, and the ratio of the cross sections is

$$\frac{\sigma_b}{\sigma_f} = \left(\frac{2A}{1 + A}\right)^2 \qquad (17.25)$$

For protons bound in a solid target, A is effectively infinite, so that

$$\frac{\sigma_b}{\sigma_f} = 4$$

This is about the increase shown in Fig. 17.2.

17.3 Scattering of Neutrons by H₂

Because there are two kinds of hydrogen molecules, those in which the nuclear spins are parallel (ortho-hydrogen) and those in which they are antiparallel (para-hydrogen), a comparison of the way they scatter neutrons is a sensitive test of the spin dependence of the n-p interaction. Experimentally, the test depends on the possibility of producing coherent elastic scattering of the neutron beam by the pairs of protons. In order for the scattering to be elastic, the neutrons must not have enough energy to excite molecules into higher vibrational or rotational states. The first excited vibrational state requires about 0.5 eV. The rotational levels are given by $0.0075J(J + 1)$ eV. For ortho-hydrogen, $J = 0, 2, 4, \ldots$, while for para-hydrogen it is $1, 3, 5, \ldots$, (why?). Thus the lowest rotational excitation occurs for ortho-hydrogen, at 0.015 eV, where it induces unwanted transitions into the para state. Even thermal neutrons which have come into equilibrium with a moderator at room temperature are too energetic, and in practice the moderator is cooled to liquid-hydrogen temperatures, about 20°K, giving neutrons of 0.002 eV. The neutron wavelength at this energy is about 6 Å, whereas the mean separation between the protons in the molecule is about

[4] J. M. Blatt and V. F. Weisskopf, *Theoretical Nuclear Physics*, John Wiley & Sons, Inc., New York, 1952.

0.75 Å. Thus the neutron wave will have almost the same phase at the positions of the protons, and the scattering will be almost perfectly coherent. There is one unavoidable complication. Para-hydrogen has a slightly lower ground-state energy than ortho-hydrogen—this is what makes it possible to prepare a pure sample of it. Therefore, even at these low energies, the neutrons can induce para-ortho transitions, and since they cannot be avoided, they must be taken into account in an exact calculation. (We shall not take them into account here.) Their effect is to increase σ_{para} by about 10 percent. The observed cross sections are[5]

$$\sigma_{\text{para}} = 4.40 \text{ b} \qquad \sigma_{\text{ortho}} = 133 \text{ b} \qquad (17.26)$$

The scattering is thus markedly spin-dependent, as we have seen before. Further, in scattering from the para system (opposite spins) the neutrons clearly undergo destructive interference. It follows that the scattering amplitudes, and hence the scattering lengths, have opposite signs for the singlet and triplet n-p interactions; this is firm proof that $a_s < 0$.

Because there are $2^3 = 8$ different spin states of the three-particle system, a direct calculation of the cross sections would be somewhat lengthy. The problem is to average the spin dependence of the neutron-hydrogen interaction over the various relative orientations of the particles, and this can be done quite simply by means of the following trick.

The effective potentials describing the n-p interactions in singlet and triplet states differ both in range and in depth; let us call then V_s and V_t. Singlet and triplet states are also distinguished by the eigenvalues of the operator $\hat{\mathbf{S}}_n \cdot \hat{\mathbf{S}}_p$, which are $-\frac{3}{4}$ for the singlet state and $\frac{1}{4}$ for the triplet. It is now easy to verify that if we form the operator

$$\hat{V} = \tfrac{1}{4}(3V_t + V_s) + (V_t - V_s)\hat{\mathbf{S}}_n \cdot \hat{\mathbf{S}}_p \qquad (17.27)$$

it satisfies

$$\hat{V}\chi_{\text{sing}} = V_s\chi_{\text{sing}} \qquad \hat{V}\chi_{\text{trip}} = V_t\chi_{\text{trip}} \qquad (17.28)$$

so that it correctly describes the spin dependence of the interaction. According to Prob. 9.23, the low-energy limit of the scattering amplitude f is the negative of the scattering length a. Putting $\hat{V}$ into (17.23) and performing the spatial integration gives an operator

$$\hat{a} = \tfrac{1}{4}(3a_t + a_s) + (a_t - a_s)\hat{\mathbf{S}}_n \cdot \hat{\mathbf{S}}_p \qquad (17.29)$$

which reduces to a_s or a_t when applied to a singlet or a triplet state. Averages over the neutron spin can now be performed very easily.

[5] R. B. Sutton et al., Phys. Rev., **72**, 1147 (1947).

Problem 17.3   Use (17.29) to rederive (17.18).

We now turn to the evaluation of the neutron-hydrogen scattering. There will be a contribution corresponding to $\hat{a}$ for each proton, giving

$$\hat{a}_{H_2} = \tfrac{1}{2}(3a_t + a_s) + (a_t - a_s)\hat{\mathbf{S}}_n \cdot \hat{\mathbf{S}}_{H_2}$$

where $\hat{\mathbf{S}}_{H_2} = \hat{\mathbf{S}}_{p_1} + \hat{\mathbf{S}}_{p_2}$, the sum of the spin operators for the two protons. To find the cross section, it is thus only necessary to consider the spin of the hydrogen molecule as a whole. For para-hydrogen, $\langle \hat{\mathbf{S}}_{H_2} \rangle = 0$, so that

$$\langle \hat{a}_{H_2}^2 \rangle_{\text{para}} = \tfrac{1}{4}(3a_t + a_s)^2$$

To get the cross section, we must correct this by a factor of

$$\left(\frac{2 \times 2}{2 + 1}\right)^2 = \frac{16}{9}$$

to take account of the change in effective mass, and we have

$$\sigma_{\text{para}} = \tfrac{16}{9}\pi(3a_t + a_s)^2 \tag{17.30}$$

The small value found experimentally shows that, by coincidence, a_s is of the order of $-3a_t$, and this establishes the sign of a_s as we have given it above. To continue, we need some spin averages. The neutron–ortho-hydrogen system has two spin states with spins $1 - \tfrac{1}{2} = \tfrac{1}{2}$ and $1 + \tfrac{1}{2} = \tfrac{3}{2}$ so that $(\hat{\mathbf{S}}_n + \hat{\mathbf{S}}_{\text{ortho}})^2 = \tfrac{1}{2}(\tfrac{1}{2} + 1)$ and $\tfrac{3}{2}(\tfrac{3}{2} + 1)$, respectively. To find $\hat{\mathbf{S}}_n \cdot \hat{\mathbf{S}}_{\text{ortho}}$, we note that

$$(\hat{\mathbf{S}}_n + \hat{\mathbf{S}}_{\text{ortho}})^2 = \hat{\mathbf{S}}_n{}^2 + \hat{\mathbf{S}}_{\text{ortho}}^2 + 2\hat{\mathbf{S}}_n \cdot \hat{\mathbf{S}}_{\text{ortho}} = \tfrac{3}{4} \text{ or } \tfrac{15}{4}$$

respectively, so that

$$\hat{\mathbf{S}}_n \cdot \hat{\mathbf{S}}_{\text{ortho}} = \begin{cases} -1 & \text{(two states with total spin } \tfrac{1}{2}) \\ \tfrac{1}{2} & \text{(four states with total spin } \tfrac{3}{2}) \end{cases}$$

and

$$\langle \hat{\mathbf{S}}_n \cdot \hat{\mathbf{S}}_{\text{ortho}} \rangle_{\text{avg}} = \tfrac{1}{6}[2 \times (-1) + 4 \times \tfrac{1}{2}] = 0$$

$$\langle (\hat{\mathbf{S}}_n \cdot \hat{\mathbf{S}}_{\text{ortho}})^2 \rangle_{\text{avg}} = \tfrac{1}{6}[2 \times (-1)^2 + 4 \times (\tfrac{1}{2})^2] = \tfrac{1}{2}$$

With this, we find

$$\langle \hat{a}_{H_2}^2 \rangle_{\text{ortho}} = \tfrac{1}{4}(3a_t + a_s)^2 + \tfrac{1}{2}(a_t - a_s)^2$$

so that

$$\sigma_{\text{ortho}} = \sigma_{\text{para}} + \tfrac{32}{9}\pi(a_t - a_s)^2 \tag{17.31}$$

For comparison with experiment this formula and (17.30) need corrections. The velocities of the target atoms are maxwellian rather than homogeneous, the scattered waves from the two protons are not quite in phase, and σ_{ortho} needs to be increased by the cross section corresponding to ortho-para conversions. The resulting formulas are 10 to 20 percent different from ours.

Problem 17.4 At a neutron energy of 1.25×10^{-3} eV, the corrected theoretical formulas are[6]

$$\sigma_{\text{ortho}} = 6.95(3a_t + a_s)^2 + 15.76(a_t - a_s)^2$$
$$\sigma_{\text{para}} = 6.95(3a_t + a_s)^2$$

The observed values are given in (17.26). What values result for a_t and a_s? Summarize the specific evidence which leads to the rejection of the spurious sets of values.

Problem 17.5 It has been assumed throughout that the spin of the neutron is $\frac{1}{2}$. If it were $\frac{3}{2}$, there could still be a ^3S ground state for the deuteron. Show that this value for the spin is inconsistent with the experimental data that have been quoted.

Problem 17.6 Evaluate the cross section for the elastic scattering of protons by hydrogen molecules at very low energies, assuming the de Broglie wavelength long enough that the interference effects of Prob. 9.14 may be neglected. The scattering amplitudes are then additive and the resultant may be written in the style of (11.42) as

$$\hat{f}(\vartheta_c) = 2f(\vartheta_c) - (1 + 2\hat{\mathbf{S}} \cdot \hat{\mathbf{\Sigma}})f(\pi - \vartheta_c)$$

where $\hat{\mathbf{S}}$ is the spin operator of the incoming proton and $\hat{\mathbf{\Sigma}}$ that of the molecule (that is, the sum of the two nuclear spins it contains). Derive the foregoing formula and apply it separately to evaluate the scattering of protons in pure para-hydrogen ($\Sigma = 0$) and pure ortho-hydrogen ($\Sigma = 1$). Express the answers in terms of scattering amplitudes and then of energy and angle in the laboratory system.

17.4 The Photodissociation of the Deuteron

We have already said that since the neutron-proton system has only a single bound state, the amount of information that can be gained from a study of the static properties of this system is rather limited. One way of introducing experiments in which some of the variables can be changed at will by the experimenter is to study scattering, but this does not bear directly on the properties of the ground state. The experiment which we shall analyze here in simple form has been performed many times, and it gives accurate information on the ground-state wave function.

If a monochromatic beam of X rays is directed at deuterons, it can dissociate them when the energy is great enough. One can meas-

[6] *Ibid.*

ure the angular dependence of the emitted neutrons and protons, and also the dependence of the total cross section on the X-ray energy. We have already discussed the effect for hydrogen in Sec. 10.5. There the angular dependence turned out to be trivial, essentially because electromagnetic radiation is transverse, but here it is not trivial, for two processes having different angular properties come into play. The first is the dissociation property called photoelectric, in which the electric field of the incoming radiation exerts a force on the proton to break it loose. The analysis here is essentially the same as that in Sec. 10.5. But there is also another process; for the magnetic moments of neutron and proton in the ground state point in opposite directions, and the radiation's magnetic field will therefore act to turn them differently. There is a certain probability that they will be turned parallel, that is, into the unbound singlet state, and the particles will then drift apart. In this process the angular distribution is isotropic and the energy dependence of the cross section is quite different.

Photoelectric effect

We shall calculate here very roughly and leave a more refined version for the problems. The coordinates will be the C.M. system of the deuteron before the X ray acts, and the matrix element of the transition will be written as $\langle f|H^{(1)}|g\rangle$, where g stands for "ground" and f for either "final" or "free." The perturbing energy which causes the photoelectric transition is

$$H^{(1)} = \tfrac{1}{2}e\mathbf{E} \cdot \mathbf{r} \qquad \mathbf{E} = \mathbf{E}_0 \cos{(\mathbf{q} \cdot \mathbf{r} - qct)} \tag{17.32}$$

where the $\tfrac{1}{2}$ is because $\mathbf{r}$, in the C.M. system, gives the separation of the two particles. The initial and final wave functions will be approximated rather roughly. In the zero-range approximation, (17.6) becomes

$$\psi_g \approx \left(\frac{\kappa}{2\pi}\right)^{\frac{1}{2}} r^{-1}e^{-\kappa r} \tag{17.33}$$

for all values of r, and the simplest form for ψ_f is

$$\psi_f \approx Q^{-\frac{1}{2}}e^{i\mathbf{k}\cdot\mathbf{r}} \tag{17.34}$$

Here Q is the volume of the entire system, $\hbar k$ is the relative momentum of the particles after dissociation, and the effect of the n-p interaction as the particles separate is completely ignored. In this approximation, we can write the conservation of energy as

$$\hbar c q = \frac{\hbar^2}{M}(\kappa^2 + k^2) \tag{17.35}$$

where $\hbar c q$ is the X-ray energy.

Only the component of $H^{(1)}$ with negative frequency contributes to the absorption, and we have

$$\langle f|H^{(1)}|g\rangle = \frac{1}{4}\, e\left(\frac{\kappa}{2\pi Q}\right)^{\!\!\frac{1}{2}} \int e^{i(\mathbf{q}-\mathbf{k})\cdot\mathbf{r}}\mathbf{E}_0\cdot\mathbf{r}r^{-1}e^{-\kappa r}\, dv$$

$$= -ie\left(\frac{2\pi\kappa}{Q}\right)^{\!\!\frac{1}{2}} \frac{\mathbf{E}_0\cdot\mathbf{k}}{[\kappa^2 + (\mathbf{q}-\mathbf{k})^2]^2}$$

where we have used $\mathbf{E}_0\cdot\mathbf{q} = 0$. (The integration is left as an exercise.)

The calculation of the cross section goes through exactly as before, and we find

$$\frac{d\sigma}{d\Omega} = \frac{e'^2}{\hbar c}\frac{\kappa k^3(\kappa^2 + k^2)}{[\kappa^2 + (\mathbf{k}-\mathbf{q})^2]^4}\sin^2\vartheta \tag{17.36}$$

where ϑ is the angle measured with respect to the incident quantum. This can be simplified if in the denominator we write

$$\kappa^2 + (\mathbf{k}-\mathbf{q})^2 = \kappa^2 + k^2 + q^2 - 2kq\cos\vartheta$$

By (17.35) this becomes

$$\kappa^2 + (\mathbf{k}-\mathbf{q})^2 = \frac{Mcq}{\hbar}\left(1 + \frac{\hbar cq}{Mc^2} - \frac{2\hbar k}{Mc}\cos\vartheta\right)$$

Since $Mc^2 \approx 0.5$ BeV, the second term is negligible. In the third, we recall that $\hbar k = \mu v_{\mathrm{rel}}$, where v_{rel} is the relative velocity of the separating particles. Thus the factor in parentheses becomes $1 - \beta\cos\vartheta$, with $\beta = v_{\mathrm{rel}}/c$, and

$$\frac{d\sigma}{d\Omega} = \frac{\alpha}{\kappa^2}\frac{B^{\frac{3}{2}}E^{\frac{3}{2}}}{(B+E)^3}\frac{\sin^2\vartheta}{(1 - \beta\cos\vartheta)^4} \tag{17.37}$$

where B is the (positive) binding energy and α is the fine-structure constant. The factor in β is only slightly different from 1.

Problem 17.7   Write out the complete derivation of (17.36).

The cross section has been written above in terms of the energy of the ejected protons, which we shall call E below. This is because a monochromatic X-ray beam at arbitrary energy is difficult to arrange, and it is easiest to identify the energies of the protons as they are counted. Integration over angles and omission of a term in β^2 gives for the total cross section

$$\sigma_{\mathrm{el}} = \frac{8\pi}{3}\frac{\alpha}{\kappa^2}\frac{B^{\frac{3}{2}}E^{\frac{3}{2}}}{(B+E)^3} = 11.4\,\frac{B^{\frac{3}{2}}E^{\frac{3}{2}}}{(B+E)^3}\qquad \mathrm{mb} \tag{17.38}$$

where the energies may be measured in any convenient unit. This starts out with a horizontal tangent as a function of E and has a maximum when $E = B$ so that the recoiling n-p system has an energy of 2.226 MeV. Thus the cross section should be greatest for photons of 4.45 MeV. The observed maximum is at about 4.1 MeV. Further, the theoretical peak value is

$$\sigma_{el}^{max} = \frac{8\pi}{3 \times 137 \times 8\kappa^2} = 1.42 \text{ mb}$$

whereas the experimental value is about 2.5 mb. Much of the discrepancy is due to having made the zero-range approximation (17.33) for the ground state. This can be partly corrected by normalizing it according to (7.75), which is approximately correct for all the wave function which lies outside the range of interaction. This increases the cross sections calculated above by a factor of $(1 + \frac{1}{2}Kr_0)^2 \approx 1 + Kr_0 \approx 1.4$, bringing σ_{el}^{max} up to almost 2.0 mb. Inclusion of the photomagnetic cross section will improve the agreement.

Photomagnetic effect

We write the magnetic moments of neutron and proton as $2\mu_n\mu_M S_n$ and $2\mu_p\mu_M S_p$, respectively, where $\mu_M = e\hbar/2M$ is the value of the proton's magnetic moment according to Dirac's theory and μ_n and μ_p are factors which give agreement with experiment,

$$\mu_n = 2.793 \qquad \mu_p = -1.913$$

The perturbing energy in a magnetic field B in the z direction is

$$\hat{H}^{(1)} = 2\mu_M B(\mu_n\hat{S}_{zn} + \mu_p\hat{S}_{zp}) \qquad B = B_0 \cos(\mathbf{q} \cdot \mathbf{r} - qct) \tag{17.39}$$

and the matrix element of the transition is

$$\langle f|\hat{H}^{(1)}|g\rangle = 2\mu_M \int \psi_f^* {}^1\chi_0^* B(\mu_n\hat{S}_{zn} + \mu_p\hat{S}_{zp})^3\chi_m\psi_g \tag{17.40}$$

where the "integration" is over spins and coordinates, $^1\chi_0$ is the singlet final spin state, and $^3\chi_m$, with $m = -1, 0, +1$, are the three possible initial triplet states. Let us write

$$\mu_n\hat{S}_{zn} + \mu_p\hat{S}_{zp} = \frac{1}{2}[(\mu_n + \mu_p)\hat{S}_z + (\mu_n - \mu_p)(\hat{S}_{zn} - \hat{S}_{zp})]$$

where $\hat{S}_z$ is the total spin operator, and use the hermitian property to operate with it on $^1\chi_0$. The first term gives zero, while in the second we find by direct computation, using (6.42) and (6.43), that

$$(\hat{S}_{zn} - \hat{S}_{zp})^1\chi_0 = {}^3\chi_0 \tag{17.41}$$

Thus, (17.35) is

$$\langle f|\hat{H}^{(1)}|g\rangle = \mu_M(\mu_n - \mu_p)\int {}^3\chi_0^* {}^3\chi_m \int \psi_f^* B\psi_g \, dv$$

$$= \mu_M(\mu_n - \mu_p)\delta_{0m}\int \psi_f^* B\psi_g \, dv \tag{17.42}$$

where δ_{0m} is the Kronecker symbol. Intuitively, this means that the magnetic field does not act to tip over a pair of spins whose magnetic moment is initially aligned parallel or antiparallel to it. On the average, only one-third of the target deuterons will be in a state which can be affected by an incident quantum. Using the same approximate wave functions as before, we find

$$\frac{d\sigma}{d\Omega} = \frac{1}{6} \frac{e'^2}{\hbar c} (\mu_n - \mu_p)^2 \left(\frac{\hbar}{Mc}\right)^2 \frac{\kappa k(\kappa^2 + k^2)}{[\kappa^2 + (\mathbf{k} - \mathbf{q})^2]^2}$$

and by the same substitutions as led to (17.37) this becomes

$$\frac{d\sigma}{d\Omega} = \frac{1}{6} (\mu_n - \mu_p)^2 \frac{\alpha}{\kappa^2} \frac{B^{3/2}E^{1/2}}{Mc^2(B + E)} \frac{1}{(1 - \beta \cos \vartheta)^2} \tag{17.43}$$

with a total cross section of

$$\sigma_{\text{mag}} = \frac{2\pi}{3} (\mu_n - \mu_p)^2 \frac{\alpha}{\kappa^2} \frac{B^{3/2}E^{1/2}}{Mc^2(B + E)} = 13.4 \frac{B^{3/2}E^{1/2}}{Mc^2(B + E)} \quad \text{mb} \tag{17.44}$$

This starts out with a vertical tangent as a function of E and so is initially larger than σ_{el}, though the factor of Mc^2 makes it a minor effect for all but the smallest energies. Figure 17.5 shows theoretical curves and their comparison with experiment.

Problem 17.8   Fill in the missing details of the last calculation.

Problem 17.9   At low energies, the photomagnetic cross section needs an important correction. Since the phase shift of the singlet n-p interaction is so large, the approximate wave function (17.34) for the singlet final state is very poor. To include the ^3S final interaction in an approximate way, we neglect the photons' momentum

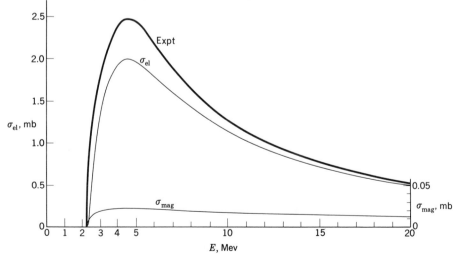

Fig. 17.5   Theoretical curves of σ_{el} and σ_{mag} (note different scales) calculated from (17.38) and (17.44) with the normalization correction of a factor of 1.4, compared with experimental values compiled from several sources.

by setting $\mathbf{q} = 0$ in (17.39) and can then restrict ourselves to the S-state part of ψ_f, since B and ψ_i have spherical symmetry. By (9.74), we can represent ψ_f by

$$\psi_f \approx \frac{e^{i\delta_s}}{kr} \sin{(kr + \delta_s)}$$

valid outside the range of interaction but here used, like (7.75), for all values of r. Carry out the integration and simplify by the low-energy approximation $k \cot \delta_s \approx - a_s^{-1}$ [see (17.15)]. Compare the general features of the result with those of (17.44). (The normalization by a factor of $1 + \kappa r_0$ applies here also.)

Problem 17.10 The weakest point in the calculation of σ_{el} is the zero-range approximation for ψ_g. The Hulthén wave function is much more realistic while remaining analytically tractable. If the binding energy is given, the range and depth of this potential are related and only one parameter remains to be varied. To see how sensitively the calculated cross sections depend on the choice of wave function (and therefore how much information the process yields) see how well it is possible to fit the observed data by a proper choice of this parameter.

Problem 17.11 Design an experiment to measure the electric and magnetic cross sections as a function of energy. The source and nature of the X rays should be specified.

REFERENCES

H. A. Bethe and P. Morrison, *Elementary Nuclear Theory*, 2d ed., John Wiley & Sons, Inc., New York, 1956.

L. R. B. Elton, *Introductory Nuclear Theory*, Sir Isaac Pitman & Sons, Ltd., London, 1959.

K. B. Mather and P. Swan, *Nuclear Scattering*, Cambridge University Press, London, 1958.

M. A. Preston, *Physics of the Nucleus* Addison-Wesley Publishing Co., Inc., Reading, Mass., 1962.

18

Thermodynamics

18.1 Thermodynamical Questions

In thermodynamics, it is customary to express the conservation of energy (the first law) in the form

$$dU = DQ - DW \qquad (18.1)$$

which states that the internal energy U of a thermodynamic system may be increased by adding to it an amount of heat DQ or by performing on it an amount of work $-DW$ (DW is the work done *by* the system). The D's are used to denote quantities which, though infinitesimal, are not differentials of anything. For example, by taking the temperature of a hot gas, it is impossible to deduce how much heat has been put into it, since the heating may have been produced by external work and not by the addition of heat at all. Thus a sample of material has no "Q" or "W," though increments DQ and DW may be supplied to change its energy.[1]

Similarly, the principal mathematical consequence of the second law is that although DQ is not a perfect differential, it is proportional to one,

$$DQ = T \, dS \qquad (18.2)$$

---

[1] It should be noted that in order to specify a thermodynamic change like DW it is necessary to specify the process by which the change occurs. One could, for example, produce an infinitesimal DW by taking the system through a very large change in which it has work W done on it and does work $W + DW$. We shall exclude this possibility by restricting our attention to infinitesimal processes in which none of the variables describing the system change more than infinitesimally. No more detailed specification is necessary.

where S is called the entropy and T the absolute temperature, and the equality holds only when the change is carried out in a quasistatic and reversible manner. Thus, although it makes no sense to talk of the heat or work in a system, there are two properties, U and S, which depend only on its actual state and not at all on which of various possible processes put it into the state.

The foregoing capsule summary of the first and second laws of thermodynamics raises some questions as to atomistic mechanism which cannot, of course, be answered from within the framework of the classical theory. Chief among these are:

1. Exactly what, on the microscopic scale, is meant by DQ and $-DW$?

2. Can these quantities be expressed in such a way that it is *obvious* that not they but their sum is a perfect differential?

3. What is the microscopic meaning of entropy, and can the mathematical truth of (18.2) be made similarly obvious?

4. What, on the microscopic scale, is a quasi-static reversible process?

These questions will be answered in this chapter in terms of the quantum theory, and a few simple applications will be pointed out.

18.2 Ensembles

The study which bridges the gap between thermodynamics and the atomic mechanisms which underlie it is known as *statistical mechanics*, and one of the principal devices by which it obtains its results is the ensemble. We imagine that together with the thermodynamic system under discussion (we shall call it the system A) there exist a large number of identical copies of A, call them A', A'', . . . , all exposed to the same external environment as A. Instead of asking for "the value" or "the average value" of a certain quantity in A, we shall now try to find its value averaged over all the subsystems of the ensemble. The purpose of this procedure is to average out random fluctuations which occur in macroscopic systems containing heat but which are rarely of experimental interest.

The external environment of A, A', . . . , may be variously chosen, and correspondingly, statistical mechanics speaks of various types of ensemble. We shall confine our attention here to one type, which Gibbs called a *canonical ensemble:* that in which the subsystems are all in thermal contact with each other and thermally isolated from the rest of the world, as shown schematically in Fig. 18.1. If there are many such subsystems, then each one is in thermal contact with an effectively infinite heat reservoir.

We now suppose that each subsystem has a set of nondegenerate quantum states of energy E_1, E_2, ... (If degeneracies occur, we

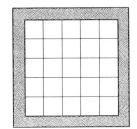

Fig. 18.1   A canonical ensemble. The subsystems are in thermal contact with each other and isolated from the rest of the world.

pretend they do not exist by counting the degenerate states as though they were all distinct.) The averaging process is carried out by means of the numbers n_i denoting how many (but not which!) of the subsystems are in their ith energy state. Clearly, if there are n subsystems, we have

$$\sum_i n_i = n \tag{18.3}$$

and

$$\sum_i n_i E_i = E_t \tag{18.4}$$

where E_t is the total energy of the whole ensemble, which we shall suppose to be a fixed quantity. The *ensemble average* of any dynamical variable Ω is now defined as

$$\bar{\Omega} = n^{-1} \Sigma n_i \langle \Omega \rangle_i \tag{18.5}$$

where $\langle \Omega \rangle_i$ is the expectation value of Ω in the ith state. It is assumed that $\bar{\Omega}$ represents the probable result of a measurement of Ω on the original system A. The arguments underlying this assumption are very clearly detailed in Tolman's book listed in the References at the end of this chapter.

Randomness

The main problem of statistical mechanics is to compute the n_i. In order to do this, it is necessary to introduce an explicit assumption of randomness. One cannot predict anything exact about the fall of a die, but if one makes the assumption (which does not follow from the ordinary principles of mechanics) that every way of falling is equally probable, then one can make statistical predictions as to the probable results of a large number of throws. Our statistical assumption is this:

> Other things being equal, every quantum state of every sub-
> system is equally probable. (18.6)

A simple example of this, derived by averaging over random phases, is given by (17.17). The proviso "other things being equal" means only that the states cannot be assigned completely at random because there is a certain amount of energy which must be distributed, as expressed by (18.4).

From this apparently chaotic assumption there usually emerges on averaging a very definite state of affairs. How this comes about is seen if we imagine a game in which four coins are thrown on to a table and a 1 is scored for each head which appears. There are 16 possible outcomes to the throw, all equally probable, but not all scores are equally probable. Let us list them (h = heads, t = tails):

Coins				Score	Relative probability
tttt				0	1
httt,	thtt,	ttht,	ttth	1	4
hhtt,	htht,	htth,			
thht,	thth,	tthh		2	6
hhht,	hhth,	hthh,	thhh	3	4
hhhh				4	1
					16

Thus, a score of 2 is 6 times more intrinsically probable than a score of 4. The n_i mentioned above are analogous to the score here, and for large enough n there is usually one n_i, or else a narrow range of n_i's, which is far more probable than any other. The student who will keep this circumstance firmly in mind can understand almost any treatise on statistical mechanics.

We define the thermodynamical probability M to be the number of ways in which a given distribution of the n subsystems can be realized with n_1 of them in the first state, n_2 in the second, and so on. The entire ensemble can be enumerated in $n!$ ways; but of these, $n_1!$ are equivalent because they involve only a relabeling of the systems in the first state, and similarly for n_2, n_3, . . . , so that finally

$$M = \frac{n!}{n_1!n_2! \cdots} = \frac{n!}{\prod_i n_i!} \tag{18.7}$$

Problem 18.1 Apply this formula to the game of heads and tails mentioned above. Graph M against n_i/n for that case ($n = 4$) and also, on the same plot, for $n = 12$. What would this lead you to expect when n is very large?

Equilibrium

We now define thermodynamic equilibrium to be that state in which a system is most likely to be found, that is, the state for which

M has the greatest value. It is easy to show that M is largest for a given n when all the n_i are equal. Owing to (18.4), however, this will not in general be a possible state of the ensemble. We must seek to maximize M subject to the condition (18.4). In practice it is more convenient to maximize $\ln M$, for this quantity is represented by a simpler formula than (18.7). We assume that n is so large that all (or almost all) the n_i are much greater than unity, and we use Stirling's approximation[2] to $\ln (n!)$,

$$\ln n! \approx n \ln n - n \tag{18.8}$$

This gives

$$
\begin{aligned}
\ln M &= \ln (n!) - \sum_i \ln (n_i!) \\
&\approx n \ln n - n - \sum n_i \ln n_i + \sum n_i \\
&= \sum n_i \ln n - \sum n_i \ln n_i
\end{aligned}
\tag{18.9}
$$

where we have used (18.3) twice in the last step.

It is convenient at this point to introduce instead of n_i the quantity

$$p_i = \frac{n_i}{n} \tag{18.10}$$

[2] Stirling's approximation to the factorial function is most easily derived by starting from Euler's integral

$$n! = \int_0^\infty x^n e^{-x}\, dx = \int_0^\infty e^{f(x)}\, dx$$

where

$$f(x) = n \ln x - x$$

This function is negative for large and small x and has a maximum at $x = n$ which contributes most of the integral. We write

$$
\begin{aligned}
f(x) &\approx f(n) + (x - n)f'(n) + \tfrac{1}{2}(x - n)^2 f''(n) \\
&= n \ln n - n - (2n)^{-1}(x - n)^2
\end{aligned}
$$

as can easily be calculated. The integral is now

$$n! \approx e^{n \ln n - n} \int_{-\infty}^\infty e^{-(2n)^{-1}(x-n)^2}\, dx$$

where we have made a negligible error in replacing the lower limit by $-\infty$. It can be evaluated to give

$$n! \approx n^n e^{-n} (2\pi n)^{1/2}$$

We shall need this form later, but for most of thermodynamics the last term is a negligible correction. Omitting it gives (18.8). The derivation is a simple example of the *method of steepest descents*, which is a general way of finding the asymptotic forms of functions defined by definite integrals.

representing the probability that any subsystem of the ensemble, chosen at random, will be found to be in the state i. In terms of this, (18.9) is

$$\ln M = -n\Sigma p_i \ln p_i \tag{18.11}$$

and the conditions (18.3) and (18.4) are

$$\Sigma p_i = 1 \tag{18.12}$$

and

$$\Sigma p_i E_i = \bar{E} \tag{18.13}$$

which is the mean energy of the subsystems.

We now ask what values of the various p_i are the most probable, that is, what values make $\ln M$ a maximum subject to the conditions (18.12) and (18.13). This can be solved by Lagrange's method of undetermined multipliers, as follows. If infinitesimal changes are made in the p_i, we have

$$d \ln M = -n\Sigma(1 + \ln p_i)\, dp_i \tag{18.14}$$

and if M is to be a maximum, this quantity must be zero for all possible dp_i. The dp_i cannot be chosen independently of one another, since they must satisfy

$$\Sigma\, dp_i = 0 \qquad \Sigma E_i\, dp_i = 0 \tag{18.15a,b}$$

by (18.12) and (18.13); but it is clear that if we choose arbitrarily all but two of them, say, dp_1 and dp_2, it will be possible to satisfy (18.15a,b) by a suitable choice of dp_1 and dp_2. Let us multiply (18.15a) and (18.15b) by constants α and β and add them to the condition $\Sigma(1 + \ln p_i)\, dp_i = 0$ which we wish to satisfy. This gives

$$(1 + \ln p_1 + \alpha + \beta E_1)\, dp_1 + (1 + \ln p_2 + \alpha + \beta E_2)\, dp_2$$
$$+ \sum_{i=3}^{n} (1 + \ln p_i + \alpha + \beta E_i)\, dp_i = 0$$

where the two dependent dp's are singled out for special treatment. By a proper choice of α and β it is possible to make

$$1 + \ln p_i + \alpha + \beta E_i = 0 \tag{18.16}$$

for $i = 1$ and 2. But now since the remaining dp_i $(i = 3, 4, \ldots)$ may be chosen independently of each other, the same quantity must vanish also for $i = 3, 4, \ldots$. Thus (18.16) holds for all i, and the probability that a subsystem of the ensemble is found in state i is

$$p_i = e^{-(1+\alpha)}e^{-\beta E_i} \tag{18.17}$$

where α and β are constants fixed by (18.12) and (18.13) but whose meaning is not at once identifiable. We can replace α at once by writing

$$\Sigma p_i = e^{-(1+\alpha)}\Sigma e^{-\beta E_i} = 1$$

so that in terms of the *partition function Z*, defined as

$$Z = e^{1+\alpha} = \Sigma e^{-\beta E_i} \tag{18.18}$$

we have

$$p_i = Z^{-1}e^{-\beta E_i} \tag{18.19}$$

This formula, due to Boltzmann, lies at the center of statistical mechanics. We shall give examples to show its meaning and its use in the next section, but we shall now go on to show how the formulas we have derived are related to thermodynamics and to identify the constant β.

Problem 18.2 Suppose the system A (and therefore each of its copies) is divided into two parts by a thermally conducting rigid wall. Show that the most probable (that is, the equilibrium) condition is described by a distribution like (18.19) for each part, but with the same value of β for each. Show that β must therefore be a function only of the temperature of A.

It follows from (18.13) and (18.19) that the mean energy of a subsystem of the ensemble is

$$\bar{E} = \sum E_i p_i = Z^{-1}\sum E_i e^{-\beta E_i} = -Z^{-1}\frac{\partial Z}{\partial \beta} \tag{18.20}$$

and since $\bar{E}$ is related to the temperature T of the ensemble, we see from Prob. 18.2 that it is related to β. It is also intuitively clear that the probability M will have something to do with the entropy of the ensemble, since like the entropy it is a maximum when the ensemble is in equilibrium. More specifically, (18.11) leads us to examine $\ln M$; for it, like the entropy, is proportional to the size of the ensemble.

Let

$$\sigma = -\Sigma p_i \ln p_i \tag{18.21}$$

and consider the change produced in σ when the ensemble, starting at equilibrium, is altered by the addition of a small amount of heat. The equilibrium value of σ is found using the equilibrium value of the p_i,

$$\sigma_{\text{eq}} = \Sigma p_i(\beta E_i + \ln Z)$$

or

$$\sigma_{\text{eq}} = \beta\bar{E} + \ln Z \tag{18.22}$$

by (18.12) and (18.13). The addition of heat $d\bar{E}$ per subsystem changes this by an amount

$$d\sigma_{eq} = \beta\, d\bar{E} + \bar{E}\, d\beta + Z^{-1}\frac{\partial Z}{\partial\beta}\, d\beta$$

$$d\sigma_{eq} = \beta\, d\bar{E} \tag{18.23}$$

by (18.20), where we have used the fact that since the energy levels themselves are not changed by the addition of heat, the partition function will be changed only through its dependence on β. Now $d\sigma_{eq}$ is, by its derivation, a perfect differential, and $d\bar{E}$ may in this instance be written as DQ, so that βDQ is a perfect differential, β being an integrating factor. But we know already that T^{-1} is the integrating factor for DQ, and except for a constant multiple there is no other.[3] Therefore, we see that there exists some constant κ such that

$$\beta = \frac{1}{\kappa T} \qquad S = \kappa\sigma_{eq} \tag{18.24}$$

We have thus answered question 3 posed at the beginning of this chapter: the entropy has a definite specification in mechanical terms for systems at equilibrium, and it satisfies (18 2) when heat is added. In ordinary thermodynamics one does not talk of the entropy of systems far from equilibrium; but $\kappa\sigma$, with σ given by (18.21), is defined for any state, and this is the starting point of discussions of how a system initially disturbed approaches equilibrium.

It will be shown in the next section that the constant κ is equal to R, the gas constant, divided by N_0, Avogadro's number. This ratio, called Boltzmann's constant, is denoted by k, but we shall continue to use κ until the identity has been proved.

[3] To see this, let

$$dS = \frac{DQ}{T} = \frac{\partial S}{\partial V}\, dV + \frac{\partial S}{\partial T}\, dT$$

and

$$dS' = \frac{DQ}{f(T)} = \frac{\partial S'}{\partial V}\, dV + \frac{\partial S'}{\partial T}\, dT$$

where $f(T)$ is some function of T and dS' is also assumed to be a perfect differential. Since $dS' = \dfrac{T}{f(T)}\, dS$, we have

$$\frac{\partial S'}{\partial V} = \frac{T}{f(T)}\frac{\partial S}{\partial V} \qquad \frac{\partial S'}{\partial T} = \frac{T}{f(T)}\frac{\partial S}{\partial T}$$

Now calculate $\partial^2 S'/\partial V\,\partial T$. From the two expressions we get

$$\frac{\partial^2 S'}{\partial V\,\partial T} = \frac{d}{dT}\left[\frac{T}{f(T)}\right]\frac{\partial S}{\partial V} + \frac{T}{f(T)}\frac{\partial^2 S}{\partial V\,\partial T} = \frac{T}{f(T)}\frac{\partial^2 S}{\partial T\,\partial V}$$

which can be satisfied only if $T/f(T)$ is independent of T, that is, if $f(T) = cT$.

We can now use (18.22) and (18.23) to see how the partition function fits into the scheme of thermodynamics. Noting that $\bar{E}$ has now a definite meaning as an ensemble average, we find

$$-\kappa T \ln Z = \bar{E} - TS \qquad (18.25)$$

The quantity $\bar{E} - TS$ is known as the Helmholtz free energy F and it tends toward a minimum in any system which (like the subsystems of the ensemble) is kept at constant volume and temperature. This is analogous to the increase in entropy of a system which (like the ensemble itself) is kept at constant volume and energy. We have, therefore,

$$Z = e^{-F/\kappa T} \qquad (18.26)$$

and we see that there is a complete correspondence between the quantities α, β, Z, σ_{eq} which occur in the course of a purely statistical discussion of equilibrium and the quantities $\bar{E}$, S, T, F which arise in thermodynamics.

Problem 18.3 Derive the Gibbs-Helmholtz formula

$$\bar{E} = -T^2 \frac{\partial}{\partial T}\left(\frac{F}{T}\right)_V \qquad (18.27)$$

from the above formulas, and then show that

$$S = -\left(\frac{\partial F}{\partial T}\right)_V \qquad (18.28)$$

Problem 18.4 Show from fundamental principles that the entropy of a system consisting of two parts separated by a rigid, thermally conducting wall ,is equal to the sum of the individual entropies.

Practically the whole of thermodynamics may thus be based on the evaluation of the partition function. In order to give some insight into the nature of the results that can be obtained in this way, to prepare for the next chapter and to establish the identification of κ with Boltzmann's constant, we shall now detour from the main argument and discuss some consequences of the results we have obtained.

18.3 The Boltzmann Distribution

In order to evaluate κ, we must relate our results so far to some suitable definition of T. This may be done in several ways. The simplest way, which we shall follow here, is to calculate the equation of state of a perfect gas in terms of κ and then find κ by comparing it with the well-known formula

$$PV = NkT \tag{18.29}$$

for a gas containing N molecules. [This approach, however, has the disadvantage that there is no such thing as a perfect gas, and so (18.29) is hardly a good theoretical specification of T.]

The perfect gas

We define a perfect gas as a collection of N molecules which do not interact. Further, we ignore entirely for the moment the consequences arising from the indistinguishability of molecules, expressed by the symmetric and antisymmetric wave functions of Chap. 11. They will be discussed in detail in the next chapter. Since in a perfect gas the molecules do not interact appreciably, their energy is entirely kinetic, and we can write for the partition function of the system A

$$Z = \sum_{i,j,\ldots,z} e^{-\beta[E_i(1)+E_j(2)+\cdots+E_z(N)]}$$

where $E_i(1)$ represents the ith stationary energy state of the first molecule, and so on, and the sum is over all possible states of each molecule. Since the set of states available to each molecule is the same, and the states are occupied independently of each other, we have

$$Z = \sum_i e^{-\beta E_i(1)} \sum_j e^{-\beta E_j(2)} \cdots \sum_z e^{-\beta E_z(N)}$$
$$= \left(\sum_i e^{-\beta E_i}\right)^N \tag{18.30}$$

where the sum represents the partition function for a single molecule.

It is a great convenience to carry out the sum over the different *energies* of the system rather than over the individual *states*, which are often highly degenerate. We therefore introduce the number $g(E_i)$ of states corresponding to the single energy E_i so that

$$\sum_i e^{-\beta E_i} = \sum_E g(E)e^{-\beta E} \tag{18.31}$$

and

$$Z = \left(\sum_E g(E)e^{-\beta E}\right)^N \tag{18.32}$$

summed over all the possible energy eigenvalues of the system. Since for an ordinary container volume the energy levels lie very close together, we make the approximation of introducing a continuous function $\rho(E)$, defined as the number of states per unit energy range around E, so that

$$\Delta n = \rho(E)\,\Delta E \tag{18.33}$$

is the number of states between E and $E + \Delta E$. Using this, the sum in (18.32) becomes

$$\int_0^\infty \rho(E)e^{-\beta E}\, dE \tag{18.34}$$

where we have replaced the finite upper limit by infinity because at large energies the exponential becomes so small as not to matter.

The density of states appropriate to a cubical container is derived in Chap. 9.[4] Taking all directions of motion into account, we replace $d\Omega$ in (9.26) by 4π, and we denote the volume by V instead of Q to make it look more like thermodynamics. Then

$$\rho(E) = \frac{4\pi m V}{(2\pi\hbar)^3}\, p \tag{18.35}$$

where p is the molecule's momentum. It is convenient to use p as the variable of integration; we find

$$Z = \left[V\left(\frac{m}{2\pi\beta\hbar^2}\right)^{3/2} \right]^N \tag{18.36}$$

Problem 18.5 Carry out the integrations leading to (18.36) in cartesian and then in polar coordinates.

To find the pressure in the gas, we start with (18.25). It follows from the definition of F that

$$dF = d\bar{E} - T\, dS - S\, dT$$

Further, by (18.1),

$$d\bar{E} = DQ - DW$$
$$= T\, dS - \bar{P}\, dV \tag{18.37}$$

where $\bar{P}$ is the mean pressure in the subsystems, because $\bar{P}\, dV$ is the work done by a gas in changing its volume. Thus

$$dF = -\bar{P}\, dV - S\, dT \tag{18.38}$$

and the pressure of the gas is given by

$$\bar{P} = -\left(\frac{\partial F}{\partial V}\right)_T = \frac{1}{\beta}\left(\frac{\partial \ln Z}{\partial V}\right)_T \tag{18.39}$$

Differentiation of (18.36) gives the equation of state,

$$\bar{P}V = \frac{N}{\beta}$$

---

[4] It is, however, valid for a large container of any simple shape. See R. Courant and D. Hilbert, *Methods of Mathematical Physics*, Interscience Publishers, Inc., New York, 1953, vol. 1, p. 429.

Comparing this with (18.29) gives

$$\beta = \frac{1}{kT} \tag{18.40}$$

as promised. We can also use (18.27) to find the mean energy of a subsystem,

$$\bar{E} = \tfrac{3}{2} NkT \tag{18.41}$$

from which follows the well-known fact that the mean kinetic energy per molecule is $\tfrac{3}{2} kT$.

The Gibbs paradox

One of the striking features of the results we have just found is that they do not depend on $\hbar$, and in fact they can readily be obtained from arguments based on classical physics. This is not true, however, of the entropy, which is calculated from (18.28) to be

$$S = Nk \left\{ \ln \left[V \left(\frac{mkT}{2\pi\hbar^2} \right)^{3/2} \right] + \frac{3}{2} \right\} \tag{18.42}$$

and in which $\ln \hbar$ appears in the role of an additive constant. Such a specific value of S is not given by classical thermodynamics, which defines it only up to an undetermined constant; but we shall see in Chap. 19 that the value of this constant plays a crucial part in certain calculations, notably of the vapor pressure of a monatomic solid.

There is a significant inconsistency in our formula for S, which was first noted by Gibbs in the corresponding classical formula. Suppose we apply (18.42) to the situation shown in Fig. 18.2, where the gases in the two sides are chemically identical and have the same pressures and densities. The total entropy is given (cf. Prob. 18.4) by the sum of two terms like (18.42). Now let the partition be removed. Since nothing happens, the total entropy will be unchanged, but it will be given by (18.42) with $N = N_1 + N_2$ and $V = V_1 + V_2$. This is not equal to the sum of the initial entropies, and therefore something is wrong.

To see what is wrong, let us examine an assumption that was made in deriving (18.30). It is that a state with molecule 1 in state i and molecule 2 in state j is significantly different from that with 1 in state j and 2 in state i, and it is therefore to be counted separately. Since molecules are not in fact distinguishable, and since if their

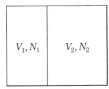

Fig. 18.2 The two chambers contain samples of the same gas under identical conditions of temperature and pressure.

wave functions overlap they may even be said to lose their identity
(cf. Chap. 11), this assumption is open to question. Let us see what
is the effect of the opposite assumption, that the two states are the
same and should be counted only once. There are $N!$ ways of distributing N molecules among N states. We have therefore counted
every indistinguishable state $N!$ times and must therefore divide
our previous value of Z by $N!$ to get

$$Z_i = \frac{1}{N!}\left[V\left(\frac{m}{2\pi\beta\hbar^2}\right)^{3/2}\right]^N \tag{18.43}$$

where the subscript i refers to the assumed indistinguishability of
the particles. This amounts to subtracting $k \ln N!$ from (18.42),
which with Stirling's approximation gives

$$S_i = Nk\left\{\ln\left[\frac{V}{N}\left(\frac{mkT}{2\pi\hbar^2}\right)^{3/2}\right] + \frac{5}{2}\right\}$$

This formula has the desired additivity, since the two cells of
Fig. 18.2 have $V_1/N_1 = V_2/N_2$. Put in another way, S_i has the
property that the entropy of a gas of a given density and temperature is directly proportional to the amount of gas, and this is not true
of (18.42). Of course, whether this formula is correct, only experiment can decide, but we shall see in Chap. 19 that the measured
vapor pressures of monatomic solids support it and that the factor
of $N!$ occurs naturally in a calculation more rigorously based on
quantum mechanics.

By using the property of additivity, we can generalize relations
like (18.37) to situations in which the number of particles is allowed
to vary. Write for example

$$d\bar{E} = \bar{E}\frac{d\bar{N}}{\bar{N}} + (d\bar{E})_{\bar{N}}$$

and similarly for the other variables, where the first term represents
the increase due to changing the number of particles and the second,
that due to all the other changes Thus,

$$d\bar{E} = \bar{E}\frac{d\bar{N}}{\bar{N}} + (T\,dS - \bar{P}\,dV)_{\bar{N}}$$

$$= \bar{E}\frac{d\bar{N}}{\bar{N}} + T\,dS - TS\frac{d\bar{N}}{\bar{N}} - \bar{P}\,dV + \bar{P}V\frac{d\bar{N}}{\bar{N}}$$

or

$$d\bar{E} = T\,dS - \bar{P}\,dV + (\bar{E} + \bar{P}V - TS)\frac{d\bar{N}}{\bar{N}} \tag{18.44}$$

which we shall need later.

Problem 18.6   Nernst's heat theorem, the third law of thermodynamics, states that the entropy of any pure substance (together

with its specific heat) vanishes at absolute zero. Real gases condense, of course, but our idealized perfect gas would not condense,
and the results obtained above conflict with the third law. Show
that the difficulty here is with the introduction of the level density
$\rho(E)$ in (18.33). Taking account only of the two lowest energy states
of the gas, show that at low temperatures, with Z uncorrected by
$N!$, the entropy approaches

$$ S = 3Nk \left(1 + \frac{E_g}{kT} \right) e^{-E_g/kT} \qquad E_g = \frac{3\pi^2 \hbar^2}{2mV^{2/3}} $$

for a cubical container and find the specific heat. At about what
temperature do our earlier approximations fail?

Maxwell's distribution

By considering the special case in which $N = 1$ we can easily derive
Maxwell's formula for the distribution of molecular velocities.
Suppose we ask what is the probability dP_E of finding the molecule
with its energy between E and $E + dE$. This will be given by the
sum of the p_i's corresponding to all the states in this range or, by
(18.33),

$$ dp_E = \rho(E)p_i(E) \, dE \tag{18.45} $$

where we assume that the energy range is narrow enough that all
the p_i's are approximately equal. Using (18.19), (18.35), and (18.36),
we find

$$ dp_E = \frac{\pi}{(\pi kT)^{3/2}} e^{-E/kT} E^{1/2} \, dE \tag{18.46} $$

or, in terms of the velocity v, the probability that the magnitude of
the velocity lies between v and $v + dv$ is

$$ dp_v = 4\pi \left(\frac{m}{2\pi kT} \right)^{3/2} e^{-mv^2/2kT} v^2 \, dv \tag{18.47} $$

This formula (again independent of $\hbar$) was first derived in 1859 by
Maxwell. It is plotted in Fig. 18.3.

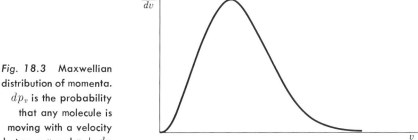

Fig. 18.3 Maxwellian
distribution of momenta.
dp_v is the probability
that any molecule is
moving with a velocity
between v and $v + dv$.

Problem 18.7 Give the details in the derivation of (18.47) from (18.46). Show that the sum of all the dp_v's is equal to 1. Find the molecule's mean kinetic energy.

A paramagnetic system

The following is a simple model of paramagnetic behavior such as might be exhibited in a gas or in a crystal in which the magnetic ions are quite widely spaced and do not interact appreciably with each other. We assume that the ion's angular momentum is $\frac{1}{2}$, so that its magnetic moment M is directed either parallel or antiparallel to the magnetic field. First let the system A consist of only a single ion. Since there are only two states, with energies

$$E_1 = -MB \qquad (\mathbf{M} \Uparrow \mathbf{B})$$
$$E_2 = MB \qquad (\mathbf{M} \Updownarrow \mathbf{B})$$

the partition function has only two terms,

$$Z_1 = e^{MB/kT} + e^{-MB/kT} = 2 \cosh \frac{MB}{kT} \qquad (18.48)$$

where the subscript 1 refers to the single ion. The mean energy of the spin is

$$\bar{E} = -MB \tanh \frac{MB}{kT} \qquad (18.49)$$

by (18.20), and the specific heat is

$$C = \frac{\partial \bar{E}}{\partial T} = k \left(\frac{MB}{kT} \right)^2 \operatorname{sech}^2 \frac{MB}{kT} \qquad (18.50)$$

These quantities are shown in Fig. 18.4.

Suppose now that we wish to calculate the susceptibility of a sample of matter containing n ions per unit volume. We can con-

Fig. 18.4 Energy and specific heat of a system of noninteracting spins.

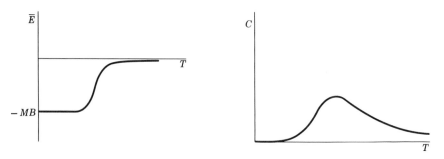

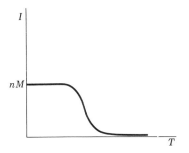
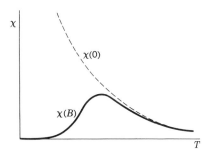

Fig. 18.5   Magnetization and susceptibility of a system
of noninteracting spins.

sider the entire sample as the ensemble, and we readily find that its
magnetic moment per unit volume is

$$I = nM \tanh \frac{MB}{kT} \tag{18.51}$$

and its susceptibility is

$$\chi = \frac{\partial I}{\partial B} = \frac{nM^2}{kT} \operatorname{sech}^2 \frac{MB}{kT} \tag{18.52}$$

These are shown in Fig. 18.5.

Problem 18.8   Derive (18.51) and (18.52). Write down the expression for χ_0, the susceptibility at zero field, and explain it
qualitatively.

Problem 18.9   Calculate the entropy of the ensemble, and
verify that it satisfies the third law.

The sharpness of ensemble averages

Now let us look at the same calculation except that the system A
and all its copies are supposed to contain N ions each, where N is
very large. We have to evaluate the partition function, and this
can best be done by replacing the sum over states by a sum over
energies as in (18.31). Suppose that of the N ions in a subsystem,
s are pointed down and $N - s$ are pointed up. The energy of the
subsystem is

$$E_s = sMB - (N - s)MB = -(N - 2s)MB$$

and the number of states corresponding to this energy is equal to the
number of ways in which s ions may be selected from among N. This
number is

$$g(E_s) = \frac{N!}{s!(N - s)!} \tag{18.53}$$

and the partition function is accordingly

$$Z_N = \sum_{s=0}^{N} \frac{N!}{s!(N-s)!} e^{(N-2s)MB/kT}$$

Writing $e^{-MB/kT} = x$, we have

$$Z_N = x^{-N} \sum_{s=0}^{N} \frac{N!}{s!(N-s)!} x^{2s}$$

and the series will be recognized as the binomial expansion whose sum is $(1 + x^2)^N$, so that

$$Z_N = x^{-N}(1 + x^2)^N = (x^{-1} + x)^N = \left(2 \cosh \frac{MB}{kT}\right)^N = Z_1{}^N$$

The energy, calculated from $\ln Z_N$, is accordingly N times that given in (18.49), just as one would expect, and similarly for the magnetic quantities.

But we can learn more than that from the calculation. Let us ask what is the probability that the subsystem is in a state with energy equal to E_s. Clearly, it is

$$p(E_s) = Z^{-1} e^{NMB/kT} \frac{N!}{s!(N-s)!} e^{-2sMB/kT} \tag{18.54}$$

The first two factors of this are independent of s, and the last two are shown in Fig. 18.6. Since the graph of $g(E_s)$ has such a narrow peak at $s = \frac{1}{2}N$, the product of the two functions will (unless MB/kT is large and the curve a is accordingly very steep) again have the form of a narrow peak with its maximum shifted slightly. Therefore, even though the probability of a given *state* decreases uniformly with increasing energy, the probability of a given *energy* has a sharp maximum, and the system A has an energy that is quite narrowly limited even though there is, strictly speaking, nothing except the law of averages to prevent it from taking all or none of the energy of the ensemble into itself. It is this sharpness that makes the notion of an ensemble useful—the behavior of A as a member of the ensemble is, in the long run, almost exactly what it would be if A were an isolated system. Thus it is conceptually better to have

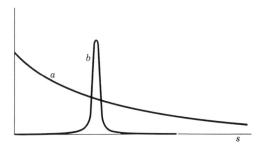

Fig. 18.6 The Boltzmann factor (a) and the statistical weight (b) of a system of noninteracting spins.

each member of the ensemble consist of a large number of particles, even though in the case we have just considered the partition function can be more easily evaluated if each member is taken to be one particle.

To give a quantitative idea of the width of $g(E_s)$, and hence of the distribution in values of E_s, it can be shown by a careful use of Stirling's theorem that if $s = \frac{1}{2}N + \delta$, where δ is much smaller than $\frac{1}{2}N$,

$$g(E_s) \approx 2^N \left(\frac{2}{\pi N} \right)^{\frac{1}{2}} e^{-2\delta^2/N} \tag{18.55}$$

from which we see that if $\delta = N^{\frac{1}{2}}$, the curve is already down to less than one-seventh of its peak value. If N is, say, 10^{26}, then this value of δ is enormous, but compared to N it is very small indeed, for $\delta/N = 10^{-13}$. The following problem will show that this definiteness of energy, arising not from the Boltzmann factor $e^{-\beta E_s}$, but from the weighting factor that goes with it, is a general feature of ensembles (failing only if the system is close to making a phase transition).

Problem 18.10   Investigate the mean size of fluctuations away from the average energy by the techniques of Chap. 3, showing as with (3.36) that

$$(\Delta E)^2 = \overline{(E - \bar{E})^2} = - \frac{\partial \bar{E}}{\partial \beta} = kT^2 \frac{\partial \bar{E}}{\partial T} \tag{18.56}$$

Similarly, show that the square of the relative fluctuation is

$$\left(\frac{\Delta E}{\bar{E}} \right)^2 = \frac{\partial}{\partial \beta} \frac{1}{\bar{E}} = -kT^2 \frac{\partial}{\partial T} \left(\frac{1}{\bar{E}} \right) \tag{18.57}$$

Problem 18.11   Use these formulas to discuss the energy fluctuations in a perfect gas at ordinary and at extra-low temperatures and in the paramagnetic system discussed above.

Problem 18.12   In the earliest form of the theory of the specific heats of solids, Einstein considered a solid as an ensemble of simple harmonic oscillators, all at the same frequency ω. Evaluate the specific heat of such a system, verify that it satisfies the third law, and give a qualitative comparison of the result with experimental data.

Problem 18.13   According to the correspondence principle, quantum phenomena in the limit of high quantum numbers approach their classical analogues. Accordingly, thermodynamic formulas at high temperatures should be expected to become independent of $\hbar$. In the early days of quantum theory it was thought that the energy levels of a simple harmonic oscillator are given by $n\hbar\omega$; quantum mechanics changes this to $(n + \frac{1}{2})\hbar\omega$. Calculate $\bar{E}$ for a harmonic oscillator in equilibrium with its surroundings at a temperature T, using both expressions for the energy levels. Discuss the high-temperature limit in each case. Include sketches of $\bar{E}$ as a function of T. Is the correspondence principle obeyed?

18.4 Work and Heat

We are now ready to finish answering the questions posed at the beginning of this chapter on the microscopic interpretation of the first law of thermodynamics. We have in (18.13) an expression for the average energy of the system A,

$$\bar{E} = \Sigma p_i E_i \tag{18.58}$$

and if an infinitesimal change is made in the ensemble, we have

$$d\bar{E} = \Sigma E_i\, dp_i + \Sigma p_i\, dE_i \tag{18.59}$$

The first term reflects a redistribution of the systems among the existing energy levels, and the second describes a mechanical change in the systems which changes the energy levels themselves without changing their populations. These are two quite distinct ways in which the system's energy can change. We now define the infinitesimal heat and work by

$$DQ = \Sigma E_i\, dp_i \tag{18.60}$$

and

$$DW = -\Sigma p_i\, dE_i \tag{18.61}$$

so that the truth of (18.1) becomes automatic. We have still, however, to show that these definitions have something to do with thermodynamics.

The consistency of (18.60) follows at once from the arguments used to establish (18.23). Defining σ as in (18.21), we have for an infinitesimal change in the p_i away from equilibrium

$$d\sigma = -\Sigma(1 + \ln p_i)\, dp_i$$
$$= -\Sigma(1 - \ln Z - \beta E_i)\, dp_i$$
$$= \beta\Sigma E_i\, dp_i = \beta DQ$$

the same as (18.23). Using (18.24) with κ equal to k shows that DQ is indeed an element of heat.

The fact that (18.61) defines work in the usual sense can best be shown by considering a simple system. Let it be a cylinder of length l, closed by a piston and containing a single gas molecule. The energy of its ith state is

$$E_i = \frac{1}{2m}\,(p_x{}^2 + p_y{}^2 + p_z{}^2)$$

where the boundary condition in the x direction requires that l be an integral number of half de Broglie wavelengths, so that

$$p_x = s\frac{\pi\hbar}{l} \qquad (s = 1,2, \ldots)$$

If the piston is moved slowly so as to change l without changing s, the change in energy is

$$dE_i = \frac{2p_x\,dp_x}{2m}$$

But

$$dp_x = -s\left(\frac{\pi\hbar}{l^2}\right)dl = -p_x\frac{dl}{l}$$

so that

$$dE_i = -2\frac{p_x^2}{2m}\frac{dl}{l} \tag{18.62}$$

We now assume that at equilibrium, p_x^2, p_y^2, and p_z^2 are all equal on the average, so that (18.62) is

$$dE_i = -\tfrac{2}{3}E_i\frac{dl}{l}$$

Returning to (18.61) (and noting that p_i there denotes probability, not momentum!) we have

$$DW = \frac{2}{3}\sum p_i E_i\frac{dl}{l} = \tfrac{2}{3}\bar{E}\frac{dl}{l}$$

But $\bar{E} = \tfrac{3}{2}PV$, where P is the pressure exerted by the molecule and V is the volume of the cylinder. Thus

$$DW = PV\frac{dl}{l} = PAl\frac{dl}{l} = P\,dV$$

where A is the area of the cylinder. This result agrees with the usual macroscopic definition of work and is familiar in thermodynamics. It is easy to generalize this result to the case of many noninteracting molecules.

It is clear from this example that the quantity which we have called DW corresponds to what is usually denoted as external work in thermodynamics, just as DQ corresponds to heat. The work produces a change in the energy levels of a system without affecting their populations, whereas the heat changes the populations without affecting the energy levels. Their sum is evidently a perfect differential.

Finally, we must discuss the assumption that the piston moves so as not to change the energy state s of the molecule bouncing against it. It is a general principle in quantum mechanics that if the mechanical parameters describing a system are altered very slowly, so as to change the positions of the system's energy levels, this will not induce any transitions, and the system will end up in the new state which corresponds exactly to the one in which it began. This principle is known as the adiabatic theorem. It is expressed in (8.102) and explained in the paragraphs following that equation.

The correspondence between external work and the DW defined in (18.61) thus requires that the transition be carried out adiabatically in the quantum sense. This corresponds to the requirement, usual in thermodynamics, that thermodynamic changes be carried out in a quasi-static, reversible way. Adiabatic transitions have to be quasi-static, and they are also reversible, since if a system is taken adiabatically through a cycle ending in a return to the initial configuration, it is clear that nothing will have changed. This answers the final question, 4, with which the chapter began.

Adiabatic demagnetization

A well-known use of adiabatic transitions is in the achievement of very low temperatures by demagnetization. In this technique a sample of a paramagnetic salt in a strong magnetic field B is allowed to come to thermal equilibrium with its surroundings at a low temperature, perhaps that of liquid helium. If the atoms of the salt have a spin of $\frac{3}{2}$, say, the populations of the four states at equilibrium will vary as $e^{-\beta E}$. (We are here regarding the individual atoms of the salt as the systems A, A', etc. of the ensemble.) Now the magnetic field is reduced adiabatically, to a value B', so that the same relative populations remain. The new distribution corresponds to a lower temperature than the old (see Fig. 18.7). Quantitatively, we know that the potential energy of a magnetic system in a field B is proportional to B. Since the probabilities $p \propto \exp(-E/kT)$ are unchanged by adiabatic cooling, it follows that T must decrease proportionally to B as the substance is demagnetized. Thus the spins in the cryostat become suddenly

Fig. 18.7 Adiabatic cooling. The populations remain the same while the energies decrease. The new Boltzmann distribution is characterized by $T' < T$.

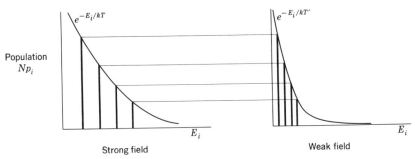

Population
Np_i

$e^{-E_i/kT}$

$e^{-E_i/kT'}$

E_i

E_i

Strong field

Weak field

colder than the other degrees of freedom (vibrational, etc.) of the same system, and equilibrium is reestablished by the passage of energy from the other degrees of freedom into the spins.

How this actually occurs can be understood qualitatively from (18.49). If B is decreased (for a given T) the energy $\bar{E}$ tends to rise. If the spins are isolated, it cannot rise, and T must decrease. If they are not isolated, they absorb heat from their surroundings, and at the new equilibrium everything is a little colder. One might suppose that by removing the external field entirely, absolute zero would be reached. Unfortunately, a paramagnetic substance has an internal field, and this condition cannot be reached. The internal field depends in a detailed way on the crystalline structure of the salt, and an exact analysis becomes rather complicated.

REFERENCES

Section 1

A. B. Pippard, *Classical Thermodynamics*, Cambridge University Press, London, 1957.

E. Fermi, *Thermodynamics*, Dover Publications, Inc., New York, 1956.

F. H. Crawford, *Heat, Thermodynamics, and Statistical Physics*, Harcourt, Brace & World, Inc., New York, 1963.

Sections 2 and 3

D. Ter Haar, *Elements of Statistical Mechanics*, Holt, Rinehart and Winston, Inc., New York, 1954.

L. D. Landau and E. M. Lifschitz, *Statistical Physics*, Addison-Wesley Publishing Company, Inc., Reading, Mass., 1958.

R. C. Tolman, *The Principles of Statistical Mechanics*, Clarendon Press, Oxford, 1938.

Section 4

Simon, Kurti, Allen, and Mendelssohn, *Low Temperature Physics*, Academic Press Inc., New York, 1952.

H. B. G. Casimir, *Magnetism and Very Low Temperatures*, Cambridge University Press, London, 1940.

D. de Klerk, in *Handbuch der Physik*, Springer-Verlag OHG, Berlin, vol. XV, 1956.

19

Quantum Statistics

19.1 Introduction

In a sense, all statistical mechanics is quantum statistical mechanics, since it all deals ultimately with the behavior of matter on the atomic or molecular scale. The remarkable thing is how good an approximation the classical theory provides. To be sure, it needs to be amended by some factors of $\hbar$, cf. (18.42), and a factor of $(N!)$, cf. (18.43), but many of its results are independent of such constants, and it provides great insight into the behavior of complex systems. The real difficulties arise when one begins to consider systems which interact slightly, like the molecules of a real gas, or strongly, like those of a solid.

It is characteristic of quantum mechanics that it treats "simple" many-particle systems more easily than classical mechanics can—in Chap. 15, for example, we have solved a three-body problem with considerable accuracy. In the mechanics of large numbers of particles, however, such simplifications are more than overbalanced by difficulties which arise in the attempt to enumerate the states of the system. This enumeration is easy if the interactions are neglected, but it becomes very difficult when the energy of each particle can no longer be considered constant. Therefore much of our discussion will be about non-interacting particles. Surprisingly, we shall see that this approximation provides insight into a variety of interesting physical systems. This is partly because "no interaction" in quantum physics, when translated into classical terms, does not cor-

NOTE: This chapter is independent of the main argument of Chap. 18, but it requires familiarity with Secs. 18.2 and 18.3.

respond with the classical notion of no interaction; for, as we have seen in Sec. 11.1, the mere existence of symmetrized or antisymmetrized wave functions involving several particles introduces correlations in position and momentum which have no classical explanation but which have effects roughly similar to those of a force. If there is no interaction between molecules, the mere correlations in position have no effect on the energy and hence on the statistical distribution in energy, but a correlation in momentum may have a very marked effect. The exclusion principle, for example, prevents any state from being occupied by more than one particle. This effect is felt especially at low temperatures and high densities, when in the absence of the exclusion principle the particles would tend to congregate in a relatively small number of low-lying states. But if in the absence of exclusion the probability of finding more than one particle in the same state is small, exclusion makes little difference.

It is clear that the statistical methods to be used must refer explicitly to the number of particles in each state. There are two principal methods of treating these situations. The first is to study in some detail the counting of states in which the particles are described by symmetric and antisymmetric wave functions, leading to an argument similar to that of Sec. 13.2 but involving different formulas.[1] The second, which we shall follow here because it has wider implications, is to start by generalizing the canonical ensemble of the preceding chapter to cover situations in which the number of particles in a subsystem is allowed to vary. This theory, first developed by Gibbs, is the natural framework in which to discuss chemical reactions, in which molecules and ions of a given species actually appear and disappear; but we shall use it to describe quantum transitions out of one state and into another. This can, of course, be done perfectly well by means of the canonical ensemble, but mathematical difficulties arise which make our approach much simpler. The requisite mathematical apparatus is rather long; it is given in the next section. Having made a large investment in equipment, we should expect to get a lot done with it, and accordingly the six sections thereafter will give applications of the basic ideas to a wide variety of physical systems, both idealized and real.

19.2 The Grand Canonical Ensemble

Let us imagine an ensemble of systems similar to that in Fig. 18.1 except that the internal walls are porous and allow particles to flow in and out. It can be diagrammed as in Fig. 19.1. The number of particles in a subsystem will be called N, and a subsystem containing

[1] J. Mayer and M. G. Mayer, *Statistical Mechanics*, John Wiley & Sons, Inc., New York, 1940.

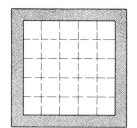

Fig. 19.1 A grand canonical ensemble. The subsystems may exchange both heat and particles but are thermally isolated from the rest of the world.

N particles will have a set of states (normally infinite in number) available to it. The states will be numbered by the index i, and since the energy levels of a subsystem depend on the number of particles in it, we shall sometimes (but not always) write $i(N)$. The total number of subsystems in the ensemble is $\mathbf{n}$, and the number containing N particles and in state i is $n_i(N)$. The number of subsystems containing N particles is

$$n(N) = \sum_{i(N)} n_i(N) \tag{19.1}$$

and

$$\mathbf{n} = \sum_N n(N) = \sum_{N,i(N)} n_i(N) \tag{19.2}$$

where the sum over $i(N)$ must be carried out first because $i(N)$ depends on N. The probability of finding a subsystem selected at random in the state $i(N)$ is

$$p_i(N) = \frac{n_i(N)}{\mathbf{n}} \tag{19.3}$$

so that (19.2) is

$$\sum_{N,i(N)} p_i(N) = 1 \tag{19.4}$$

Let the total number of particles in the ensemble be $\mathbf{N}$ and the total energy be $\mathbf{E}$. Clearly

$$\mathbf{N} = \sum_N N n(N) = \sum_{N,i(N)} N n_i(N) \tag{19.5}$$

and

$$\mathbf{E} = \sum_{N,i(N)} E_i(N) n_i(N) \tag{19.6}$$

where $E_i(N)$ is the energy of the ith state in a system containing N particles. Dividing the last two equations by n gives

$$\sum_{N,i(N)} N p_i(N) = \frac{\mathbf{N}}{\mathbf{n}} = \bar{N} \tag{19.7}$$

$$\sum_{N,i(N)} E_i(N) p_i(N) = \frac{\mathbf{E}}{\mathbf{n}} = \bar{E} \tag{19.8}$$

where $\bar{E}$ and $\bar{N}$ are the (fixed) averages of energy and particle number for the members of the ensemble. Before continuing, the reader should be sure that he has the meanings of all these symbols fixed in his mind (see Table 19.1), and he would do well to review briefly the argument of Sec. 18.2, which is the prototype of the work to follow.

Table 19.1

	n	total number of subsystems
	$n(N)$	number of subsystems containing N particles
	$i(N)$	the ith quantum state of a subsystem containing N particles
	$n_i(N)$	number of subsystems which contain N particles and are in the state $i(N)$
$p_i(N) = n_i(N)/n$		probability of finding a subsystem in the state $i(N)$
	$E_i(N)$	energy of a subsystem in the state $i(N)$
	E	total energy of the ensemble
	N	total number of particles in the ensemble
$\bar{E} = E/n$		mean energy per subsystem
$\bar{N} = N/n$		mean particle number per subsystem

As before, we assume that all the different states are equally probable, subject to the constancy of **N** and **E**. Defining the thermodynamic probability M as in Chap. 18 to be the logarithm of the total number of arrangements which correspond to a given set of $n_i(N)$, we have exactly as in (18.11)

$$M = -\mathbf{n} \sum_{N,i(N)} p_i(N) \ln p_i(N) \tag{19.9}$$

We wish to maximize this subject to the three conditions (19.4), (19.7), and (19.8). This requires three lagrangian multipliers instead of the previous two, and we find

$$1 + \ln p_i(N) + \alpha + \beta E_i(N) + \gamma N = 0$$

or

$$p_i(N) = e^{-(1+\alpha)}e^{-\beta E_i(N)}e^{-\gamma N} \tag{19.10}$$

As before, the condition (19.4) leads to

$$\sum_{N,i(N)} p_i(N) = e^{-(1+\alpha)}Q = 1$$

where

$$Q = \sum_{N,i(N)} e^{-\beta E_i(N) - \gamma N} \tag{19.11}$$

is the *grand partition function*. Comparison with (18.18) shows that

$$Q = \sum_N Z_N e^{-\gamma N} \tag{19.12}$$

where Z_N is the earlier "canonical" partition function for a system of exactly N particles. The probability

$$p_i(N) = Q^{-1}e^{-\beta E_i(N)-\gamma N} \tag{19.13}$$

still contains two arbitrary constants which we must identify as we did β in Chap. 12.

Suppose now that we have two grand canonical ensembles and place them in thermal contact, but do not allow them to exchange any particles. It is now easy to show (see Prob. 19.1) that at equilibrium their values of β will be equal. This leads to the conclusion that β is a function of the temperature T only, and in fact it is equal to $1/kT$ (Prob. 19.1). Now let the two ensembles exchange particles through a porous partition as well. They will remain at the same value of β, and the number of particles will adjust itself until the two values of γ are equal (Prob. 19.2). Thus, γ plays the same part in the exchange of particles that β does in the exchange of energy; in ordinary thermodynamic usage it is related to the *chemical potential* μ by

$$\mu = -\gamma kT \tag{19.14}$$

Problem 19.1 Show that if two grand canonical ensembles are placed in thermal contact, they will come to equilibrium with their values of β equal. Imagine a grand canonical ensemble in thermal contact with a vessel containing a perfect gas, and show that $\beta = 1/kT$.

Problem 19.2 Show that if two grand canonical ensembles are allowed to exchange particles as well as energy, they will come to equilibrium with their values of β and γ respectively equal.

We now go on to establish the relation between the properties of the grand canonical ensemble and thermodynamics. From (19.7) and (19.8) we construct the two averages

$$\bar{N} = -Q^{-1}\frac{\partial Q}{\partial \gamma} \tag{19.15}$$

and

$$\bar{E} = -Q^{-1}\frac{\partial Q}{\partial \beta} \tag{19.16}$$

Further, we define a quantity

$$\sigma = -\sum_{N,i(N)} p_i(N) \ln p_i(N)$$

as in (18.21), which, tending toward a maximum with constant N and E at equilibrium, is, of course, proportional to the entropy just as before. Its equilibrium value is

$$\sigma_{eq} = \sum_{N,i(N)} p_i(N)[\beta E_i(N) + \gamma N + \ln Q]$$

$$= \beta \bar{E} + \gamma \bar{N} + \ln Q \tag{19.17}$$

Suppose now that a small amount of heat, amounting to $d\bar{E}$ per subsystem, is added to the ensemble and it is once again allowed to come into equilibrium. This will change the values of β, γ, and Q along with $\bar{E}$, so that

$$d\sigma_{eq} = \beta \, d\bar{E} + \bar{E} \, d\beta + \bar{N} \, d\gamma + \frac{\partial \ln Q}{\partial \beta} \, d\beta + \frac{\partial \ln Q}{\partial \gamma} \, d\gamma$$

$$= \beta \, d\bar{E}$$

by (19.15) and (19.16). Therefore, as before, $\beta = 1/kT$ and

$$\sigma_{eq} = S/k$$

where S is the mean entropy per subsystem of the ensemble. Thus we can write a thermodynamic formula for $\ln Q$ as

$$-kT \ln Q = \bar{E} - TS - \mu \bar{N} \tag{19.18}$$

where we have used (19.14). This relation, analogous to (18.25), defines a thermodynamic potential for systems in which the number of particles is variable. It is called the *grand potential* Ω, with

$$\Omega = -kT \ln Q$$
$$Q = e^{-\Omega/kT} \qquad \Omega = \bar{E} - TS - \mu \bar{N} \tag{19.19}$$

Regarding Ω as a function of the variables β and γ, we can write the relations (19.15) and (19.16) as

$$\bar{N} = \left[\frac{\partial}{\partial \gamma} (\beta \Omega) \right]_\beta = \beta \left(\frac{\partial \Omega}{\partial \gamma} \right)_\beta \tag{19.20}$$

$$\bar{E} = \left[\frac{\partial}{\partial \beta} (\beta \Omega) \right]_\gamma = \Omega + \beta \left(\frac{\partial \Omega}{\partial \beta} \right)_\gamma \tag{19.21}$$

Problem 19.3 Starting from the definitions (19.11) and (19.19), show that $(\partial \Omega / \partial V)_{\beta,\gamma} = -\bar{P}$, the average pressure in a subsystem of the ensemble.

Solution. Differentiate (19.11) with respect to V,

$$\frac{\partial Q}{\partial V} = \beta \sum_{N,i(N)} - \frac{\partial E_i(N)}{\partial V} e^{-\beta E_i(N) - \gamma N}$$

The derivative $-\partial E_i(N)/\partial V$ represents the change in the energy of an N-particle system in its ith energy state per unit decrease in volume. This is the pressure of the system, which we can write as

$$- \frac{\partial E_i(N)}{\partial V} = P_i(N) \tag{19.22}$$

From (19.13), we can write

$$\frac{\partial Q}{\partial V} = \beta Q \sum_i P_i(N) p_i(N)$$

and this is of the form (2.3), giving

$$\frac{\partial Q}{\partial V} = \beta Q \bar{P} \tag{19.23}$$

The desired result follows at once.

Now let us make an arbitrary infinitesimal change in the system. Remembering that Ω is a function of β, γ, and V, we find as before

$$d\sigma_{\text{eq}} = \beta \, d\bar{E} + \bar{E} \, d\beta + \bar{N} \, d\gamma + \gamma \, d\bar{N} + \frac{\partial \ln Q}{d\beta} \, d\beta$$

$$+ \frac{\partial \ln Q}{d\gamma} \, d\gamma + \frac{\partial \ln Q}{dV} \, dV$$

$$= \beta \, d\bar{E} + \gamma d\bar{N} + \beta \bar{P} \, dV$$

or

$$d\bar{E} = T \, dS - \bar{P} \, dV + \mu \, d\bar{N} \tag{19.24}$$

Comparison with (18.44) shows that

$$\bar{E} + \bar{P}V - TS = \mu \bar{N} \tag{19.25}$$

and (19.19) shows the meaning of the grand potential,

$$\Omega = -\bar{P}V \tag{19.26}$$

The perfect gas

Let us use the formalism of the grand canonical ensemble to calculate the equation of state of a perfect gas. The equation of state is

$$\bar{P}V = -\Omega \tag{19.27}$$

so that we have only to calculate Ω from its definition and then express it as a function of $\bar{N}$ and T.

We start with the grand partition function Q defined in (19.11). The summation

$$\sum_{i(N)} e^{-\beta E_i(N)}$$

has already been carried out in Chap. 18; the value is given by (18.43) as

$$Z_N = \frac{1}{N!} \left[V \left(\frac{mkT}{2\pi\hbar^2} \right)^{3/2} \right]^N \tag{19.28}$$

The further sum gives

$$Q = \exp\left[e^{-\gamma} V \left(\frac{mkT}{2\pi\hbar^2}\right)^{3\!/\!2} \right] \tag{19.29}$$

To express things in terms of the desired variables, we evaluate $\bar{N}$ by (19.20), which gives

$$\bar{N} = \frac{1}{kT} \frac{\partial\Omega}{\partial\gamma} \tag{19.30}$$

with

$$\Omega = -kTe^{-\gamma} V \left(\frac{mkT}{2\pi\hbar^2}\right)^{3\!/\!2} \tag{19.31}$$

so that

$$\bar{N} = e^{-\gamma} V \left(\frac{mkT}{2\pi\hbar^2}\right)^{3\!/\!2} = -\frac{\Omega}{kT} \tag{19.32}$$

Thus $\Omega = -\bar{N}kT$, and (19.27) gives the usual equation of state

$$\bar{P}V = \bar{N}kT \tag{19.33}$$

The chemical potential is

$$\mu = -kT\gamma = kT \ln\left[\frac{\bar{N}}{V} \left(\frac{2\pi\hbar^2}{mkT}\right)^{3\!/\!2} \right] \tag{19.34}$$

Problem 19.4   Calculate the internal energy and entropy of a perfect gas. Show that if a perfect gas is compressed isothermally, the increase in μ equals the work done per particle in compressing the gas.

Problem 19.5   Recalculate the heat capacity and magnetization of the paramagnetic spin system discussed in Chap. 18.

Problem 19.6   Suppose we have an arbitrary system of non-interacting particles for which, as in (18.43), $Z_N = Z_1{}^N/N!$. Show that $Q = e^{\bar{N}}$ and that $p(N)$, the probability that any subsystem contains exactly N particles, is

$$p(N) = \frac{\bar{N}^N e^{-\bar{N}}}{N!} \tag{19.35}$$

This formula represents what is known as a Poisson distribution, and it may be found in books on statistics. Sketch $p(N)$ for large $\bar{N}$ and show that (19.35) was to be expected on the basis of Poisson's reasoning.

Problem 19.7   Show from the result of the preceding problem or by an argument analogous to that of Prob. 18.11 that even though the subsystems of a grand canonical ensemble are free to exchange particles, the dispersion ΔN is the value of N from one subsystem to another is only of the order of $\sqrt{N}$. Suppose the ensemble to be a one-story office building with identical offices of reasonable size. By what mass will the amount of air vary from office to office? Comment on the relationship of results obtained from a grand canonical ensemble to those obtained from a canonical ensemble.

19.3 Quantum Statistics

Except for use of the density of states in evaluating Q for a perfect gas, we have proceeded up to this point as though quantum mechanics did not exist. When we come to take it into account, we find that, at least in the simple, non-interacting systems that have occupied us so far, the only difference that arises is in the counting of states. In carrying out the sums in (19.11), it is logically necessary to sum first over $i(N)$, then over N. Suppose, however, that the particles do not interact appreciably, so that it makes sense to talk of the energy ε_s of an individual particle in its sth state, rather than the energy of a system of N of them. There is then another way to look at the evaluation of Q. It is to think of all the particles with energy ε_1 as being counted together as one ensemble, those with energy ε_2 is another which can exchange both particles and energy with the first one, and so on, as in Fig. 19.2. (The ensembles are not localized in space!) It follows from the preceding section, and especially Prob. 19.2, that these ensembles will finally all come into equilibrium with the same value of β $(= 1/kT)$ and γ $(= -\mu/kT)$. The energy of a subsystem containing N particles in the sth ensemble is $N\varepsilon_s$, replacing the old $E_i(N)$, which referred to an N-particle system considered as a whole, and its grand partition is

$$Q_s = \sum_N \frac{1}{N!} e^{-N(\beta\varepsilon_s + \gamma)} \tag{19.36}$$

summed over all values of N, where we have put in the semiempirical $1/N!$ to take account of the fact that interchanging the labels on particles does not change the state.

Equation (19.36) is fundamental for the classical theory of identical, non-interacting particles approached through the grand

Fig. 19.2 A quantized system represented as a set of grand canonical ensembles in equilibrium with each other under exchange of heat and of particles. Each particle in the sth ensemble is in quantum state s.

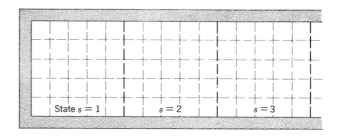

State $s = 1$ $s = 2$ $s = 3$

canonical ensemble. The general success of classical statistical mechanics shows that it has a large range of validity. We shall therefore examine the orders of magnitude it contains before turning to the different sums over s required when wave functions are symmetrical or antisymmetrical.

Classical theory

We find

$$Q_s = \exp e^{-\beta \varepsilon_s - \gamma} \qquad (19.37)$$

and

$$\Omega_s = -kTe^{-\beta \varepsilon_s - \gamma} \qquad (19.38)$$

The mean number of particles per subsystem in state s is, by (19.30),

$$\bar{N}_s = e^{-\beta \varepsilon_s - \gamma} \qquad (19.39)$$

Since Ω is an additive quantity, the grand potential of the entire ensemble is

$$\Omega = -kT \sum_s e^{-\beta \varepsilon_s} e^{-\gamma} \qquad (19.40)$$

To get an idea of the size of $\bar{N}_s$, let us take the value of $e^{-\gamma}$ for a perfect gas from (19.32),

$$e^{-\gamma} = \frac{\bar{N}}{V} \left(\frac{2\pi \hbar^2}{mkT} \right)^{3/2}$$

If a particle has an energy equal to $\frac{3}{2}kT$, its momentum is found from $p^2/2m = \frac{3}{2}kT$, and

$$\left(\frac{2\pi \hbar^2}{mkT} \right)^{1/2} = \left(\frac{3}{2\pi} \right)^{1/2} \frac{h}{p}$$

which, except for an unimportant numerical factor, is the de Broglie wavelength corresponding to the temperature T. We shall accordingly write it (including the numerical factor) as λ, so that

$$e^{-\gamma} = \bar{N} \frac{\lambda^3}{V} \qquad \lambda = \left(\frac{2\pi \hbar^2}{mkT} \right)^{1/2} \qquad (19.41)$$

Expressed in angstroms, typical values of λ are

$$\lambda = \frac{745}{\sqrt{T}} \,\text{Å} \qquad \text{electrons}$$

$$= \frac{17.4}{\sqrt{T}} \,\text{Å} \qquad \text{nucleons} \qquad (19.42)$$

$$= \frac{8.7}{\sqrt{T}} \,\text{Å} \qquad \text{He}^4 \text{ atoms}$$

If there are $\bar{N}/V$ particles per unit volume, then the average volume per particle is $V/\bar{N}$ and the average spacing between particles is $d = (V/\bar{N})^{1/3}$. Thus,

$$e^{-\gamma} = \left(\frac{\lambda}{d}\right)^3 \tag{19.43}$$

and we see that at all temperatures and densities at which a real substance might conceivably be a gas, $e^{-\gamma}$ is extremely small. Hence, by (19.39),

$$\bar{N}_s \ll 1 \tag{19.44}$$

and

$$\gamma \gg 1 \tag{19.45}$$

Thus it will be a very rare event that a system contains two particles in the same quantum state.

One might conclude from all this that quantum statistics is a wild-goose chase, but that is by no means so; for a number of systems which do not satisfy (19.44) exist in nature. Such systems, having $\bar{N}_s \gtrless 1$, are termed *degenerate*. There is the photon gas inside a cavity at equilibrium, where there are great numbers of low-frequency photons and $\bar{N}_s$ becomes infinite as s approaches zero. Exactly the same situation is found in the thermal oscillations of solid bodies. Here, since the particles of the material are tightly bonded together and there is no possibility of considering them in isolation, one transfers one's attention to their collective motions, the normal modes of oscillation, in the language of classical mechanics, in which they all participate. These motions take the form of waves which move through the crystal as light moves through space. Their quanta, called phonons, obey Bose-Einstein statistics.

Another system whose behavior is dominated by its quantum properties is liquid helium. Here the considerations are of two kinds. First, the mean spacing d is 3.58 Å at very low temperatures, so that λ/d is of the order of unity or larger over a range of several degrees above absolute zero. There are, of course, intermolecular forces strong enough to cause the gas to condense into a liquid, though only at 4.2°K at atmospheric pressure. But we shall find nevertheless that the behavior of the liquid resembles that of the corresponding ideal gas in quite a remarkable way, and we shall see that at the same time the phonon concept is of use.

The Fermi-Dirac formulas also have their domains of interest. Foremost is the gas of electrons in a metal, where although the existence of a structure of energy bands (Chap. 13) shows that the electrons are not to be considered as entirely free, there are nevertheless many properties which may be understood as if they were, and λ in (19.42) greatly exceeds the mean spacing between electrons up to very high temperatures. Two other degenerate systems, which we shall not discuss, are the mixture of protons and neutrons inside a nucleus[2] and the state of matter inside a star, where although it is very hot, the gravitational force compresses it to great densities.[3]

Problem 19.8 Over what range does $\bar{N}_s$ vary for air at ordinary conditions?

Quantum theory

Now let us return to (19.36) and evaluate it by quantum mechanics. We have learned that two types of particle exist in nature: bosons, having spins of $0, \hbar$, and sometimes higher, and fermions, with spins $\frac{1}{2}$ and sometimes $\frac{3}{2}$ and higher. A state containing N bosons is described by a wave function symmetrical in all N sets of coordinates, and there is one such quantum state for each energy state s and not $N!$ of them. (As explained at the beginning of this chapter, it is not necessary to consider the symmetries of wave functions involving different states of the particles if they do not interact directly.) On the other hand, there can never be more than one fermion in a given state, so that N can only be 0 or 1. Thus, instead of (19.36) we have

$$\text{bosons} \qquad Q_s = \sum_{N=0}^{\infty} e^{-N(\beta\varepsilon_s+\gamma)} = \frac{1}{1 - e^{-\beta\varepsilon_s-\gamma}} \qquad (19.46)$$

$$\text{fermions} \qquad Q_s = \sum_{N=0}^{1} e^{-N(\beta\varepsilon_s+\gamma)} = 1 + e^{-\beta\varepsilon_s-\gamma} \qquad (19.47)$$

Note that the series (19.46) converges only if $\gamma + \beta\varepsilon_s > 0$ and therefore, since the lowest ε is very small, only $\gamma > 0$ can be used, whereas (19.47) is valid for any γ. The corresponding grand potentials corresponding to the individual quantum states are

$$\text{bosons} \qquad \Omega_s = kT \ln (1 - e^{-\beta\varepsilon_s-\gamma}) \qquad (19.48)$$

$$\text{fermions} \qquad \Omega_s = -kT \ln (1 + e^{-\beta\varepsilon_s-\gamma}) \qquad (19.49)$$

and those for the whole ensembles are

$$\text{bosons} \qquad \Omega = kT \sum_s \ln (1 - e^{-\beta\varepsilon_s-\gamma}) \qquad (19.50)$$

$$\text{fermions} \qquad \Omega = -kT \sum_s \ln (1 + e^{-\beta\varepsilon_s-\gamma}) \qquad (19.51)$$

From (19.20), the average numbers of particles in state s are

$$\text{bosons} \qquad \bar{N}_s = \frac{1}{e^{\beta\varepsilon_s+\gamma} - 1} \qquad (19.52)$$

$$\text{fermions} \qquad \bar{N}_s = \frac{1}{e^{\beta\varepsilon_s+\gamma} + 1} \qquad (19.53)$$

[2] D. ter Haar, see under References at the end of this chapter.
[3] S. Chandrasekhar, *Introduction to the Study of Stellar Structure*, University of Chicago Press, Chicago, 1939.

while the classical way of counting, which goes under the name of Boltzmann, gave:

Boltzmann $\bar{N}_s = \dfrac{1}{e^{\beta\varepsilon_s+\gamma}}$ (19.54)

midway between the other two. For the large values of γ encountered in ordinary gases, these three modes of distribution are indistinguishable. Equations (19.50) and (19.51) become the same as (19.40), and we have at last achieved a derivation of the Maxwell-Boltzmann formulas[4] which does not depend on introducing *ad hoc* our earlier factor of $1/N$!

The preceding formulas are usually referred to as those of Bose-Einstein, Fermi-Dirac, and Boltzmann statistics after their originators, but the word "statistics" is perhaps a misnomer here. There is only one statistical argument, and it leads to the general formulas for the partition function and its uses. These are the same in all three cases. The only thing that varies is the list of states to be counted. It might therefore have been better to refer to Bose-Einstein *counting* and so on, but the other term is firmly established and we shall have to live with it.

Dilute gases

In order to see the effect of the modifications we have made in the Boltzmann formulas without becoming involved in mathematical complications, let us find the equations of state of the gases they describe in the limit where $e^{-\gamma}$ is small and the method of counting makes very little difference. Taking only the first two terms in a series expansion of the logarithms in (19.48) and (19.49), we have

$$\Omega_s = -kT[e^{-(\beta\varepsilon_s+\gamma)} \pm \tfrac{1}{2}e^{-2(\beta\varepsilon_s+\gamma)}]$$

where the upper sign refers to the bosons. The total partition function is

$$\Omega = -kT \sum_s [e^{-(\beta\varepsilon_s+\gamma)} \pm \tfrac{1}{2}e^{-2(\beta\varepsilon_s+\gamma)}]$$

and this is evaluated exactly like (18.31) to give

$$\Omega = -kTV \left[\left(\frac{m}{2\pi\beta\hbar^2}\right)^{3/2} e^{-\gamma} \pm \frac{1}{2}\left(\frac{m}{4\pi\beta\hbar^2}\right)^{3/2} e^{-2\gamma} \right]$$
$$= -kTV\lambda^{-3}(e^{-\gamma} \pm 2^{-5/2}e^{-2\gamma})$$

As before, we use (19.30) to express γ in terms of $\bar{N}$

$$\bar{N} = V\lambda^{-3}(e^{-\gamma} \pm 2^{-3/2}e^{-2\gamma})$$

---

[4] The limiting case of the Boltzmann distribution is discussed by Landau and Lifschitz (see References at the end of this chapter), section 37.

This is

$$e^{-\gamma} = \frac{\bar{N}}{V} \lambda^3 \mp 2^{-3/2} e^{-2\gamma}$$

or, since the second term is a small correction,

$$e^{-\gamma} = \frac{\bar{N}}{V} \lambda^3 \left(1 \mp 2^{-3/2} \frac{\bar{N}}{V} \lambda^3 \right) \tag{19.55}$$

Putting this back into Ω gives

$$\Omega = -\bar{N}kT \left(1 \mp 2^{-5/2} \frac{\bar{N}}{V} \lambda^3 \right) \tag{19.56}$$

so that the (approximate) equation of state is

$$\bar{P}V = \bar{N}kT(1 \mp 2^{-5/2} \bar{N}\lambda^3/V) \tag{19.57}$$

We see that bosons tend to exert a little less pressure, and fermions a little more, than they would under classical statistics. These effects have already been encountered in the form of a sort of "statistical attraction and repulsion," which has nothing to do with actual forces, in Sec. 11.1.

Problem 19.9 What is the energy calculated for the dilute gases discussed above? (Remember that λ and γ are functions of T.)

19.4 Photons and Phonons

We have mentioned above two kinds of boson, which may be called permanent and ephemeral. Atoms and molecules are permanent, for their total number does not change, but phonons and photons are continually being emitted and absorbed, and their number is purely a statistical matter. The treatment given above is for permanent particles; the number γ was introduced as the lagrangian multiplier of the condition (19.7) which expresses this fact. If there is no such condition, then there is no such multiplier, and the corresponding formulas are readily obtained from those of the preceding section by setting $\gamma = 0$.

Photons

The average occupation number of the state s is

$$\bar{N}_s = \frac{1}{e^{\beta \varepsilon_s} - 1} \tag{19.58}$$

and the grand potential is

$$\Omega = kT \sum_s \ln (1 - e^{-\beta \varepsilon_s}) \tag{19.59}$$

To evaluate this, we introduce the density of states for the electromagnetic field given by (10.34), integrated over angles and with a factor of 2 for the polarization states,

$$\rho(\varepsilon) = \frac{V\varepsilon^2}{\pi^2\hbar^3c^3} \tag{19.60}$$

Therefore

$$\Omega = \frac{VkT}{\pi^2\hbar^3c^3}\int_0^\infty \varepsilon^2 \ln{(1 - e^{-\beta\varepsilon})}\,d\varepsilon \tag{19.61}$$

$$\Omega = -\frac{V}{3\pi^2\hbar^3c^3}\int_0^\infty \frac{\varepsilon^3\,d\varepsilon}{e^{\beta\varepsilon}-1} \tag{19.62}$$

after integration by parts. To evaluate this we let $\beta\varepsilon = x$. Then

$$\Omega = -\frac{V}{3\pi^2\beta^4(\hbar c)^3}\int_0^\infty \frac{x^3\,dx}{e^x-1} \tag{19.63}$$

Integrals of this kind cannot be evaluated by elementary means without the use of elaborate artifice, but they may be expanded in series and expressed in terms of the zeta function $\varsigma(k)$ defined as

$$\varsigma(k) = \sum_{n=1}^\infty \frac{1}{n^k} \tag{19.64}$$

Zeta functions of even integers can be expressed in terms of integers and powers of π: $\varsigma(2) = \frac{1}{6}\pi^2$, $\varsigma(4) = \frac{1}{90}\pi^4$, etc., but the rest have no such simple representation. Defining a general class of integrals by I_k, we have

$$I_k = \int_0^\infty \frac{x^k\,dx}{e^x-1} = \sum_{n=1}^\infty \int_0^\infty x^k e^{-nx}\,dx = \sum_{n=1}^\infty \frac{k!}{n^{k+1}}$$

$$I_k = k!\varsigma(k+1) \tag{19.65}$$

If k is not an integer, we write $\Gamma(k+1)$ instead of $k!$; some relevant values are given in Table 19.2. It will also be useful in doing Fermi-Dirac statistics to have the integrals

$$J_k = \int_0^\infty \frac{x^k\,dx}{e^x+1} \tag{19.66}$$

and these can be expressed in terms of I_k by the identity

$$\frac{1}{e^x+1} = \frac{1}{e^x-1} - \frac{2}{e^{2x}-1}$$

On writing down the integral, we find

$$J_k = (1 - 2^{-k})I_k \tag{19.67}$$

and we can now fill out Table 19.2.

Table 19.2   Functions and integrals encountered in quantum statistics

k	$\Gamma(k+1)$	$\zeta(k+1)$	$I_k = \int_0^\infty \dfrac{x^k\,dx}{e^x - 1}$	$J_k = \int_0^\infty \dfrac{x^k\,dx}{e^x + 1}$
0	1	∞	∞	$\ln 2 = 0.6931$
$\frac{1}{2}$	$\frac{1}{2}\sqrt{\pi}$	2.612	2.315	0.6780
1	1	$\frac{1}{6}\pi^2 = 1.645$	$\frac{1}{6}\pi^2 = 1.645$	$\frac{1}{12}\pi^2 = 0.8225$
$\frac{3}{2}$	$\frac{3}{4}\sqrt{\pi}$	1.341	1.783	1.152
2	2	1.202	2.404	1.803
3	6	$\frac{1}{90}\pi^4 = 1.082$	$\frac{1}{15}\pi^4 = 6.494$	$\frac{7}{120}\pi^4 = 5.682$

We find

$$\Omega = -\frac{\pi^2 V}{45\beta^4 (\hbar c)^2} \tag{19.68}$$

so that by (19.27) the pressure of the radiation in a cavity at temperature T is

$$\bar{P} = \frac{\pi^2 (kT)^4}{45(\hbar c)^3}$$

and by (19.21) the mean energy of the radiation is

$$\bar{E} = \frac{\pi^2 V (kT)^4}{15(\hbar c)^3} \tag{19.69}$$

Note that

$$\bar{E} = 3\bar{P}V \tag{19.70}$$

instead of the $\frac{3}{2}\bar{P}V$ which characterizes a perfect gas. Equation (19.69) is the Stefan-Boltzmann law for the energy of radiation in a hot cavity. The proportionality to T^4 was measured by Stefan in 1879; five years later Boltzmann derived it by a thermodynamical argument. It can be shown that if the cavity has a small hole in it, the radiant energy emerging per unit area per second is given by

$$\Re = \sigma T^4 \qquad \sigma = \frac{\pi^2 c k^4}{60(\hbar c)^3} \tag{19.71}$$

where σ is called the Stefan-Boltzmann constant, is equal to 5.669×10^{-16} Jm^{-2} sec^{-1} deg^{-4}.

To find the spectrum of the emitted radiation, we return to (19.58) and (19.60). The number of photons with energy between ε and $\varepsilon + d\varepsilon$ is

$$d\Re(\varepsilon) = \frac{V}{\pi^2 \hbar^3 c^3} \frac{\varepsilon^2\,d\varepsilon}{e^{\beta\varepsilon} - 1} \tag{19.72}$$

and the energy in the same range is found by multiplying this by the energy ε of a quantum,

$$d\mathcal{E}(\varepsilon) = \frac{V}{\pi^2\hbar^3 c^3} \frac{\varepsilon^3 \, d\varepsilon}{e^{\beta\varepsilon} - 1} \tag{19.73}$$

On integrating this we again find (19.69). The spectral distribution of the radiation in frequency is

$$d\mathcal{E}(\nu) = \frac{8\pi V h}{c^3} \frac{\nu^3 \, d\nu}{e^{h\nu/kT} - 1} \tag{19.74}$$

where we have reinstated the constant $h = 2\pi\hbar$, or, in terms of the wavelength,

$$d\mathcal{E}(\lambda) = 8\pi V h c \frac{\lambda^{-5} \, d\lambda}{e^{hc/kT\lambda} - 1} \tag{19.75}$$

This is the famous law for the distribution in wavelength, first discovered by Planck in 1900 by interpolating the formula for the entropy of radiation between two limiting expressions known to be true at large and small wavelengths. It is illustrated for several temperatures in Fig. 19.3.

Problem 19.10   Calculate the frequency at which (19.74) has its maximum. To what wavelength does this correspond? Calculate the wavelength at which (19.75) has its maximum. Comment on the statement often heard that the Sun ($T \approx 6000°K$) "has its maximum radiation in the green." (The exact calculation requires solution of simple transcendental equations, but estimates accurate to a few percent may be made almost at sight.)

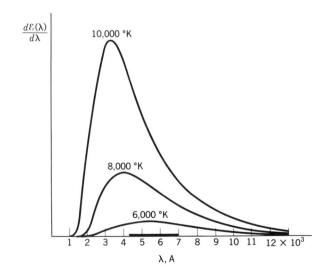

Fig. 19.3 The distribution of energy in black-body radiation, with $d\mathcal{E}(\lambda)$ equal to the energy per unit volume in the wavelength range λ to $\lambda + d\lambda$. The horizontal bar shows the visible range.

Problem 19.11 Calculate the radiation pressure in a furnace (2000°K) and in a hot star (10^7°K). In order to generate thermonuclear energy by fusion reactions in a plasma, it is necessary for the temperature to exceed 10^7°K. What hope is there for operating such a machine? (This requires some thought.)

Problem 19.12 Prove that if $\rho(\varepsilon)$ is of the form $C\varepsilon^m$, then $\bar{E} = (m + 1)\bar{P}V$ for all three statistics. Apply the result to photons and gas molecules.

Problem 19.13 How many photons are there per unit volume in a cavity in equilibrium at temperature T? What is their mean energy? Find the equation of state of a gas of photons.

Phonons

The theory of the assembly of photons in a solid in thermal equilibrium is largely analogous to that for radiation; it was first given by Debye in 1912. We assume that the phonons run freely through the solid, though this is clearly not so, for in that case heat would travel almost instantaneously, instead of slowly in the manner of a diffusion. There are two kinds of wave, longitudinal and transverse. We shall assume that their speeds, c_l and c_t, are independent of the frequency and that, as with light, the energy of a quantum is equal to $\hbar c_l$ or $\hbar c_t$ times its wave number. Thus, since there are two independent transverse states and one longitudinal, the density of states is

$$\rho(\varepsilon) = \frac{V\varepsilon^2}{2\pi^2\hbar^3}\left(\frac{1}{c_l^3} + \frac{2}{c_t^3}\right) \tag{19.76}$$

There is a further important difference from Planck's theory in that the total number of independent modes of motion is not infinite, being the same as the number of degrees of freedom of the system. Suppose that the solid contains N_s atoms. There are $3N_s$ degrees of freedom, so that assuming (19.76) to hold up to a limiting energy ε_m, we have

$$\frac{V}{2\pi^2\hbar^3}\left(\frac{1}{c_l^3} + \frac{2}{c_t^3}\right)\int_0^{\varepsilon_m} \varepsilon^2\,d\varepsilon = 3N_s$$

or

$$\frac{V\varepsilon_m^3}{2\pi^2\hbar^3}\left(\frac{1}{c_l^3} + \frac{2}{c_t^3}\right) = 9N_s \tag{19.77}$$

We now proceed as with (19.61) with one significant difference. This is that the phonons consist of mechanical oscillations which have a zero-point energy. The sum in (19.46) therefore becomes

$$Q_s = \sum_{N=0}^{\infty} e^{-(N+\frac{1}{2})\beta\varepsilon_s} = \frac{e^{-\frac{1}{2}\beta\varepsilon_s}}{1 - e^{-\beta\varepsilon_s}}$$

and the grand potential is

$$\Omega = \frac{V}{2\pi^2\hbar^3\beta}\left(\frac{1}{c_l{}^3} + \frac{2}{c_t{}^3}\right)\int_0^{\varepsilon_m} \varepsilon^2[\tfrac{1}{2}\beta\varepsilon + \ln(1 - e^{-\beta\varepsilon})]\,d\varepsilon$$

instead of (19.61). With (19.77) this is

$$\Omega = \frac{9N_s}{\varepsilon_m{}^3\beta^4}\int_0^{\beta\varepsilon_m} x^2[\tfrac{1}{2}x + \ln(1 - e^{-x})]\,dx \tag{19.78}$$

It is customary to express the energy ε_m in terms of an equivalent temperature ϑ, the *Debye temperature*, by

$$\varepsilon_m = k\vartheta \tag{19.79}$$

so that the upper limit of the integral is ϑ/T. For most materials, ϑ is in the range between 100 and 400°K. When T is also in this range, the evaluation of (19.78) has to be taken care of numerically, and for this we refer the reader to the literature.[5] Here we shall discuss only the value when T is well below ϑ, and we can replace the upper limit by infinity. The logarithm can again be integrated by parts as with (19.61), and we get

$$\Omega = N_s\left[\tfrac{9}{8}k\vartheta - \frac{\pi^4}{5\beta^4(k\vartheta)^3}\right] \tag{19.80}$$

so that the mean thermal energy is

$$\bar{E} = N_s k\vartheta\left[\tfrac{9}{8} + \tfrac{3}{5}\pi^4\left(\frac{T}{\vartheta}\right)^4\right] \tag{19.81}$$

where the first term represents the zero-point energy. The heat capacity is

$$\mathcal{C}_v = \frac{\partial\bar{E}}{\partial T} = 1\tfrac{2}{5}\pi^4 k N_s\left(\frac{T}{\vartheta}\right)^3 \quad \text{cal/deg} \tag{19.82}$$

If N_s is taken equal to Avogadro's number, we have the molar specific heat

$$c_v = 1\tfrac{2}{5}\pi^4 R\left(\frac{T}{\vartheta}\right)^3 = 464.6\left(\frac{T}{\vartheta}\right)^3 \quad \text{cal/mole deg} \tag{19.83}$$

For the detailed verification of Debye's formula and its high-temperature extension we refer the reader to the literature.[6] It fits quite well, which is remarkable in view of the crudity of the assumptions made. Chief among these is that the density of energy states is given by the simple quadratic law (19.76). This is in fact totally untrue except at the very lowest energies—the real distributions

[5] G. Joos, *Theoretical Physics*, Hafner Publishing Company, New York, 1953, 1958.

[6] See chap. 6 in C. Kittel, reference at the end of this chapter.

have at least two peaks at which the slope becomes logarithmically infinite.[7] The resulting formulas must be evaluated numerically.[8]

Vapor pressure

Even though grand potentials such as (19.31) and (19.68) depend on the value of $\hbar$, many of the results obtained from them do not, and one would perhaps conclude that the only results which depend on the quantum theory are those arising from the counting of states. Actually, however, equilibrium phenomena generally depend on the magnitudes of thermodynamic functions such as the entropy, into which $\hbar$ enters explicitly. To illustrate this, let us calculate the equilibrium vapor pressure of a monatomic solid at low temperatures. The procedure will be to consider the vapor and the solid as two subensembles in equilibrium with respect to exchange of particles and energy. This equilibrium is expressed by the equality of β and γ, that is, of μ and T. We shall calculate μ_s of the solid and μ_g of the gas and set them equal.

Let N_s be the number of atoms in the solid phase and N_g that in the vapor phase. Then by (19.19),

$$\mu_s = N_s^{-1}(\bar{E}_s - TS_s - \Omega_s)$$

Let us consider these terms one at a time. The energy of the solid will consist of two parts: the energy $\bar{E}_0$ if there were no phonons present and the energy $\bar{E}_p$ of the phonons. To find $\bar{E}_0$, we imagine that the solid is taken gently to pieces, atom by atom, without exciting any phonons. The work required to do this is the latent heat of the sample, and it is represented by λ_0 per atom in Fig. 19.4. Let u_0 be the total binding energy per atom, and e_0 be the zero-point energy contributed by phonons which tends to loosen the binding. Then

$$\lambda_0 = u_0 - e_0 \tag{19.84}$$

and

$$\bar{E}_s = -N_s u_0 + \bar{E}_p \tag{19.85}$$

The entropy of the solid is due entirely to the phonons, since by the third law, entropy vanishes at absolute zero. Finally,

$$\Omega_s = -PV_s$$

and since at the temperatures under consideration the pressure is very low, it is easy to see that this term is quite negligible. (Note however that the pressure of the phonons, almost exactly balanced by the cohesive energy of the solid, is not itself negligible.) Putting

[7] L. Van Hove, Phys. Rev., **89**, 1189 (1953).
[8] J. de Launay in Solid State Phys., **2** (1956).

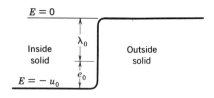

$$E = 0$$

Inside
solid

Outside
solid

$$E = -u_0$$

Fig. 19.4   Energies of atoms in a solid; λ_0 is
the latent heat per atom and e_0 is the
zero-point energy per atom.

these results together, we have

$$\mu_s = N_s^{-1}(-N_s u_0 + \bar{E}_p - TS_p)$$

Remembering that the chemical potential of phonons is zero, we find from (19.19) that

$$\mu_s = -u_0 + \frac{\Omega_p}{N_s}$$

and putting in the low-temperature approximation to Ω_p given by (19.80) gives

$$\mu_s = \tfrac{9}{8}k\vartheta - u_0 - \frac{\pi^4 k T^4}{5\vartheta^3}$$

The first term represents the mean zero-point energy e_0 per atom, so that by (19.84)

$$\mu_s = -\lambda_0 - \frac{\pi^4 k T^4}{5\vartheta^3} \tag{19.86}$$

On the other hand, (19.33) and (19.34) tell us that for the vapor,

$$\mu_g = kT \ln\left[\frac{\bar{P}}{kT}\left(\frac{2\pi\hbar^2}{mkT} \right)^{3/2} \right]$$

Setting the two chemical potentials equal and solving for $\bar{P}$ gives

$$\bar{P} = \left(\frac{m}{2\pi\hbar^2} \right)^{3/2} (kT)^{5/2} e^{-\frac{1}{5}\pi^4(T/\vartheta)^3} e^{-\lambda_0/kT} \tag{19.87}$$

In this formula the number $\hbar$ occurs explicitly; and since all the other quantities are known, it may be determined by direct measurements. Historically, this approach stems from the work of Sakur, Tetrode, and Stern in 1912 and 1913, and it was one of the first revelations of the part that Planck's constant was later to play in physics.

Problem 19.14   Clapeyron's equation, derived in thermodynamics, states that when solid and vapor are in equilibrium,

$$\frac{d\bar{P}}{dT} = \frac{\lambda}{T(V_g/N_g - V_s/N_s)}$$

Neglecting V_s (this corresponds to the earlier neglect of Ω_s), use this equation together with (19.87) to find how the latent heat varies with temperature. Interpret the resulting formula qualitatively.

Problem 19.15   Evaluate the sublimation vapor pressure at temperatures well above the Debye temperature. [The resulting formula is less accurate than (19.87) but qualitatively still correct.] A convenient approach is to expand the integrand of (19.78) in powers of x. (Why?) Retain correction terms up to the order of $(\vartheta/T)^2$. The exact integration is given by N. C. Wickramasinghe, Proc. Cambridge Phil. Soc., **59**, 255 (1963).

19.5   A Gas of Permanent Bosons

The main interest in studying the behavior of a gas of permanent bosons is in the light it throws on the behavior of He^4 at low temperatures. Since the gas liquefies at 4.2°K, and exhibits its most interesting behavior in the range below this, it is clear there is no a priori reason to expect that any understanding of its properties can be reached through the study of an ideal gas. The logical system to discuss is a system of strongly interacting particles, but this discussion is extraordinarily difficult; and the whole subject at present is one in which progress is being made with great effort. But what is surprising is that the behavior of an ideal gas seems to offer a deep insight into that of liquid helium, and to that end we shall study it in some detail.

We can analyze the ideal boson gas just like the nondegenerate gas discussed earlier in this chapter. The grand partition function per molecule is

$$\Omega = kT \sum_s \ln (1 - e^{-\beta\varepsilon_s - \gamma}) \tag{19.88}$$

and the density of states is

$$\rho(\varepsilon) = C\varepsilon^{1/2} \qquad C = \frac{(2m)^{3/2}V}{4\pi^2\hbar^3} \tag{19.89}$$

Therefore

$$\Omega = \frac{C}{\beta} \int_0^\infty \ln (1 - e^{-\beta\varepsilon - \gamma})\varepsilon^{1/2}\, d\varepsilon \tag{19.90}$$

$$\Omega = -\tfrac{2}{3}C \int_0^\infty \frac{\varepsilon^{3/2}\, d\varepsilon}{e^{\beta\varepsilon + \gamma} - 1} \tag{19.91}$$

on integration by parts. To find the mean energy per subsystem, we use (19.21) with (19.90) to get

$$\bar{E} = C \int_0^\infty \frac{\varepsilon^{3/2}\, d\varepsilon}{e^{\beta\varepsilon + \gamma} - 1} \tag{19.92}$$

so that

$$\bar{E} = \tfrac{3}{2}PV \tag{19.93}$$

by (19.26), exactly as for a nondegenerate gas. In order to get any further, we have to evaluate Ω, and we cannot do that in terms of any simple functions. The best we can do is to let $e^{-\gamma} = y$, say, in (19.92) and expand the integrand in powers of the exponential, that is, in powers of y. This gives

$$\Omega = -\tfrac{2}{3}C \sum_1^\infty y^n \int_0^\infty \varepsilon^{3/2} e^{-n\beta\varepsilon}\, d\varepsilon$$

$$= -\tfrac{2}{3}C\Gamma(\tfrac{5}{2})\beta^{-5/2} \sum_1^\infty \frac{y^n}{n^{5/2}}$$

$$= -kT \frac{V}{\lambda^3} F_{5/2}(y) \qquad y = e^{-\gamma} \tag{19.94}$$

where we have introduced the thermal de Broglie wavelength by writing C as

$$C = \frac{2V}{\pi^{1/2}\lambda^3(kT)^{3/2}} \qquad \lambda = \left(\frac{2\pi\hbar^2}{mkT}\right)^{1/2} \tag{19.95}$$

Also, $\Gamma(\tfrac{5}{2})$ has been evaluated from $\Gamma(n+1) = n\Gamma(n)$ and $\Gamma(\tfrac{1}{2}) = \pi^{1/2}$, and we have written $F_k(y)$ for the series

$$F_k(y) = \sum_{n=1}^\infty \frac{y^n}{n^k} \tag{19.96}$$

The parameter y has been encountered before. By (19.43) it is equal to $(\lambda/d)^3$ for a gas under ordinary conditions and is therefore very close to zero. On the other hand, we noted in summing (19.46) that γ must be >0, so that we have

$$0 \leqslant y < 1 \tag{19.97}$$

The limiting values of $F_{5/2}(y)$ are

$$F_{5/2}(0) = 0 \qquad F_{5/2}(1) = \zeta(\tfrac{5}{2}) = 1.341$$

the latter from Table 19.2. When y is very small, a few terms of (19.96) suffice; whereas if it is near 1, the following approximate series has been given by Opechowski:[9]

$$F_{5/2}(y) = 2.36\left(\ln\frac{1}{y}\right)^{3/2} + 1.34 - 2.61\ln\frac{1}{y} - 0.73\left(\ln\frac{1}{y}\right)^2$$
$$+ \cdots$$

$$= 2.36\gamma^{3/2} + 1.34 - 2.61\gamma - 0.73\gamma^2 + \cdots$$

The first two terms of (19.96) lead to the expression (19.56) for Ω.

[9] W. Opechowski, Physica, **4**, 722 (1937).

Bose-Einstein condensation

To continue, we must find the relation between y and the number of particles, and it is here that the principal interest of the subject lies. We find from (19.20)

$$\bar{N} = \frac{V}{\lambda^3} F_{3/2}(y) \tag{19.98}$$

Let us look at the range of values possible for $\bar{N}$. We have

$$0 \leqslant y < 1$$
$$0 \leqslant \bar{N} < 2.612 V \lambda^{-3}$$

or

$$0 \leqslant \frac{\bar{N}}{V} < 2.612 \left(\frac{mkT}{2\pi\hbar^2} \right)^{3/2} \tag{19.99}$$

where we have taken $F_{3/2}(1)$ from Table 19.2.

Problem 19.16   Derive (19.98).

The right-hand side of (19.99) says that $T > T_0$, where

$$T_0 = \frac{2\pi\hbar^2}{mk} \left(\frac{\bar{N}}{2.612 V} \right)^{2/3} \tag{19.100}$$

If we have one mole of gas, so that $\bar{N}$ is Avogadro's number, this is

$$T_0 = \frac{115}{MV^{2/3}} \quad °\mathrm{K} \tag{19.101}$$

where M is the molecular weight and V is the volume per mole in cubic centimeters. Now suppose we start with a gas whose temperature is T_0 and cool it down without changing $\bar{N}$ or V. It is clear that this is possible physically; we have therefore made a mathematical error somewhere. It turns out that the error is in replacing the sum by an integral in (19.88) and that we can correct it by taking into account the ground state, which we shall take to be at zero energy and which does not contribute at all to integrals like (19.91) because of the factor $\varepsilon^{3/2}$ which vanishes there. We therefore write the first term in (19.88) explicitly and sum the rest by integration,

$$\Omega = kT \left[\ln (1 - e^{-\gamma}) + C \int_0^\infty \ln (1 - e^{-\beta\varepsilon - \gamma}) \varepsilon^{1/2} \, d\varepsilon \right]$$
$$= kT \left[\ln (1 - y) - \frac{V}{\lambda^3} F_{5/2}(y) \right] \tag{19.102}$$

We then have

$$\bar{N} = \bar{N}_0 + \bar{N}' \tag{19.103}$$

with

$$\bar{N}_0 = \frac{y}{1 - y} \qquad \bar{N}' = \frac{V}{\lambda^3} F_{3/2}(y) \tag{19.104}$$

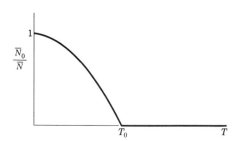

Fig. 19.5   Fractional occupation of the lowest
quantum state of an ideal Bose gas at
temperatures below T_0.

Clearly, $\bar{N}_0$ is the average number of particles in the lowest state and $\bar{N}'$ refers to all the rest. Let us now see what happens as we cool the gas down. Initially, $y \approx (\lambda/d)^3$ and is very small. As T decreases towards T_0, λ increases until y arrives very close to its limiting value of 1. Even when $y = 0.999$, $\bar{N}_0$ is only 999, which is negligible compared with the number of particles in a macroscopic sample of gas. When y is very close to 1, $\bar{N}'$ is close to its limiting value of $2.612V\lambda^{-3}$. Further, at T_0, $\bar{N}' = \bar{N}$, so that

$$\frac{\bar{N}'}{\bar{N}} = \frac{\lambda^{-3}}{\lambda_0{}^{-3}} = \left(\frac{T}{T_0}\right)^{3/2}$$

and

$$\frac{\bar{N}_0}{\bar{N}} = 1 - \left(\frac{T}{T_0}\right)^{3/2} \qquad (T < T_0)$$

The behavior of $\bar{N}_0$ as a function of T is shown in Fig. 19.5.

The foregoing results are obtained by a rather casual taking of limits, but they are very nearly correct. (An exact discussion is quite elaborate.) We can now use them to write down an amended formula for Ω. Above the transition temperature T, we have from (19.56) and (19.100)

$$\Omega = -\bar{N}kT\left[1 - 0.462\left(\frac{T_0}{T}\right)^{3/2} + \cdots\right] \qquad (T > T_0) \qquad (19.105)$$

and when $T < T_0$,

$$\Omega = kT\left[\ln\left(1 - y\right) - \frac{1.341V}{\lambda^3}\right]$$

$$= -kT\left[\ln\left(1 + \bar{N}_0\right) + \frac{1.341}{2.612}\bar{N}\left(\frac{T}{T_0}\right)^{3/2}\right]$$

The first term in the brackets is much smaller than the second, being at most of the order of 50 when the second is of the order of 10^{23}. And as well as being negligible it is also obviously wrong, since Ω is an extensive quantity that increases linearly with the number of particles. It comes from the improper use of limits above, and we omit it:

$$\Omega = - \frac{0.513\bar{N}kT^{5/2}}{T_0^{3/2}} \quad (T < T_0) \tag{19.106}$$

From these we have the equations of state

$$\bar{P}V = \bar{N}kT \left[1 - 0.462 \left(\frac{T_0}{T}\right)^{3/2} + \cdots \right] \quad (T > T_0) \tag{19.107}$$

and

$$\bar{P}V = \frac{0.513\bar{N}kT^{5/2}}{T_0^{3/2}} \quad (T < T_0) \tag{19.108}$$

If (19.100) is substituted into this, we get

$$\bar{P} = 1.341 \left(\frac{m}{2\pi\hbar^2}\right)^{3/2} (kT)^{5/2} \quad (T < T_0) \tag{19.109}$$

independent of the volume. This behavior, illustrated in Fig. 19.6, is reminiscent of the condensation of an imperfect gas; it is called *Bose-Einstein condensation*. The similarities as well as the differences are most interesting. The imperfect gas condenses into a small volume because of attractive forces between its molecules which do not exist in the case we have been discussing. Here we have, rather, a condensation into a single quantum state, that having the lowest energy, and this, of course, has no classical analogue. Suppose, however, that some force is present, say a downward gravitational force. The atoms with the lowest energy will then be found at the bottom of the container, and except for the fact that they have no size and hence cannot flow around like a liquid, they will very much resemble an ordinary condensed vapor.

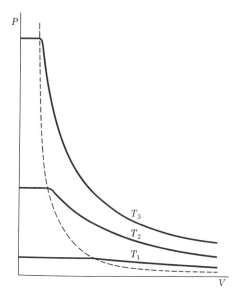

Fig. 19.6   Pressure-volume relation for ideal Bose gas showing the Bose-Einstein condensation. T_1, T_2, and T_3 are successively higher temperatures. The dashed transition curve is of the form $PV^{5/3} = \text{const}$

To find the energy of the gas, we have from (19.93)

$$\bar{E} = \tfrac{3}{2}\bar{N}kT\left[1 - 0.462\left(\frac{T_0}{T}\right)^{\frac{3}{2}} + \cdots\right] \qquad (T > T_0) \qquad (19.110)$$

and

$$\bar{E} = \frac{0.770\bar{N}kT^{\frac{5}{2}}}{T_0{}^{\frac{3}{2}}} \qquad (T < T_0) \qquad (19.111)$$

The molar specific heats have $\bar{N}$ equal to Avogadro's number,

$$c_v = \frac{\partial \bar{E}}{\partial T} = \tfrac{3}{2}R\left[1 + 0.231\left(\frac{T_0}{T}\right)^{\frac{3}{2}} + \cdots\right] \qquad (T > T_0) \qquad (19.112)$$

and

$$c_v = 1.925R\left(\frac{T}{T_0}\right)^{\frac{3}{2}} \qquad (T < T_0) \qquad (19.113)$$

The behavior of c_v just above T_0 needs a more exact discussion, but it turns out that there is a cusp at T_0, as shown in Fig. 19.7.

The foregoing phenomena were first described by Einstein in 1924 as consequences of the method of counting the states of indistinguishable particles which had recently (and prior to quantum mechanics) been proposed by the Indian physicist S. N. Bose. They would have remained a minor statistical curiosity if it were not for their relevance to the problem of explaining the anomalous behavior of helium at low temperatures.

Problem 19.17   It is reasonable to suspect that not only the lowest state but also the next-lowest and a few states above that may participate in the Bose-Einstein condensation. By considering the next-lowest (degenerate) state of a gas in a cubical box, show that the population of this state is of the order of $\bar{N}^{-\frac{1}{3}}\bar{N}_0$ and may therefore be neglected.

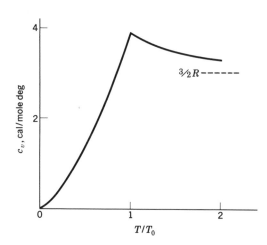

Fig. 19.7   The specific heat of an ideal Bose gas. The dashed line gives the Maxwell-Boltzmann value.

19.6   Liquid Helium

The behavior of helium at low temperatures seems to be unique in nature in several respects. First, it is the only substance which does not freeze at ordinary pressures. It is easy to understand why this is so. An atom confined to a region of size Δx has a momentum at least of the order of $\hbar/\Delta x$ and a kinetic energy at least $\hbar^2/2m(\Delta x)^2$. The Van der Waals attraction between two helium atoms, even at the optimum separation of about 3 Å, is only about 10^{-16} ergs, and for binding to occur, the zero-point kinetic energy would have to be less than this. But that would require $\Delta x > 8$ Å, much greater than the range of the attractive force, and so there is no binding. This peculiarity of helium is therefore due at once to its weak binding and its low mass. But a still more remarkable peculiarity is found if one measures the specific heat at low temperatures. At 4.2°K the isotope He^4 condenses into a liquid, and at 2.18° the specific heat becomes infinite, indicating that a change of state is taking place. There is no latent heat, so the phase transition is of the second kind. From the appearance of the specific-heat curve (and also that of the density), the temperature at which the transition occurs is called the *lambda point*. Down to about 0.6° the specific heat decreases about as T^6; below this point it is given quite accurately by the formula

$$C = (0.0204 \pm 0.0004)T^3 \qquad \text{J/g deg} \tag{19.114}$$

The isotope He^3 shows no such anomaly. Figure 19.8 shows a phase diagram of He^4 and distinguishes the two phases of the liquid by the terms He I and He II.

The behavior of He II is thoroughly anomalous.[10] The viscosity depends on how it is measured, but is fantastically small, and the heat conductivity is some 3×10^6 that of He I. In 1938, F. London[11] called attention to Einstein's calculations on the ideal Bose gas and pointed out that if in (19.101) we put the values $M = 4$ and $V = 27.6$ cm³ per mole, we get $T_0 = 3.14°$, which is remarkably close to the lambda temperature. The resemblance between the specific-heat curves then becomes much more remarkable than the difference, inasmuch as one ordinarily expects the behavior of matter at low temperature to be controlled by the intermolecular forces. And if He^3, with substantially the same forces, shows no such transition, this is almost certainly because it does not obey Bose-Einstein statistics.

[10] K. Mendelssohn, in *Encyclopedia of Physics*, Springer-Verlag OHG, Berlin, 1956, vol. 15, p. 570; *Cryophysics*, Interscience Publishers, Inc., New York, 1961. An excellent introductory survey of the field is given by Simon, Kurti, Allen, and Mendelssohn, *Low Temperature Physics*, Academic Press Inc., New York, 1952.

[11] F. London, Phys. Rev., **54**, 947 (1938).

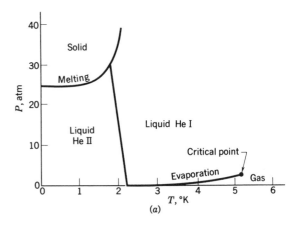

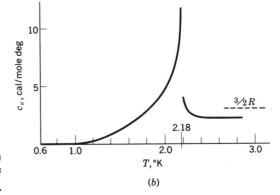

Fig. 19.8 Properties of He⁴. (a) Phase diagram. (b) Specific heat of liquid He⁴.

Below 2.18°, then, there is expected to be an increasing number of He atoms which are in some sense in the lowest energy state available to them and which therefore contribute nothing to the specific heat or the entropy. But it does not really mean very much to talk of the energy of an atom which is in close interaction with others as though the energy were a constant. The empirical dependence on T^3 in (19.114) suggests that we should consider that the thermal excitation below 0.6° is in the form of phonons and that Debye's theory may explain the specific heat. There are no transverse waves in a liquid, so that with $\varepsilon_m = k\vartheta$ we have from (19.77)

$$(k\vartheta)^3 = 18\pi^2\hbar^3 c^3 N V^{-1}$$

where c is the speed of sound in the liquid, N is the number of helium atoms, and V is the volume. Putting this into (19.82) gives

$$\mathcal{C}_v = \frac{2\pi^2 k^4}{15\hbar^3 c^3} V T^3 \qquad \text{J/deg}$$

whence the specific heat is

$$C_v = \frac{2\pi^2 k^4}{15\hbar^3 c^3 \rho} \, T^3 \qquad \text{J/g deg}$$

where ρ is the mass density. The value of c at zero degrees, extrapolated from low-temperature measurements, is 238.3 ± 0.1 m/sec, and $\rho = 0.124$ g/cm³. We find

$$C_v = 0.0206 T^3 \text{ J/g deg}$$

which agrees with (19.114). (The experimental value was not obtained at constant volume, but the difference is negligible.) The phonons should also have long mean free paths at low temperatures where they are rare, and this explains qualitatively why the heat conductivity is so great—the energy moves freely and at great speed in the form of phonons.

Above 0.6°, the situation becomes more complicated. Clearly, a liquid has many modes of motion which are not simple compressional waves, and the quanta corresponding to some of them, called *rotons*, begin to play a part and increase the specific heat. From here on, the theory is essentially that of the collective oscillations of an assembly of interacting bosons. It has received much attention in recent years and a number of results have been obtained, though few that can be applied directly to liquid helium. The interested reader will find an illuminating intuitive discussion of some of these points in two articles by Feynman.[12]

Problem 19.18   Calculate the vapor pressure of He⁴ at low temperatures. Take the latent heat at 0° as 59.50 J/mole. Experimental data to check your calculation:[13]

T, °K	0.5	1.0	1.5	2.0
P, mm Hg	1.6×10^{-5}	0.120	3.60	23.77

Discuss the adequacy of the Debye approximation in the region for which data are given.

19.7   A Gas of Fermions

An assembly of particles which obey the exclusion principle behaves altogether differently from a boson gas at low temperatures because the particles cannot lose their energy even at absolute zero. We have already investigated it at moderate temperatures and found behavior qualitatively similar to that predicted by classical physics. We shall now examine three more cases: absolute zero, a temperature

[12] R. P. Feynman, Progr. Low Temp. Phys. (North-Holland Publishing Company, Amsterdam), **1**, 17 (1955); Rev. Mod. Phys., **29**, 205 (1957).
[13] H. van Dijk and M. Durieux, Progr. Low Temp. Phys. (North-Holland Publishing Co., Amsterdam), **2**, 431 (1957).

T_F which corresponds in some ways with the boson critical temperature, and the region between these two. That above T_F is what is meant by "moderate temperatures."

Absolute zero

It will be most convenient to abandon the parameter γ in favor of the chemical potential μ, since μ approaches the finite value μ_0 at absolute zero whereas γ becomes negatively infinite. The mean number of particles in state s is thus given by

$$\bar{N}_s = \frac{1}{e^{\beta(\varepsilon_s - \mu)} + 1}$$

and as $T \to 0$, $\beta \to \infty$, and $\mu \to \mu_0$, we see that

$$\bar{N}_s \to \begin{cases} 1 & (\varepsilon_s < \mu_0) \\ 0 & (\varepsilon_s > \mu_0) \end{cases}$$

This is clearly the limiting behavior of the distributions of Fig. 19.9. The value of μ_0 is thus the top of the energy distribution at zero degrees, and it is commonly referred to as the *Fermi energy* E_F of the distribution. At higher temperatures the top becomes somewhat smeared out, but we shall still often call $\mu(T)$ the Fermi energy. The reason for calling it an energy is obvious from Fig. 19.9, and the importance of the idea stems from the fact that if two different materials at the same temperature are allowed to exchange electrons, they will do so until their μ's become equal, and it is convenient to think of this as an alignment of their Fermi energies. It will be seen in the next section that for electrons in metals, $\mu_0 \approx 5$ eV.

For material particles, the density of states is of the form (19.89), except that spin degeneracy increases it by a factor of $2s + 1$, the number of distinct spin states corresponding to a given

Fig. 19.9 Average occupation of quantum state s as a function of the energy ε_s. T_1, T_2, and T_3 are successively higher temperatures.

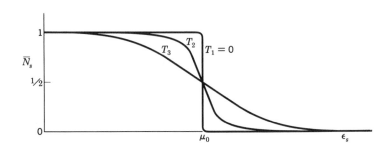

translational state. Anticipating that our principal interest will be in particles with spin $\frac{1}{2}$, we have

$$\rho(\varepsilon) = 2C\varepsilon^{\frac{1}{2}} \qquad C = \frac{(2m)^{\frac{3}{2}}V}{4\pi^2\hbar^3} \tag{19.115}$$

The total number of particles is

$$\bar{N} = \int_0^{\mu_0} \rho(\varepsilon)\,d\varepsilon = \frac{4}{3}C\mu_0^{\frac{3}{2}} \tag{19.116}$$

and the total energy is

$$\bar{E} = \int_0^{\mu_0} \varepsilon\rho(\varepsilon)\,d\varepsilon = \frac{4}{5}C\mu_0^{\frac{5}{2}}$$

The first of these gives

$$\mu_0 = \left(\frac{\frac{3}{4}\bar{N}}{C}\right)^{\frac{2}{3}} = \frac{\hbar^2}{2m}\left(\frac{3\pi^2\bar{N}}{V}\right)^{\frac{2}{3}} \tag{19.117}$$

while the second is

$$\bar{E} = \frac{3}{5}\bar{N}\mu_0 \tag{19.118}$$

The mean energy per particle is three-fifths the Fermi energy. For electrons in metals this is 2 to 5 eV, some hundred times kT at room temperatures.

The degeneracy temperature

The principal new feature of (19.117) is that we have found a positive value of μ at $T = 0$. This is to be contrasted with (19.55), which in terms of μ is

$$e^{\beta\mu} = \left(\frac{\lambda}{d}\right)^3\left[1 + 2^{\frac{3}{2}}\left(\frac{\lambda}{d}\right)^3\right] \tag{19.119}$$

which is $\ll 1$ for ordinary gases, so that μ is large and negative. We shall define as the *degeneracy temperature* T_F the temperature at which μ passes through zero; this is analogous to the temperature, called T_0, at which μ becomes effectively zero for a boson gas. To find T_F, we have

$$\bar{N} = 2C\int_0^\infty \frac{\varepsilon^{\frac{1}{2}}\,d\varepsilon}{e^{\beta\varepsilon} + 1} = 1.356C\beta^{-\frac{3}{2}}$$

so that

$$kT_F = \left(\frac{\bar{N}}{1.356C}\right)^{\frac{2}{3}} = 0.459\mu_0 = 1.42T_0$$

on comparison with (19.117) and (19.100). For temperatures below this, we can say that the gas exhibits low-temperature behavior, and from this standpoint even the electrons in white-hot metal are "cold."

Low temperatures

For temperatures well below T_F, we can proceed as usual by evaluating the grand partition function. From (19.51) it is

$$\Omega = -\frac{2C}{\beta} \int_0^\infty \ln\left(1 + e^{-\beta(\varepsilon-\mu)}\right)\varepsilon^{\frac{1}{2}} \, d\varepsilon \tag{19.120}$$

$$\Omega = -\frac{2}{3}C \int_0^\infty \frac{\varepsilon^{\frac{3}{2}} \, d\varepsilon}{e^{\beta(\varepsilon-\mu)} + 1} \tag{19.121}$$

and just as for bosons, we find that (at all temperatures)

$$\bar{E} = -\frac{3}{2}\Omega = \frac{3}{2}PV \tag{19.122}$$

To evaluate integrals like (19.121) requires a little ingenuity. Suppose we have to calculate

$$G_n = \int_0^\infty \frac{\varepsilon^n \, d\varepsilon}{e^{\beta(\varepsilon-\mu)} + 1}$$

We let $\varepsilon - \mu = x$ and write

$$G_n = \int_{-\mu}^0 \frac{(\mu + x)^n}{e^{\beta x} + 1} \, dx + \int_0^\infty \frac{(\mu + x)^n}{e^{\beta x} + 1} \, dx$$

Write the first of these as

$$\int_{-\mu}^0 (\mu + x)^n \left[\frac{1}{e^{\beta x} + 1} - 1\right] dx + \int_{-\mu}^0 (\mu + x)^n \, dx$$

The point of doing so is that, as $x \to -\mu$, the term in square brackets vanishes rapidly and we can replace the lower limit by $-\infty$. Thus

$$G_n \approx -\int_{-\infty}^0 \frac{(\mu + x)^n}{e^{-\beta x} + 1} \, dx + \frac{\mu^{n+1}}{n + 1} + \int_0^\infty \frac{(\mu + x)^n}{e^{\beta x} + 1} \, dx$$

Now change the sign of x in the first integral.

$$G_n \approx \frac{\mu^{n+1}}{n + 1} + \int_0^\infty \frac{(\mu + x)^n - (\mu - x)^n}{e^{\beta x} + 1} \, dx \tag{19.123}$$

Expanding the terms $(\mu + x)^n$ by the binomial theorem leads to a series of integrals of the form of J_k in (19.66) which can readily be written down by using Table 19.2. With $n = \frac{3}{2}$, for example, we find

$$G_{\frac{3}{2}} \approx \frac{2}{5}\mu^{\frac{5}{2}} \left[1 + \frac{5}{8}\pi^2(\beta\mu)^{-2} - \frac{7}{384}\pi^4(\beta\mu)^{-4} + \cdots\right]$$

and the grand partition function is

$$\Omega = -\frac{8}{15}C\mu^{\frac{5}{2}} \left[1 + \frac{5}{8}\pi^2\left(\frac{kT}{\mu}\right)^2 - \cdots\right] \tag{19.124}$$

The first two terms will suffice for our purposes.

Problem 19.19 Find the relation between PV and $\bar{N}kT$ for a perfect gas of fermions when $T = T_F$.

Problem 19.20 The density of liquid He³ at low temperatures is about 0.08 g/cm³. What is the relation between PV and $\bar{N}kT$ for a perfect gas of this density at temperatures near absolute zero?

Problem 19.21 What formula corresponds to (19.123) when no approximations are made? Estimate the error in (19.123) when $\mu = 50kT$.

To find the relation between μ and T, we find $\bar{N}$ from Ω,

$$\bar{N} = -\left(\frac{\partial\Omega}{\partial\mu}\right)_{T,V} = \tfrac{2}{3}C\mu^{3\!/\!2}\left[1 + \tfrac{1}{8}\pi^2\left(\frac{kT}{\mu}\right)^2 + \cdots\right]$$

and comparison with (19.116) gives

$$\mu_0^{3\!/\!2} = \mu^{3\!/\!2}\left[1 + \tfrac{1}{8}\pi^2\left(\frac{kT}{\mu}\right)^2 + \cdots\right]$$

If the second term is a small correction, we can replace μ by μ_0 in it and solve for μ, getting

$$\mu^{3\!/\!2} = \mu_0^{3\!/\!2}\left[1 - \tfrac{1}{8}\pi^2\left(\frac{kT}{\mu_0}\right)^2 + \cdots\right]$$

$$\mu = \mu_0\left[1 - \tfrac{1}{12}\pi^2\left(\frac{kT}{\mu_0}\right)^2 + \cdots\right] \tag{19.125}$$

The variation of μ with temperature for ideal Bose and Fermi gases is shown in Fig. 19.10.

The mean energy per particle is given by (19.122) and (19.124) as

$$\bar{E} = \tfrac{2}{5}C\mu^{5\!/\!2}\left[1 + \tfrac{5}{8}\pi^2\left(\frac{kT}{\mu}\right)^2 + \cdots\right]$$

and putting in μ from (19.125) gives

$$\bar{E} = \tfrac{3}{5}\bar{N}\mu_0\left[1 + \tfrac{5}{12}\pi^2\left(\frac{kT}{\mu_0}\right)^2 + \cdots\right] \tag{19.126}$$

The fact that the total energy depends only slightly on the temperature is striking, but it can easily be understood from Fig. 19.9. The heat capacity is

$$\mathcal{C}_v = \tfrac{1}{2}\pi^2\bar{N}\frac{k^2T}{\mu_0} = \tfrac{1}{3}\pi^2\frac{kT}{\mu_0}\left(\frac{3}{2}\bar{N}k\right) \tag{19.127}$$

and since in the region of greatest interest $kT \ll \mu_0$, we see that $\mathcal{C}_v$ is far below its classical value of $\tfrac{3}{2}\bar{N}k$. This is a consequence of the particles' relative lack of freedom—the addition of heat can affect only the particles with energies close to μ_0. In fact, if the fraction of particles affected is of the order of kT/μ_0 (see Prob. 19.23) and their average excitation energy is of the order of kT per particle,

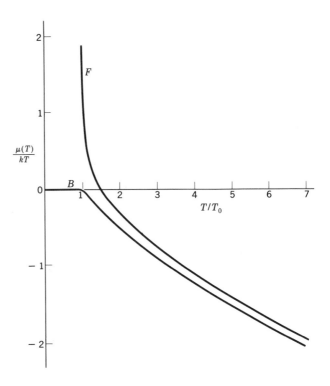

Fig. 19.10 Variation of μ/kT with temperature for ideal Bose and Fermi gases having equal densities of atoms of the same mass.

then the total excitation energy is about $\bar{N}(kT)^2/\mu_0$ and the specific heat is about $2\bar{N}k^2T/\mu_0$, which is essentially the value found above.

We have seen that the low-temperature specific heat of liquid He⁴ can be understood in terms of phonons. The behavior of the isotope He³ is quite different; for not only is this isotope a gas of fermions, but the nuclei also have a magnetic interaction which, though feeble, influences the low-temperature properties. He³ is a liquid below its critical point at about 3.3°K and 10 mm Hg, and at the lowest temperatures its specific heat is linear in T (Fig. 19.11). This overshadows any possible phonon contribution in T^3, and it can be understood from (19.127) as a consequence of the exclusion principle. The effect of the interaction between atoms is to give them an effective mass m^* different from the real one. Taking the value of μ_0 from (19.117) and replacing m by m^*, we find

$$\mathcal{C}_v = \frac{\bar{N}m^*k^2T}{\hbar^2}\left(\frac{\pi V}{3\bar{N}}\right)^{\!2/3}$$

from which m^* may be evaluated. The experimental values are in the neighborhood of $2m$.

Problem 19.22   Taking the density of liquid He³ at 14 mm Hg as 0.0822 g/cm³, calculate the value of m^*/m from Fig. 19.11.

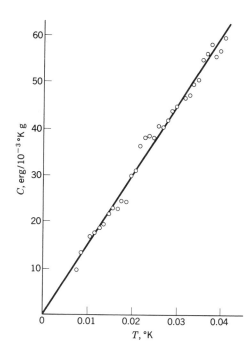

Fig. 19.11   Low-temperature specific heat
of He³. [From *Anderson, Salinger, Stegert,
and Wheatley, Phys. Rev. Letters, 6, 331*
(1961). Reprinted by permission.]

Problem 19.23   Show how one can estimate the number of
electrons in a degenerate Fermi-Dirac distribution at temperature T
which are free to make transitions up and down if a little heat is
added to or subtracted from the system.

Problem 19.24   Find approximate equations of state for a perfect Fermi gas with $T > T_F$ and $T < T_F$, giving PV in terms of
μ_0 and T. Figure 19.12 shows the general character of the equations
of state for bosons and fermions.

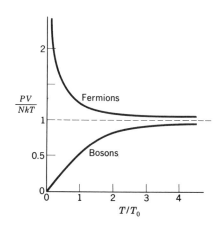

Fig. 19.12   Equations of state for perfect
Bose and Fermi gases.

19.8   Electrons in a Metal

A simplified but convenient way of looking at a metal is to suppose that the valence electrons move freely among the ions in the manner of a perfect Fermi gas, their mutual repulsions being effectively screened by the ionic charge. This picture ignores the band structure of electronic energies, and it is certainly incorrect in ignoring the electrons' mutual interactions, but it is nevertheless very useful in understanding orders of magnitude.

The Fermi level

To find μ_0, we consider 1 mole of substance having z free valence electrons per atom. Then (19.117) gives

$$
\begin{aligned}
\mu_0 &= \frac{\hbar^2}{2m}\left(\frac{3\pi N_0 z}{V_0}\right)^{\frac{2}{3}} \\
&= 4.16 \times 10^{-7}\left(\frac{z}{V_0}\right)^{\frac{2}{3}} \text{ J/electron} \\
&= 26.0\left(\frac{z}{V_0}\right)^{\frac{2}{3}} \text{ eV/electron}
\end{aligned}
$$

where V_0 is the molar volume of the metal, in most cases about 10 cm³. The value of z is found to be only approximately equal to the valence. For the alkali metals it is about 1; in other cases it is difficult to estimate.

Specific heat

Including the contributions from lattice and electrons, the specific heat of a metal at low temperatures should be in the form

$$
c_v = \alpha T^3 + \gamma T
$$

where α and γ are factors whose theoretical values are derived above. One way to check this dependence is to write

$$
\frac{c_v}{T} = \alpha T^2 + \gamma
$$

so that a plot of c_v/T against T^2 should give a straight line. Figure 19.13 shows such a plot for Sr in which, as in many other cases, the prediction is borne out.

Problem 19.25   Find the constants α and γ for Sr from Fig. 19.13 and compare them with the rough theory. Use $\vartheta_D = 144°K$.

Problem 19.26   What is the pressure, in atmospheres, exerted by the electrons in a sample of Na at 0° and at room temperature? Why do the electrons not fly off into space?

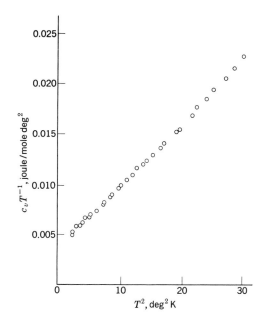

Fig. 19.13   Low-temperature specific heat
of strontium plotted to exhibit
contributions from electrons and from
lattice. [From *L. M. Roberts, Proc. Phys. Soc.
(London) 70B, 738 (1957).* Reprinted
by permission.]

Thermionic emission

To calculate the rate at which electrons are emitted from a hot
metal surface, let us first consider a stationary situation in which the
metal evaporates electrons into a closed region. Inside the metal
the Fermi level of the electrons is $\mu(T)$. Outside, we assume that
the electrons are scarce enough to form a nondegenerate gas whose
distribution among its energy states is given closely by the Boltzmann formula (19.54). Figure 19.14 shows the energies involved.
Owing to the attraction between electrons and ions, it takes a certain
amount of work ε_0 to remove an electron from the lattice, some of
which will be supplied by its kinetic energy in the lattice. With the
zero of energy as shown, however, the energy of the free electrons
will start at ε_0, and the number of free electrons in the state whose
kinetic energy is ε_s is

$$\bar{N}_s = e^{-\beta(\varepsilon_0 + \varepsilon_s - \mu)}$$

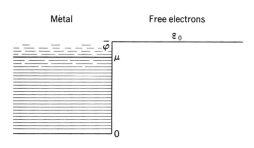

Fig. 19.14   Energies of electrons in a metal.

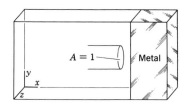

Fig. 19.15 For calculating the rate
of thermionic emission.

Introducing the *work function* φ, the energy necessary to remove an electron from the Fermi level, we have

$$\bar{N}_s = e^{-\beta\varphi}e^{-\beta\varepsilon_s}$$

To calculate the emission current per unit area s we consider the equilibrium between free electrons and metal in more detail (Fig. 19.15). Let A be a unit area just to the left of the metal surface. At equilibrium, we suppose that s, the current flowing out of the metal through A, is equal to that flowing in. The latter, however, is easy to calculate. We have several times written down the number of states in a certain energy range. Wishing now to distinguish between directions, we pause to derive the basic formula for the number of states in a certain range of momenta. In the three-dimensional analogue of Fig. 9.8 there is one state per unit volume of n space, so that (for small but finite dn's) the number of states in a cell of volume $dn_x\,dn_y\,dn_z$ is just equal to the volume, $dN = dn_x\,dn_y\,dn_z$. Using (9.24), we write this as

$$dN = \left(\frac{L}{2\pi\hbar}\right)^3 dp_x\,dp_y\,dp_z = \frac{V}{(2\pi\hbar)^3}\,dp_x\,dp_y\,dp_z$$

so that the density of states in p space is constant. Including a factor of 2 for the electron spin, we have

$$d\bar{N}_e = \frac{2V}{(2\pi\hbar)^3}\,e^{-\beta\varphi}e^{-\beta p^2/2m}\,dp_x\,dp_y\,dp_z$$

If the particle density is $n_e = \bar{N}_e/V$, the mean current density toward the right is

$$s = \overline{en_ev_x} = \frac{e}{m}\,\overline{n_ep_x}$$

averaged over all states of motion. Since only the electrons with $p_x > 0$ pass through and enter the metal, we have

$$s = \frac{e}{m}\frac{2}{(2\pi\hbar)^3}\,e^{-\beta\varphi}\int_0^\infty p_x\,dp_x\iint_{-\infty}^\infty dp_y\,dp_z\,e^{-\beta p^2/2m}$$

$$s = e\,\frac{m(kT)^2}{2\pi^2\hbar^3}\,e^{-\varphi/kT}\qquad \text{A/m}^2 \tag{19.128}$$

This formula is usually written as

$$s = A\,T^2 e^{-\varphi/kT} \tag{19.129}$$

where A, calculated from (19.128), is

$$A = 1.20 \times 10^6 \text{ A/m}^2 \tag{19.130}$$

It was originally given by Dushman, and since it resembles in form an earlier expression derived from classical statistics by Richardson, it is often called the Richardson-Dushman law. In practice, the general form of (19.129) is verified by experiment, but observed values of A are often much smaller than (19.130).[14] This is probably because the ideal situation of a flat metal surface at uniform temperature is not realized and surface films and irregularities play a dominant part.

Problem 19.27   Calculate the rate of evaporation of a monatomic solid at temperatures well below the Debye temperature. At what rate are atoms lost from 1 cm² of surface of a piece of clean iron in a vacuum at 300°K? At 800°K? The Debye temperature is 467° and the heat of sublimation is 4.10 eV/atom.

Spin paramagnetism

If the energy of the electrons in a metal depends upon their spins, it is convenient to break the grand canonical ensemble into two subensembles, in equilibrium with each other, corresponding to the two different spin states. Suppose, for example, that a field B is present. Then the electrons will have potential energies $\mp M_B B$ according as they are oriented parallel or antiparallel to the field, where M_B is the Bohr magneton. The number of electrons with kinetic energy in state s and spin parallel to B is

$$N_s^{(+)} = \frac{1}{e^{\beta(\varepsilon_s - M_B B - \mu)} + 1}$$

and similarly for $N_s^{(-)}$, so that the total moment per unit volume of an assembly of electrons is

$$I = \frac{M_B}{V} \sum_s \left[\frac{1}{e^{\beta(\varepsilon_s - M_B B - \mu)} + 1} - \frac{1}{e^{\beta(\varepsilon_s + M_B B - \mu)} + 1} \right]$$

If B is small, this is approximately

$$I = -\frac{2M_B^2 B}{V} \sum_s \frac{\partial}{\partial \varepsilon_s} \frac{1}{e^{\beta(\varepsilon_s - \mu)} + 1}$$

and replacing the sum by an integral in the usual way gives

$$I = -\frac{2M_B^2 B}{V} C \int_0^\infty \varepsilon^{1/2} \frac{\partial}{\partial \varepsilon} \frac{1}{e^{\beta(\varepsilon - \mu)} + 1} d\varepsilon$$

$$= \frac{M_B^2 B}{V} C \int_0^\infty \frac{\varepsilon^{-1/2} d\varepsilon}{e^{\beta(\varepsilon - \mu)} + 1}$$

[14] C. Herring and M. H. Nichols, Rev. Mod. Phys., **21**, 185 (1949).

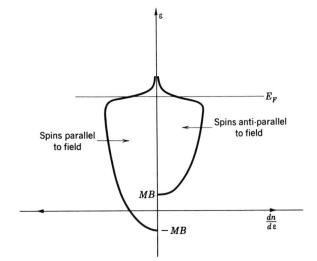

Fig. 19.16 To explain electron spin paramagnetism. The electrons' total energy is ε, and $dn/d\varepsilon = C\varepsilon^{\frac{1}{2}}f(\varepsilon)$ is the number of states per unit energy range. The two groups of spins have the same Fermi level, but the energies of corresponding states are shifted by the field so that the populations differ.

Using the first term of (19.123) gives an estimate valid at low temperatures,

$$I = \frac{2M_B{}^2B}{V}C\mu_0{}^{\frac{1}{2}} = \frac{3}{2}\frac{\bar{N}}{V}\frac{M_B{}^2B}{\mu_0}$$

by (19.117), so that the paramagnetic susceptibility is

$$\chi = \frac{\bar{N}}{V}\frac{3M_B{}^2}{2\mu_0} \tag{19.131}$$

This result, first derived by Pauli in 1927, is explained qualitatively by Fig. 19.16. It is applicable to the alkali metals, but only after a number of corrections have been made.[15]

Problem 19.28 Find, to a first approximation, how χ depends on B and on T.

Concluding remarks

Throughout this discussion we have skirted around the main technical problem of statistical mechanics, which is the introduction of the forces between the particles. This did not entirely prevent us from treating interacting systems, for their collective motions can to some extent be treated as phonons, but looking at the matter more carefully one finds that the phonons themselves interact.

The most natural approach to an exact calculation is to introduce the interactions as a perturbation, but if this is done, it is found that the perturbation theory as we have developed it often fails, for the individual terms do not approach a finite limit as the size of

---

[15] C. Kittel (see References at end of this chapter), p. 261; R. H. Fowler (see References at end of this chapter), p. 473.

the system is made very large. It is necessary to rearrange the mathematical treatment (without, however, changing its essential content) so as to obtain finite limits, and the most convenient techniques for doing this involve the formalism of second quantization which, although not difficult, has not been treated here. The resulting perturbation expansions, though their convergence is difficult to assess, have proved very useful when applied to actual problems. There are also a number of nonperturbation approaches, and by now the phenomena of superconductivity and superfluidity are now essentially understood. The technical difficulties are however extreme, and no reasonably simple general approach to the problem of interacting systems has yet been found.

REFERENCES

L. Landau and L. Lifschitz, *Statistical Physics*, Addison-Wesley Publishing Company, Inc., Reading, Mass., 1958.

D. ter Haar, *Elements of Statistical Mechanics*, Holt, Rinehart and Winston, Inc., New York, 1954.

R. C. Tolman, *The Principles of Statistical Mechanics*, Clarendon Press, Oxford, 1938.

R. H. Fowler, *Statistical Mechanics*, 2d ed., Cambridge University Press, London, 1936.

W. Band, *Quantum Statistics*, D. Van Nostrand Company, Inc., Princeton, N.J., 1955.

C. Kittel, *Solid State Physics*, 2d ed., John Wiley & Sons, Inc., New York, 1955.

The study of interacting systems can be begun in Landau and Lifschitz, *op. cit.*, and continued in

D. J. Thouless, *The Quantum Mechanics of Many-Body Systems*, Academic Press Inc., New York, 1961.

K. Huang, *Statistical Mechanics*, John Wiley & Sons, Inc., New York, 1963.

An excellent introduction to modern methods is

C. Fronsdal, ed., *The N-Body Problem*, W. A. Benjamin, Inc., New York, 1961.

Appendixes

In the solution of algebraic equations it is necessary to use two types of number. For example, if the equation is $x^2 + 25 = 0$, and 25 is a number of type 1, then the solutions must be of type 2. Because numbers of type 1 are used for counting things, they are called real. Type 2, for contrast, is called imaginary, though the term is misleading, since all numbers are equally imaginary. (It is worth remembering that in the seventeenth century the term "imaginary" was applied to numbers less than zero.) All mystical remarks based on the explicit occurrence of imaginary numbers in the equations of quantum theory should be regarded as groundless.

The basic real number is 1; the basic imaginary number is called i, where $i^2 = -1$. A complex number is a number of the form

$$z = a + bi$$

where a and b are both real. Here, a and b are called the *real* and *imaginary parts* of z, written

$$a = \text{Re } z \qquad b = \text{Im } z$$

It is a basic fact of algebra that algebraic equations whose coefficients are complex numbers have solutions which are complex numbers ($x^2 + 25 = 0$ is an example).

The rule for adding complex numbers is that one keeps the two types distinct,

$$(a_1 + b_1 i) + (a_2 + b_2 i) = (a_1 + a_2) + (b_1 + b_2)i$$

For multiplying, one combines them,

$$(a_1 + b_1 i)(a_2 + b_2 i) = a_1 a_2 + (a_1 b_2 + a_2 b_1)i + b_1 b_2 i^2$$
$$= (a_1 a_2 - b_1 b_2) + (a_1 b_2 + a_2 b_1)i$$

Corresponding to any number

$$z = a + bi$$

we define another, called z^*, the *complex conjugate* of z, equal to

$$z^* = a - bi$$

The product of z^* and z is a nonnegative real number

$$z^* z = a^2 + b^2 \geqslant 0$$

equal to zero only if a and b are both zero. This quantity has a special notation,

$$z^* z = |z|^2$$

and the positive square root of this, called

$$|z| = (a^2 + b^2)^{1/2}$$

is called the *modulus* of z.

It is convenient to think of z in the form

$$z = a1 + bi$$

and consider 1 and i as unit vectors in a plane. Thus, z becomes a point in the plane (or it may be thought of as the vector leading to the point) whose coordinates are a and b (Fig. 1). Clearly, the length of the vector is equal to the modulus $|z|$. If now ϑ is defined as in Fig. 1, we can write

$$a = |z| \cos \vartheta \qquad b = |z| \sin \vartheta$$

so that

$$z = |z| (\cos \vartheta + i \sin \vartheta)$$

The angle ϑ is called the *phase*, or the *argument* of z. A complex number is determined by its modulus and its argument just as well as by its real and imaginary parts.

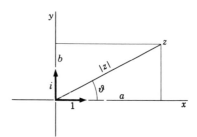

Fig. 1   Representation of a complex number z as a
point in the complex plane.

One of the cardinal facts of complex arithmetic is that the combination $\cos \vartheta + i \sin \vartheta$ has another notation,

$$\cos \vartheta + i \sin \vartheta = e^{i\vartheta}$$

There are a number of ways to prove this; the simplest is to expand each side in a Taylor series about the origin and see that they are the same. One can also verify that

$$(\cos \vartheta_1 + i \sin \vartheta_1)(\cos \vartheta_2 + i \sin \vartheta_2) = e^{i\vartheta_1}e^{i\vartheta_2} = e^{i(\vartheta_1+\vartheta_2)}$$
$$= \cos(\vartheta_1 + \vartheta_2) + i \sin(\vartheta_1 + \vartheta_2)$$

by direct calculation. Thus another way of writing z is

$$z = |z|e^{i\vartheta}$$

where (see Fig. 1) ϑ is given by

$$\tan \vartheta = \frac{\text{Im } z}{\text{Re } z}$$

The special convenience in this notation is that the formula for multiplication is very simple,

$$z_1 z_2 = |z_1|e^{i\vartheta_1}|z_2|e^{i\vartheta_2} = |z_1|\,|z_2|e^{i(\vartheta_1+\vartheta_2)}$$

so that the phase of $z_1 z_2$ is the sum of the individual phases, whereas the modulus is the product of the moduli. (It should be noted, however, that in general, $|z_1 + z_2| \neq |z_1| + |z_2|$.)

Any function of a complex number is again a complex number. Of particular interest is the type of function known as *analytic*. We shall not need to use this concept, and so it will be described here only in a rough and intuitive way. The functions

$$z,\ z^2,\ \sin z,\ e^{iz},\ \text{etc.}$$

are analytic, while the functions

$$\text{Re } z,\ \text{Im } z,\ z^*,\ |z|^2,\ \text{etc.}$$

are not. The former treat the whole of z at once, whereas the latter distinguish between real and imaginary parts. The most important elementary property of analytic functions is embodied in the *reflection principle*. Let $w(z)$ be some function of z. It is in general a complex number, $w = u + iv$. There are many analytic functions, including the first three of the examples given above, which have the property that they are real (that is, have $v = 0$), when z is real. The reflection principle says that if w is such a function, then

$$w(z^*) = [w(z)]^*$$

which means that if one knows the value of the function for a certain complex z, then the value of the function for z^* is found by taking the

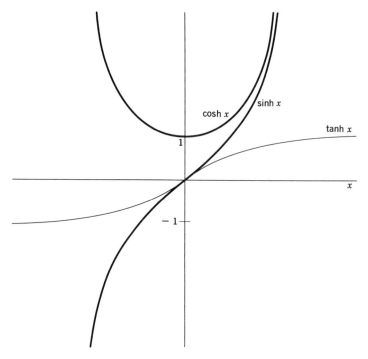

Fig. 2   Plots of sinh x, cosh x, and tanh x.

complex conjugate of its value for z. As an example,

$$e^z = e^{a+ib} = e^a e^{ib} = e^a(\cos b + i \sin b)$$

whereas

$$e^{z^*} = e^{a-ib} = e^a e^{-ib} = e^a[\cos(-b) + i \sin(-b)]$$
$$= e^a(\cos b - i \sin b) = (e^z)^*$$

since it is the complex conjugate of the preceding. The proof of the reflection principle requires the use of advanced methods.[1]

To end with, we note that from

$$e^{\pm i\vartheta} = \cos \vartheta \pm i \sin \vartheta$$

it follows that

$$\cos \vartheta = \tfrac{1}{2}(e^{i\vartheta} + e^{-i\vartheta}) \qquad \sin \vartheta = \frac{1}{2i}(e^{i\vartheta} - e^{-i\vartheta})$$

If in these expressions we let ϑ be an imaginary number, say, ix, with x real, we have

$$\cos(ix) = \tfrac{1}{2}(e^{-x} + e^x) = \cosh x$$

[1] R. V. Churchill, *Complex Variables and Applications*, 2d ed., McGraw-Hill Book Company, Inc., New York, 1960.

defining cosh x, the *hyperbolic cosine* of x. Similarly, we have

$$\sin (ix) = \frac{1}{2i} (e^{-x} - e^{x}) = i\tfrac{1}{2}(e^{x} - e^{-x})$$

$$= i \sinh x$$

defining the *hyperbolic sine* of x. Since $\cos^{2} \vartheta + \sin^{2} \vartheta = 1$, it follows that

$$\cosh^{2} x - \sinh^{2} x = 1,$$

as may easily be seen from their expressions in exponentials. These functions behave qualitatively as shown in Fig. 2; the reader should familiarize himself with their general properties.

appendix 2
Fourier Series and Integrals

Suppose we have a function of x which is periodic in the length L,

$$f(x + L) = f(x) \tag{1}$$

The function may be either real or complex. Let, for convenience, $K = 2\pi/L$. Then the function e^{iKx} also satisfies (1). The basic content of Fourier's theorem is that, subject to certain restrictions of form, any $f(x)$ satisfying (1) may be expanded in integral powers of e^{iKx},

$$f(x) = \sum_{n=-\infty}^{\infty} a_n e^{inKx} \tag{2}$$

where the range from $-\infty$ to $+\infty$ should be noted. If (2) holds, any coefficient a_m can be found by multiplying both sides by e^{-imKx} and integrating over a complete cycle of x, say from $-\frac{1}{2}L$ to $+\frac{1}{2}L$. Since

$$\int_{-\frac{1}{2}L}^{\frac{1}{2}L} e^{i(n-m)Kx}\, dx = \begin{cases} 0 & (n \neq m) \\ L & (n = m) \end{cases}$$

all terms of the sum drop out except one, and

$$a_m = \frac{1}{L} \int_{-\frac{1}{2}L}^{\frac{1}{2}L} f(x) e^{-imKx}\, dx \tag{3}$$

This result is valid if the integral (3) exists and if (2) is correct, that is, if the series in (2) converges, *and* converges, moreover, to the function $f(x)$. It is easy to find functions for which these things are not true, but they do not ordinarily arise in physical problems.

In case of doubt, a book on advanced calculus should be consulted for the conditions in which (2) is valid.

If $f(x)$ is real, the values of a_m are restricted. Let us calculate a_m^* from (3). Since f is real,

$$a_m^* = \frac{1}{L} \int_{-\frac{1}{2}L}^{\frac{1}{2}L} f(x) e^{imKx}\, dx = a_{-m} \tag{4}$$

since m may be either positive or negative. The sum (1) may now be written

$$f(x) = \sum_{-\infty}^{-1} a_n e^{inKx} + a_0 + \sum_{1}^{\infty} a_n e^{inKx}$$

$$= a_0 + \sum_{1}^{\infty} (a_n e^{inKx} + a_n^* e^{-inKx})$$

Let us write a_n as $\frac{1}{2}(b_n - ic_n)$, where b_n and c_n are both real. Then

$$f(x) = a_0 + \sum_{1}^{\infty} [\frac{1}{2}b_n(e^{inKx} + e^{-inKx}) - \frac{1}{2}ic_n(e^{inKx} - e^{-inKx})]$$

or

$$f(x) = a_0 + \sum_{1}^{\infty} (b_n \cos nKx + c_n \sin nKx) \tag{5}$$

which is the form in which the series is often given. Nevertheless, (2) is simpler in form, and it is generally used for the purposes of this book.

Fourier's integral representation is the limit taken by the series (2) when L becomes infinite. The function represented now need not be periodic, since it may be thought to repeat itself only after an infinite interval. To carry out the limiting process, we substitute (3) into (2) to get

$$f(x) = \frac{1}{L} \sum_{n=-\infty}^{\infty} \int_{-\frac{1}{2}L}^{\frac{1}{2}L} f(t) e^{-inK(x-t)}\, dt$$

where we have changed the name of the variable of integration in (3) from x to t to avoid confusion with the other x outside. Since $K = 2\pi/L$, this is

$$f(x) = \frac{1}{2\pi} \int_{-\frac{1}{2}L}^{\frac{1}{2}L} f(t) \left(K \sum_{n=-\infty}^{\infty} e^{inK(x-t)} \right) dt \tag{6}$$

The limit $L \to \infty$ is now the same as $K \to 0$, and the sum is of the general form

$$\lim_{K \to 0} K \sum_{n=-\infty}^{\infty} F(nKz)$$

For the smoothly varying functions ordinarily encountered, the limit exists and is equal to $\int_{-\infty}^{\infty} F(kz)\,dk$. This may be understood if the region of integration is thought to be divided up into an infinite number of strips of width K. The integral is then the sum of the areas of these strips in the limit as they are made infinitely narrow. In the general case, this limit requires very careful discussion, but we shall ignore here the question of its convergence. Equation (6) becomes

$$f(x) = \frac{1}{2\pi} \int_{-\infty}^{\infty} f(t) \left(\int_{-\infty}^{\infty} e^{ik(x-t)}\,dk \right) \tag{7}$$

which can be factored into

$$f(x) = \int_{-\infty}^{\infty} g(k)e^{ikx}\,dk \tag{8}$$

where

$$g(k) = \frac{1}{2\pi} \int_{-\infty}^{\infty} f(t)e^{-ikt}\,dt \tag{9}$$

These are the analogues of (2) and (3) when the region of periodicity is infinite. The reciprocal relationship expressed by (8) and (9) is known as Fourier's integral theorem, and f and g are said to be *Fourier transforms* of one another. Equation (8) and (9) are certainly valid if $\int_{-\infty}^{\infty} f(x)\,dx$ is absolutely convergent and if $f(x)$ contains no infinite discontinuities and only a finite number of maxima, minima, and finite discontinuities in any finite interval.[1]

Comparing (7) with (8.105), we see that the delta function can be represented by a definite integral

$$\delta(x - t) = \frac{1}{2\pi} \int_{-\infty}^{\infty} e^{ik(x-t)}\,dk \tag{10}$$

which is a useful formula even though the integral itself does not converge.   (See especially Lighthill's book cited below.)

---

[1] A good general introduction is H. S. Carslaw, *Fourier Series and Integrals*, 2d ed., The Macmillan Company, New York, 1921. See also P. M. Morse and H. Feshbach, *Methods of Theoretical Physics*, McGraw-Hill Book Company, Inc., New York, 1953. An excellent elementary discussion of recent developments is M. J. Lighthill, *Introduction to Fourier Analysis and Generalized Functions*, Cambridge University Press, London, 1958.

Transformations to Moving Coordinate Systems

One learns a great deal in mechanics and electrodynamics by looking at simple systems from systems of reference which are in motion with respect to one another. This is, of course, the primary analytical device whereby the equations of relativity are derived, but it is of great use also in gaining an insight into the connections of things at a more elementary level. As an example of this, suppose we consider a one-dimensional collision between two objects of masses m_1 and m_2, whereby their velocities are changed from u_1 and u_2 to v_1 and v_2. If the collision is elastic, we have

$$\tfrac{1}{2}m_1u_1{}^2 + \tfrac{1}{2}m_2u_2{}^2 = \tfrac{1}{2}m_1v_1{}^2 + \tfrac{1}{2}m_2v_2{}^2 \tag{1}$$

Suppose that we observe the collision from a system of reference moving to the right with respect to the first at a velocity V. The velocity v_1 is now replaced by

$$v_1' = v_1 - V \tag{2}$$

and similarly for all the others. Let us now assume that (1) holds also in the new system of reference, so that we have

$$\tfrac{1}{2}m_1u_1'{}^2 + \tfrac{1}{2}m_2u_2'{}^2 = \tfrac{1}{2}m_1v_1'{}^2 + \tfrac{1}{2}m_2v_2'{}^2 \tag{3}$$

Writing this out in detail and using (1) we find

$$m_1u_1V + m_2v_2V = m_1v_1V + m_2v_2V$$

or

$$m_1u_1 + m_2u_2 = m_1v_1 + m_2v_2$$

which expresses the conservation of momentum in the collision. This is something new. It is not contained in the conservation of energy

511

(1), but it is contained if we add the requirement that the energy be conserved when viewed from a coordinate system in motion with respect to the first. It is easy to see, by adding a Q to represent dissipated energy on the right-hand sides of (1) and (3), that the argument does not depend on the collision's being elastic.

Having seen this preliminary example from classical physics, let us now look at something equally elementary in quantum mechanics, the transformation analogous to (2) which one has to make in order to go from one coordinate system to another. It will be instructive if we first do it wrong. Let us distinguish by primes the variables in the moving system. If we use the transformation

$$x \rightarrow x' = x - Vt \qquad t' = t \tag{4}$$

in the expression for a plane wave, we have

$$e^{i(kx-\omega t)} = e^{i(kx'+kVt'-\omega t')} = e^{i(k'x'-\omega't')}$$

where

$$k' = k \qquad \omega' = \omega - kV \tag{5}$$

These are wrong, if $\hbar k$ and $\hbar k'$ represent momenta, because the momentum of a particle clearly depends on the coordinate system from which it is observed. The mistake was to think that a matter wave is like a sound wave or a water wave in having a definite wavelength which is independent of the observer's state of motion. That this is not so emphasizes still further the nonobservable character of ψ.

We must now look for some criterion which will tell us how the values of k and ω vary from one observer to another. One such criterion is to demand that the results of the transformation be consistent with the particle interpretation of the wave function. Thus, if the particle's mass is m and its velocity is v, we have

$$\hbar k = mv \qquad \hbar k' = mv' = m(v - V)$$

so that

$$k' = k - \frac{mV}{\hbar} \tag{6}$$

and similarly, for a free particle,

$$\hbar\omega = \tfrac{1}{2}mv^2 \quad \hbar\omega' = \tfrac{1}{2}mv'^2 = \tfrac{1}{2}m(v - V)^2$$

so that

$$\omega' = \omega - kV + \frac{mV^2}{2\hbar} \tag{7}$$

But it is objectionable to have to go outside the mathematical structure of the theory to learn how the various quantities transform. The best way to proceed is to start from Schrödinger's equation, whose validity is clearly not restricted to any particular system of coordinates, and demand that it take the same form in primed and unprimed coordinates. Since a potential energy anchors a particle down to a particular coordinate system, we shall consider only the free-particle equation

$$\frac{\hbar^2}{2m}\frac{\partial^2\psi}{\partial x^2} + i\hbar\frac{\partial\psi}{\partial t} = 0 \tag{8}$$

To go to the primed coordinates, we see from (4) that for a function of x' and t',

$$\frac{\partial}{\partial x} = \frac{\partial}{\partial x'} \tag{9a}$$

and

$$\frac{\partial}{\partial t} = \frac{\partial t'}{\partial t}\frac{\partial}{\partial t'} + \frac{\partial x'}{\partial t}\frac{\partial}{\partial x'}$$

$$= \frac{\partial}{\partial t'} - V\frac{\partial}{\partial x'} \tag{9b}$$

so that (8) becomes

$$\frac{\hbar^2}{2m}\frac{\partial^2}{\partial x'^2} - i\hbar V\frac{\partial\psi}{\partial x'} + i\hbar\frac{\partial\psi}{\partial t'} = 0 \tag{10}$$

where ψ is now regarded as a function of x' and t'. This is not of the same form as (8). It must therefore be that ψ itself is different in the two systems in such a way as to compensate for the change which has appeared. But ψ cannot be completely different, for its square $|\psi|^2$ has a physical interpretation which is independent of the coordinate system with respect to which it is specified. Thus ψ', the wave function in the new coordinate system, cannot differ from ψ by more than a phase. We shall assume that this phase is a linear function of x and t, the assumption being justified by the fact that we shall obtain a consistent answer. The reader is invited to see for himself that it is in fact the only answer.

We therefore write in (10)

$$\psi(x',t') = e^{i(\alpha x' + \beta t')}\psi'(x',t') \tag{11}$$

and find by direct substitution that

$$\frac{\hbar^2}{2m}\left(\frac{\partial^2\psi'}{\partial x'^2} + 2i\alpha\frac{\partial\psi'}{\partial x'} - \alpha^2\psi'\right) - i\hbar V\left(\frac{\partial\psi'}{\partial x'} + i\alpha\psi'\right)$$
$$+ i\hbar\left(\frac{\partial\psi'}{\partial t'} + i\beta\psi'\right) = 0$$

and determine α and β by the requirement that Schrödinger's equation in the new coordinate system take the same form as it did in the old,

$$\frac{\hbar^2}{2m}\frac{\partial^2\psi'}{\partial x'^2} + i\hbar\frac{\partial\psi'}{\partial t'} = 0 \tag{12}$$

This is readily seen to imply that

$$\alpha = \frac{mV}{\hbar} \qquad \beta = \frac{mV^2}{2\hbar} \tag{13}$$

and the transformation to moving coordinates is now completely specified. Written out, it is

$$\psi'(x',t') = \left\{ \exp\left[-i\frac{mV}{\hbar}(x' + \tfrac{1}{2}Vt') \right] \right\} \psi(x',t') \tag{14}$$

where ψ is the original function and x' and t' are given in terms of the old x and t by $x' = x - Vt$ and $t' = t$.

We can most easily interpret the above result by applying it to the plane wave. Let it be in the fixed coordinate system

$$\psi(x,t) = e^{i(kx-\omega t)}$$

On the left side of (11) this is expressed in terms of the primed coordinates; by (4), it is

$$\psi(x',t') = e^{i(kx'+kVt'-\omega t')}$$

On the right side of (11), we assume that the transformed ψ is of exactly the same form as the old,

$$\psi'(x',t') = e^{i(k'x'-\omega' t')}$$

and ask what k' and ω' have to do with the old k and ω. Substitution into (11) gives

$$kx' + kVt' - \omega t' = \alpha x' + \beta t' + k'x' - \omega' t'$$

from which we find

$$k' = k - \alpha \qquad \omega' = \omega - kV + \beta$$

and this, with (13), is exactly the same as (6) and (7).

The transformation (4) is called a Galilean transformation, and our postulate that Schrödinger's equation shall take exactly the same form in two systems related by such a transformation is called the postulate of *Galilean invariance*. We see that this postulate is sufficient to determine the transformation property of ψ under Galilean transformations and that furthermore, by enabling us to derive (6) and (7) without reference to the particle interpretation of the theory, it adds a new element of plausibility and self-consistency to this interpretation.

As a historical note it may be added that in his earliest work de Broglie was concerned with this same problem of self-consistency, except that he had no wave equation from whose invariance he could deduce the transformation properties of a matter wave. He therefore based his whole approach on relativistic invariance, arguing that whatever might be the final form of the theory (and its wave equation) the theory and its results would have to be invariant under a

Lorentz transformation. His results, when v and V are small, are the same as we have obtained.

Uniform acceleration

Considerations of the same kind have a bearing on the introduction of forces into the free-particle Schrödinger equation. In Chap. 4 we postulated the addition of a term of the form $V(x)\psi$, with the remark that it is not possible to derive all the equations of quantum mechanics from classical considerations. But we can, guided by our intuition of classical physics, imagine an interaction which would give a particle (or a system of particles) a uniform acceleration, say, a, in the positive x direction, and we can alter the free-particle Schrödinger equation so as to take account of it in a rigorous manner. In classical physics the interaction would be a uniform, constant force $F = ma$, where m is the mass of the particles. In quantum mechanics we can simulate its effect by viewing a free particle from a coordinate system which has an acceleration a in the negative x direction. Let

$$x \rightarrow x' = x + \tfrac{1}{2}at^2 \qquad t' = t$$

where the new coordinates coincide with the old, and are momentarily at rest with respect to them, when $t = 0$. The transformed Schrödinger equation is

$$\frac{\hbar^2}{2m}\frac{\partial^2 \psi}{\partial x'^2} - i\hbar at\frac{\partial \psi}{\partial x'} + i\hbar \frac{\partial \psi}{\partial t'} = 0 \tag{15}$$

analogous to (10). This is a perfectly good equation to describe what we have in mind, but it is more conventional to use equations of motion which do not explicitly involve t. A little work shows that t can be removed if we go to a new wave function which differs from the old by a phase factor,

$$\psi = e^{i(\alpha x' t' + \beta t'^3)}\psi' \qquad \alpha = -\frac{ma}{\hbar} \qquad \beta = \frac{ma^2}{6\hbar}$$

With this, (15) becomes

$$\frac{\hbar^2}{2m}\frac{\partial^2 \psi'}{\partial x'^2} + max'\psi' + i\hbar \frac{\partial \psi'}{\partial t'} = 0$$

It is of the form

$$-\frac{\hbar^2}{2m}\frac{\partial^2 \psi'}{\partial x'^2} + V(x')\psi' = i\hbar \frac{\partial \psi'}{\partial t'} \tag{16}$$

where $V(x') = -max'$, and when we note that this is the classical potential energy of a particle subject to the given force, we are encouraged (though not of course compelled) to try the same sort of equation for more general forces.

Spherical Harmonics and Angular Functions

In this appendix we shall gather together some properties of spherical harmonics which are of use in quantum mechanics. In order to make this book mathematically less demanding, no use is made of this material except in Chap. 14. The reader should not be misled by that fact, however. These functions, together with their underlying theoretical significance, are used all the time, in all parts of the subject.

Spherical harmonics occur in two essentially distinct aspects, both of which must be understood. The first is as the angular part of the solution of a partial differential equation containing the laplacian operator. The second is as the eigenfunctions of the angular-momentum operators $\hat{L}^2$ and $\hat{L}_z$. We shall try to explain and connect the two roles as we go along.

Suppose we have to solve an equation of the form

$$\nabla^2 F + p(r)F = 0 \tag{1}$$

where $p(r)$ is some function of the radial distance only. [This is the usual situation with Schrödinger's equation; with $p(r) = 0$ we get Laplace's equation.] Transforming the laplacian operator into spherical coordinates is laborious at best, and it can best be approached via the general theory of orthogonal systems of coordinates.[1] The result is

$$\frac{1}{r}\frac{\partial^2}{\partial r^2}(rF) + \frac{1}{r^2 \sin\vartheta}\frac{\partial}{\partial\vartheta}\left(\sin\vartheta\,\frac{\partial F}{\partial\vartheta}\right) + \frac{1}{r^2 \sin^2\vartheta}\frac{\partial^2 F}{\partial\varphi^2} + p(r)F = 0 \tag{2}$$

[1] See textbooks on applied mathematics and theoretical physics.

Let us try to solve this equation by factoring $F(r,\vartheta,\varphi)$ into a radial part $R(r)$ and an angular part $Y(\vartheta,\varphi)$. Putting this into (2) and multiplying the results by r^2/RY gives

$$\frac{r}{R}\frac{\partial^2}{\partial r^2}(rR) + r^2 p(r) + \frac{1}{Y\sin\vartheta}\frac{\partial}{\partial\vartheta}\left(\sin\vartheta\frac{\partial Y}{\partial\vartheta}\right)$$

$$+ \frac{1}{Y\sin^2\vartheta}\frac{\partial^2 Y}{\partial\varphi^2} = 0$$

and since the variables are now completely separated, we must have, as usual,

$$\frac{r}{R}\frac{\partial^2}{\partial r^2}(rR) + r^2 p(r) = K$$

and

$$\frac{1}{Y\sin\vartheta}\frac{\partial}{\partial\vartheta}\left(\sin\vartheta\frac{\partial Y}{\partial\vartheta}\right) + \frac{1}{Y\sin^2\vartheta}\frac{\partial^2 Y}{\partial\varphi^2} = -K$$

where K is some constant. Cross-multiplying these gives a radial equation

$$\frac{d^2}{dr^2}(rR) + \left[p(r) - \frac{K}{r^2}\right](rR) = 0 \tag{3}$$

and an angular equation

$$\frac{1}{\sin\vartheta}\frac{\partial}{\partial\vartheta}\left(\sin\vartheta\frac{\partial Y}{\partial\vartheta}\right) + \frac{1}{\sin^2\vartheta}\frac{\partial^2 Y}{\partial\varphi^2} + KY = 0 \tag{4}$$

The first of these is an ordinary differential equation for R. We can further separate the second into ordinary differential equations in ϑ and φ, but before doing so let us first compare the above formulas with some which come from the theory of angular momentum.

Angular momentum

The cartesian coordinates are given in terms of the polar coordinates by

$$x = r\sin\vartheta\cos\varphi \qquad y = r\sin\vartheta\sin\varphi \qquad z = r\cos\vartheta$$

and the inverse relations are

$$r = (x^2 + y^2 + z^2)^{1/2} \qquad \vartheta = \cos^{-1}\frac{z}{r} \qquad \varphi = \tan^{-1}\frac{y}{x}$$

We can use these to transform the operator $\hat{\mathbf{L}}$ into polar coordinates by writing for example

$$\hat{L}_z = -i\left(y\frac{\partial}{\partial z} - z\frac{\partial}{\partial y}\right)$$

$$= -i\left[r\sin\vartheta\sin\varphi\left(\frac{\partial r}{\partial z}\frac{\partial}{\partial r} + \frac{\partial\vartheta}{\partial z}\frac{\partial}{\partial\vartheta}\right)\right.$$

$$\left. - r\cos\vartheta\left(\frac{\partial r}{\partial y}\frac{\partial}{\partial r} + \frac{\partial\varphi}{\partial y}\frac{\partial}{\partial\varphi}\right)\right]$$

When the partial derivatives are worked out, we find

$$\hat{L}_x = i\left(\sin\varphi\,\frac{\partial}{\partial\vartheta} + \cot\vartheta\,\cos\varphi\,\frac{\partial}{\partial\varphi}\right) \tag{5}$$

$$\hat{L}_y = i\left(-\cos\varphi\,\frac{\partial}{\partial\vartheta} + \cot\vartheta\,\sin\varphi\,\frac{\partial}{\partial\varphi}\right) \tag{6}$$

$$\hat{L}_z = -i\,\frac{\partial}{\partial\varphi} \tag{7}$$

and finally,

$$\hat{L}^2 = -\frac{1}{\sin\vartheta}\,\frac{\partial}{\partial\vartheta}\,\sin\vartheta\,\frac{\partial}{\partial\vartheta} - \frac{1}{\sin^2\vartheta}\,\frac{\partial^2}{\partial\varphi^2} \tag{8}$$

Comparison of this with (4) shows the remarkable fact that the two differential operators are the same and that (2) may be written as

$$\frac{1}{r}\,\frac{\partial^2}{\partial r^2}\,(r\,F) - \frac{\hat{L}^2}{r^2}\,F + p(r)F = 0 \tag{9}$$

and (4) is

$$\hat{L}^2 Y = K Y \tag{10}$$

We have found the eigenvalues K in Sec. 5.6. They are of the form $l(l+1)$ with $l = 0, 1, 2, \ldots$. Thus (3) becomes

$$\frac{d^2}{dr^2}\,(rR) + \left[p(r) - \frac{l(l+1)}{r^2}\right]rR = 0 \tag{11}$$

and the radial wave function is now specified except for normalization. Further, the separation of variables in (4), which is simple enough anyhow, is taken care of automatically if we require that, as in (5.32),

$$\hat{L}_z Y = m Y \qquad (-l \leqslant m \leqslant l) \tag{12}$$

Noting the simple form of $\hat{L}_z$ in (7), we can factor the angular-momentum eigenfunction $Y(\vartheta,\varphi)$ into a part depending on ϑ, which we shall call $P_l{}^m(\cos\vartheta)$, and a part depending on φ which from (12) is $e^{im\varphi}$, with m a positive or negative integer.

$$Y(\vartheta,\varphi) = P_l{}^m(\cos\vartheta)e^{im\varphi} \tag{13}$$

We find from (4) that $P_l{}^m$ satisfies the equation

$$\frac{1}{\sin\vartheta}\,\frac{d}{d\vartheta}\left(\sin\vartheta\,\frac{dP_l{}^m}{d\vartheta}\right) + \left[l(l+1) - \frac{m^2}{\sin^2\vartheta}\right]P_l{}^m = 0 \tag{14}$$

We shall also need the form taken by this equation if the independent variable is taken as $\cos\vartheta = \mu$,

$$\frac{d}{d\mu}\left[(1-\mu^2)\,\frac{dP_l{}^m}{d\mu}\right] + \left[l(l+1) - \frac{m^2}{1-\mu^2}\right]P_l{}^m = 0 \tag{15}$$

This equation can be solved in a straightforward way,[2] but the procedure is difficult and not very illuminating. We shall learn more by reducing the problem to a consideration of the special case $m = 0$. That such a reduction is possible is already clear from Sec. 5.6, in which it was shown how to construct eigenvalues of $\hat{L}^2$ corresponding to any eigenvalue of $\hat{L}_z$ by successive applications of the operators $\hat{L}_+$ and $\hat{L}_-$. Even this procedure, though simpler than the above, is laborious, however, and we shall follow an equivalent method, via a transformation of the differential equation (15).

Relation between $P_l{}^m(\mu)$ and $P_l(\mu)$

Let us start with the differential equation for $P_l{}^0$, which we shall call P_l, obtained by setting $m = 0$ in (15),

$$(1 - \mu^2) \frac{d^2 P_l}{d\mu^2} - 2\mu \frac{dP_l}{d\mu} + l(l + 1)P_l = 0 \tag{16}$$

and differentiate it m times with respect to μ. The first term gives

$$(1 - \mu^2) \frac{d^2}{d\mu^2} \left(\frac{d^m P_l}{d\mu^m} \right) - 2m\mu \frac{d}{d\mu} \left(\frac{d^m P_l}{d\mu^m} \right) - m(m - 1) \frac{d^m P_l}{d\mu^m}$$

the second gives

$$-2 \left[\mu \frac{d}{d\mu} \left(\frac{d^m P_l}{d\mu^m} \right) + m \frac{d^m P_l}{d\mu^m} \right]$$

and the third is $l(l + 1)d^m P_l/d\mu^m$. Adding these gives

$$\left[(1 - \mu^2) \frac{d^2}{d\mu^2} - 2(m + 1)\mu \frac{d}{d\mu} + l(l + 1) - m(m + 1) \right] \frac{d^m P_l}{d\mu^m} = 0$$

which can also be written as

$$\left[(1 - \mu^2) \frac{d^2}{d\mu^2} - 2\mu \frac{d}{d\mu} + l(l + 1) - \frac{m^2}{1 - \mu^2} \right] (1 - \mu^2)^{m/2} \frac{d^m P_l}{d\mu^m} = 0$$

(The reader should verify all these differentiations.) This is the same as the equation for $P_l{}^m$, so we can conclude that the two are proportional. We shall take the factor of proportionality to be $(-1)^m$, giving

$$P_l{}^m(\mu) = (-1)^m (1 - \mu^2)^{m/2} \frac{d^m P_l(\mu)}{d\mu^m} \tag{17}$$

For negative m this equation makes no sense. One way out of this is to note that the defining equation (15) is the same for positive

[2] J. C. Jaeger, *Introduction to Applied Mathematics*, Clarendon Press, Oxford, 1951, p. 341 and also many other books of this kind.

as for negative m, so that we can define $P_l{}^m$ with negative m to be $P_l{}^{|m|}$ without loss of consistency, and (13) would become

$$Y(\vartheta,\varphi) = P_l{}^{|m|}(\vartheta)e^{im\varphi}$$

This is often done, but it has the disadvantage of treating m differently in the two factors. We shall have to wait for a moment before formulating a more convenient definition.

Construction of $P_l(\mu)$

Now let us examine equation (16), called Legendre's equation, which gives $P_l(\mu)$. Two approaches may be used. The first is a straightforward expansion in series, such as was used in solving (4.102). The reader is invited to verify our results by trying this method himself. It has the disadvantage that there emerges no short and general formula analogous to (18), below. The second approach is analogous to that used for $P_l{}^m$. Consider first the polynomial in μ of degree $2l$, $q_l = (\varphi^2 - 1)^l$. One can verify at once that it satisfies the equation·

$$(1 - \mu^2)\frac{d^2 q_l}{d\mu^2} + 2(l - 1)\mu\frac{dq_l}{d\mu} + 2lq_l = 0$$

Now differentiate this equation l times with respect to μ. Exactly as above, we find

$$\left[(1 - \mu^2)\frac{d^2}{d\mu^2} - 2\mu\frac{d}{d\mu} + l(l + 1)\right]\frac{d^l q_l}{d\mu^l} = 0$$

so that $d^l q_l/d\mu^l$ satisfies the same equation as does $P_l(\mu)$. We therefore conclude that the two are proportional. The factor of proportionality is established by convention so that

$$P_l(\mu) = \frac{1}{2^l l!}\frac{d^l}{d\mu^l}(\mu^2 - 1)^l \tag{18}$$

(The reason for this definition will be seen in the next section.) From (18) we can see at once one of the most important properties of $P_l(\mu)$. We have remarked that q_l is a polynomial in μ of degree $2l$, and it contains only even powers. When differentiated l times, it becomes a polynomial of degree l, and furthermore it contains only even or odd powers of μ according as l is even or odd. Thus

$$P_l(-\mu) = (-1)^l P_l(\mu)$$

The functions $P_l(\mu)$ are known as *Legendre polynomials*, and a few are listed in Table 1 and graphed in Fig. 1.
    Combining (17) and (18), we find

$$P_l{}^m(\mu) = \frac{(-1)^m}{2^l l!}(1 - \mu^2)^{m/2}\frac{d^{l+m}}{d\mu^{l+m}}(\mu^2 - 1)^l \tag{19}$$

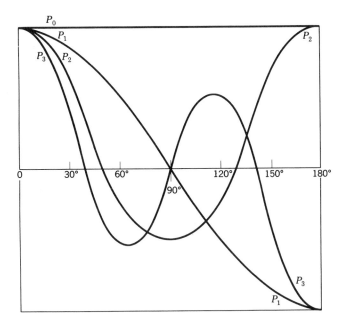

Fig. 1 The first four Legendre polynomials as functions of the angle.

with the special values

$$P_l^{-l}(\mu) = \frac{1}{2^l l!}\,(1 - \mu^2)^{l/2} \qquad P_l^l(\mu) = (-1)^l\,\frac{(2l)!}{2^l l!}\,(1 - \mu^2)^{l/2} \qquad (19a)$$

It can easily be verified that the function P_l^m satisfies (15) for either positive or negative m $(-l \leqslant m \leqslant l)$, and we shall therefore use this equation, rather than (17), to define what is meant by P_l^m for all values of m. P_l^{-m} now differs from $P_l^{|m|}$ in both magnitude and sign. The magnitude is unimportant, since we are going to normalize Y_l^m anyhow, but the sign is $(-1)^{\frac{1}{2}(|m|+m)}$, that is, -1 for positive odd m and $+1$ otherwise.

The functions P_l^m are known as the *associated Legendre functions*. If m is even, they are polynomials of degree l in μ, or $\cos \vartheta$, as can be seen from (19). If m is odd, they can be written as $\sin \vartheta$ multiplied by a polynomial in $\cos \vartheta$ of degree $l - 1$.

Table 1 Legendre Polynomials

l	$P_l(\mu)$
0	1
1	μ
2	$\frac{1}{2}(3\mu^2 - 1)$
3	$\frac{1}{2}(5\mu^3 - 3\mu)$
4	$\frac{1}{8}(35\mu^4 - 30\mu^2 + 3)$
5	$\frac{1}{8}(63\mu^5 - 70\mu^3 + 15\mu)$

Spherical harmonics

All the properties of the P_l's and $P_l{}^m$'s are, of course, contained in the definitions just given, but many of them are easier to extract if we adopt a different approach by way of Laplace's equation and some of its simple solutions. Setting $p(r) = 0$ in (11) gives

$$\frac{d^2}{dr^2}(rR_l) = \frac{l(l+1)}{r^2}rR_l$$

where we have added a subscript for convenience. This is solved by putting $rR = r^\alpha$. Differentiation gives $\alpha(\alpha-1) = l(l+1)$, whence $\alpha = l+1$ or $-l$, and

$$R_l(r) = a_l r^l + b_l r^{-l-1}$$

Thus there are solutions of Laplace's equation which are of the form

$$H_l{}^m(r,\vartheta,\varphi) = (a_l r^l + b_l r^{-l-1})P_l{}^m(\cos\vartheta)e^{im\varphi}$$

The letter H reflects the fact that solutions of Laplace's equation are known generally as *harmonic functions*. We are going to investigate a particularly simple class of them, independent of φ and therefore, by (13), having $m = 0$.

It can be shown that any harmonic function H independent of φ can be represented by a sum of H_l's with suitably chosen a_l's and b_l's,

$$H = \sum_{l=0}^{\infty}(a_l r^l + b_l r^{-l-1})P_l(\cos\vartheta) \tag{20}$$

Such functions represent, for example, the electrostatic potentials of axially symmetrical distributions of charge evaluated at points on the axis. Let us choose a particularly simple example, in which we already know the answer, and work it out. Knowing the answer will lead to a simple formula for the Legendre polynomials.

The example is that illustrated in Fig. 2, which shows a point charge located on the z axis. The potential at the point P is axially symmetric and is therefore given as a function of r and ϑ by an

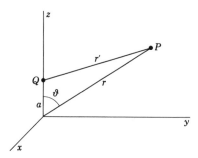

Fig. 2 To find the potential of a point charge Q.

expansion of the form (20). On the other hand, we know that, neglecting irrelevant factors, it is equal to $1/r'$. By the law of cosines, this is

$$V(r,\mu) = (a^2 - 2ar\mu + r^2)^{-\frac{1}{2}} \qquad (21)$$

We wish to expand this in ascending or descending powers of r for comparison with (20). Let us assume for a moment that $r > a$ and write

$$V(r,\mu) = \frac{1}{r}\left(1 - 2\frac{a}{r}\mu + \frac{a^2}{r^2}\right)^{-\frac{1}{2}}$$

This can be expanded in the convergent series (why is it convergent?)

$$\left(1 - 2\frac{a}{r}\mu + \frac{a^2}{r^2}\right)^{-\frac{1}{2}} = 1 - \frac{1}{2}\left(-2\frac{a}{r}\mu + \frac{a^2}{r^2}\right)$$
$$+ \frac{3}{8}\left(-2\frac{a}{r}\mu + \frac{a^2}{r^2}\right)^2 + \cdots \qquad (r > a)$$

Expanding these terms and collecting powers of r, we find

$$V(r,\mu) = \frac{1}{r}\left(1 + \frac{\mu}{r} + \frac{3\mu^2 - 1}{2r^2} + \frac{5\mu^3 - 3\mu}{2r^3} + \cdots\right)$$

and this is of the form (20), with all a_l's equal to zero and all b_l's equal to 1 and P_l's as defined in (18). The reader can easily see that in the other case, with $r < a$, an exactly similar series results with $a_l = 1$ and $b_l = 0$. The Legendre polynomials were first encountered and defined in this way, which accounts for the numerical factors appearing in the definition (18). The functions $P_l{}^m(\cos \vartheta)e^{im\varphi}$ are known as *spherical harmonics*.

Recurrence relations

The above specification of $P_l(\mu)$ may be condensed into the following formula:

$$(1 - 2t\mu + t^2)^{-\frac{1}{2}} = \sum_{l=0}^{\infty} t^l P_l(\mu) \qquad (|t| < 1) \qquad (22)$$

where the function on the left is known as the *generating function* for the Legendre polynomials. Most of the sets of special functions of analysis can be characterized in a similar way by a generating function, and such functions, generally fairly simple in form and containing a complete specification of every member of the set, often provide an excellent approach to the study of the functions. We shall use (22) to study the *recurrence relations* among successive Legendre polynomials and then to study their integral properties.

If (22) is differentiated with respect to t and rearranged, there results

$$(\mu - t)\Sigma t^l P_l(\mu) = (1 - 2\mu t + t^2)\Sigma l t^{l-1} P_l(\mu)$$

Since this is true for all values of t (and μ), we can equate corresponding powers of t on each side of the equation to get

$$(l + 1)P_{l+1}(\mu) - (2l + 1)\mu P_l(\mu) + l P_{l-1}(\mu) = 0 \tag{23}$$

This is an example of a *recurrence relation*, and it gives an easy means of finding P_{l+1} when the preceding two polynomials are known. Similarly, by differentiating (22) with respect to μ it can be shown that

$$\mu \frac{dP_l}{d\mu} - \frac{dP_{l-1}}{d\mu} - l P_l = 0 \tag{24}$$

The proof is left to the reader as an exercise. A slightly more difficult exercise is the derivation of the same results from (18).

By substituting (19) back into the original differential equation and expressing the result in terms of $P_l{}^m$, we find the recurrence formula relating adjacent values of m,

$$P_l{}^{m+1}(\mu) + \frac{2m\mu}{(1 - \mu^2)^{\frac{1}{2}}} P_l{}^m(\mu) + (l + m)(l - m + 1)P_l{}^{m-1}(\mu)$$
$$= 0 \tag{25}$$

valid for all m. A formula relating adjacent values of l is

$$(2l + 1)\mu P_l{}^m(\mu) - (l - m + 1)P_{l+1}^m(\mu) - (l + m)P_{l-1}^m(\mu) = 0 \tag{26}$$

By differentiating (22) and using (19a) it is easy to find a generating function for $P_l{}^m$ with a given value of m,

$$\frac{t^m}{(1 - 2t\mu + t^2)^{m+\frac{1}{2}}} P_m{}^m(\mu) = \sum_{l=m}^{\infty} t^l P_l{}^m(\mu) \qquad (|t| < 1)$$

Orthogonality relations

Let us write (15) as

$$\hat{D}P_l{}^m(\mu) + \left[l(l + 1) - \frac{m^2}{1 - \mu^2} \right] P_l{}^m = 0$$

where the operator $\hat{D}$ may easily be verified to be hermitian in the sense that

$$\int_{-1}^{1} P_l{}^m \hat{D}P_{l'}^{m'} \, d\mu = \int_{-1}^{1} (\hat{D}P_l{}^m)P_{l'}^{m'} \, d\mu$$

It follows from the procedure of Sec. 5.1 that we have for any two $P_l{}^m$

$$[l(l + 1) - l'(l' + 1)] \int_{-1}^{1} P_l{}^m P_{l'}^{m'} \, d\mu$$
$$- (m^2 - m'^2) \int_{-1}^{1} P_l{}^m P_{l'}^{m'} \frac{d\mu}{1 - \mu^2} = 0$$

from which, by setting in turn $m = m'$ and $l = l'$, we find

$$\int_{-1}^{1} P_l^m P_{l'}^m \, d\mu = 0 \qquad (l \neq l') \tag{27}$$

and

$$\int_{-1}^{1} P_l^m P_l^{m'} \frac{d\mu}{1 - \mu^2} = 0 \qquad (m^2 \neq m'^2) \tag{28}$$

Special values

Put $\mu = \pm 1$ in (22), which becomes

$$(1 \mp t)^{-1} = \Sigma t^l P_l(\pm 1)$$

Equating coefficients of equal powers of t gives

$$P_l(\pm 1) = (\pm 1)^l \tag{29}$$

and finally, with $\mu = 0$ and

$$(1 + t^2)^{-\frac{1}{2}} = \sum_n (-1)^n \frac{1 \times 3 \times 5 \cdots (2n - 1)}{2 \times 4 \times 6 \cdots (2n)} t^{2n}$$

we find

$$P_l(0) = \begin{cases} 0 & (l \text{ odd}) \\ (-1)^{\frac{1}{2}l} \dfrac{1 \times 3 \times 5 \cdots (l - 1)}{2 \times 4 \times 6 \cdots l} & (l \text{ even}) \end{cases} \tag{30}$$

The value of $P_l^m(\pm 1)$ is most simply found by letting μ approach ± 1 in (25). The first and last terms are finite, while the middle one becomes infinite unless m or P_l^m (or both) becomes zero. If m is not zero, we have

$$P_l^m(\pm 1) = 0 \qquad (m \neq 0) \tag{31}$$

whereas if $m = 0$, the value is given by (29). The value of $P_l^m(0)$ is found by carrying out the differentiations in the one term in (19) that does not vanish on setting $\mu = 0$. This gives

$$P_l^m(0) = (-1)^{\frac{1}{2}(l+m)} 2^{-l} \frac{(l + m)!}{\left(\dfrac{l - m}{2}\right)! \left(\dfrac{l + m}{2}\right)!} \tag{32}$$

if $l - m$ is even and zero otherwise.

An important property of the spherical harmonics is their behavior under the reflection of coordinates denoted by $\hat{P}$, the parity operator, which sends x into $-x$, y into $-y$, and z into $-z$, or, in spherical coordinates, ϑ into $\pi - \vartheta$ and φ into $\pi + \varphi$. Since $\cos(\pi - \vartheta) = -\cos\vartheta$, we have

$$\hat{P} Y_l^m(\vartheta, \varphi) = P_l^m(-\mu) e^{im(\varphi + \pi)}$$

It is clear from (19) that $P_l^m(\mu)$ is equal to $(1 - \mu^2)^{m/2}$ times a polynomial of degree $l - m$, which is even or odd according as

$l - m$ is even or odd. Thus,

$$\hat{P} Y_l{}^m(\vartheta,\varphi) = (-1)^{l-m} P_l{}^m(\mu)(-1)^m e^{im\varphi}$$
$$= (-1)^l Y_l{}^m(\vartheta,\varphi) \tag{33}$$

and the parity of $Y_l{}^m$ is the same as that of l.

Integral relations

To evaluate definite integrals involving products of Legendre polynomials, we can again use the generating function. Writing down the series (22) twice gives

$$[(1 - 2a\mu + a^2)(1 - 2b\mu + b^2)]^{-\frac{1}{2}} = \sum_{k=0}^{\infty} \sum_{l=0}^{\infty} a^k b^l P_k(\mu) P_l(\mu)$$

We can integrate this over μ,

$$\int_{-1}^{1} \frac{d\mu}{[(1 + a^2 - 2a\mu)(1 + b^2 - 2b\mu)]^{\frac{1}{2}}}$$
$$= \sum_{k,l}^{\infty} a^k b^l \int_{-1}^{1} P_k(\mu) P_l(\mu) \, d\mu$$

The integral on the left is easily evaluated[3] as

$$\frac{1}{(ab)^{\frac{1}{2}}} \ln \frac{1 + (ab)^{\frac{1}{2}}}{1 - (ab)^{\frac{1}{2}}}$$

Now expand this in series and compare it with the right-hand side.

$$2 \left[1 + \tfrac{1}{3} ab + \tfrac{1}{5}(ab)^2 + \cdots + \frac{1}{2l + 1}(ab)^l + \cdots \right]$$
$$= \sum_{k,l} a^k b^l \int_{-1}^{1} P_k(\mu) P_l(\mu) \, d\mu$$

We notice first that a and b never occur on the left with different exponents. Thus the integral on the left is zero unless $k = l$, as we have already found in (27). If $k = l$, we can read off the value of the integral from the coefficient on the left. Thus,

$$\int_{-1}^{1} P_k(\mu) P_l(\mu) \, d\mu = \begin{cases} 0 & (k \neq l) \\ \dfrac{2}{2l + 1} & (k = l) \end{cases} \tag{34}$$

Most of the special functions can be treated in this way, but not the associated Legendre polynomials, since they have no simple generating function. We must therefore adopt a different approach.

The normalized spherical functions

The apparatus for normalizing the functions $Y_l{}^m$ lies ready to hand in Sec. 4.10, where we constructed normalized wave functions for the harmonic oscillator by the algebraic method.

---

[3] Use, for example, Dwight's *Tables*, 3d ed., no. 195.01.

The procedure here involves the use of the shift operators $\hat{L}_+$ and $\hat{L}_-$, which are given in terms of μ by

$$\hat{L}_+ = e^{i\varphi}(1 - \mu^2)^{-\frac{1}{2}}\left[-(1 - \mu^2)\frac{\partial}{\partial\mu} + i\mu\frac{\partial}{\partial\varphi}\right] \tag{35}$$

$$\hat{L}_- = e^{-i\varphi}(1 - \mu^2)^{-\frac{1}{2}}\left[(1 - \mu^2)\frac{\partial}{\partial\mu} + i\mu\frac{\partial}{\partial\varphi}\right] \tag{36}$$

and by direct calculation one finds easily that

$$\hat{L}_+ Y_l{}^m = Y_l{}^{m+1} \tag{37}$$

The operation of $\hat{L}_-$ is not quite so simple; it is easiest to apply the operator

$$\begin{aligned}
\hat{L}_-\hat{L}_+ &= \hat{L}_x{}^2 + \hat{L}_y{}^2 - i[\hat{L}_x,\hat{L}_y] \\
&= \hat{L}^2 - \hat{L}_z{}^2 - \hat{L}_z
\end{aligned} \tag{38}$$

to $Y_l{}^{m-1}$:

$$\hat{L}_-\hat{L}_+ Y_l{}^{m-1} = \hat{L}_- Y_l{}^m = [l(l + 1) - m(m - 1)]Y_l{}^{m-1}$$

or

$$\hat{L}_- Y_l{}^m = (l + m)(l - m + 1)Y_l{}^{m-1} \tag{39}$$

[Equation (39) is given here for reference; we shall not need it below.]

To normalize $Y_l{}^m$, we proceed as in the derivation of (4.122).

$$\begin{aligned}
A_l{}^m &= \int Y_l{}^{m*}Y_l{}^m \, d\Omega && (d\Omega = \sin\vartheta \, d\vartheta \, d\varphi) \\
&= \int(\hat{L}_+ Y_l{}^{m-1})^*(\hat{L}_+ Y_l{}^{m-1}) \, d\Omega && \text{by (37)} \\
&= \int Y_l{}^{m-1*}\hat{L}_-\hat{L}_+ Y_l{}^{m-1} \, d\Omega && \text{by (36)} \\
&= [l(l + 1) - (m - 1)^2 - (m - 1)]\int Y_l{}^{m-1*}Y_l{}^{m-1} \, d\Omega \\
&&& \text{by (38)} \\
&= (l + m)(l - m + 1)A_l{}^{m-1}
\end{aligned}$$

Continuing this process, we see that

$$\begin{aligned}
A_l{}^m &= [(l + m)(l + m - 1) \cdots (l + 1)][(l - m + 1)(l - m \\
&\qquad + 2) \cdots l] A_l{}^0 \\
&= \frac{(l + m)!}{l!}\frac{l!}{(l - m)!} A_l{}^0 = \frac{(l + m)!}{(l - m)!} A_l{}^0
\end{aligned}$$

But

$$A_l{}^0 = \int [P_l(\mu)]^2 \, d\Omega = 2\pi\int_{-1}^{1} [P_l(\mu)]^2 \, d\mu = \frac{4\pi}{2l + 1}$$

by (34). Therefore

$$A_l{}^m = \frac{4\pi}{2l + 1}\frac{(l + m)!}{(l - m)!} \tag{40}$$

Table 2   Normalized Spherical Harmonics

$$P_0 = 1$$

$$\mathcal{Y}_0{}^0 = \left(\frac{1}{4\pi}\right)^{\frac{1}{2}}$$

$$P_1{}^1 = -\sin\vartheta$$

$$\mathcal{Y}_1{}^1 = -\frac{1}{2}\left(\frac{3}{2\pi}\right)^{\frac{1}{2}}\sin\vartheta\ e^{i\varphi}$$

$$P_1{}^0 = \cos\vartheta$$

$$\mathcal{Y}_1{}^0 = \frac{1}{2}\left(\frac{3}{\pi}\right)^{\frac{1}{2}}\cos\vartheta$$

$$P_1{}^{-1} = \tfrac{1}{2}\sin\vartheta$$

$$\mathcal{Y}_1{}^{-1} = \frac{1}{2}\left(\frac{3}{2\pi}\right)^{\frac{1}{2}}\sin\vartheta\ e^{-i\varphi}$$

$$P_2{}^2 = 3\sin^2\vartheta$$

$$\mathcal{Y}_2{}^2 = \frac{1}{4}\left(\frac{15}{2\pi}\right)^{\frac{1}{2}}\sin^2\vartheta\ e^{2i\varphi}$$

$$P_2{}^1 = -3\sin\vartheta\cos\vartheta$$

$$\mathcal{Y}_2{}^1 = -\frac{1}{2}\left(\frac{15}{2\pi}\right)^{\frac{1}{2}}\sin\vartheta\cos\vartheta\ e^{i\varphi}$$

$$P_2{}^0 = \tfrac{1}{2}(3\cos^2\vartheta - 1)$$

$$\mathcal{Y}_2{}^0 = \frac{1}{4}\left(\frac{5}{\pi}\right)^{\frac{1}{2}}(3\cos^2\vartheta - 1)$$

$$P_2{}^{-1} = \tfrac{1}{2}\sin\vartheta\cos\vartheta$$

$$\mathcal{Y}_2{}^{-1} = \frac{1}{2}\left(\frac{15}{2\pi}\right)^{\frac{1}{2}}\sin\vartheta\cos\vartheta\ e^{-i\varphi}$$

$$P_2{}^{-2} = \tfrac{1}{8}\sin^2\vartheta$$

$$\mathcal{Y}_2{}^{-2} = \frac{1}{4}\left(\frac{15}{2\pi}\right)^{\frac{1}{2}}\sin^2\vartheta\ e^{-2i\varphi}$$

$$P_3{}^3 = -15\sin^2\vartheta$$

$$\mathcal{Y}_3{}^3 = -\frac{1}{8}\left(\frac{35}{\pi}\right)^{\frac{1}{2}}\sin^3\vartheta\ e^{3i\varphi}$$

$$P_3{}^2 = 15\sin^2\vartheta\cos\vartheta$$

$$\mathcal{Y}_3{}^2 = \frac{1}{4}\left(\frac{105}{2\pi}\right)^{\frac{1}{2}}\sin^2\vartheta\cos\vartheta\ e^{2i\varphi}$$

$$P_3{}^1 = -\tfrac{3}{2}\sin\vartheta(5\cos^2\vartheta - 1)$$

$$\mathcal{Y}_3{}^1 = -\frac{1}{8}\left(\frac{21}{\pi}\right)^{\frac{1}{2}}\sin\vartheta(5\cos^2\vartheta - 1)e^{i\varphi}$$

$$P_3{}^0 = \tfrac{1}{2}(5\cos^3\vartheta - 3\cos\vartheta)$$

$$\mathcal{Y}_3{}^0 = \frac{1}{4}\left(\frac{7}{\pi}\right)^{\frac{1}{2}}(5\cos^3\vartheta - 3\cos\vartheta)$$

$$P_3{}^{-1} = \tfrac{1}{8}\sin\vartheta(5\cos^2\vartheta - 1)$$

$$\mathcal{Y}_3{}^{-1} = \frac{1}{8}\left(\frac{21}{\pi}\right)^{\frac{1}{2}}\sin\vartheta(15\cos^2\vartheta - 3)e^{-i\varphi}$$

$$P_3{}^{-2} = \tfrac{1}{8}\sin^2\vartheta\cos\vartheta$$

$$\mathcal{Y}_3{}^{-2} = \frac{1}{4}\left(\frac{105}{2\pi}\right)^{\frac{1}{2}}\sin^2\vartheta\cos\vartheta\ e^{-2i\varphi}$$

$$P_3{}^{-3} = \tfrac{1}{48}\sin^3\vartheta$$

$$\mathcal{Y}_3{}^{-3} = \frac{1}{8}\left(\frac{35}{\pi}\right)^{\frac{1}{2}}\sin^3\vartheta\ e^{-3i\varphi}$$

where, as usual, 0! is taken to be unity, and the functions

$$\mathcal{Y}_l{}^m(\vartheta,\varphi) = \left[\frac{2l + 1}{4\pi}\frac{(l - m)!}{(l + m)!}\right]^{\frac{1}{2}} P_l{}^m(\cos\vartheta)e^{im\varphi} \tag{41}$$

are the *normalized spherical harmonics*. Those for $l = 0$, 1, and 2 are listed in Table 2.

Rewriting (37) and (39) in terms of these functions, we have

$$\hat{L}_+ \mathcal{Y}_l{}^m = [(l - m)(l + m + 1)]^{\frac{1}{2}} \mathcal{Y}_l{}^{m+1} \tag{42}$$

$$\hat{L}_- \mathcal{Y}_l{}^m = [(l + m)(l - m + 1)]^{\frac{1}{2}} \mathcal{Y}_l{}^{m-1} \tag{43}$$

As mentioned above, some authors use $P_l{}^{|m|}$ to construct $\mathcal{Y}_l{}^m$ when m is negative. Since (40) gives the correct normalization for either positive or negative m, it follows that

$$\left[\frac{2l + 1}{4\pi} \frac{(l - |m|)!}{(l + |m|)!}\right]^{\frac{1}{2}} P_l{}^{|m|}(\cos \vartheta) e^{im\varphi}$$

$$= \pm \left[\frac{2l + 1}{4\pi} \frac{(l - m)!}{(l + m)!}\right]^{\frac{1}{2}} P_l{}^m(\cos \vartheta) e^{im\varphi}$$

where the uncertainty in sign reflects the fact that one loses track of it in normalization. If $m < 0$, the sign is $(-1)^{\frac{1}{2}(|m|-m)}$, found by calculating the leading term of each side when expanded in powers of μ. We then have

$$P_l{}^{-m}(\mu) = (-1)^m \frac{(l - m)!}{(l + m)!} P_l{}^m(\mu) \qquad (m > 0) \tag{44}$$

Putting together these results, we have the final recipe for the normalized solutions of (1): Solve the equations (11) for $R_l(r)$, where $l = 0, 1, 2, \ldots$. In an eigenvalue problem, where $p(r)$ contains the unknown eigenvalue, there will in general be a number of well-behaved solutions of this equation, corresponding to different eigenvalues. Let R_{nl} be the nth one, normalized so that

$$\int_0^\infty r^2 R_{nl}{}^2(r) \, dr = 1$$

Then the normalized solutions of (1) are of the form

$$F(r,\vartheta,\varphi) = R_{nl}(r) \mathcal{Y}_l{}^m(\vartheta,\varphi) \qquad (-l \leqslant m \leqslant l) \tag{45}$$

Other notations

Though everyone seems to agree on the definition of Legendre's polynomial $P_l(\mu)$, there are a number of definitions current for $P_l{}^m(\mu)$ and even more for the normalized spherical harmonics. In Table 3 we give some of the definitions used in widely quoted works. The quantity $\mathcal{P}_l{}^m(\mu)$ is defined in terms of our $\mathcal{Y}_l{}^m$ by

$$\mathcal{Y}_l{}^m = \mathcal{P}_l{}^m e^{im\varphi}$$

In defining $P_l{}^m$ we have used the sign convention of Magnus and Oberhettinger. It yields positive signs in (37), (39), (42), and (43), and leads to the sign convention followed by Condon and Shortley, Landau and Lifshitz, and other more recent writers in writing the normalized spherical harmonics.

Table 3 Other Notations

Author	Notation	Equivalent in Our Notation
Bateman[a]	P_l^m	$(-1)^m P_l^m$
Bethe and Salpeter[b]	P_l^m	$(-1)^m P_l^m$
Bohm[c]	P_l^m	$(-1)^m P_l^{|m|}$
Condon and Shortley[d]	$\Theta(lm)$	$(2\pi)^{1/2} \mathcal{P}_l^m$
Landau and Lifschitz[e]	P_l^m	$(-1)^m P_l^m$ ($m \geq 0$ only)
Magnus and Oberhettinger[f]	P_l^m	P_l^m
Merzbacher[g]	P_l^m	$(-1)^m P_l^m$ ($m \geq 0$ only)
Schiff[h]	P_l^m	$(-1)^m P_l^{|m|}$
Bethe and Salpeter	Φ_{lm}	$(-1)^m \mathcal{Y}_l^m$
Bohm	Y_l^m	$(-1)^{\frac{1}{2}(m+|m|)} \mathcal{Y}_l^m$
Edmonds[i]	Y_{lm}	$\mathcal{Y}_l^m$
Landau and Lifschitz	Θ_{lm}	$(2\pi)^{1/2} \mathcal{P}_l^m$
Merzbacher	Y_l^m	$\mathcal{Y}_l^m$
Schiff	Y_{lm}	$(-1)^{\frac{1}{2}(m+|m|)} \mathcal{Y}_l^m$

[a] See references at end of this appendix.

[b] Bethe and Salpeter in *Encyclopedia of Physics*, Springer-Verlag OHG, Berlin, 1957.

[c] D. Bohm, *Quantum Theory*, Prentice-Hall, Inc., Englewood Cliffs, N.J., 1951.

[d] Condon and Shortley, *The Theory of Atomic Spectra*, The Macmillan Company, New York, 1935.

[e] Landau and Lifschitz, *Quantum Mechanics.* Addison-Wesley Publishing Company, Inc., Reading, Mass., 1958.

[f] Magnus and Oberhettinger, *Formulas and Theorems for the Special Functions of Mathematical Physics*, Chelsea Publishing Company, New York, 1949.

[g] E. Merzbacher, *Quantum Mechanics*, John Wiley & Sons, Inc., New York, 1961.

[h] E. L. Schiff, *Quantum Mechanics*, 2d ed., McGraw-Hill Book Company, Inc., New York, 1955.

[i] A. R. Edmonds, *Angular Momentum in Quantum Mechanics*, Princeton University Press, Princeton, N.J., 1957.

REFERENCES

H. Bateman, *Partial Differential Equations of Mathematical Physics*, Dover Publications, Inc., New York, 1944, chap. VI

I. S. and E. S. Sokolnikoff, *Higher Mathematics for Engineers and Physicists*, McGraw-Hill Book Company, Inc., New York, 1941.

P. M. Morse and H. Feshbach, *Methods of Theoretical Physics*, McGraw-Hill Book Company, Inc., New York, 1953.

Outline of Electromagnetic Theory

The following is intended, not to teach the reader much about physical content or experimental basis, but merely to provide a convenient summary of these aspects of electromagnetism encountered in this book. In particular, we shall omit many of the qualifications and restrictions which ought to be made if one is being careful about details.

1. *Electric field or intensity* **E**. Defined as the force per unit charge.

$$\mathbf{F} = q\mathbf{E} \tag{1}$$

2. *Path independence of electrostatic forces.* If a charge is transported along a closed path in an electrostatic field, no work is done.

$$\oint \mathbf{E} \cdot \mathbf{ds} = 0 \qquad \text{(any closed path)}$$

By Stokes's theorem, this is

$$\int \mathbf{\nabla} \times \mathbf{E} \cdot \mathbf{dA} = 0$$

integrated over any surface bounded by any path, that is, over any surface. Therefore

$$\mathbf{\nabla} \times \mathbf{E} = 0 \tag{2}$$

3. *Electric displacement* **D**. Defined as the density of a flux issuing from a charge,

$$\int \mathbf{D} \cdot \mathbf{dA} = q \qquad \text{(any volume)}$$

where the integral on the left extends over the surface bounding any volume and q is the charge contained in the volume. If ρ is the corresponding charge density, then

$$\int \mathbf{D} \cdot \mathbf{dA} = \int \rho \, dv$$

or, by Gauss's theorem,

$$\int \boldsymbol{\nabla} \cdot \mathbf{D} \, dv = \int \rho \, dv \qquad \text{(any volume)}$$

from which

$$\boldsymbol{\nabla} \cdot \mathbf{D} = \rho \tag{3}$$

Thus 1 defines $\mathbf{E}$ by the effects it produces, whereas 3 defines $\mathbf{D}$ in terms of what produces it.

4. *In a vacuum, $\mathbf{D}$ and $\mathbf{E}$ are proportional,*

$$\mathbf{D} = \varepsilon_0 \mathbf{E} \tag{4}$$

As an example of this, one derives Coulomb's law of force between two charges from (1), (3), and (4).

5. *Electric polarization* $\mathbf{P}$. This is defined as the electric dipole moment per unit volume of a material substance. By calculating the field due to both free charges (which produce $\mathbf{D}$) and polarization charges, one can show that $\mathbf{E} = \varepsilon_0^{-1}\mathbf{D} - \mathbf{P}$, or

$$\mathbf{D} = \varepsilon_0(\mathbf{E} + \mathbf{P}) \tag{5}$$

6. *Susceptibility and dielectric constant.* In gases and many solids, the polarization is caused by the field and is at least approximately proportional to it. This is written as

$$\mathbf{P} = \chi_e \mathbf{E} \tag{6}$$

where χ_e, the electric susceptibility, is at least approximately independent of $\mathbf{E}$. The relation between $\mathbf{D}$ and $\mathbf{E}$ is then

$$\mathbf{D} = \kappa\varepsilon_0\mathbf{E} = \varepsilon\mathbf{E} \qquad \kappa = 1 + \chi_e \tag{7}$$

where κ is called the dielectric constant and ε the permittivity.

7. *Conservation of electric charge.* The rate of decrease of the charge q in any region is given by the rate of flow through the boundaries of the region. Let $\mathbf{s}$ represent the current per unit area (called somewhat misleadingly the current density). Then

$$\int \mathbf{s} \cdot \mathbf{dA} = -\frac{dq}{dt} = -\frac{d}{dt}\int \rho \, dv$$
$$\| \qquad\qquad\qquad \|$$
$$\int \boldsymbol{\nabla} \cdot \mathbf{s} \, dv \quad = \quad -\int \frac{\partial \rho}{\partial t} \, dv \qquad \text{(any region)}$$

if we regard the boundaries of the region as fixed. It follows that the conservation of electric charge at each point of space is expressed by the differential *equation of continuity*

$$\boldsymbol{\nabla} \cdot \mathbf{s} + \frac{\partial \rho}{\partial t} = 0 \tag{8}$$

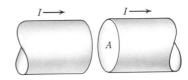

Fig. 1   Broken wire to illustrate the continuity of the
total current.

8. *Displacement current.* Combining (3) and (8), we see that

$$\mathbf{\nabla} \cdot \mathbf{C} = 0 \qquad \text{where } \mathbf{C} = \mathbf{s} + \dot{\mathbf{D}} \tag{9}$$

This is the relation which characterizes the flow of an incompressible fluid. The meaning of C is shown in Fig. 1. Inside the broken wire, the average current density is $s = I/A$. At the break, charge accumulates at a rate of I C/sec. Since one line of D comes from each coulomb (see 3), this gives I lines of displacement per second in the gap. Their density is D, so that

$$\dot{D} = \frac{I}{A} = s$$

Thus, $\dot{D}$ starts where s leaves off, and $C = s + \dot{D}$ is continuous. The density of what is usually called the current in physics and engineering is given by $\mathbf{C}$, not $\mathbf{s}$.

9. *Magnetic induction* **B**. This is defined, analogously to **E**, by the force it exerts. On a straight segment of wire of length **L** carrying a current I the force is

$$\mathbf{F} = I\mathbf{L} \times \mathbf{B} \tag{10}$$

Consider a current made up of elements of charge dq moving with a velocity **v** separated by intervals **ds**. Since $I = dq/dt$,

$$d\mathbf{F} = \frac{dq}{dt}\,\mathbf{ds} \times \mathbf{B} = dq\,\frac{\mathbf{ds}}{dt} \times \mathbf{B} = dq\,\mathbf{v} \times \mathbf{B}$$

so that the force on a point charge q moving in a magnetic field is

$$\mathbf{F} = q\mathbf{v} \times \mathbf{B} \tag{11}$$

10. *Closure of lines of induction.* It is found that one can pretend that lines of induction are continuous,[1] so that all lines entering a region must leave it,

$$\int \mathbf{B} \cdot \mathbf{dA} = 0$$

or

$$\int \mathbf{\nabla} \cdot \mathbf{B}\, dv = 0 \qquad \text{(any region)}$$

Thus

$$\mathbf{\nabla} \cdot \mathbf{B} = 0 \tag{12}$$

---

[1] For a discussion of this often misunderstood point, see J. Slepian, Am. J. Phys., **19**, 87 (1951).

11. *Faraday's law.* When the flux of **B** through a closed circuit changes, an electromotive force is developed in the circuit such that

$$\oint \mathbf{E} \cdot \mathbf{ds} = -\frac{d}{dt} \int \mathbf{B} \cdot \mathbf{dA}$$

where the line integral is around the edge of the area on the right. By Stokes's theorem, this is

$$\int \boldsymbol{\nabla} \times \mathbf{E} \cdot \mathbf{dA} = -\int \dot{\mathbf{B}} \cdot \mathbf{dA} \qquad \text{(any area)}$$

so that the infinitesimal form of Faraday's law is

$$\boldsymbol{\nabla} \times \mathbf{E} = -\dot{\mathbf{B}} \tag{13}$$

This, in the dynamic case, replaces the static relation (2).

12. *Production of a magnetic field.* Experimentally, it is found that the magnetic induction along any closed loop enclosing a current i is proportional to the current in such a way that

$$\oint \mathbf{B} \cdot \mathbf{ds} \propto i$$

This suggests defining a quantity **H**, analogous to **D**, so that

$$\oint \mathbf{H} \cdot \mathbf{ds} = i$$
$$\int \boldsymbol{\nabla} \times \mathbf{H} \cdot \mathbf{dA} = \int \mathbf{s} \cdot \mathbf{dA} \qquad \text{(any area)}$$

and therefore $\boldsymbol{\nabla} \times \mathbf{H} = \mathbf{s}$. This is inconsistent, however, for taking the divergence of both sides gives $\boldsymbol{\nabla} \cdot \mathbf{s} = 0$ instead of (8). Thus it is clear that instead of **s** we must use the "ordinary" current density **C**,

$$\boldsymbol{\nabla} \times \mathbf{H} = \mathbf{C} \tag{14}$$

The question of names for B and H is an annoyance. For historical reasons B is usually called the magnetic induction and H the field. This no longer makes sense in the mks system of units where it is B that exerts the force and should properly be called the field. We have tended to call it so elsewhere in this book, but only in conjunction with the letter B for clarity. Sommerfeld calls H the magnetic excitation, which correctly describes its role.

13. *In empty space,* **B** *and* **H** *are proportional,*

$$\mathbf{B} = \mu_0 \mathbf{H} \tag{15}$$

This, like 4, is an experimental fact.

14. *The magnetization* **I**. This is defined as the magnetic dipole moment per unit volume, and it can be shown that in material media

$$\mathbf{B} = \mu_0(\mathbf{H} + \mathbf{I})$$

In many substances (though not in ferromagnetic ones) **I** is at least roughly proportional to the applied **H**, so that

$$\mathbf{I} = \chi_m \mathbf{H}$$

and

$$\mathbf{B} = \mu \mathbf{H} \qquad \mu = \mu_0(1 + \chi_m)$$

where χ_m, the magnetic susceptibility, and μ, the permeability, are at least roughly independent of **H**. Substances with $\chi_m < 0$ are called diamagnetic; those with $\chi_m > 0$ are paramagnetic. Ferromagnetic behavior is not very conveniently described by a susceptibility.

15. *The energy of an electromagnetic field* may be written as an integral,

$$U = \tfrac{1}{2}\!\int(\mathbf{E}\cdot\mathbf{D} + \mathbf{B}\cdot\mathbf{H})\,dv$$

It is consistent with this, and generally useful, to assume that the energy resides in the field and define the energy density[2] as

$$\varepsilon = \tfrac{1}{2}(\mathbf{E}\cdot\mathbf{D} + \mathbf{B}\cdot\mathbf{H}) \tag{16}$$

16. *The potentials.* Collecting the field equations, we have

(a) $\nabla \times \mathbf{E} = -\dot{\mathbf{B}}$ (b) $\nabla \times \mathbf{H} = \mathbf{s} + \dot{\mathbf{D}}$

(c) $\nabla \cdot \mathbf{D} = \rho$ (d) $\nabla \cdot \mathbf{B} = 0$

These are Maxwell's equations; they describe the relations of the fields with their sources and with each other. Because the field variables are so much intertwined in these equations, one introduces potentials as follows. Let

$$\mathbf{B} = \nabla \times \mathbf{A} \tag{17}$$

This satisfies (d) identically. Then (a) becomes

$$\nabla \times (\mathbf{E} + \dot{\mathbf{A}}) = 0$$

If we set $\mathbf{E} + \dot{\mathbf{A}} = -\nabla V$, or

$$\mathbf{E} = -\nabla V - \dot{\mathbf{A}} \tag{18}$$

then (a) is identically satisfied also. **A** and V are called the vector and scalar potentials respectively.

We now turn to the relations between the fields and their sources. In vacuo, the only case we shall consider, (b) gives

$$\nabla \times \mathbf{B} = \nabla \times \nabla \times \mathbf{A} = \mu_0(\mathbf{s} + \varepsilon_0\dot{\mathbf{E}})$$

In cartesian coordinates, the double curl becomes

$$\nabla(\nabla \cdot \mathbf{A}) - \nabla^2\mathbf{A} = \mu_0\mathbf{s} - \mu_0\varepsilon_0(\nabla\dot{V} + \ddot{\mathbf{A}})$$

[2] This is discussed by D. Park, Am. J. Phys., **24**, 78 (1956).

where $\nabla^2\mathbf{A}$ is a vector whose components are $\nabla^2 A_x$, $\nabla^2 A_y$, and $\nabla^2 A_z$. This is

$$\nabla^2\mathbf{A} - \frac{1}{c^2}\ddot{\mathbf{A}} = -\mu_0\mathbf{s} + \nabla\left(\nabla\cdot\mathbf{A} + \frac{1}{c^2}\dot{V}\right)$$

where $(\mu_0\varepsilon_0)^{1/2}$ has been written as c, which will turn out to be the speed of light. It can now be shown that it is always possible to choose $\mathbf{A}$ and V, which are not uniquely determined by (17) and (18), so that

$$\nabla\cdot\mathbf{A} + \frac{1}{c^2}\dot{V} = 0 \tag{19}$$

This is known as the Lorentz condition, and if it is satisfied, we find three equations

$$\nabla^2\mathbf{A} - \frac{1}{c^2}\ddot{\mathbf{A}} = -\mu_0\mathbf{s} \tag{20}$$

in which the variables are completely disentangled.

Finally, we write (c) as

$$\nabla\cdot\mathbf{E} = \frac{\rho}{\varepsilon_0}$$

or, by (18),

$$\nabla^2 V = -\frac{\rho}{\varepsilon_0} - \nabla\cdot\dot{\mathbf{A}}$$

Differentiating (19) gives

$$\nabla\cdot\dot{\mathbf{A}} + \frac{1}{c^2}\ddot{V} = 0$$

whence

$$\nabla^2 V - \frac{1}{c^2}\ddot{V} = -\frac{\rho}{\varepsilon_0} \tag{21}$$

in which the electric variable V stands alone. In the absence of charges and currents, (20) and (21) are of the form of d'Alembert's equation for a wave progressing with velocity c. These are the electromagnetic waves, and c may be calculated from μ_0 and ε_0. In practice, one usually determines electric and magnetic fields by solving the equations for the potentials and then using (17) and (18) to find the fields.

17. *Radiation.* In empty space, with $\mathbf{s} = \rho = 0$, plane-wave solutions of (20) and (21) are given by

$$\begin{aligned}\mathbf{A} &= \mathbf{a}\sin(\mathbf{k}\cdot\mathbf{r} - \omega t)\\ V &= v\sin(\mathbf{k}\cdot\mathbf{r} - \omega t)\end{aligned} \qquad (\omega = ck) \tag{22}$$

where **a** and v are constant amplitudes. The Lorentz condition (19) now tells us that **a** and v are not entirely arbitrary, but are connected by

$$\mathbf{k} \cdot \mathbf{a} - \frac{\omega v}{c^2} = 0 \tag{23}$$

The field strengths are

$$\mathbf{B} = (\mathbf{k} \times \mathbf{a}) \cos (\mathbf{k} \cdot \mathbf{r} - \omega t) \tag{24}$$

$$\mathbf{E} = (-\mathbf{k}v + \omega \mathbf{a}) \cos (\mathbf{k} \cdot \mathbf{r} - \omega t) \tag{25}$$

and one can easily verify using (23) that

$$\mathbf{E} \cdot \mathbf{k} = \mathbf{B} \cdot \mathbf{k} = \mathbf{E} \cdot \mathbf{B} = 0$$

so that **E**, **B**, and **k** are all perpendicular, as is required for transverse radiation.

To compute the energy density (16),

$$\mathcal{E} = \frac{1}{2} \left(\epsilon_0 E^2 + \frac{B^2}{\mu_0} \right) \tag{26}$$

we readily find that

$$B^2 = [k^2 a^2 - (\mathbf{k} \cdot \mathbf{a})^2] \cos^2 (\mathbf{k} \cdot \mathbf{r} - \omega t)$$

$$E^2 = c^2 [k^2 a^2 - (\mathbf{k} \cdot \mathbf{a})^2] \cos^2 (\mathbf{k} \cdot \mathbf{r} - \omega t)$$

so that $B^2 = \mu_0 \epsilon_0 E^2$, and the two terms of (26) are equal in magnitude.

18. *Gauge transformations.* The potentials **A** and V are not experimental quantities as are **B** and **E**, and they are even to some extent arbitrary. Consider the *gauge transformation*

$$\mathbf{A} \to \mathbf{A} + \nabla X \qquad V \to V - \dot{X} \tag{27}$$

where X is some scalar function of x,y,z,t. Comparison with (17) and (18) shows that under this transformation $\mathbf{B} \to \mathbf{B}$ and $\mathbf{E} \to \mathbf{E}$, so that the change of variables is without physical content (but see Prob. 7.39). Equation (19) becomes

$$\nabla \cdot \mathbf{A} + \frac{1}{c^2} \dot{V} \to \nabla \cdot \mathbf{A} + \frac{1}{c^2} \dot{V} + \nabla^2 X - \frac{1}{c^2} \ddot{X}$$

so that if X satisfies d'Alembert's equation (but is otherwise arbitrary), the Lorentz condition is preserved. If we transform (22) by

$$X = \frac{v}{\omega} \cos (\mathbf{k} \cdot \mathbf{r} - \omega t)$$

we find

$$\mathbf{A} \to \left(\mathbf{a} - \frac{\mathbf{k}v}{\omega} \right) \sin (\mathbf{k} \cdot \mathbf{r} - \omega t) \qquad V \to 0$$

The new amplitude of **A** in this "radiation gauge" is perpendicular to k; for $\mathbf{k} \cdot \mathbf{a} - k^2 v/\omega = 0$ by (23), so that V is zero and **A** is transverse. This is an economical description of a field of plane radiation in terms of two functions, say, A_x and A_y, if **k** is along the z axis, instead of A_x, A_y, A_z, and V as in the general case.

REFERENCES

These brief notes may be supplemented by any text on elementary electricity and magnetism. In order of increasing difficulty, the following are recommended:

R. P. Winch, *Electricity and Magnetism*, 2d ed., Prentice-Hall, Inc., Englewood Cliffs, N.J., 1963.

W. T. Scott, *The Physics of Electricity and Magnetism*, John Wiley & Sons, Inc., New York, 1959.

A. Sommerfeld, *Electrodynamics*, Academic Press Inc., New York, 1952.

appendix 6
Symbols and Notations

a	scattering length at zero energy
$a_0 = 4\pi\varepsilon_0\hbar^2/me^2$	radius of first Bohr orbit
$\mathbf{A}$	vector potential of electromagnetic field
A_{mn}	Einstein coefficient for spontaneous emission
b	barn (1 b $= 10^{-24}$ cm^2)
B_{mn}	Einstein coefficient for induced processes
$\mathbf{B}$	magnetic induction
$c = (\mu_0\varepsilon_0)^{-1/2}$	speed of light
$C = \dfrac{(2m)^{3/2}V}{4\pi^2\hbar^3}$	see Eq. (19.89)
C_v	specific heat (cal/g deg)
c_v	molar specific heat (cal/mole deg)
$\mathfrak{C}_v$	heat capacity (cal/deg)
e	elementary charge (electronic charge $= -e$)
$e' = e(4\pi\varepsilon_0)^{-1/2}$	
$\mathbf{e}$	unit polarization vector
E	energy
$\mathbf{E}$	electric field
f	Fermi (or fentometer), 10^{-15}m
$f(\vartheta)$	scattering amplitude
F	Helmholtz free energy; electric field

NOTE: See also Table 19.1.

	g	g factor
	h	Planck's constant
$\hbar = h/2\pi$		
	I	magnetization (magnetic moment per unit volume)
	j	quantum number of total angular momentum
	J	moment of inertia
	$\mathbf{J}$	total angular momentum, $\mathbf{L} + \mathbf{S}$
	k	wave number (λ^{-1}); Boltzmann's constant
$k(x) = \{2m\hbar^{-2}[E - V(x)]\}^{\frac{1}{2}}$		wave number of particle in a field of force
	l	quantum number of orbital angular momentum
$\mathbf{L} = \mathbf{P}/\hbar$		dimensionless angular momentum
	L_0	Loschmidt's number
	m	electron mass (sometimes m_e); azimuthal quantum number (sometimes m_l)
	m_s	spin azimuthal quantum number
	M	nucleon mass
$M_{\mathrm{B}} = e\hbar/2m$		Bohr magneton
	$\mathbf{M}$	magnetic moment
	n	radial quantum number
	N_0	Avogadro's number
	$\mathbf{p}$	linear momentum
	$\mathbf{P}$	angular momentum; polarization (electric dipole moment per unit volume)
	Q	volume; grand partition function
	r_0	effective range
	R	gas constant
$\mathrm{Ry} = \dfrac{me^4}{2(4\pi\varepsilon_0)^2\hbar^2}$		Rydberg constant
	$\mathbf{s}$	current density (current per unit area)
	S	entropy; $e^{2i\delta}$
	$\mathbf{S}$	spin angular momentum in units of $\hbar$
	T	Kelvin temperature
	$u(\omega)$	spectral distribution function
$u(r) = r\psi(r)$		radial wave function
	U	energy density
	V	electric potential; volume
	Z	atomic number; canonical partition function

α electric polarizability; fine-structure constant

$\beta = 1/kT$

γ gyromagnetic ratio (magnetic moment to angular momentum); $-\mu/kT$

δ scattering phase shift

ε_0 permittivity of free space

ϑ polar angle; Debye temperature

$\kappa = \{2m\hbar^{-2}[V(x) - E]\}^{1/2}$

λ wavelength; thermal de Broglie wavelength $\left(\dfrac{2\pi\hbar^2}{mkT}\right)^{1/2}$

$\lambdabar = \lambda/2\pi$

μ reduced mass; chemical potential; $\cos\vartheta$

μ_0 permeability of free space; chemical potential at absolute zero

ν frequency (cycles per second)

$\rho(\varepsilon)$ density of states

σ scattering cross section

$\dfrac{d\sigma}{d\Omega}$ differential scattering cross section

φ azimuthal angle; phase of wave function; time-dependent wave function

χ susceptibility; spin eigenfunction

ψ wave function

ω angular frequency $2\pi\nu$

Ω grand potential

$d\Omega$ element of solid angle $= \sin\vartheta\,d\vartheta\,d\varphi$

$\hat{Q}$ operator representing the dynamical variable Q

$\langle A \rangle$ expectation value of the variable A

$\langle \hat{O} \rangle$ expectation value of the quantity represented by the operator $\hat{O}$

$\langle b|\Omega|a \rangle$ matrix element for transition from state a to state b, induced by the interaction Ω

$[\hat{A},\hat{B}]$ the commutator $\hat{A}\hat{B} - \hat{B}\hat{A}$

Values of Physical Constants

$$a_0 = 5.2917 \times 10^{-11} \text{ m}$$
$$c = 2.99793 \times 10^8 \text{ m/sec}$$
$$e = 1.6021 \times 10^{-19} \text{ C}$$
$$h = 6.626 \times 10^{-34} \text{ J sec}$$
$$\hbar = 1.0545 \times 10^{-34} \text{ J sec}$$
$$k = 1.3805 \times 10^{-23} \text{ J/deg}$$
$$L_0 = 2.687 \times 10^{25} \text{ molecules/m}^3$$
$$m_e = 9.109 \times 10^{-31} \text{ kg}$$
$$m_e c^2 = 0.51101 \text{ MeV}$$
$$m_p c^2 = 938.26 \text{ MeV}$$
$$m_n c^2 = 939.55 \text{ MeV}$$
$$1 \text{ amu} = 931.48 \text{ MeV}$$
$$N_0 = 6.023 \times 10^{23} \text{ molecules/mole}$$
$$R = 8.314 \text{ J/mole deg}$$
$$\text{Ry} = 13.605 \text{ eV}$$
$$\alpha = \frac{e^2}{\hbar c} = 7.2972 \times 10^{-4}$$
$$\alpha^{-1} = \frac{\hbar c}{e^2} = 137.039$$
$$\varepsilon_0 = 8.854 \times 10^{-12} \text{ C}^2/\text{N m}^2$$
$$\frac{1}{4\pi\varepsilon_0} = 8.987 \times 10^9 \text{ N m}^2/\text{C}^2$$
$$\mu_0 = 4\pi \times 10^{-7} \text{ Wb/A m}$$

Unit of magnetic field: 1 tesla = 1 Wb/m^2 = 10^4 G
$$1 \text{ cal} = 4.1840 \text{ J}$$

* Nat. Bur. of Standards Tech. News Bull., **47**, 175 (1963). This reference should be consulted for more significant figures and for uncertainties.

Index